G000144656

STATISTICS FOR BEHAVIORAL SCIENCES

KENNETH M. ROSENBERG

State University of New York/College at Oswego

Wm. C. Brown Publishers

To the memory of three devoted parents and grandparents, Harold A. and Marion W. Rosenberg, and Alma D. Davidson.

Book Team

Editor *Michael Lange*
Developmental Editor *Carla J. Aspelmeier*
Production Editor *Daniel Rapp*
Permissions Editor *Vicki Krug*
Visuals Processor *Andé Meyer*

Wm. C. Brown Publishers

President *G. Franklin Lewis*
Vice President, Publisher *Thomas E. Doran*
Vice President, Operations and Production *Beverly Kolz*
National Sales Manager *Virginia S. Moffat*
Advertising Manager *Ann M. Knepper*
Marketing Manager *Kathy Law Laube*
Production Editorial Manager *Colleen A. Yonda*
Production Editorial Manager *Julie A. Kennedy*
Publishing Services Manager *Karen J. Slaght*
Manager of Visuals and Design *Faye M. Schilling*

Cover image © The Image Bank/Pete Turner

Cover design by Dick Kharibian

Library of Congress Catalog Card Number: 89-061704

ISBN 0-697-09740-4

Printed in the United States of America by Wm. C. Brown Publishers, 2460 Kerper Boulevard, Dubuque, IA 52001

10 9 8 7 6 5 4 3 2

Brief Contents

Expanded Contents

CHAPTER 13 Nonparametric Two-Group Tests 269

CHAPTER 14 Chi-Square 289

CHAPTER 15 Inside the Analysis of Variance (ANOVA) 308

CHAPTER 18 An Introduction to the Multifactor Analysis of Variance: The Two-Factor Experiment 370

CHAPTER 19 Using Statistics: What's Next? 404

Preface

This introductory level statistics text was written principally to meet the needs of students in the behavioral sciences. It is based upon teaching strategies that I have used successfully in my own teaching of statistics during the past twenty years. Although the majority of students in my classes tend to be psychology majors, the formal content of this statistics text, the examples that are used, and the chapter exercises, are suitable for a wide variety of disciplines, including education, business administration, agricultural science, medicine, and biology.

Any instructor who has taught a course in statistics to college students with academic majors in the social sciences knows that some students in this population lack confidence in their ability to learn statistical concepts and data analysis skills. *Statistics for Behavioral Sciences* was written in an informal style with the mathematically anxious student in mind. Every effort has been made to offer clear, nonthreatening explanations without sacrificing completeness or accuracy.

The coverage of topics in this introductory level text are rather traditional. In the introductory chapter, basic terminology, statistical notation, and measurement scales are discussed. Graphs, tables, and statistics (measures of central tendency and dispersion) are presented throughout Part I, Descriptive Statistics, as devices for extracting the elements of information that reside in a set of data. Coverage of linear regression and correlation complete the descriptive statistics section of the text.

Next, as a transition to Part II, Inferential Statistics (hypothesis testing), some necessary background is provided in the chapters on basic probability theory and the binomial distribution. Then the logic and mechanics of hypothesis testing are introduced within the context of the binomial distribution. Even though the binomial is seldom applied to analyze the type of data gathered by behavioral scientists, I adopted this somewhat nontraditional approach after finding that the fundamental concepts of hypothesis testing are more easily communicated using the relatively simple single-sample scenarios to which the binomial test may be applied.

Another noteworthy feature of Part II, Inferential Statistics, is "the five steps of hypothesis testing"—a way of approaching the data analysis phase of hypothesis testing as a uniform series of five steps that apply to any type of statistical analysis. This presentation is used throughout the chapters on hypothesis testing and allows students to grasp the logical foundation that is common to all statistical tests.

Following the binomial test, the next two chapters deal with the other single-sample tests (the single-sample z-test and the single-sample t-test). The next two chapters cover the two-sample parametric tests (the independent groups and correlated groups t-test) and the two-sample nonparametric tests (the Mann-Whitney, sign, and Wilcoxon tests). The final chapters deal with multiple samples or categories. These tests include the chi-square goodness-of-fit test, the chi-square test of independence, the independent groups and correlated groups single-factor analysis of variance, and the analysis for the fixed factor randomized groups factorial experiment.

Ancillaries that you may use with the text include a Student Study Guide and *Stat/Tutor*, a computer (I.B.M.–P.C. or compatible) software package of twenty-five demonstration/tutorial and data analysis programs that complement and are carefully coordinated with the text. Also, for instructors, there is an Instructor's Manual that contains multiple choice, fill in, and true/false test items.

Although *Statistics for Behavioral Sciences* has been written to stand alone as a complete instructional resource, the *Stat/Tutor* package (including *Manual for Stat/Tutor*), which has been used in various forms by students at S.U.N.Y.C.O. since 1981, has proven to be a very effective teaching device. The demonstrations and sampling experiments help to make abstract statistical concepts such as the sampling distribution of the sample mean, confidence intervals, and the structural model of the analysis of variance, more concrete and understandable. Other programs allow students to practice problem-solving skills and get immediate feedback on details of the solution. Even the data analysis programs have instruction as the primary focus. The formulae are displayed with appropriate substitutions and the intermediate steps are explained to foster complete awareness of the computational process. All but the two introductory chapters are coordinated with one or more companion *Stat/Tutor* programs.

In a perfect world, the instructional environment for the use of this text/software combination would include easy access to desktop personal computers. Unfortunately, while most colleges are working toward easy computer access for a variety of educational purposes (word processing, business/accounting applications, data management and analysis, etc.), and while great strides have been made, not all schools have achieved this worthy goal. Even though computer availability and utilization may still have a long way to go at your college or university, this need not preclude your use of *Stat/Tutor* with this text.

In my own case, before the creation of our microcomputer laboratory, I used a personal computer as an instructional aid while I lectured. I did (and still do) sampling experiments and data analysis during lectures in seconds that would take hours to do with a hand calculator. I do hypothesis testing in a variety of experimental contexts with computer generated data, the characteristics of which are user controlled, and I can quickly analyze my own data or data brought to class by the students from an assignment. This use of the computer works very well with a projection system so the class can follow the whole process, but copying a few values or a formula from the computer display to the chalkboard or making handouts before class by duplicating screen dumps to a printer works fine.

In 1982, when the number of computers designated for use by psychology students grew to about five, it became practical to use the software as part of the laboratory curriculum and as a remedial teaching device. The students who wanted to supplement my lectures and the text presentation with additional lessons could run computer tutorials at their leisure. In particular, *Stat/Tutor* has proven very effective in helping students to catch up who miss class due to illness, etc.

Now at S.U.N.Y.C.O., as in many other colleges and universities, any student who needs to use a microcomputer can go to one of several campus locations where microcomputer laboratories are staffed from late morning through the evening hours. My students are comfortable working independently in the microcomputer laboratories because each has his or her own copy of the software and no previous familiarity with computers is needed to run the programs other than knowing how to insert the diskettes and turn on the computer. It is not necessary to learn a command syntax, as one must do to run high-powered mainframe packages such as MINITAB and SPSS.

Many individuals, some unknowingly, have made great contributions to shape my approach to the teaching of statistics. As a graduate student, my mentors at Purdue University (Vic Denenberg, Don Brown, and the late Ben Winer) taught me most of what I know about statistics as a formal discipline. As a teacher of statistics, the texts I have used have also left their mark on my approach to the subject. In particular, like Robert Pagano, I present the topic of regression before rather than after the topic of correlation (*Understanding Statistics*, St. Paul, MN: West Publishing, 1981). The use of sampling experiments to explain the properties of sampling distributions was pioneered by Jerome C. R. Li of the University of Oregon (*Introduction to Inferential Statistics*, Ann Arbor: Edwards Brothers, 1957). (Unlike Dr. Li's students who had to do their sampling experiments manually using a basket of metal-rimmed cardboard tags, today we can use remarkably fast computer simulations.)

I am grateful for the sabbatical leave, granted to me by the administration of the State University of New York College at Oswego, that enabled me to complete the *Stat/Tutor* software. I also thank the editorial staff at Wm. C. Brown Publishers and the peer reviewers who made so many valuable contributions to the manuscript:

Janice Adams, *Middle Tennessee State University*

Gordon A. Allen, *Miami University*

Richard Colker, *University of D.C.*

John M. Davis, *Southwest Texas State University*

Steven Falkenberg, *Eastern Kentucky University*

Norman Greenfeld, *SUNY—Albany*

James F. Juola, *University of Kansas*

William McDaniel, *Georgia College*

Randall M. Potter, *Calrion University*

Jacqueline Reihman, *SUNY—Oswego*

Robert B. Tallarico, *University of Miami*

Kenneth M. Rosenberg

PART I

DESCRIPTIVE STATISTICS

CHAPTER 1

Introduction

DECISIONS! DECISIONS! DECISIONS!

Life places many demands upon us, and one of them is the burden of making decisions that affect our lives and careers. On an abstract level, controlling one's destiny through the decision-making process should be a fulfilling and enjoyable experience. On a more realistic level, however, it often seems that we don't have enough information or the right kinds of information available when we are faced with making an important decision. Because some decisions cannot be put off and because of demands that are placed upon us and that we place on ourselves, some decisions are inevitably made in the face of substantial uncertainty—without all the relevant information and with incomplete understanding of the information we do have.

Before we make decisions that affect us personally, we tend to gather as much relevant information as possible. By making a decision based upon information rather than on impulse we can minimize any uncertainty we may have about the correctness of the decision. In science the goal is fundamentally the same. To minimize uncertainty and maximize the availability of relevant information, scientists collect data (measurements from observations that are usually recorded using numbers). Whether in the context of formal research activity ("Is this advertising campaign working?") or our personal lives ("Where should I go to college?") the goal is to make as informed a decision as possible, backed up with as much relevant data as we can collect.

In a formal research setting, data are carefully collected under controlled conditions so that they will hold the promise of containing needed information. As sound and potentially valuable as data may be, however, they will not yield their information without a struggle. Information is coy. It likes to disguise itself and stay hidden in a jumble of numbers. We have to flush it out into the open using special tools—the tools that comprise statistical analysis. By subjecting the data to formal computational procedures, we can distill the information that is in the data into forms that can be assimilated, understood, communicated, and used for practical purposes. Without the organizing and summarizing of information that is accomplished by statistical analysis, we would tend to be overwhelmed and confused—aimlessly adrift in a sea of numbers.

To understand the role of statistical analysis as an information-gathering tool, it helps to regard the numerical representation of data as a code. If numbers are the coded representations of our observations, we need to crack the code to make available all the information the numbers hold. The techniques of descriptive statistics are, in a sense, decoding devices that pull the information from the data and allow us to see properties and relationships that could otherwise go unnoticed.

NUMBED BY NUMBERS: MATH ANXIETY

Some students who enroll in an introductory level statistics course are social science majors who have a negative perception of their ability to handle mathematics. Perhaps it is the prospect of grinding through complex formulae and computational procedures that triggers the anxiety, or maybe the various symbols that are used to write mathematical expressions give mathematics its alien and threatening aura.

The course of study presented in this text and in the accompanying computer software has been designed to be as nonthreatening as possible. The primary objective is *not* to train you in the mechanics of statistical computation, although some is indeed necessary. Nor is the primary objective to familiarize you with complex mathematical derivations and proofs of various sorts. This we leave to the teachers of mathematical statistics. Rather, the primary objective is to give you a conceptual understanding of the subject matter with the ultimate goal of preparing you to design, analyze, and interpret experiments.

This applied emphasis in the teaching of descriptive and inferential statistics is in keeping with modern developments because, in the present computer age, one is rarely faced with the prospect of doing a statistical analysis by hand. Nevertheless, although computational drudgery may be all but gone, a thorough understanding of the conceptual underpinnings of statistical analysis cannot be replaced by a machine. It is, therefore, the understanding of statistics that shall be stressed and, in this regard, you as social science majors are no less capable than any other group of students.

SOME BASIC TERMINOLOGY

To begin your study of statistics you will need to build a vocabulary of some basic terminology. We shall start with some definitions of the most common terms.

Population. All members of a specified group. The specification can be broad (e.g., all members of the human race) or relatively narrow (e.g., all male heads of household whose income exceeds $40,000 per year).

Sample. A subset of a population.

Population. A **population** is an entire set of people, places, or things. The term *universe* is also used in statistics to convey the notion of a complete set. In research the ultimate goal is to understand the behavior and characteristics of an entire population, but, if the population is large, it is usually impossible or impractical to collect information on every element of a population. Instead, the researcher is usually limited to studying a sample.

Sample. A **sample** is a subset of a population. To make valid conclusions about a population from studying a sample the sample must be *representative* of the population. There are special procedures that help to insure the selection of representative samples, and these will be covered at the appropriate time (chapter 7).

Population versus Sample. Populations may be arbitrarily defined with varying degrees of breadth. Consider the following definitions of population: the human race, males only, men over the age of 18, men in the armed forces, officers in the armed forces, Naval officers, etc. Each definition is more restrictive than the previous one. In fact, each of these defined populations can be regarded as a *subset* (sample) of some other population. Even the human race is a subset of all primates, which is a subset of all mammals, which is a subset of . . . , etc. In simple terms, the population, whether defined narrowly or broadly, is the true focus of the researcher's information-gathering effort. As mentioned above, a realistic alternative to having complete information on a population is having information on a representative sample from the population.

Although it may appear so from the definitions above, a population is not necessarily large and a sample is not necessarily small. For example, you know that a flip of a coin can result in only two outcomes: heads or tails. When you flip a coin you are sampling from a population that has only two possible values, and yet you may sample from this population (i.e., flip the coin) as many times as you wish. Thus, while the population consists of only two values, the sample size may be infinitely large.

VARIABLES

When the word variable is used as an adjective to describe a measurable characteristic of a person, event, phenomenon, behavior, etc., it means that whatever is being measured has the potential to change quantitatively and/or qualitatively over time. For example, let us say that the number of automobile collisions at a busy intersection varies with the seasons, reaching a peak during the winter months when the roads tend to be very slippery. Because the values recorded for the measurable characteristic "number of collisions" change over time, it is a variable. Moreover, fluctuations in the value of this variable reflect a *quantitative* change: the higher the value of the variable, the more accidents we know have taken place.

When the police reports describing accidents at this intersection are inspected, you may notice that the typical winter accident is a fender bender with a very low incidence of personal injury and modest property damage. The summertime accidents, though fewer in number, typically do involve significant personal injuries and property damage because of increased speed at the moment of collision. The difference in the type of collision, serious versus minor, is a qualitative difference.

Dependent Variable. The variable that is measured in an experiment. It is assumed to vary as a function of the independent variable.

Independent Variable. A variable that is manipulated by the experimenter (e.g., the treatment administered to a subject in an experiment).

Independent versus Dependent Variable. In a research context, however, *variable* is more likely to be used as a noun. It refers to that which is varying. If the intersection referred to above were the subject of a traffic accident analysis, the **dependent variable** would be the number of accidents that occur at the intersection. The variable is called dependent because the number of accidents depends upon another variable—the season of the year. The dependent variable refers to the measurements that are being recorded (the number of accidents), and the **independent variable** refers to the changing condition that affects the value of the dependent variable (the season of the year).

It is interesting to note that many variables (e.g., intelligence, muscular coordination, family income, etc.) can be either independent or dependent variables in different experimental contexts. For example, let us say an experimenter is studying the intelligence of adolescents as a function of whether they did or did not attend a day-care center during their preschool years. In this context the intelligence test scores of the adolescents would be the dependent variable because intelligence is expected to vary as a function of the presence or absence of day-care experience, the independent variable. If, on the other hand, an experimenter studying sleep and dreaming wished to determine whether persons of above average intelligence dream any more frequently than persons of below average intelligence, intelligence would be the independent variable. This is because the frequency of dreaming episodes, the dependent variable, is being studied as a function of the intelligence of the experimental subjects.

Dichotomous Variable. A variable that can take only one of two possible values (e.g., true/false, on/off, etc.).

Continuous Variable. A variable is continuous if, as it changes from value *A* to value *B*, it passes through all the possible values that exist between *A* and *B* (e.g., height and weight).

Discontinuous Variable. A variable is discontinuous if, as it changes from value *A* to value *B*, it changes abruptly without passing through all the values that exist between *A* and *B* (e.g., family size).

Other Attributes of Variables. Besides the distinction that is drawn between dependent and independent variables, there are other distinctions of which you should be aware. Some variables are **dichotomous variables.** That is, they can take on only two values such as true/false, yes/no, on/off, male/female, etc. Another distinction is between **continuous variables** and **discontinuous variables.** For example, a person's body weight is a continuous variable. If it changes from 150 to 155 between weighings, the person knows that with each mouthful of overindulgence his/her weight passed through all of the small increments that exist between 150 and 155. The change was not abrupt, but took place in a continuous fashion. On the other hand, other variables *do* change abruptly. For example, family size changes in discontinuous steps with the birth of each new child.

The True Limits of a Continuous Variable

As discussed above, when one's body weight changes from one value to another, the weight values flow through all of the very small increments that exist between the two points on the weight scale. With every mouthful of food or intake of fluid one's weight increases, and from such processes as perspiration, hair loss, and elimination of wastes, one's body weight decreases. Yet, our measuring instrument (a bathroom scale) is not sensitive enough to record a weight change for every morsel we eat or every drop of perspiration that evaporates. Consequently, measurement of body weight using a bathroom scale, or measurement of any continuous variable using an instrument of limited accuracy, is approximate. The real weight value may be somewhat above or somewhat below the indicated reading on the measuring instrument.

True Limits. The value of a continuous variable plus and minus one-half a scale measuring unit. For example, the true limits of 10 pounds are 9.5 to 10.5 pounds.

The **true limits** of a continuous variable are the values that are above and below the recorded value by one-half of the smallest measuring unit of the scale. These limits will contain the real value that the measuring instrument is approximating. Thus, if an accurate bathroom scale reads 155 lbs., the person weighs somewhere between 154.5 lbs. (the lower true limit) and 155.5 lbs. (the upper true limit). Because of the limitations of the measuring instrument, we know that the person's weight is unlikely to be exactly 155.000000000. . . lbs. and that any weight between 154.5 and 155.5 will show up on the scale readout as 155.

Parameter. A measurable characteristic of a population.

Statistic. A measurable characteristic of a sample.

Parameter versus Statistic. A **parameter** is a measurable characteristic of an entire population, whereas a **statistic** is a measurable characteristic of a sample. Researchers often use sample statistics to estimate population parameters, such as when the television-viewing habits of the so-called Nielsen households are used to estimate the viewing habits of the population of the United States.

As mentioned earlier, we can only use sample statistics to estimate population parameters if the sample is representative of the population. We would not, for example, wish to use the television-viewing habits of Sun City, Arizona, a community made up largely of senior citizens, to profile the viewing habits of the broad cross section of American society. We would call such a sample a *biased* sample because not all elements of the population have an equally likely chance of being included. For the same reason, using all the students taking advanced physics as a sample to represent the general population of liberal arts majors would be a biased approach to sampling. All subsets of populations may be considered samples, but only samples that meet certain conditions (to be presented in chapter 7) have a chance to be free of sampling bias.

DESCRIPTIVE VERSUS INFERENTIAL STATISTICS

Descriptive Statistic. A number that reflects a specific characteristic of a set of data.

The first part of this text is devoted to the topic of **descriptive statistics.** As you shall see in the coming chapters, applying descriptive statistics to data involves designing graphic and tabular displays (chapter 2) and/or computing special numbers (chapters 3, 4, 5, and 6) that can reveal some specific, useful, and important characteristics of the data. You are probably more familiar with descriptive statistics than you may realize because some of the most basic descriptive statistics are widely used in the news media. You may have read, for example, that in the early part of 1988 the *median* cost of a new home rose to $92,000, or that admission to the most selective colleges is difficult for those students who score lower than the 90th *percentile* on the Scholastic Aptitude Test.

Inferential Statistics. Drawing conclusions about the characteristics of populations from the information in sample data.

The topic of **inferential statistics,** the subject of the second part of the text, focuses upon the use of statistics in evaluating the accuracy of experimental predictions. These predictions are called *hypotheses* and evaluating the predictions is called *hypothesis testing*. At the end of an experiment, a decision must be made about whether the data are consistent with the researcher's prediction ("The data support the hypothesis that taking an aspirin a day lowers the risk of heart attack."), or attributable only to chance factors ("The data fail to show that the experimental rocket fuel delivers significantly more thrust than the standard fuel.").

Another mission of inferential statistics is to describe the characteristics of sample data with the eventual goal of generalizing the sample characteristics to entire populations. For example, the television-viewing habits of the Nielsen households are carefully monitored, and because the households are carefully selected to represent a broad cross section of American society, projections are made from the sample data to the overall viewing population. When you hear that 52 million persons watched at least part of Superbowl XXIII, you probably recognize this as a projection made from sample data. Polling data is routinely used to make projections about characteristics of a population.

This projection is called an inference and rests upon the assumption that the sample is representative of the population. The application of inferential statistics takes many forms, depending upon the questions that are being asked and the characteristics of the data that are available. These considerations will be covered in detail in the second section of the text when we take up the topics of hypothesis testing and parameter estimation.

STATISTICAL NOTATION

Statistics, parameters, and the mathematical operations that are used to compute them are represented with special symbols called *statistical notation*. Several different notational systems exist, and examining some statistics books in a library will make that painfully clear. Although there is no universal standard, the system used in this text is the most common, at least for statistics geared to the needs of the behavioral sciences.

Notation exists to increase the efficiency of communication. It is a shorthand that, with a single character, can indicate a series of computations to be performed or label an important statistical entity. As you progress through this text you will be introduced to many different notational symbols. Let us begin with some of the most basic ones.

Labelling Data

A set of original, unprocessed experimental observations is called *raw data*, and the scores in the set of raw data are represented with capital letters such as X and Y. The positions of scores within a set are indicated with subscripts.

So, for the set 2, 4, 5, 9, 10:

$$X_1 = 2, \quad X_2 = 4, \quad X_3 = 5, \quad X_4 = 9, \text{ and } X_5 = 10$$

This symbolic representation is much easier than saying, "The first score in the set equals 2, the second score in the set equals 4, etc." In general, a set may be represented as

$$X_1, X_2 \ldots X_i \ldots X_n,$$

where the subscript i can take any value from 1 to n. The letter n is used to designate the size of a set, and so X_n is the last score in the set. Later, in the coverage of inferential statistics, you will notice that capital N is used to designate the size of a population, whereas the lower case n is the size of a sample. Thus, a computation completed on N scores is a parameter, while a computation completed on n scores is a statistic.

The Summation Operation

The Greek letter Σ (sigma) is the symbol that directs us to add. If the addition refers to a subset of a collection of scores, additional notation below the Σ tells us where in the set to begin addition and notation on top of the Σ tells us when to stop adding. Thus,

$$\sum_{i=1}^{n} X_i$$

tells us to add all the scores in the set from the first one ($i = 1$) to the last one ($i = n$) and

$$\sum_{i=2}^{4} X_i$$

tells us to add the second, third, and fourth scores. For the set 2, 4, 5, 9, 10, the former expression equals 30, the sum of the entire set, while the latter expression equals 18, the sum of 4, 5, and 9, the second, third, and fourth scores in the set.

In practice, at least at this introductory level, all addition operations will refer to an entire set, and so the additional notation above and below Σ is unnecessary and will be omitted.

Instead of the complete expression

$$\sum_{i=1}^{n} X_i$$

the simplified expression ΣX will be used. So, for the set 2, 4, 5, 9, 10:

$$\Sigma X = X_1 + X_2 + X_3 + X_4 + X_5$$
$$\Sigma X = 2 + 4 + 5 + 9 + 10$$
$$\Sigma X = 30$$

Summation Notation. The use of the Greek Σ to stand for the "add" instruction in performing computations.

A simple application of this **summation notation** appears in the formula for the *arithmetic mean* (also called the average). The mean of a population is represented by the Greek letter μ or mu (pronounced myoo) and the mean of a sample is represented by $\overline{X}$ (read as "X bar"). Using the summation notation introduced above,

$$\mu = \frac{\Sigma X}{N} \quad \text{and} \quad \overline{X} = \frac{\Sigma X}{n}$$

Let us compute the mean of the set 2, 4, 5, 9, 10 using the formula for the mean of a sample

$$\overline{X} = \frac{\Sigma X}{n}$$
$$\overline{X} = \frac{30}{5}$$
$$\overline{X} = 6$$

In general, the population parameters you shall encounter in this text (e.g., μ) will be represented by Greek letters, while their corresponding sample statistics (e.g., $\overline{X}$) will be represented with English letters.

ROUNDING

In the latter section on statistical notation a mean was computed for the set 2, 4, 5, 9, 10: $\overline{X} = \Sigma X/n = 30/5 = 6$. The result was an integer (i.e., a whole number as opposed to one with a fractional remainder such as 6.23751). In the case of noninteger results it is important, if we are to maintain a degree of uniformity in our computational procedures, to treat remainders according to fixed guidelines. For example, consider the following set:

1, 2, 2, 3, 3, 5, 6

The mean of this set is

$$\overline{X} = \frac{\Sigma X}{n} = \frac{(1 + 2 + 2 + 3 + 3 + 5 + 6)}{7} = \frac{22}{7} = 3.1428571$$

Do we say the answer is 3 and let it go at that, or do we dutifully report all the decimal places that appear on our calculator display? In the physical sciences the convention is to report the results of such a division in terms of the same number of significant figures that appear in the raw data. In other words, since the raw data consists of all integer values (1, 2, 2, 3, 3, 5, 6), the average of these scores should be reported as an integer as well (average = 3). Only if the raw data were reported in decimals (e.g., 1.2, 2.7, 3.4, etc.) would their average be computed out to one decimal place.

This convention has not been followed in the behavioral sciences. Instead, most computational results are reported to two or three decimal places regardless of the number of significant figures in the raw data. Calculations are generally carried out to three or four decimal places more than appear in the raw data, and then the result is rounded off to two decimal places. (Some computations, as when solving for probability values, are often reported out to four decimal places. Such exceptions to the latter convention of two decimal places will be noted as we encounter them in the coming chapters.)

Rounding Convention. Take computations out to three more decimal places than exist in the original data and round back to two places.

The **rounding convention** that is observed in the behavioral sciences and in this text is as follows:

Rule 1. If the number three places to the right of the decimal point (thousandths) is less than 5, simply discard all but the first two decimal places. For example, 3.1428571 becomes 3.14 because the 2 in the thousandths position is less than 5.

Rule 2. If the number three places to the right of the decimal point (thousandths) is greater than 5, then increase the number in the hundredths position by 1. For example, 6.23751 becomes 6.24. The 3 in the hundredths position is increased to 4 because the 7 in the thousandths position is greater than 5.

Rule 3. If the number three places to the right of the decimal point (thousandths) is exactly 5 (i.e., zeros for the remaining decimal places) and the value in the hundredths position is an odd number, increase the number in the hundredths position by 1. If the number in the hundredths position is even, leave the result as is and discard all but the first two decimal places.

Thus, both 6.245000 and 6.235000 would be rounded off to 6.24. In the first case (6.245000) the exact remainder of 5 thousandths is preceded by an even number, and so we simply chop off the 5000 and are left with 6.24. In the second case the exact remainder of 5 thousandths is preceded by an odd number, 3, and so the convention dictates that we raise the three to the next even number, and the answer is 6.24.

Using Summation Notation with Parentheses

To prepare you for learning the computation of some statistics you will encounter in chapter 3, you should become familiar with use of Σ together with parentheses.

For example, ΣX^2 is not the same as $(\Sigma X)^2$. In the first expression all the scores in the set are squared before they are added, and in the second expression the set is added and the sum is squared. Thus, for the set 1, 2, 3, 4, 5:

$$\Sigma X^2 = 1^2 + 2^2 + 3^2 + 4^2 + 5^2 = 1 + 4 + 9 + 16 + 25 = 55$$

but

$$(\Sigma X)^2 = (1 + 2 + 3 + 4 + 5)^2 = (15)^2 = 225$$

The two expressions ΣX^2 and $(\Sigma X)^2$ may be combined, as in the following formula:

$$\Sigma X^2 - \frac{(\Sigma X)^2}{n}$$

If we solve this expression for the set 1, 2, 3, 4, 5 we get:

$$55 - \frac{225}{5} = 10$$

Another common use of Σ with parentheses is in expressions such as $\Sigma(X - \overline{X})^2$. This expression directs us to subtract the mean from each score in the original set, square the difference scores, and then add the results. The computation within the parentheses is done first, then the squaring operation, and the addition is done last. This procedure can be represented in tabular form as shown below for the set 1, 2, 3, 4, 5. The mean of the set is 3 since $\Sigma X/n = 3$.

X	$\overline{X}$	$(X - \overline{X})$	$(X - \overline{X})^2$
1	3	−2	4
2	3	−1	1
3	3	0	0
4	3	1	1
5	3	2	4
$\Sigma X = 15$		$\Sigma(X - \overline{X}) = 0$	$\Sigma(X - \overline{X})^2 = 10$

MEASUREMENT SCALES

The numerical representations of our experimental observations, the research data we collect and wish to analyze, can exist in four different types of measurement scales: Ratio, Interval, Ordinal, and Nominal.

Even though the scaling of data is a topic that is not widely addressed outside of a formal course, this material is very important because specific statistical tests assume that the data reflect a certain level of measurement. Later, when you are aware of the assumptions that apply to the various statistical tests and are familiar with the tests themselves, knowing the measurement scale of a set of data will point you toward the correct statistical analysis. Selection of a statistical test is one task even sophisticated computers cannot help you with. Machines will do any statistical analysis you wish on any numbers you input, but it still takes a human to load the correct program and to interpret the results of the analysis.

Rather than simply naming the four scales and listing their specific properties, the following brief exercise will allow you to discover for yourself that there are four different scales of measurement. We shall ask the same set of four questions about the same score values in four different measurement contexts.

The Ratio Scale

For the first context we shall assume that the scores are weight scores.

0 lbs. 25 lbs. 50 lbs. 75 lbs. 100 lbs.

Ratio Scale. The highest level of measurement that has all the characteristics of the interval scale plus a true zero point. Physical measures are commonly ratio (e.g., height, weight, distance, pressure, etc.).

Here are four questions about these **ratio scaled** numbers followed by the answers:

1. Does a score of zero represent the true absence of that which is being measured?

Answer: Yes. If the weighing scale is empty, a zero does represent the absence of any weight.

2. Does the difference between 25 and 50 represent the exact same quantity of that which is being measured that exists between 50 and 75, or between 75 and 100?

Answer: Yes. The difference is 25 pounds for any two points on the scale that are 25 units apart. Equal intervals represent equal quantity.

3. Does a number with a higher numerical value represent more of what is being measured than a number with a lower numerical value (e.g., 50 vs. 25)?

Answer: Yes. The higher the number the more weight that is present. Fifty pounds is more weight than twenty-five pounds.

4. Does a number that has a different value from another number (e.g., 50 vs. 75) represent either a quantitative or qualitative difference?

Answer: Yes. There is a quantitative difference. Fifty pounds represents a different amount of weight than seventy-five pounds.

Many of the variables we use on a daily basis (time, distance, volume, etc.) are ratio scaled.

The Interval Scale

Interval Scale. A measurement scale with an arbitrary zero point in which numerically equal intervals at different locations on the scale reflect the same quantitative difference (e.g., temperature in Celsius or Fahrenheit).

Now let us change the context. The numbers will remain the same, except that now they are temperature values on a Celsius scale. On this **interval scale** zero is the temperature at which water freezes and 100 is the temperature at which water boils.

$$0°\ C,\quad 25°\ C,\quad 50°\ C,\quad 75°\ C,\quad 100°\ C$$

1. Does a score of zero represent the true absence of that which is being measured?

Answer: No. The true absence of heat is not 0° C. This temperature scale has an arbitrary zero point: the temperature at which water freezes. The true absence of heat is 0° K, which is −273 degrees on the centigrade scale.

2. Does the difference between 25 and 50 represent the exact same quantity of that which is being measured that exists between 50 and 75, or between 75 and 100?

Answer: Yes. The difference in heat between any two values that are 25 units apart is the same. Equal intervals represent equal quantity.

3. Does a number with a higher numerical value represent more of what is being measured than a number with a lower numerical value (e.g., 50 vs. 25)?

Answer: Yes. The higher the number the more heat that is present. Fifty degrees is hotter than twenty-five degrees.

4. Does a number that has a different value from another number (e.g., 50 vs. 75) represent either a quantitative or qualitative difference?

Answer: Yes. There is a quantitative difference. Fifty degrees represents a different amount of heat than seventy-five degrees.

Notice that the interval scale retains all the properties of the ratio scale except that the value of zero does not represent the true absence of that which is being measured. The principal effect of the arbitrary zero point is that ratio statements are not correct. For example, 75° C is not twice as hot as 37.5° C. Instead, as shown in figure 1.1, 75° C is twice as hot as −99° C.

With respect to the earlier statement that "knowing the measurement scale of a set of data will point you toward the correct statistical analysis," the distinction between interval and ratio scaling is largely academic. In choosing an appropriate statistical test for our data we do not need to make the fine distinction between the two scales. This is because several statistical analyses assume at least interval level scaling of the data, but none assumes only ratio scaling. Therefore, in practice one need only meet the requirements of interval scaling for even the most demanding test assumptions.

The Ordinal Scale

Ordinal Scale. A measurement scale in which values reflect only rank order (e.g., the order of finishing a race).

Now the context will be changed again. This time the scores represent an **ordinal scale** from zero to 100 that judges are using to rate the quality of baked goods at a county fair.

0 pts. 25 pts. 50 pts. 75 pts. 100 pts.

1. Does a score of zero represent the true absence of that which is being measured?

Answer: Not necessarily. Relative to the other baked goods, a lot rated with a zero may be on the bottom rung as far as taste and texture are concerned, but next to raw octopus they may seem downright tasty. In a subjective rating

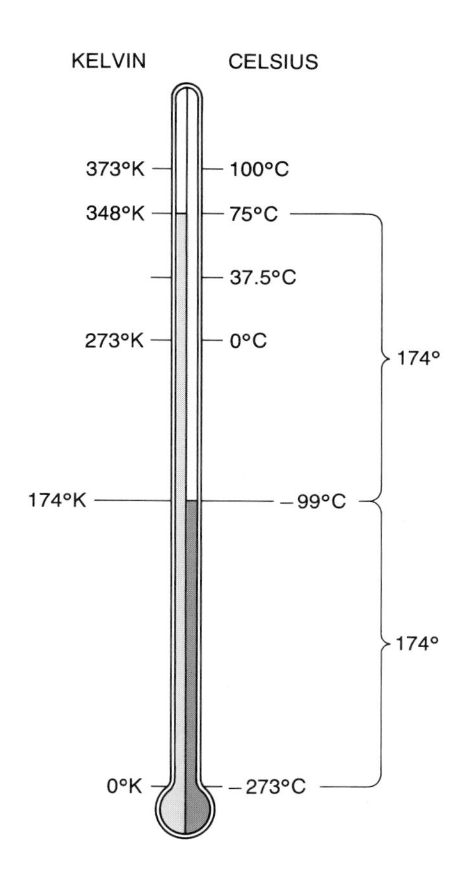

Figure 1.1

Temperatures in Kelvin and Celsius to show that 75° C is twice as hot as −99° C.

scale we cannot defend the notion that zero represents the complete absence of any of the quality being measured.

2. Does the difference between 25 and 50 represent the exact same quantity of that which is being measured that exists between 50 and 75, or between 75 and 100?

Answer: No. The difference between baked goods given a score of 25 and those given a score of 50 is not necessarily the exact same difference in quality that exists between a score of 75 and 100. Again, as in the previous question, this is because scores are assigned on the basis of a subjective rating.

3. Does a number with a higher numerical value represent more of what is being measured than a number with a lower numerical value (e.g., 50 vs. 25)?

Answer: Yes. Even though the scale does not have a true zero point and even though equal intervals do not necessarily represent equal quantity, one may assume that for any given judge, the higher the score is, the higher the quality of the baked goods. Fifty represents higher quality than twenty-five.

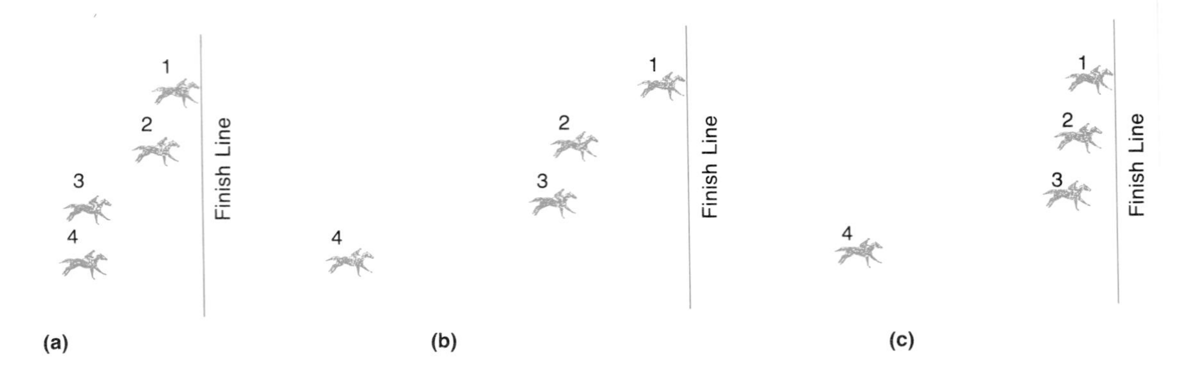

Figure 1.2

A few patterns of finishing a horse race to illustrate 1,2,3,4 as an ordinal scale.

4. Does a number that has a different value from another number (e.g., 50 vs. 75) represent either a quantitative or qualitative difference?

Answer: Yes. There is a qualitative difference. Baked goods that are assigned different score values (e.g., 50 vs. 75) are regarded to be of different quality. In the ordinal scale the values convey quantity, but this scale has no true zero point and equal intervals between numbers do not necessarily imply equal quantity.

Scaling and Statistics: An Illustration. Having discussed three of the measurement scales, let us digress briefly for a simple illustration of why the scaling of data must be considered when we compute statistics. We may compute a statistic such as the mean (average) for any set of data, regardless of the scaling. All that is required is to add up all the score values and divide by the number of scores in the set. If, however, the mean is computed on other than interval or ratio data the result will be uninterpretable. For example, in figure 1.2 a few patterns of finishing a horse race are illustrated. Applying the criteria above, you should see that these data (1, 2, 3, and 4) are ordinal. In part (c) of figure 1.2, if horses #1 and #4 are owned by Calumet Stables and horses #2 and #3 are owned by Fallbrook Stables, did the entries of the two stables perform the same on the average? (Both the average of 1 and 4 and the average of 2 and 3 are the same—2.50.) I think you will agree that the Fallbrook horses turned in the better performance overall even though the average of the two finishing orders are the same. In short, plugging ordinal data into a statistical formula that assumes ratio or interval data gives a meaningless result.

Some examples of ordinally scaled variables include scores determined by judges at a diving competition, essay contest, talent contest, etc. Also, minerals may be ordered in terms of their hardness by determining which specimen is capable of scratching (or being scratched by) another specimen. The resulting numbers (e.g., diamond = 1) are ordinal.

The Nominal Scale

In the final question/answer scenario the numbers will be the labels on the jerseys of the starting five members of a basketball team. Because the values are being used only as labels, this is called a **nominal** (naming) **scale.** Notice in answering the following questions how very little information is conveyed by nominal scores.

Nominal Scale. A measurement scale in which numbers are used as labels or names rather than to reflect quantitative information (e.g., the numbers on athletic uniforms).

1. Does a score of zero represent the true absence of that which is being measured?

Answer: No. Nothing is being measured. The number is being used only as a label like a Social Security number, license number, etc.

2. Does the difference between 25 and 50 represent the exact same quantity of that which is being measured that exists between 50 and 75, or between 75 and 100?

Answer: No. The intervals between the jersey numbers of different players have no meaning. The numbers are used only to distinguish the players from each other.

3. Does a number with a higher numerical value represent more of what is being measured than a number with a lower numerical value (e.g., 50 vs. 25)?

Answer: No. Numbers are not assigned to team players to reflect ability, speed, strength, or anything else. They are just labels, and their magnitude is arbitrary.

4. Does a number that has a different value from another number (e.g., 50 vs. 75) represent either a quantitative or qualitative difference?

Answer: Yes. There is no quantitative difference, but there is a qualitative difference. The player wearing 50 is a different person than the player wearing 75. Each number gives each player a unique identity on his team.

From the above answers we see that the numerical values of nominal data serve only as labels. No quantitative information is expressed or implied by the numerical values. As we saw above with ordinal data, when certain statistics, such as the mean, are computed on nominal data, they cannot be interpreted. For example, it tells you nothing about the team to know that the average value of the jersey labels is 50.

Some common examples of nominal data include telephone numbers, Social Security numbers, apartment numbers, street address numbers, bank account numbers, model numbers, etc.

Table 1.1

A summary of the properties of the four measurement scales.

	Measurement Scales			
Scale properties:	Nominal	Ordinal	Interval	Ratio
a true zero point	No	No	No	Yes
equal intervals represent equal quantity	No	No	Yes	Yes
different values represent different quantity	No	Yes	Yes	Yes
different values represent either a quantitative (**) or a qualitative (*) difference	Yes*	Yes**	Yes**	Yes**

COMPARING THE FOUR MEASUREMENT SCALES

The results of the preceding exercise are summarized in table 1.1. The answers to all the questions were "yes" only for the ratio scaled weight scores. Only when a scale has a true zero point can 50 be counted on to mean twice as much as 25. Fifty pounds, 50 miles, 50 apples, etc., all represent twice as much as 25, but 50° C does not represent twice as much heat as 25 because 0° C is an arbitrary zero point. Similarly, it is a misrepresentation of the information in the ratings to say that a pie given a score of 75 by a judge at the county fair is three times better than one with a score of 25. We cannot defend the notion that subjective impressions convey enough precision to interpret them in that way.

The interval scale differed from the ratio scale only by the absence of a true zero point. Unlike the lower levels of measurement (ordinal and nominal) equal intervals mean the same thing in an interval scale. The difference in heat between 60° F and 65° F is the same as between 75° F and 80° F.

On the other hand, in an ordinal scale, such as that used to represent the positions of horses at the end of a race, the distance between the second horse and the third horse at the finish (by a nose to several lengths back) may be quite different from the difference between the third horse and the fourth horse. The numerical difference between 2 and 3 and between 3 and 4 is one unit in both cases, but in an ordinal scale the equality of the intervals is meaningless. Only the relative value of the numbers is important (1st, 2d, 3d, 4th, etc.). In fact, an infinite number of spatial arrangements between horses can exist at the finish of a race while, at the same time, preserving the same order of finishing. A few of the possible patterns are shown in figure 1.2 to convey the point that the numerical differences between horses 1, 2, 3, and 4 convey only order information. As you can see from this illustration, the difference between horse #1 and horse #2 is not necessarily the same as between horse #2 and horse #3 even though 2 − 1 and 3 − 2 both equal one unit on the scale.

Nominal versus Ratio

You would think it would be easy to distinguish nominal data from ratio data. The former is the lowest level of measurement while the latter is the highest. Sometimes, however, it can be tricky. Consider the following example.

A pollster placed telephone calls to a random sample of households in a city to survey the public opinion of three candidates who were soon to compete in a local mayoral election. The data represent the voters' responses to the question, "If the election were held today, for whom would you vote?"

Candidate	Votes
Powers	25
Briggs	50
O'Shea	75

The three numbers are called *cell frequencies* and represent the results of 150 separate telephone calls. The table shows that 25 persons voted for Powers, 50 persons voted for Briggs, and 75 persons voted for O'Shea. On the face of it these data appear to be on a scale with a true zero point. After all, there is such a thing as a candidate getting zero votes, even though it did not actually happen in this case. Also, it does appear to be a fair statement that O'Shea got three times the votes of Powers and twice as many as Briggs. These characteristics exist only in ratio data.

If these data are not ratio, surely they are at least interval. After all, isn't the difference between 25 votes and 50 votes the same as between 50 and 75 votes? Equal intervals mean the same thing for these data, don't they?

The requirement for ordinal data seems the easiest of all to meet with regard to election results because the candidate with the most votes wins. O'Shea, with 75 votes, would be reported as having won the preelection poll because her vote total exceeded all the others. In an ordinal scale the larger the number is, the greater quantity there is of whatever is being measured.

As reasonable as the above comments on the scaling of the poll data may appear to be, none reveals the fact that the data are really nominal, the lowest level of measurement. To identify correctly the scaling of data we have to ask, "What is the nature of one single experimental observation (a datum)?" When we reconstruct a mental picture of the pollster collecting data and

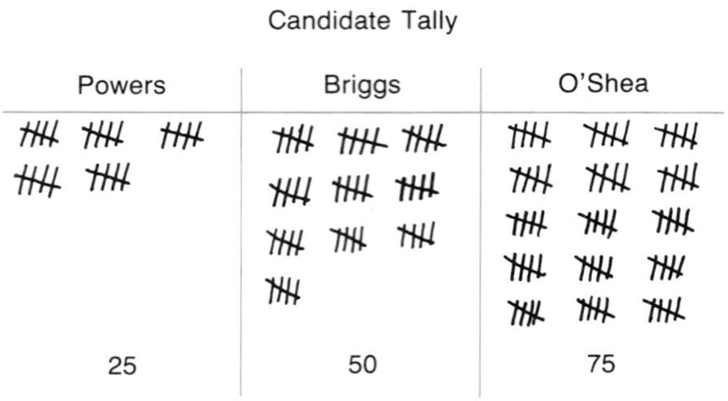

Figure 1.3

A tally of election results to show the nominal scaling of the data.

Candidate Tally

Powers	Briggs	O'Shea
25	50	75

recording the results of a single telephone call, we can appreciate that the data represent a simple tally. The original data sheet probably would look like the representation in figure 1.3. The data are so low level that a voter's response may be recorded with a simple tally mark in one of three categories (Powers vs. Briggs vs. O'Shea). No numbers are required to record each voter's response. Only when the tally marks are added are the data represented with numbers. The data we see (25, 50, and 75) may look like three ratio scaled numbers, but these values are really 150 separate categorical responses distributed over the three voting categories and, for this reason, these data are nominally scaled.

If you understand the above description of the typical data-gathering process for nominal data, it should be no surprise that nominal data are also called frequency data and categorical data. Notice that when the data are nominal the individual datum conveys absolutely no quantitative information. The measurement, if it can even be called measurement, is qualitative in nature.

Summary

Statistics, as a discipline, was described as a tool for extracting information from data with the eventual goal of making decisions based upon that information. Following a discussion of some basic terminology, you were introduced to some of the symbols that are used to compute statistics and the measurement scales that typify various kinds of experimental data.

Key Terms

Continuous Variable
Dependent Variable
Descriptive Statistics
Dichotomous Variable
Discontinuous Variable
Independent Variable
Inferential Statistics
Interval Scale
Nominal Scale
Ordinal Scale
Parameter
Population
Ratio Scale
Rounding Convention
Sample
Statistic
Summation Notation
True Limits

Exercises

1. Assume you are the Director of Admissions for a college. You must look at a variety of data to help you make the decision to admit or not to admit a particular student applicant. How are the data (e.g., rank in high school class, S.A.T. scores, letters of recommendation, quality of essay on college application, high school grade average, I.Q., etc.) scaled?
2. If you are in the college athletic department and are examining college applications to make recruitment and athletic scholarship decisions, what data would you want the applicant to provide for your inspection? (Pick your favorite sport: swimming, gymnastics, football, basketball, baseball, hockey, or any other with which you are familiar.) After listing some of the data you would want to inspect, identify the scaling of each variable you inspected.
3. For each of the following sets of scores solve the expressions:

I. a. ΣX

b. ΣX^2

c. $(\Sigma X)^2$

II. $\Sigma X^2 - \frac{(\Sigma X)^2}{n}$

III. $\frac{\Sigma X}{n}$

IV. $\Sigma(X - \overline{X})^2$

a. 4, 5, 6, 7, 8
b. 16, 32, 30, 16, 20, 24
c. 1.9, 6.9, 4.9, 2.9, 3.4

4. Round each of the following numbers to two decimal places.

a. 11.42563
b. 15.15412
c. 22.67500
d. 85.50499
e. 10.76500
f. 32.36502
g. 47.50001

5. There are four scales in the laboratory that weigh to different levels of precision. Scale 1 is capable of weighing to the nearest gram, scale 2 is capable of weighing to the nearest 0.1 gram, scale 3 is capable of weighing to the nearest 0.01 gram, and scale 4 will weigh to the nearest milligram (0.001 gram). What are the true limits of the following weight scores if they were obtained on the various scales as shown below?

Scale 1	Scale 2	Scale 3	Scale 4
43 grams	76.7 grams	84.23 grams	31.177 grams

6. Explain the distinction between an independent variable and a dependent variable, dichotomous and nondichotomous variables, and continuous vs. discontinuous variables.
7. Explain the distinction that is drawn between a statistic and a parameter.
8. Explain the distinction that is drawn between descriptive statistics and inferential statistics.

9. An experimental psychologist wants to evaluate three breeds of dogs for their suitability as Seeing Eye dogs. What behavioral attributes would be consistent with suitability for Seeing Eye duty? What behavioral measures can you think of that would reflect the presence of these attributes? Design some experiments to evaluate the three breeds, listing the independent variable, the dependent variable, and the scaling of the dependent variable (nominal, ordinal, interval, ratio) for each experiment.
10. Substitute the following values in the expressions that appear below: 10, 4, 3, 5, 9, 6, 12.
    - **a.** ΣX^2
    - **b.** $(\Sigma X)^2$
    - **c.** $\Sigma X^2 - \frac{(\Sigma X)^2}{n}$
    - **d.** $\overline{X}$
    - **e.** $\Sigma(X - \overline{X})^2$
    - **f.** $\frac{\Sigma X^2}{n} - \overline{X}^2$
11. Only the ______________ scale has a true zero point, representing the true absence of quantity of the variable being measured.
12. Data that belong to the ______________ scale are also called categorical or frequency data.
13. An example of a dichotomous variable is ______________ .
14. An example of a discontinuous variable is ______________ .
15. What are the true limits of the following numbers:
    - **a.** 12
    - **b.** 17.8
    - **c.** 18.65
    - **d.** 9.017
    - **e.** 100
16. Using the rounding convention described in the text, present the results of the following expressions:
    - **a.** 20/3
    - **b.** 20.5/3
    - **c.** 20.15/3

17. Using the following data, calculate the value of the expressions that appear below.

a. ΣX

b. $\Sigma X - 4$

c. $\Sigma(X - 4)$

d. $\Sigma X + 3$

e. $\Sigma(X + 3)$

f. $(\Sigma X)(\Sigma Y)$

g. $\Sigma(X - Y)$

h. $\Sigma X + \Sigma Y$

i. $\Sigma(X + Y)$

j. ΣX^2

k. ΣY^2

l. ΣXY

X	Y
14	8
8	9
7	12
10	17
6	14
5	10

18. What is the difference between quantitative measurement and qualitative measurement?

19. Using the following data, calculate the value of the expressions that appear below.

a. ΣX

b. $\Sigma X - 2$

c. $\Sigma(X - 2)$

d. $\Sigma X + 3$

e. $\Sigma(X + 3)$

f. $(\Sigma X)(\Sigma Y)$

g. $\Sigma(X - Y)$

h. $\Sigma X + \Sigma Y$

i. $\Sigma(X + Y)$

j. ΣX^2

k. ΣY^2

l. ΣXY

X	Y
12	6
7	9
4	10
9	5
6	2

CHAPTER 2

Frequency Distributions

There are two fundamental approaches to describing data, and the two tend to complement each other. One is essentially a visual approach that relies upon the use of graphic and tabular displays. The other approach is the application of specific computational procedures to the data that reveal the important properties and relationships that are present. The results of these computations are called *statistics*, and statistical representation of data is, for the most part, the subject of the subsequent chapters in this text.

In this chapter the principal emphasis will be on the interpretation of a tabular representation of data called the **grouped frequency distribution.** The actual preparation of the table will also be discussed because, by understanding how a grouped frequency distribution is constructed, you will more easily understand its descriptive power. You are not, however, expected to apply these hand methods to the analysis of large volumes of real data. In today's world we use computers for such tasks. Data base managers, spreadsheet programs, and both mainframe- and microcomputer-based commercial statistics packages commonly contain routines that form computer graphic and tabular displays of data. Even if you have never seen a computer actually produce complex charts, graphs, and tables from raw data, you have probably seen the computer advertisements on television and in magazines with the color pie charts, histograms, etc. It's very impressive. After selecting the correct program module, all the user has to do is input the data and select the display mode from a list of choices called a *menu*. Because of the existence of such powerful and readily available tools, the

Grouped Frequency Distribution. The tabular summary of an ungrouped frequency distribution that is accomplished by dividing the entire range of the data into 15 or so equal-sized ranges called class intervals. A tally is taken to determine how many scores fall within the range of each class interval.

hand calculation procedures, which are described below, are not intended to be a how-to guide for table preparation. Rather, they are presented to help you understand better the information in the table and how to pull it out.

Preparing raw data for display in the form of a grouped frequency distribution means imposing organization on a disordered array of scores. The scores that appear below represent the number of units sold by a group of ninety salespersons during one three-month period.

Assume you are one of the ninety salespersons and you arrive at work one day to find these scores posted outside the main conference room. You happen to have sold seventy-one units, and it would be normal for you to want to compare your performance to the performance of a "typical" coworker. Perhaps your intuitive statistical sense would direct you to get a general idea of how clustered the scores are about some *central value* (average). By comparing your personal sales performance to an average performance of all the salespersons, you could determine if your performance was better, worse, or the same as that "typical" level of salesmanship.

Maybe you would take a different approach and simply inspect the ninety scores to determine the highest and the lowest scores to see where your score of seventy-one falls relative to these two extremes. Naturally, the closer your seventy-one is to the higher of the two extreme values, the better you did relative to your coworkers, and the closer your score is to the lower of the two extremes, the worse you did.

Whatever approach you choose to evaluate your performance relative to your coworkers, it would be difficult to get the information you seek without extensive inspection of the raw data. Even if you did search carefully through the entire set of ninety scores to find the lowest and highest values, the clustering of scores around certain values would most likely elude you.

THE FIRST LEVEL OF ORGANIZATION: THE SORT

Imposing a very simple level of organization on these data, a simple descending sort, partially enhances our ability to gain impressions of the clustering of scores about some central value(s) in the distribution and how

Table 2.1

The number of units sold by 90 salespersons.

112, 102, 92, 83, 83, 75, 128, 33, 42, 58, 68, 65, 44, 76, 72, 24, 90, 54, 62, 32, 55, 104,
122, 95, 89, 60, 48, 64, 86, 68, 33, 51, 73, 55, 37, 43, 22, 82, 94, 77, 72, 100, 65, 50, 63, 130,
67, 47, 52, 28, 80, 74, 78, 82, 95, 107, 76, 81, 106, 69, 35, 45, 49, 51, 109, 72, 57, 28, 30,
46, 55, 60, 61, 138, 93, 86, 86, 79, 117, 53, 62, 58, 65, 73, 65, 71, 114, 85, 98, 38

Table 2.2

Sales data in sorted form.

138, 130, 128, 122, 117, 114, 112, 109, 107, 106, 104, 102, 100, 98, 95, 95, 94, 93, 92, 90, 89, 86, 86, 86, 85, 83, 83, 82, 82, 81, 80, 79, 78, 77, 76, 76, 75, 74, 73, 73, 72, 72, 72, 71, 69, 68, 68, 67, 65, 65, 65, 65, 64, 63, 62, 62, 61, 60, 60, 58, 58, 57, 55, 55, 55, 54, 53, 52, 51, 51, 50, 49, 48, 47, 46, 45, 44, 43, 42, 38, 37, 35, 33, 33, 32, 30, 28, 28, 24, 22

Frequency. The number of times a particular score value or range of score values appears in a distribution.

Dispersal. The degree to which the score values in a distribution are spread about the central (i.e., average) value. The range is a measure of dispersal.

Range. The highest score in a distribution minus the lowest score plus one. For example, the range of the distribution 11, 12, 12, 12, 13, 13, 14, 15 is $15 - 11 + 1 = 5$.

broadly spread out the scores are above and below the central value(s). When you look at the sorted array of scores, it becomes more obvious that some scores appear more than once (e.g., 65). The number of times a score appears in a distribution is its **frequency.** Inspection of the data reveals that 65 has a frequency of four, 62 has a frequency of two, 55 has a frequency of three, etc.

The Range. With the data now sorted, the range, a crude measure of the **dispersal** of the scores, can now be easily computed. The **range** is the top score minus the bottom score plus one. For the data in table 2.1 the range is $138 - 22 + 1 = 117$. Sometimes the range is described as simply the top score in a distribution minus the bottom score, and the plus one is omitted from the computation. The range is such a crude measure that, in most cases, it would be too strong a statement to say that failing to use the "plus one" in the computation of the range presents a misleading or incorrect description of the dispersal of the scores in a distribution. Nevertheless, to be entirely accurate, the "plus one" should be included in the computation. For example, let us say a crate of eggs falls off a delivery truck and you have the job of inspecting all the egg cartons that were in that crate for broken eggs. If there were originally one dozen intact eggs per carton, your data could include numbers ranging from a low score of zero (no eggs in a particular carton were found to be broken) to twelve (all eggs in a particular carton were found to be broken). Simple inspection reveals that the set:

$$0, 1, 2, 3, 4, 5, 6, 7, 8, 9, 10, 11, 12$$

has 13 values ($12 - 0 + 1 = 13$) *not* just 12 ($12 - 0 = 12$). Only by including the "plus one" in the computation do we get the correct answer of 13 for the range.

True Limits Revisited

In the first chapter the **true limits** of a continuous variable were defined as the score value plus and minus one-half a measuring unit. The data in table

2.1 are all integers (no decimals or fractions), and so the true limits of each score equal (score value) − 0.5 to (score value) + 0.5. For example, the true limits of the score 71 are 70.5 to 71.5. If the smallest measuring unit were in tenths and there were scores such as 35.5 or 40.2, their true limits would be 35.45 to 35.55 and 40.15 to 40.25.

Computing the Range Using True Limits

To compute the range using true limits we take the upper limit of the top score (138.5) and subtract the lower limit of the bottom score (21.5). This gives us the same answer as the "plus one" method that we used earlier with the actual lowest and highest scores (22 and 138).

true limits method: $138.5 - 21.5 = 117$

"plus one" method: $138 - 22 + 1 = 117$

To find the middle of the range we add one-half of the range to the lowest score: $22 + 1/2 \cdot 117 = 80.5$. You can now see that your score of 71 falls in the lower half of the range, and the score of 71 begins to take on meaning.

Central Tendency. A statistical description of a distribution using a single value that is usually located exactly in the middle or near the middle of the distribution. The mean or *average* of a sample or population is an example of a statistic that describes central tendency.

Central Tendency. In addition to pinpointing the middle of the range, by inspecting the sorted array we can also get a rough idea of the **central tendency** of the scores. The measures of central tendency will be the topic of the next chapter, and detailed definitions of these measures and a discussion of their properties will be put off until that time. In the present context of the frequency distribution it will be sufficient to think of central tendency as a value somewhere near the middle of the range about which you are likely to find a clustering of scores. The average (or mean) of a set that was computed using statistical notation in chapter 1 is one measure of central tendency.

As you inspect the sorted array notice that there is a clustering of scores in the 50s, 60s, 70s, and 80s with some repetition of some of the score values (e.g., 65, 65, 65, 65). When you evaluate your score of 71 with reference to the vague impression of central tendency projected by the clustering and repetition of score values in the sorted array, it suggests a sales performance more towards the top half of the sales force. The contradiction between the latter impression of the meaning of a score of 71 and the earlier computation that showed your score of 71 to be lower than 80, the middle of the range, will be resolved as our description of these sales data continues.

Table 2.3

Ungrouped frequency distribution (X = score, f = frequency).

X	f	X	f	X	f	X	f
138	1	90	1	68	2	47	1
130	1	89	1	67	1	46	1
128	1	86	3	65	4	45	1
122	1	85	1	64	1	44	1
117	1	83	2	63	1	43	1
114	1	82	2	62	2	42	1
112	1	81	1	61	1	38	1
109	1	80	1	60	2	37	1
107	1	79	1	58	2	35	1
106	1	78	1	57	1	33	2
104	1	77	1	55	3	32	1
102	1	76	2	54	1	30	1
100	1	75	1	53	1	28	2
98	1	74	1	52	1	24	1
95	2	73	2	51	2	22	1
94	1	72	3	50	1		
93	1	71	1	49	1		
92	1	69	1	48	1		

THE SECOND LEVEL OF ORGANIZATION: THE UNGROUPED FREQUENCY DISTRIBUTION

Ungrouped Frequency Distribution. The sequential arrangement of a distribution presented with the frequency tally for each score value.

Compared to your experience inspecting the array of raw data (table 2.1), you are no doubt finding it easier to grasp certain features of the data from the sorted array (table 2.2). Nevertheless, there is much room for improvement. You still do not have a firm impression about the relative merit of your score of 71 because your evaluation using the range and central tendency resulted in conflicting impressions. Your 71 was in the lower half of the range but appeared to be slightly above the middle of the sorted array. To make it even easier to see trends in the data we can organize the scores into an **ungrouped frequency distribution** (table 2.3). The table is set up by listing every score value that exists in descending sequence and recording the number of times each score value occurs in the data (i.e., the score frequency). There is nothing wrong with including scores that do not exist, except that it requires additional space. For example, in the ungrouped frequency distribution shown in table 2.3 there are no entries for score values 137, 136, 135, 134, 133, 132, and 131. This is because these score values do not exist in the raw data. If you wish the ungrouped frequency distribution to reflect such gaps in the data, as some prefer, simply include the values for the nonexistent scores in the X column and enter a zero in the frequency column.

Now you can more easily place the score of 71 in the context of all the other scores. For example, by counting the frequencies of all scores greater than 71 you could determine that forty-three salespersons sold more than you, and by counting the frequencies of all scores less than 71 you could determine that forty-six salespersons sold less than you. This presentation may meet your personal need to know how you compare to the other workers, but the company executives are less likely to be satisfied with such a sprawling table. They would want the table presented in a way that would permit more information to be retrieved from the data.

THE THIRD LEVEL OF ORGANIZATION: THE GROUPED FREQUENCY DISTRIBUTION

Much more information can be fit into roughly the same table size by imposing one more level of organization on the data—the formation of a **grouped frequency distribution** that includes three new descriptive statistics, which will be defined and discussed in the next section of this chapter: relative frequency, cumulative frequency, and cumulative percent. The process of grouping involves summarizing the data, and summarizing always results in the loss of specific information. We want to summarize to increase the efficiency of communication, but we do not want to lose so much information that important aspects of the data are obscured. To strike a reasonable balance between summarization and preserving information, a convention has been established for making grouped frequency distributions. These rules will be described below and will be applied to our data for *demonstration* purposes. (Again, the principal purpose for presenting hand computation procedures is to give you a fundamental grasp of the process. With the widespread availability of computers and appropriate software, the type of hand calculations described next are seldom done.)

Class Interval. The range that is used to group the scores in a distribution into discrete clusters or "classes." According to convention, the ideal size of the class interval is usually fairly close to the range of the data divided by 15.

Step 1. *Find the range of the scores.* We have done that for our data, and the range is 117.

Step 2. *Determine the width of each class interval.* One approach is to divide the range by 15 to determine the size of the **class interval.** Some statisticians take the position that a grouped frequency distribution should have between

10 and 20 intervals. Others recommend 12 to 15 intervals, and still others recommend "around 10." All will agree, however, that fewer than 10 is to risk oversummarizing the data, and over 20 is to risk undersummarizing. After all, if you have too many class intervals your table would resemble an ungrouped frequency distribution.

The number 15 is midway between 10 and 20, and so that is a good starting point. If the results are unsatisfactory with 15 intervals, by all means experiment with values less than or greater than 15. (You shall have an opportunity to do this in the GROUPED.BAS tutorial.) For our data 116/15 = 7.73, and so 8 is a reasonable size for the class interval.

Some prefer to set the size of the interval to an odd number so that the midpoint of the interval can be more easily determined. This makes it easier to construct a graphic representation (a frequency polygon) from the data in the grouped frequency table, but an odd-sized class interval is by no means required.

Step 3. *Enter the class intervals in the table in descending order.* As you can see in table 2.4, the first entry in the "Class Interval" column is 131–138. This was established by taking the score with the highest value in the distribution (138) and counting down until the range of the interval equals the interval size of 8 that was set in Step 2. (To verify the range of this interval, 138 − 131 + 1 = 8.)

Nominal Limits and True Limits

Nominal Limits. The limits of a class interval in whole units of measurement.

True Limits (of an interval). The range of an interval plus and minus one-half a measuring unit. For example, if the nominal limits of a class interval are 12 to 18, the true limits are 11.5 to 18.5.

The values listed in the table as the interval limits (e.g., 131 and 138 for the top interval) are called the **nominal limits** as distinguished from the **true limits** of the interval. (In describing a limit as nominal we mean "in name only" or "not real." No information about the scaling of the variable, as in the **nominal scale** (chapter 1) is implied.) The true limits of an interval are the lower real limit of the bottom of the interval and the upper real limit of the top of the interval. As discussed earlier, the lower real limit of a score is the score value minus one-half a measuring unit and the upper real limit of a score is the score value plus one-half a measuring unit. Thus, the true limits of the top interval are 130.5 to 138.5.

Failure to appreciate the difference between the nominal limits and the true limits of a class interval can lead to a common error: making the class intervals too large by one unit. For example, if you started with 138 and counted down eight more score values you would set the lowest score in the top interval at 130 (130 − 8 = 130). The interval 130–138, however, has a size of nine (138, 137, 136, 135, 134, 133, 132, 131, 130), and the class interval that we determined in the previous step was set for eight. There are nine scores in the interval rather than eight because the top score was not included in the count, as it should have been. To clarify this point further, consider the true limits of the class interval 131–138 as 130.5–138.5. If you think of the class interval in terms of its true limits, as illustrated below, you can see that the interval 131–138 is eight units wide:

130.5 131.5 132.5 133.5 134.5 135.5 136.5 137.5 138.5
1 2 3 4 5 6 7 8

Completing the Class Interval Column

Convention dictates that the table be set up in descending order so that the scores with the high values appear at the top of the table. This convention has been observed in table 2.4 by placing the interval 131–138 at the top. Next, we must list the remaining nominal intervals in descending widths of the preset interval size. Because we are using an interval size of eight for our data, the remaining intervals, as shown in table 2.4, are 123–130, 115–122, etc. Notice that the true *upper* limit of the letter interval, 122.5, is the same as the true *lower* limit of the next highest interval. Thus, true limits are shared across intervals and nominal limits are not.

Flexibility in Setting the Intervals

It is possible for either the lowest score in the lowest interval or the highest score in the highest interval to be outside the actual range of the data. For example, after counting down from the top score of 138 in intervals of eight, the bottom interval turns out to be 19–26 even though the lowest actual score in the data set is 22. This is not a problem as long as you understand that the range of the scores in the data set has not suddenly and magically increased.

Some statisticians prefer to set up the intervals so that the lower nominal limit of each interval is a multiple of the selected interval size. For us to abide by this convention all lower nominal limits would have to be multiples of eight. For example, we could have set the top interval to be 136–143, the next interval to be 128–135, etc. Notice that eight divides evenly into 136 and 128. As mentioned in the previous paragraph, it is not a problem for the upper limit of the top interval (143) to be greater than the highest score in the data set (138), as long as the reasons for the apparent extension of the range for the data set are understood and taken into consideration in any interpretation of the data.

The fact that there is a degree of flexibility in how to set up the intervals in a grouped frequency distribution should not confuse you. It just means

Table 2.4

The grouped frequency distribution with relative frequency, cumulative frequency, and cumulative percent.

Class Interval	*f*	*Relative f*	*Cum f*	*Cum %*
131–138	1	.011	90	100
123–130	2	.022	89	98.9
115–122	2	.022	87	96.7
107–114	4	.044	85	94.4
99–106	4	.044	81	90.0
91–98	6	.067	77	85.6
83–90	8	.089	71	78.9
75–82	10	.111	63	70.0
67–74	11	.122	53	58.9
59–66	11	.122	42	46.7
51–58	11	.122	31	34.4
43–50	8	.089	20	22.2
35–42	4	.044	12	13.3
27–34	6	.067	8	8.9
19–26	2	.022	2	2.2

that constructing a grouped frequency distribution that does a good job of revealing important characteristics of the data is more an artistic endeavor than an exercise in mathematical precision.

Step 4. *Using either the sorted array or the ungrouped frequency distribution, enter the appropriate frequencies into the various class intervals.* Only two scores in the data set exist between 19 and 26, and so this interval has a frequency of two. There are six scores that exist between 27 and 34 (28, 28, 30, 32, 33, and 33), and so the interval 27–34 has a frequency of six. This process is repeated until the frequency column is complete. As a check, the frequency column must add up to the total number of scores in the data set ($N = 90$). Notice how information is lost in this procedure. If the raw data were unavailable and all we had reference to was the grouped frequency distribution, the distribution of the specific scores within the interval 27–34 (28, 28, 30, 32, 33, 33) would be unknown.

RELATIVE FREQUENCY, CUMULATIVE FREQUENCY, AND CUMULATIVE PERCENTAGE

Relative Frequency. The proportion of scores in a data set that fall within a specific class interval.

Cumulative Frequency. The frequency of scores in a distribution that have values equal to or less than the true upper limit of a class interval.

Cumulative Percent. The percent of scores in a distribution that have values equal to or less than the true upper limit of a class interval.

The addition of three more columns to the grouped frequency table helps to reveal even more information in the data set. In the **relative frequency** column the proportions of the total data set that exist within specific class intervals are listed. The proportions are computed by dividing the number of scores in each class interval by the total number of scores in the data set. Thus, the proportion of scores that are in the interval 67–74 is $11/90 = 0.122$.

The **cumulative frequency** column lists the number of scores that fall below the upper real limit of each class interval. To compute cumulative frequency, start at the lowest class interval and copy its frequency into the bottom of the cumulative frequency column. Next, add the frequency of the next highest interval to your first entry. For example, the class interval 19–26 has a frequency of two. This is copied into the bottom position of the cumulative frequency column. The next highest interval (27–34) has a frequency of six. The six is added to the two in the lower interval to reflect the fact that eight scores fall below the upper real limit of the interval 27–34. To get the cumulative frequency entry for the third highest interval, the cumulative frequency of eight that we just computed for the second highest interval is added to the frequency of the third highest interval ($8 + 4 = 12$), and this value of 12 is entered in the cumulative frequency column. This process is repeated all the way to the top of the table. As a check, the top entry in the cumulative frequency column must equal the size of the data set.

The **cumulative percent** is a simple conversion of the cumulative frequency column to percentages. This is accomplished by dividing each cumulative frequency by the size of the data set. Instead of telling us *how many* scores exist below the upper real limit of each class interval, the cumulative percent value for an interval tells us the *percentage* of scores in the data set that exist below the upper real limit of the class interval. For example, a quick look at table 2.4 reveals that 58.9% of the scores have values equal to or less than 74.5, the upper real limit of the interval 67–74. The 58.9% value was computed by dividing 53, the cumulative frequency for the interval 67–74, by the total number of scores in the data set ($53/90 = .5888$) and multiplying by 100 to convert to a percent. The top entry in the cumulative percent column will always be 100% since all the scores are below the upper real limit of the top class interval.

GROUPED.BAS

The very same data set, the performance scores for the ninety salespersons, is presented in the GROUPED.BAS computer tutorial. The same levels of organization are imposed on the data set as were imposed in this chapter except that you get to select the size of the class interval to be used in setting up the grouped frequency distribution. If you select an interval of eight you will get a table identical to table 2.4. Try a variety of interval sizes to assess the impact of using too small or too large a class interval size. The effects of oversummarizing (class interval too large) or undersummarizing (class interval too small) will be apparent.

Graphic Description of Data

The same data that appear in the grouped frequency distribution table may be presented using graphs. The graphs will not add to the information that is present in the grouped frequency table, but they may make some aspects of the data more obvious and understandable.

Frequency Polygon. A graph of a distribution with score frequency on the *Y*-axis and score value on the *X*-axis. Inspection of the graph will reveal how many times each score occurs in the distribution.

The Frequency Polygon. The **frequency polygon** is a plot of the number of score values that exist within specific intervals (i.e., the *frequency* of the various intervals) against the *midpoints* of the intervals. By convention, we assign the frequency variable to the vertical or *Y*-axis and the score values at the class interval midpoints to the horizontal or *X*-axis. The data from table 2.4 are presented as a frequency polygon in figure 2.1. The graph of the sales data is no more or less descriptive than the table. It is simply more visual and, for some persons, easier to comprehend than the table.

The Plot of Cum *f* and Cum %: The Ogive Curve. When the Cum *f* or Cum % of a normal distribution is plotted against the midpoints of the class intervals, a characteristic S-shaped curve is the result. This is also called an **ogive curve.** The plot of the Cum *f* from table 2.4 is presented in figure 2.2.

Ogive Curve. The S-shaped curve that results from the graphic plot of cumulative frequency or cumulative percent data.

Histogram. A graphic representation of interval or ratio data in which the frequencies of score values or class intervals appear as contiguous bars.

The Histogram. The same data that were used to construct the frequency polygon may be used to construct a **histogram.** The frequency in each class interval determines the height of the bar for that interval, and the midpoints of the class intervals are on the *X*-axis. The histogram for the data in table 2.4 are presented in figure 2.3.

The Bar Graph. Bar graphs and histograms are really quite similar in appearance except that, according to convention, the bar graph is used for categorical (nominal) data or ordinal data. For example, when the variable on the *X*-axis is a series of discrete categories rather than a continuum, this is a clear signal that a bar graph is called for rather than a histogram. By

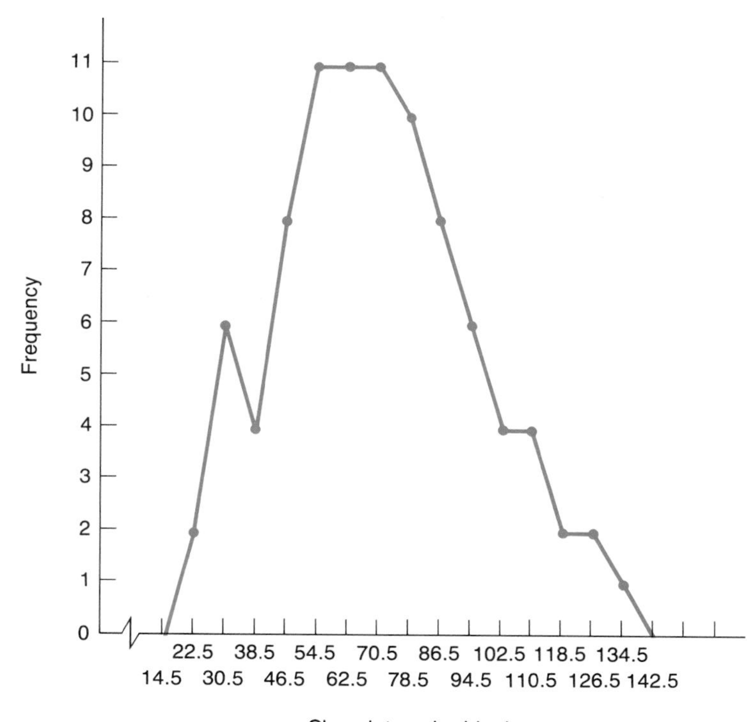

Figure 2.1

A frequency polygon for the sales data of table 2.4.

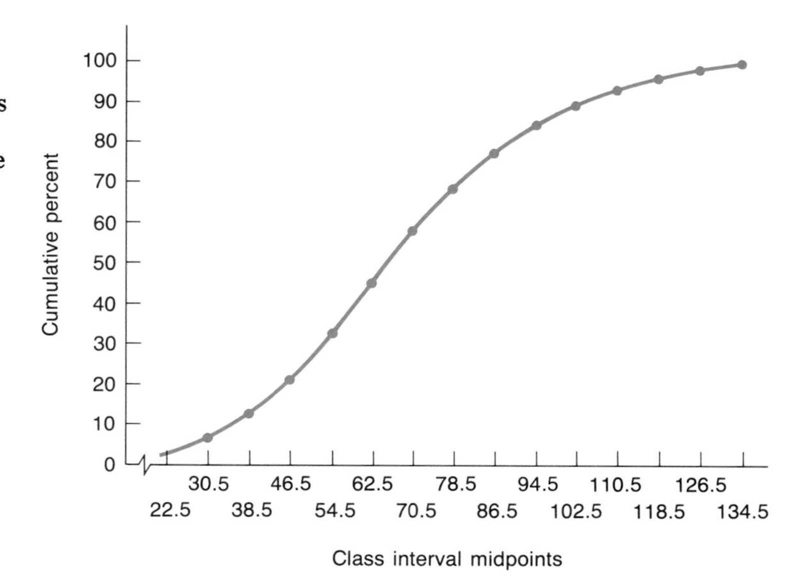

Figure 2.2

The S-shaped ogive curve that results when the class interval midpoints are plotted against cumulative percent.

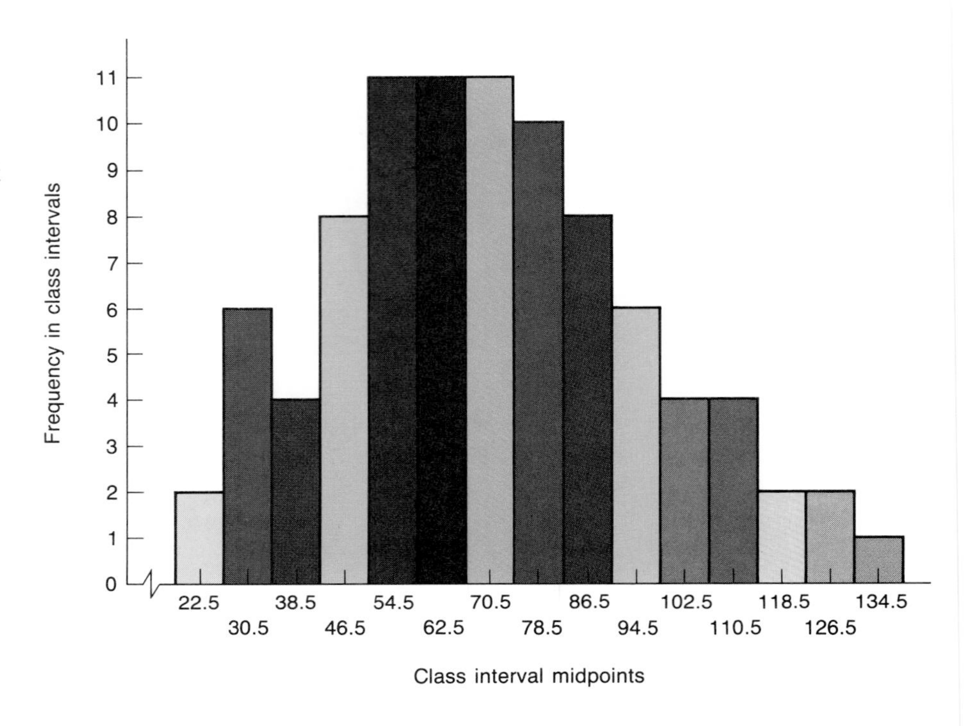

Figure 2.3

A histogram of the sales data from table 2.4. The frequency of each class interval is plotted against its midpoint.

Table 2.5

The number of units sold by 90 salespersons reported separately for the six sales districts.

District A: 112, 102, 92, 83, 75, 128, 33, 42, 58, 68, 65, 44, 76, 72, 83
District B: 24, 90, 54, 62, 32, 55, 104, 122, 95, 89, 60, 48, 64, 86, 68
District C: 33, 51, 73, 55, 37, 43, 22, 82, 94, 77, 72, 100, 65, 50, 63
District D: 130, 67, 47, 52, 28, 80, 74, 78, 82, 95, 107, 76, 81, 106, 69
District E: 35, 45, 49, 51, 109, 72, 57, 28, 30, 46, 55, 60, 61, 138, 93
District F: 86, 86, 79, 117, 53, 62, 58, 65, 73, 65, 71, 114, 85, 98, 38

drawing the graph so that the bars do not touch, the discontinuity of the categorical variable is emphasized. Conversely, when the scaling of the variable is either interval or ratio, the bars should touch to emphasize the continuity of the variable.

In table 2.5 the same sales data of the ninety salespersons have been broken down according to sales district. A bar graph may now be used to compare the sales performances of the six sales districts, and this is done in figure 2.4.

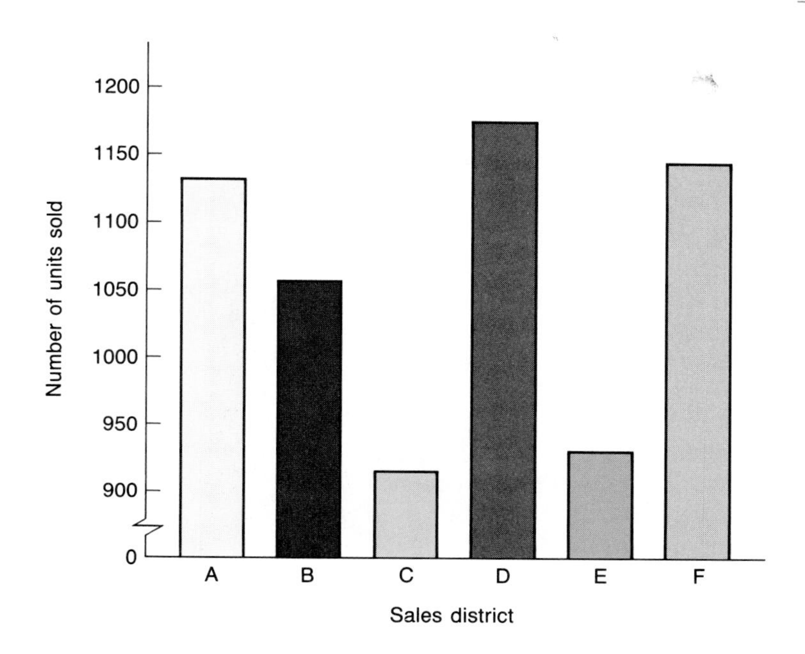

Figure 2.4

A bar graph showing the number of units sold in each sales district.

Summary

Using successive levels of organization of an unordered array of data (a simple descending sort, an ungrouped frequency distribution, and a grouped frequency distribution), we were able to extract successive amounts of detailed and useful information from the raw data. Along with the description of the data through the use of tables, some graphing techniques were discussed.

Key Terms

Central Tendency
Class Interval
Cumulative Frequency
Cumulative Percent
Dispersal
Frequency
Frequency Polygon
Grouped Frequency Distribution
Histogram
Nominal Limits
Ogive Curve
Range
Relative Frequency
True Limits
Ungrouped Frequency Distribution

BOX 2.1

Pictures that Lie: The Effects of *X*- and *Y*-axis Distortions

In drawing graphs it is possible to create a visual image from the data that does not display an accurate representation of the information that is really in the data. This is done by collapsing or expanding the scale on either the *X*- or *Y*-axis usually with the intention to create a specific impression in the viewer that will not hold up following close scrutiny of the data. Deep hills and valleys in a frequency polygon or histogram can be compressed into shallow undulations by compressing the *Y*-axis and expanding the *X*-axis, and shallow undulations can be magnified to look steep and abrupt by expanding the *Y*-axis and compressing the *X*-axis. To avoid this type of deception, a convention has been adopted that calls for plotting the data so that the *Y*-axis will be about three-quarters the length of the *X*-axis.

For example, assume the quality control data for the first three months of the year show that in January four lots of merchandise were returned by buyers because they were flawed. In February six lots were returned, and in March seven lots were returned. The histogram drawn in accordance with the three-quarter rule is shown in figure 2.5. If the quality control engineer wanted to save his job and minimize the apparent increase in the shipping of flawed merchandise, he could shorten the *Y*-axis as shown in figure 2.6. The impression of stability in the company's quality control is greater when

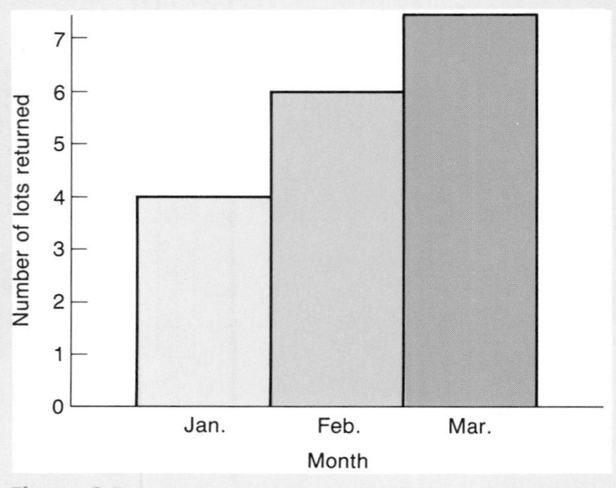

Figure 2.5

The number of lots of merchandise returned during the first quarter. The three-quarter high rule has been observed.

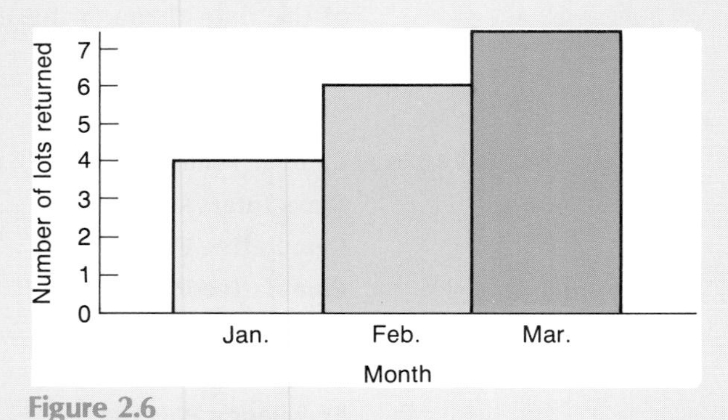

Figure 2.6

The number of lots of merchandise returned during the first quarter. The *Y*-axis has been shortened.

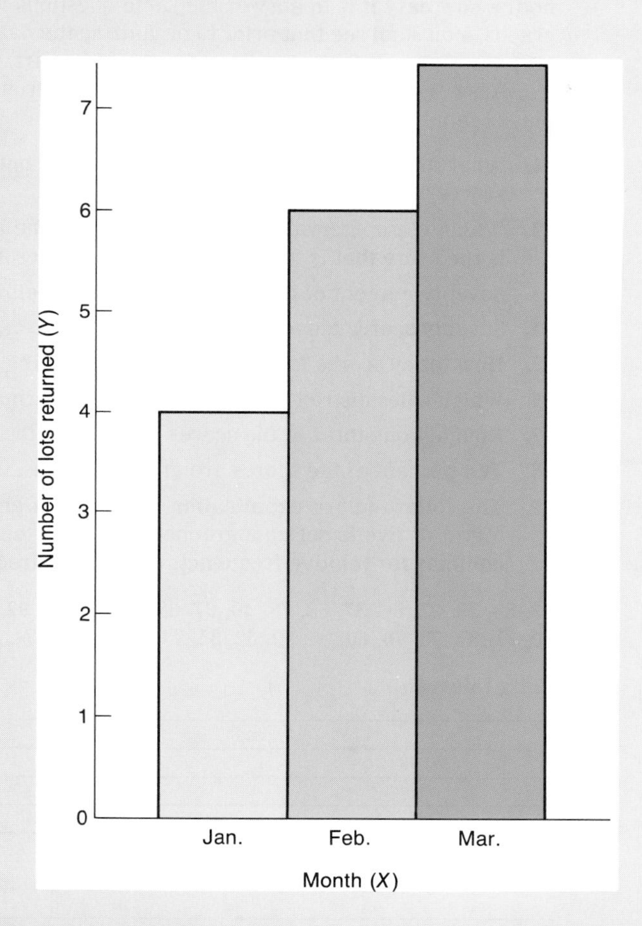

Figure 2.7
The number of lots of merchandise returned during the first quarter. The Y-axis has been extended.

viewing figure 2.6 because the increase from four to six to seven appears to be relatively modest, and the rate of increase from February to March appears to be levelling off.

The opposite impression could be conveyed by shortening the X-axis (figure 2.7). An executive wishing to shake up the management of the company might use the latter representation to create the impression of a precipitous and unabating increase in the shipping of damaged or incorrectly made merchandise.

Exercises

With both tabular and graphic representations of the sales data at our disposal, there are many questions that relate to these data that can now be answered. To appreciate how effective the tables and graphs are in helping us to wring out the information in the data, try answering the exercises that follow by looking only at the raw data. Then notice how easy it is to answer the same questions when you consult the tables and graphs. You shall see that prior to organizing the data into tables and graphs, important descriptive information was, for the most part, unavailable.

Answer the following questions using the grouped frequency distribution displayed in table 2.4 and the data in table 2.5:

1. What are three consecutive intervals that contain more than one-third of the scores?
2. Which class interval contains the score in the middle of the distribution? This is the score that is higher than half the scores and lower than half the scores.
3. Seventy percent of the scores have values below ______________________.
4. Seventy scores have values greater than ______________________.
5. How many scores fall between 50.5 and 82.5?
6. Which sales district turned in the best performance?
7. Roughly one-third of the scores are greater than ______________________.
8. Ten percent of the scores are greater than ______________________.
9. The following are examination scores for a group of students. Use a class interval of five to set up a grouped frequency distribution of these data. Include columns for relative frequency, cumulative frequency, and cumulative percent.

63, 88, 79, 92, 86, 87, 83, 78, 40, 67, 68, 76, 46, 81, 92, 77, 84, 76, 70, 66, 77, 75, 98, 81, 82, 81, 87, 78, 70, 60, 94, 79, 52, 82, 77, 81, 77, 70, 74, 61

Class Interval	*f*	Rel. *f*	Cum *f*	Cum %

10. Using the table you completed for question 9, plot the frequencies of the class intervals (Y-axis) against the midpoints of the class intervals (X-axis) to form a frequency polygon.

11. Plot the cumulative percent column against the midpoints of the class intervals to form an ogive curve.

12. Plot a histogram for these data. The midpoints of the class intervals will be on the X-axis and the frequency of the intervals will be on the Y-axis. In deciding upon the proportions of the graph, make the height of the Y-axis about 3/4 the length of the X-axis.

13. What are the true limits of the top and bottom intervals?

14. For the set of scores that appears below:

a. How many scores are in the set? (n = ?)
b. What is the sum of all the scores in the set?
c. What is the mean of the set?
d. Extend the table to include a column for cumulative frequency and cumulative percent.

X	f
3	1
4	0
5	4
6	7
7	2
8	1

15. In setting up a group frequency distribution why does the convention specify that there should be between 10 and 20 class intervals?

16. The following scores represent the number of boxes of Girl Scout cookies sold by a group of eighty scouts. Construct a grouped frequency distribution for these data.

13	10	26	19	42	28	31	34	16	57	16	18
14	16	36	20	28	12	7	26	16	24	17	18
28	29	23	10	34	25	21	21	15	9	25	11
20	15	37	43	28	39	21	14	22	13	22	19
30	46	26	15	24	8	23	18	33	20	17	31
52	43	48	60	20	16	27	23	24	35	41	32
17	53	35	23	16	26	22	22	23			

17. Extend the grouped frequency distribution to include cumulative frequency and cumulative percent columns.

18. Draw a visual display that represents the cookie sales results in the form of a histogram as you did for question 12 above.

19. What was the average number of cookie sales for the group of Girl Scouts?

CHAPTER 3

Measures of Central Tendency and Dispersion

In the previous chapter you learned how to use tabular and graphic displays to reveal the information in data. The organization that is imposed on a large data set by means of a grouped frequency distribution or a histogram provides a visual impression of two important descriptive characteristics of the data: the clustering of scores about some central value **(central tendency)** and how widely spread out the scores are **(dispersion).** The visual impressions of central tendency and dispersion that we get from inspecting tables and graphs may be quantitatively vague, but they help us to capture the essence of a distribution in the same sense that the synopsis of a complex novel helps us to get a flavor of the novel's plot and subplots. Sometimes, however, we require precise quantitative information about data and wish to get it without taking the time or making the effort to study tabular or graphic displays. Tables and graphs are usually inadequate for precise, efficient descriptions of the central tendency and dispersion in a date set and for analytical comparisons between data sets.

Central Tendency. The statistical description of a distribution in terms of an average or typical value. The mean, median, and mode are measures of central tendency.

Dispersion. A statistical representation of the degree to which the scores in a distribution are dispersed about the central value. Variation (SS), variance (σ^2) and standard deviation (σ) are statistical measures of dispersion.

THE STATISTICAL REPRESENTATION OF DATA

To pursue the next level of descriptive power we must quantify central tendency and dispersion through the computation of special numbers that reflect specific properties of the data. If the computed values describe an entire population, they are called parameters, and if they describe a sample from a population, they are called statistics. Using a statistic we can express important information about the central tendency or dispersion in a data set with a single value. This both streamlines and quantifies the descriptive process, and provides a valuable supplement or alternative to tables and graphs.

In addition to these advantages, the statistical representation of central tendency and dispersion sets the stage for the future topic of **inferential statistics.** (Statistical inference, as explained in chapter 1, is the process of drawing conclusions about population characteristics from the analysis of sample data.)

CENTRAL TENDENCY

Mean. The sum of all the score values in a distribution divided by the number of scores. The mean is also called the *average*.

Median. The score value in a distribution above which and below which half the score values fall.

Mode. The most frequently occurring score value in a distribution.

The statistics of central tendency are the **mean,** the **median,** and the **mode.** These statistics will be discussed both individually and in relation to each other in different kinds of distributions.

The Arithmetic Mean

The mean of a set of sample data ($\overline{X}$, read as "X bar") is the sum of all the scores in the sample divided by the number of scores (n) in the sample. In notation:

$$\overline{X} = \frac{\Sigma X}{n} = \frac{X_1 + X_2 + \cdots X_i + \cdots + X_n}{n}$$

If the mean is computed for an entire population, it is a parameter rather than a statistic and is designated by the Greek mu (μ) as shown in the following formula.

$$\mu = \frac{\Sigma X}{N} = \frac{X_1 + X_2 + \cdots X_i + \cdots + X_N}{N}$$

Notice that the lower case n in the formula for a sample mean has been replaced by a capital N, which represents the number of scores in a population.

The mean is a very widely used descriptive statistic, and it is quite likely that you have encountered it before in a variety of contexts. You may not, however, be aware of some interesting properties that are unique to the mean.

At present these properties may only be of academic interest, but later they will be very useful in explaining certain properties of the z statistic (chapter 4) and some elements of regression analysis (chapter 5).

Property 1. **The mean is that score or potential score in a distribution about which the sum of the deviation scores is zero.** The term *potential score* is included in this definition because the value of the mean may not exist as a score in the actual data. For example, the mean of the set 1, 2, 3, 5, 6, 7 is 4 (24 divided by 6) even though 4 does not exist in the data.

In notation:

$$\Sigma(X - \overline{X}) = 0$$

The deviation in the formula above is the difference in value between a specific individual score (X) and the mean of all the scores ($\overline{X}$). When such a deviation is computed for every score in a distribution, this property of the mean stipulates that the sum of the **deviation scores** will always equal zero.

Deviation Score. The difference between a score value and the mean of the distribution to which the score belongs. In notation, the deviation score for X is written $(X - \overline{X})$.

If we regard the subtraction of the mean from each score in distribution as a transformation, Property 1 may be expressed formally as follows:

If a distribution is transformed by subtracting the mean of the distribution from every score in the original distribution, the scores in the transformed distribution will sum to zero.

The effect of such a transformation is illustrated in table 3.1.

Table 3.1

Original Set	*Mean*	Transformed Set (deviation scores) $(X - \overline{X})$
1	3	−2
2	3	−1
3	3	0
4	3	+1
5	3	+2
		$\Sigma(X - \overline{X}) = 0$

Table 3.2

X Scores	Constant	(X − c)
1	1	0
2	1	1
3	1	2
4	1	3
5	1	4
$\Sigma X = 15$	$\Sigma c = 5$	$\Sigma(X - c) = 15 - 5 = 10$ or $\Sigma(X - c) = 0 + 1 + 2 + 3 + 4 = 10$

Property 1 derives from the following summation rule:

$$\Sigma(X - c) = \Sigma X - Nc$$

In words, the sum of a set that is transformed by subtracting a constant from each of the original scores equals the sum of the original set minus N times the constant.

Table 3.2 illustrates the operation of this summation rule with the set 1, 2, 3, 4, 5, and the constant, c, set equal to 1.

Notice that the sum of the raw scores column equals 15 and the sum of the constant column equals 5. The expression Nc, the number of X scores times the value of the constant, is also 5. That this will always hold true can be proven algebraically as shown below.

$$\begin{aligned}\Sigma(X_i - c) &= (X_1 - c) + (X_2 - c) + \cdots + (X_N - c) \\ &= (X_1 + X_2 + \cdots + X_N) + (-c - c \cdots -c) \\ &= \Sigma X_i - Nc\end{aligned}$$

In the expression $\Sigma(X - \overline{X})$ the value of the mean is used for the constant. Thus,

$$\Sigma(X - c) = \Sigma X - Nc$$

becomes

$$\Sigma(X - \overline{X}) = \Sigma X - N\overline{X}$$

Table 3.3

X	$(X-5)^2$	$(X-7)^2$	$(X-6)^2$	$(X-4)^2$	$(X-3)^2$
2	9	25	16	4	1
3	4	16	9	1	0
5	0	4	1	9	4
6	1	1	0	16	9
7	4	0	1	25	16
7	4	0	1	25	16
sums:	22	46	28	80	46

and since $\overline{X} = \frac{\Sigma X}{N}$ and $\Sigma X = N\overline{X}$, then

$$\Sigma(X - \overline{X}) = N\overline{X} - N\overline{X} = 0$$

Property 2. **The mean is that score or potential score in a distribution about which the sum of the squared deviations is a minimum.** In notation:

$$\text{If } c = \overline{X}, \text{ then } \Sigma(X - c)^2 = \text{min}$$

This says that if a constant is subtracted from each score in a set and the resulting difference scores are squared, the sum of the squared difference scores will be the smallest possible value if the constant is set equal to the mean of the set. This is illustrated in table 3.3 for the set 2, 3, 5, 6, 7, 7. The constant 5, which also happens to be the mean of the set, is subtracted from each X, and then each difference score is squared and the squared values are summed. The result is 22, and you should notice that if any constant other than 5 is used, the sum of the squared difference scores will always be greater than 22. This is illustrated by letting the constant equal two values that are greater than the mean (7 and 6) and two values that are lower than the mean (4 and 3).

The special property the mean has in minimizing the value of the expression $\Sigma(X - c)^2$ is the reason this is called the **least squares** definition of the mean.

Least Squares. A definition of the mean as that score in a distribution about which the sum of the squared deviation scores is a minimum. In notation, $\Sigma(X - \overline{X})^2 =$ minimum.

Property 3. **When extreme scores are assymetrically represented in either the high or low end of a distribution, the mean is likely to give an inaccurate representation of the distribution's central tendency.**

There is a limitation the mean has in fairly representing a distribution. For example, let us say two groups of five subjects each are performing a task and error scores are tallied for each person.

Table 3.4

Number of Errors	
Group 1	*Group 2*
2	2
3	3
5	5
7	7
8	58
$\Sigma X = 25$	$\Sigma X = 75$
mean = 5	mean = 15

The mean of group 1 should strike you as a reasonable number to use to represent the number of errors committed by a typical subject in that group. It is equidistant from the extremes at both ends and falls exactly in the middle of the five scores. On the other hand, the mean of group 2 (mean = 15) is higher than all but one of the scores ($X = 58$). Also, even though the scores in the two groups are identical except for the scores of 8 and 58, the mean of group 2 ($\overline{X} = 15$) is three times larger than the mean of group 1 ($\overline{X} = 5$). The one extreme score of 58 has caused this distortion.

If we use the means to compare the group 1 and group 2 performances we could be drawn into a misleading conclusion. For example, consider the following statement, "On the average, the subjects in group 2 committed three times as many errors as the subjects in group 1." The statement is correct as it stands, but it does not give an accurate description of what really happened. In four of five cases, subjects committed *exactly the same* number of errors. Only the fifth scores in each group differed.

The distorting effect of unbalanced extreme values on the high or low end of a distribution upon the mean may be seen in some commonly reported statistics. For example, this effect is often noticeable in the reporting of real estate values. A given geographical area may have homes that, with few exceptions, have sold in a modest price range. If, however, those few exceptions are multimillion dollar estates, the mean cost of buying a house in that area will be reported as being very high. The very high selling price of a few homes introduces extreme values on the high end of the distribution of selling prices. This pulls the mean toward the high end of the price range and may create an erroneous impression in the unwary consumer regarding the availability of affordable housing in that area. In such instances of imbalance in the data, the usefulness of the mean as a descriptive statistic is diminished.

Finally, as discussed earlier under the topic of ordinal scaling (chapter 1), remember that the mean is useful as a measure of central tendency only when the data are of interval or ratio scaling. If a mean is computed for nominal or ordinal data the result is uninterpretable.

The Median

The median is that point in a distribution below which and above which half the scores fall. In other words, it is the score value (or potential score value) that is right in the middle of a distribution. For both groups of error scores presented in table 3.4, the median is 5 because, in both cases, there are two scores above 5 and two scores below 5.

To compute the median of a set of data the first step is to rank order the scores from lowest to highest. (The scores in table 3.4 were listed in numerical order, and so we could skip this step in finding the median of 5.) If the number of scores in the set is odd, the median will be the middle score in the ordered set. For example, consider the following:

original set: 1, 8, 13, 22, 6, 9, 4

ordered set: 1, 4, 6, 8, 9, 13, 22

The middle score in the ordered set is 8, and so 8 is the median.

If the number of scores in the set is even, the median is the average of the two middle scores. To illustrate this, let us add a score of 51 to the group 2 error scores shown in table 3.4 so that there will be 6 instead of 5 scores. Here is the modified set: 2, 3, 5, 7, 51, 58. This set contains an even number of scores ($n = 6$) and the two middle scores are 5 and 7. To compute the median of this set we take the average of 5 and 7, which equals 6. Notice that, like the mean, the median may take a value that is not actually present in the distribution. The set 2, 3, 5, 7, 51, 58 has a median of 6, but there is no 6 in the set. The fact that the median can equal a score value that is not in the original set is the reason for adding the phrase "or *potential* score value" in the definition of the median offered above.

The Effect of Extreme Scores on the Mean versus the Median. In the latter example, even though another relatively high error score (51) was added to the set 2, 3, 5, 7, 58, the median only increased one unit from the original value of 5 to the new value of 6. The mean, on the other hand, increased six units from 15 to 21. This demonstrates that the median can also be affected by extreme scores, but much less so than the mean.

Instead of adding an extreme score to the set as we did above, let us maintain the set at the same size and simply change the value of an extreme score (see table 3.5).

Table 3.5

		Mean	Median
Original Set:	2, 3, 5, 6, 7, 7	5	5.5
Modified Set 1:	2, 3, 5, 6, 7, 37	10	5.5
Modified Set 2:	−28, 3, 5, 6, 7, 7	0	5.5
Modified Set 3:	2, 3, 5, 6, 27, 37	13.33	5.5

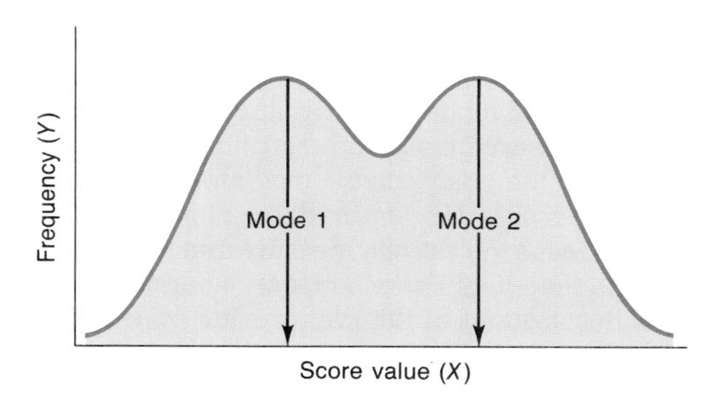

Figure 3.1

A bimodal distribution: two values of X scores tie for the high frequency.

In Modified Set 1, one of the sevens, the highest score in the original set, was increased by 30 units to 37, and in Modified Set 2, the low score of 2 in the original set was diminished by 30 units to −28. As you can see from the statistics reported on the right side of table 3.5, the effect of changing an extreme score has no effect at all on the median, but the effect on the mean is quite noticeable.

Modified Set 3 is the same as Modified Set 1 except that 20 units have been added to the one remaining 7 in Modified Set 1. The presence of two extreme scores, 27 and 37, causes a further increase in the value of the mean from the 10 of Modified Set 1 to 13.33. The value of the median, however, remains unchanged (5.5) since the two middle values of the ordered set remain the same (5 and 6).

The Mode

Of the three measures of central tendency the **mode** is the easiest to determine. It is simply the most frequently occurring score in a distribution. Sometimes a distribution has more than one mode as shown in figure 3.1.

Figure 3.2

In a normal bell-shaped curve the mean, median, and mode have the same score value.

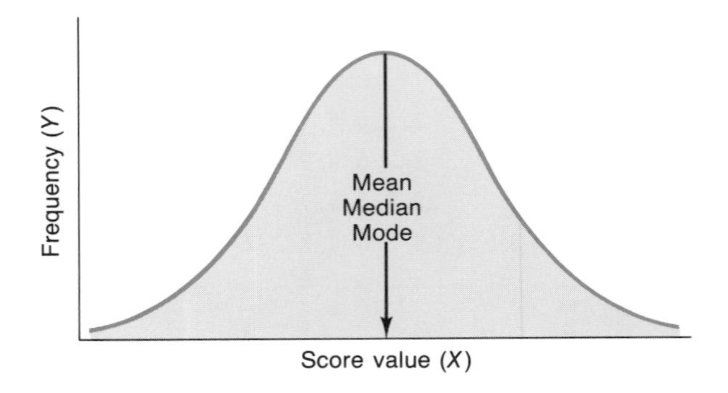

Since the mode is the result of a simple frequency count, it is an appropriate measure for summarizing nominal data. In fact, of the three measures of central tendency (mean, median, and mode), the mode is the *only* appropriate measure for summarizing nominal data. With interval or ratio data the mode is a very crude measure and has limited usefulness in summarizing central tendency. From a research perspective, for other than the most general descriptions of interval or ratio scaled data, it is seldom reported as a basis for making important decisions.

In the normal bell-shaped distribution, the distribution that characterizes so many behavioral and biological measures, the mean, the median, and the mode, equal the same value. As shown in figure 3.2, the most frequently occurring score, the middle score, and the average score are all in the same location in a normal distribution. If the distribution is *assymetrical* (this is called **skewness**), the mean is pulled toward the elongated tail, the median is pulled in the same direction to a lesser degree, and the mode stays under the hump (figure 3.3). The location of the elongated tail marks the direction of the skewness. Thus, the curve with the elongated tail to the left is said to be negatively skewed, and the curve with the elongated tail on the right is said to be positively skewed.

Skewness. A condition that denotes assymetrical dispersion of the scores in a distribution about the central value.

The Mean versus the Median. Earlier, you saw that the mean may not provide a fair representation of the central tendency in a distribution if there are unbalanced extreme scores present (see Property 3). This was also apparent in the discussion of skewness in the previous paragraph and in figure 3.3. When skewness is present the median usually gives the better representation of central tendency. For example, the *median* cost of a new home may represent the "average" cost of housing in a given area better than the *mean* cost if the distribution of housing costs is skewed toward the positive or negative end. The mean is not really an average when skewness is present because an average is supposed to represent a middle point between extremes.

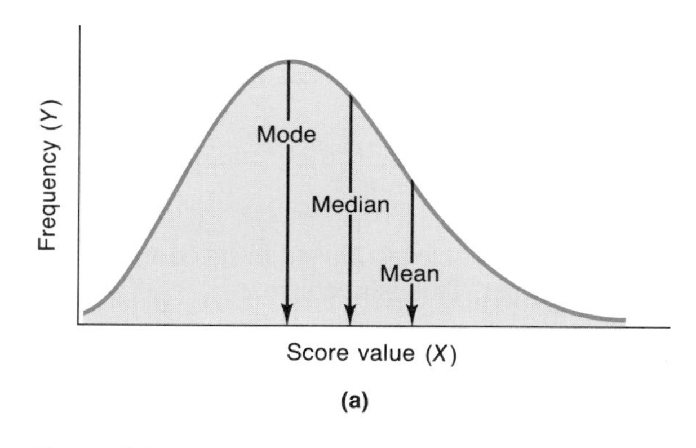

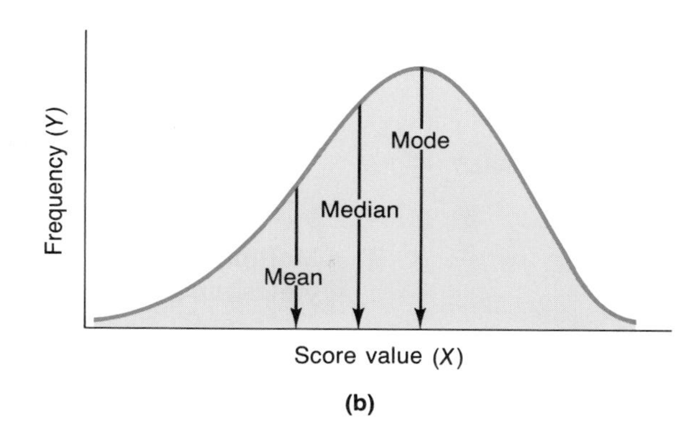

Figure 3.3
The relationship among the mean, the median, and the mode under conditions of positive (a) and negative (b) skewness.

According to Webster's Dictionary, one meaning for an average is "the usual, normal, typical, or most often encountered thing." If five homes in a neighborhood sell for $110,000 each and one sells for $650,000 does the mean of $200,000 per home represent the average cost of a house in that neighborhood?

Another point to keep in mind regarding the relative strengths and weaknesses of the measures of central tendency is that the mean is the most stable of the three measures. That is, if several samples are selected from a population and the three measures of central tendency are computed for each individual set of sample data, the values computed for the mean will show the least variability. If we are to use sample statistics to estimate population parameters, as we shall when we get to inferential statistics, stability becomes very important. This characteristic of stability, perhaps more than any other, is the reason the mean is such a widely used statistic.

The Overall Mean

Overall (Weighted) Mean. The mean of a set of means.

The **overall mean,** also called the **weighted mean,** is the mean of a set of means. Let us say a professor teaches three sections of the same course and she computes the average score on an examination separately for each of the three sections. If she later wanted to compute the overall mean for all the students she could take two different approaches. One approach would be to combine the scores for all the sections and divide by the total number of students attending all three sections. The other approach would be simply to add the three means and divide by three to get the average of the three individual means. These two approaches will give the same answer if, and only if, the three sections contain equal numbers of students.

Sometimes it becomes necessary to compute the mean of a set of means when the original raw scores are unavailable. To do this the means must be *weighted* before being added together in order to reflect the different sample sizes upon which the means are based. The formula is as follows:

$$\text{Overall Mean} = \frac{(n_1\overline{X}_1) + (n_2\overline{X}_2) + \cdots + (n_i\overline{X}_i) + \cdots + (n_k\overline{X}_k)}{n_1 + n_2 + \cdots + n_i \cdots + n_k}$$

Multiplying each mean by the number of scores (n_i) used in its computation yields the sum of the n scores for that set. This is because

$$n\overline{X} = \Sigma X.$$

This is a simple transformation of the formula for the mean:

$$\overline{X} = \frac{\Sigma X}{n}$$

The coefficients in the numerator of the formula ($n1$, $n2$, etc.) are called weights. When the group sizes are unequal and the individual means are weighted in this way, the correct overall mean for the combined groups can be found even if the original raw scores are unavailable.

This will be illustrated with the following three sets of scores:

set 1: 22, 19, 21, 28, 30
set 2: 28, 29, 22, 25, 21, 30, 28, 33
set 3: 36, 41, 37, 36, 30, 38, 29, 33, 44, 35, 37

The means of the three sets are 24, 27, and 36, respectively. Because the sets contain different numbers of scores the overall mean must be computed using the weighted mean formula. If the means (24, 27, and 36) were simply added and divided by three, we would get the incorrect answer of 29 for the overall mean. Let us compare this incorrect answer to the true answer. Here is the formula with the appropriate values filled in:

$$\text{overall mean} = \frac{5(24) + 8(27) + 11(36)}{5 + 8 + 11} = \frac{732}{24}$$

$$\text{overall mean} = 30.5$$

For these three sets, the true overall mean of the 24 scores (30.5) is higher than the average of the three individual set means (29).

MEASURES OF DISPERSION: VARIATION, VARIANCE, AND STANDARD DEVIATION

Why Must We Quantify Dispersion?

If you knew your score on an essay test was 78, without more information you would most likely be in a quandary regarding the quality of your performance. You would want to know the top possible grade. (Did you score 78 out of a possible 80 or out of a possible 100?) It would also help to know the range of scores in the class so you could make a rough comparison of your performance to the performance of the other students. (As discussed in chapter 2, the range is the top score minus the bottom score plus one.) If you knew that the class average were, say, 70, this would help you to rate your performance of 78 relative to your fellow students. But without specific quantitative information regarding the **dispersion** of the scores in the distribution, you would know only that your score of 78 was somewhere above the class average.

In figure 3.4 there are *two* distributions of examination grades. The mean of both distributions is 70, and the score of 78 exists in both distributions. Even without yet knowing about the formal computation of measures of dispersion, it is obvious in comparing the score locations that the 78 in Distribution (b) is further away from the average level of performance than the 78 in Distribution (a). You would be correct in concluding that, despite the fact that the score values are equal, the 78 in Distribution (b) reflects a level

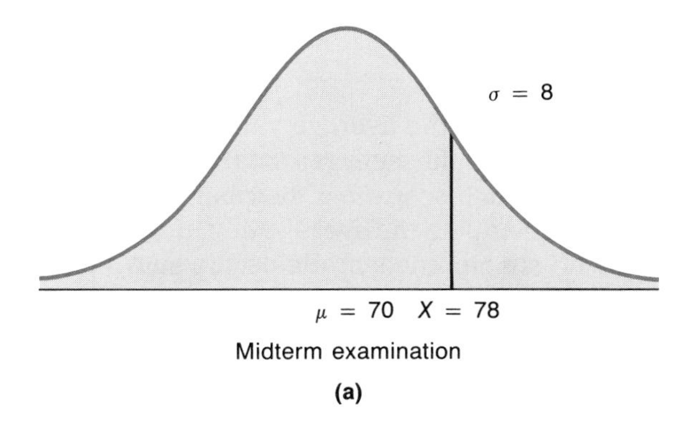

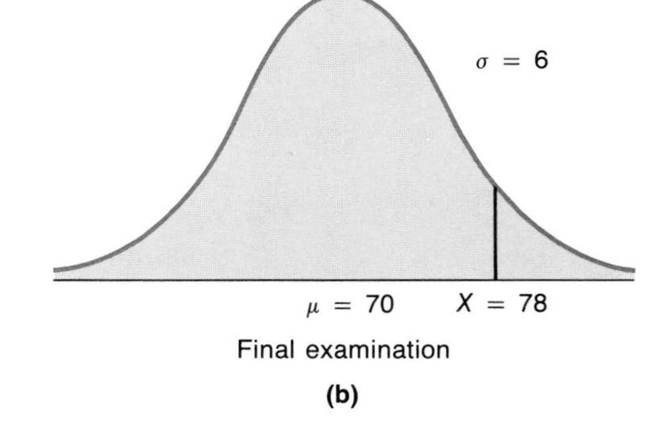

Figure 3.4

Two different distributions of examination scores. The means are the same but the standard deviations are different.

of performance that is superior to the level of performance reflected by the 78 in Distribution (a). This is because in Distribution (b), 78 is clearly near the top of the distribution, while in Distribution (a), although above average, the 78 is closer to the middle of the distribution.

We obviously need more specific quantitative information about these two distributions in order to understand the exact relationship between the two 78s and the meaning of each 78 within its own distribution. This information is supplied by a statistic called the **standard deviation.** The standard deviation is represented by the symbol σ, and if you look again at figure 3.4 you will see the σ values posted to the right of the two distributions. Notice that Distribution (b), with the smaller standard deviation ($\sigma = 6$), is more compact than Distribution (a) ($\sigma = 8$).

Standard Deviation. A descriptive statistic that reflects the amount of dispersion that exists in a distribution. The square root of the variance. σ is the symbol for the population standard deviation and s is the symbol for the sample standard deviation.

Variation. The sum of the squared deviation scores. Also called sum of squares or SS.

Variance. The average variation per population value (SS/N) or sample value (SS/n). The square of the standard deviation. σ^2 is the symbol for the variance of a population and s^2 is the symbol for the variance of a sample.

The rest of this chapter will be on the procedures for computing the standard deviation and the two statistics that are computed as steps leading up to the standard deviation: **variation** (also called sum of squares) and **variance.** This material on the measures of dispersion is also presented in great detail in the VARSD.BAS computer tutorial contained in the *Stat/Tutor* package. On the computer you will have the opportunity to review explanations similar to those that appear in the text, but, in addition, you will be able to do practice problems with your own data and see complete step-by-step solutions.

In the next chapter the focus will be on developing an understanding of the standard deviation and the practical application of this knowledge for the interpretation of data and the solution of problems. For now, we shall take a temporary leave from the discussion of Distribution (a), Distribution (b), and the real meaning of the 78s and examine some computational and abstract aspects of the measures of dispersion.

The Quantification of Dispersion

To quantify central tendency we computed the average value of a score in a distribution. To quantify dispersion it would seem reasonable to compute another average: the average amount each score in a distribution deviates from the mean of the distribution. To compute the average deviation in a set of sample data would appear to be simple enough: divide the sum of the deviation scores by n, the number of scores in the set. Here is the formula for the average of the deviation scores:

$$\frac{\Sigma(X - \overline{X})}{n}$$

The problem with this approach is that no matter what distribution is being described, the sum of the deviation scores will always be zero. This was demonstrated as Property 1 earlier in this chapter and can be seen again in table 3.6. Naturally, if the sum of the deviation scores is always zero, division by n to get an average deviation will also always be zero, no matter

Table 3.6

X	$\overline{X}$	$(X - \overline{X})$	$(X - \overline{X})^2$
1	3	−2	4
2	3	−1	1
3	3	0	0
4	3	1	1
5	3	2	4
		$\Sigma(X - \overline{X}) = 0$	$\Sigma(X - \overline{X})^2 = 10$

how dispersed or compact the distribution happens to be. The solution lies in eliminating all negative values from the set of deviation scores by means of a simple transformation: the squaring of each deviation score. The set of squared deviation scores will never sum to zero as did the original set of deviation scores except in the special case of a set of constants. For example:

Set of Constants: 7, 7, 7, 7, 7, 7

Since the mean of this set is 7 and all scores equal 7, all deviation scores $(X_i - \overline{X})$ will equal zero, their squares, $(X - \overline{X})^2$, will equal zero, and the sum of the squares, $\Sigma(X_i - \overline{X})^2$, will equal zero.

Variation (Sum of Squares)

Variation is defined as the sum of the squared deviations of each score from the mean and is represented for a population of scores by

$$\Sigma(X - \mu)^2$$

and for a set of sample data by

$$\Sigma(X - \overline{X})^2.$$

This should look familiar to you because it is the same expression that was presented as Property 2 of the arithmetic mean that was said always to equal a minimum. It is called variation or *sum of squares* (commonly abbreviated as **SS**). The computation may be done using a tabular procedure as illustrated in table 3.6. (It is unlikely that the variation of such a small set as 1, 2, 3, 4, 5 would ever be of interest to a researcher analyzing real data, but it is easier to follow the procedure if the sample size and numerical values in the sample are kept small.)

SS. An abbreviation for Sum of Squares, the variation in a distribution (i.e., the sum of the squared deviation scores). In notation, $SS = \Sigma(X - \overline{X})^2$.

Notice in table 3.6 that by squaring the individual deviation scores, the negative values are eliminated, and the sum of the squared deviation scores is a nonzero value (10).

The procedure for computing the sum of squares that is illustrated in table 3.6 is manageable if the sets are small and/or the mean is an integer (i.e., no decimals or fractions). In most cases, however, this method is impractical and tedious for hand calculations of sum of squares. Instead, we use a computational formula. This, too, should look familiar, because when you were learning to apply the symbols of statistical notation to the processing of data in chapter 1, this formula was among the examples:

$$\Sigma X^2 - \frac{(\Sigma X)^2}{n}$$

A proof that

$$\Sigma(X - \overline{X})^2 = \Sigma X^2 - \frac{(\Sigma X)^2}{n}$$

is in the Notes section at the end of this chapter.

For the set 1, 2, 3, 4, 5

$$\Sigma X^2 = 1 + 4 + 9 + 16 + 25 = 55$$

and

$$(\Sigma X)^2/n = 15^2/5 = 225/5 = 45.$$

Thus,

$$SS_X = \Sigma X^2 - \frac{(\Sigma X)^2}{n} = 55 - \frac{15^2}{5} = 10$$

The value of variation or **SS** from the computational formula is 10, the same value that was obtained with the deviation score method shown in table 3.6.

Before moving on to the computation of the variance, there is a shorthand notation that is used to designate variation that you should know. This deserves special mention because it is often a source of confusion to students when they encounter it in statistical formulae.

$$\text{variation} = \Sigma x^2$$

The lower case x is notation for $(X - \overline{X})$, and since $x = (X - \overline{X})$, the expression

$$\Sigma x^2 = \Sigma(X - \overline{X})^2$$

In summary, all these expressions are used to designate the variation of a set:

$$\text{Variation} = \text{SS} = \text{sum of squares} = \Sigma x^2$$
$$= \Sigma(X - \overline{X})^2 = \Sigma X^2 - \frac{(\Sigma X)^2}{n}$$

Variance

If you recall, the approach to the quantification of dispersion begun above was to express the dispersion in a distribution as an average—the average amount each score in a distribution deviates from the mean of the distribution. Earlier we computed the arithmetic mean of a set of sample data by dividing the sum of the scores in the set by n, the size of the set. Similarly, to get the average dispersion in a distribution we must also divide a sum by n—the sum of the squared deviation scores (the variation of a set or SS).

Dividing SS by n to get a measure of average dispersion yields a value called the *variance*. For the set 1, 2, 3, 4, 5 the SS is 10, the size of the set (n) equals 5, and so the variance is 10/5 or 2.00. When the variance is a parameter (i.e., the variance of an entire population) it is represented in notation by a squared lower case Greek sigma, σ^2. When the variance is a statistic (i.e., a measurable characteristic of a sample) it is represented by a squared lower case s (s^2). Here are the computational formulae:

for a population:

$$\sigma^2 = \frac{\Sigma X^2 - \frac{(\Sigma X)^2}{N}}{N} = \frac{SS_X}{N}$$

and for a sample:

$$s^2 = \frac{\Sigma X^2 - \frac{(\Sigma X)^2}{n}}{n} = \frac{SS_X}{n}$$

As you can see, the variation (sum of squares or SS) is in the numerator of the variance formula, and to get the variance we simply divide SS by the number of scores in the population (N) or sample (n). Thus, even though the variance is most appropriately regarded as a measure of dispersion, it is also an average—the average of the squared deviation scores.

If describing a set of scores is the sole reason for computing a variance, then the above formulae are appropriate. Later, however, when we go beyond simple description and use sample statistics to estimate the value of population parameters, we will be dividing the variation of the sample scores by $n - 1$. This will give us a variance that is the average variation per *degree of freedom* rather than the average variation per data point.

We will not deal with the concept of degrees of freedom or estimating population characteristics from sample data (i.e., parameter estimation) until we get into the topic of inferential statistics. When we do, you will find that dividing by degrees of freedom results in a more accurate (unbiased) estimate of population variance (σ^2) from sample data. Degrees of freedom is mentioned at this early point in the text only because students who decide to compute σ^2 with a scientific calculator may find that the built in function for the variance calls for dividing variation by $n - 1$ rather than n. (Often both functions are available and are labelled $\sigma^2 n$ for the descriptive statistic and $\sigma^2 n - 1$ for parameter estimation.) If the estimating function is selected, or if that is the only one built into the scientific calculator, the answer will not match your hand calculations (or the answer displayed in VARSD.BAS). The difference in the two statistics is usually not large, but it is enough to cause confusion if the reason for the discrepancy is not understood.

STANDARD DEVIATION

As you can see from the formulae that appear below, the standard deviation is found by taking the square root of the variance. Why take the square root? The story began with our attempt to reflect the dispersion in a set by computing the average amount of deviation between the individual scores and the mean. But we discovered that the sum of the deviation scores is always zero for any distribution and, therefore, the average of the deviation scores, zero divided by n, will likewise always be zero.

We dealt with the problem by squaring the deviation scores before summing them. The negative deviation scores were eliminated and we had a statistic that reflected dispersion, the sum of squares. Next, dividing SS by n gave us the average amount of variation in the set. As you now know, we call this average the variance. The variance, however, is an average of the *squared* deviation scores. To get back to the original intention of computing a statistic that represents the simple average of the deviation scores we have to "unsquare" the variance. Taking the square root of the variance accomplishes this, and the resulting value is called the **standard deviation.**

The population standard deviation is represented by σ, and the sample standard deviation is represented by s. For a population

$$\sigma = \sqrt{\frac{\Sigma X^2 - \frac{(\Sigma X)^2}{N}}{N}} = \sqrt{\frac{SS_X}{N}} = \sqrt{\sigma^2}$$

and for a sample

$$s = \sqrt{\frac{\Sigma X^2 - \frac{(\Sigma X)^2}{n}}{n}} = \sqrt{\frac{SS_X}{n}} = \sqrt{s^2}.$$

As with the variance, when a standard deviation of a sample of scores (s) is being computed with the eventual goal of estimating a population parameter (σ), we have gone beyond simple description of data into parameter estimation, and $n - 1$ is used in the denominator instead of n. (As with the variance, it is common for scientific calculators to contain both the descriptive ($\sigma\ n$) and parameter estimation functions ($\sigma\ n - 1$) for the standard deviation.)

For the set 1, 2, 3, 4, 5 the substitutions would be:

$$s = \sqrt{\frac{55 - \frac{15^2}{5}}{5}}$$

$$s = 1.414$$

The Standard Deviation as a Measure of Precision in Prediction

The dispersion that is present in a distribution relates in an important way to the concept of prediction. Prediction (chapter 5) and an in-depth interpretation of the standard deviation (chapter 4) are future topics, but it is not too early for a brief, intuitive, nontechnical introduction to these concepts. Consider the following example.

It is known that the workers in the company steno pool type an average of 60 words per minute, and, to avoid any appearance of favoritism, you plan to select a typist at random for a special assignment. Naturally, with no other information available, your best prediction is that the typist will be able to type 60 words per minute. Thus, in the absence of other relevant information, it is logical to use the mean skill level of the group to predict the randomly selected individual's skill level. Formally expressed, *the expected value of any score selected at random from a population is the mean of the population.*

How close is the actual skill level of your randomly selected typist likely to be to the predicted value of 60? The standard deviation of the distribution can be regarded as a measure of the precision of this prediction because the more widely dispersed the typing scores are about the mean of 60, the greater is the chance of selecting a typist at random that will have a skill level markedly different from 60 words per minute. In figure 3.5 two possible distributions of typing skill are shown together. If the real typing speed scores for the steno pool are as shown in the more compact distribution, the prediction of 60 could be off by as much as 10 words per minute (range = 50 − 70).

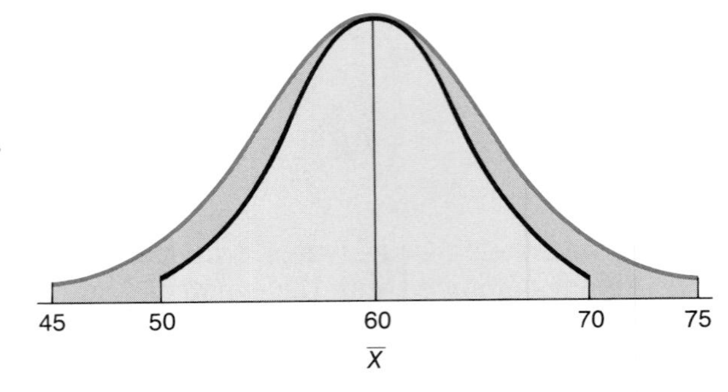

Figure 3.5

Two possible distributions of words per minute typing skill in a steno pool.

But if the real typing speed scores are as shown in the more dispersed distribution the prediction of 60 could be off by as many as 15 words per minute (range = 45 − 75). To summarize, when the standard deviation is small, the mean is more representative of the scores in its distribution than when the standard deviation is large.

TRANSFORMATIONS

Within the context of descriptive statistics, it is the standard deviation that will provide us with the most valuable information regarding the dispersion of scores in a distribution. In the next chapter you shall learn what is *standard* about the standard deviation and why it is such a useful statistic. There is one more topic, however, that must be addressed to set the stage for the next chapter and that is the effects of **transformations.**

Transformation. Applying the same change to each member of an original set, such as adding a constant to each member of a set of raw scores.

The Effects of Transformations upon the Value of the Mean and Standard Deviation

As preparation for the next chapter on the *z* statistic, it will be useful for you to understand what happens to the mean and standard deviation of a distribution of scores when the original distribution is transformed by adding a constant to each score, subtracting a constant from each score, multiplying each score by a constant, or dividing each score by a constant. The effects upon the mean of such transformations are rather straightforward. Let us begin with the addition/subtraction transformation.

The Effect of the Addition/Subtraction Transformation upon the Mean.

If a constant is added to every one of a set of original scores, the mean of the transformed set will equal the original mean plus the constant.

$$\overline{X}_T = \overline{X}_O + c$$

The subscripts *T* and *O* stand for "Transformed" and "Original."

If we take the set 2, 3, 5, 6, 7, 7 and add a constant 3 to each score, the transformed set becomes 5, 6, 8, 9, 10, 10. The mean of the original set is 5 (30/6), and the mean of the transformed set is 8 (48/6). This is consistent with the above equation, which states that the mean of the transformed set will equal the original mean (5) plus the constant (3).

Similarly, when the constant is subtracted the mean of the transformed set equals the original mean minus the constant.

$$\overline{X}_T = \overline{X}_O - c$$

For example, if we subtract 3 from each score in the set 2, 3, 5, 6, 7, 7 the transformed set becomes −1, 0, 2, 3, 4, 4. The mean of the original set is 5, and the mean of the transformed set is 2 (12/6). This is consistent with the equation, which states that the mean of the transformed set (2) will equal the mean of the original set (5) minus the constant (3).

The effect of multiplication and division by a constant on the mean is to increase (multiplication) or decrease (division) the value of the mean by a factor of the constant. These effects are expressed in the following formulae:

multiplication $\overline{X}_T = \overline{X}_O \cdot c$

and division $\overline{X}_T = \overline{X}_O / c.$

Let us double each score in the set 2, 3, 5, 6, 7, 7 and see, as indicated by the formula below, if the mean is doubled.

$$\overline{X}_T = \overline{X}_O \cdot 2$$

The transformed set is 4, 6, 10, 12, 14, 14, and the mean has indeed been doubled from the original 5 (30/6) to 10 (60/6). Notice also that the range of the set has doubled from the original $7 - 2 + 1 = 6$ to $14 - 4 + 1 = 12$.

Similarly, dividing each of the original scores by two,

$$\overline{X}_T = \overline{X}_O / 2,$$

changes the set from 2, 3, 5, 6, 7, 7 to 1, 1.5, 2.5, 3, 3.5, 3.5. The mean is half its original value, 2.5 versus 5, and the range of the transformed set is also half of the original range: $3.5 - 1.5 + 1 = 3$ compared to $7 - 2 + 1 = 6$.

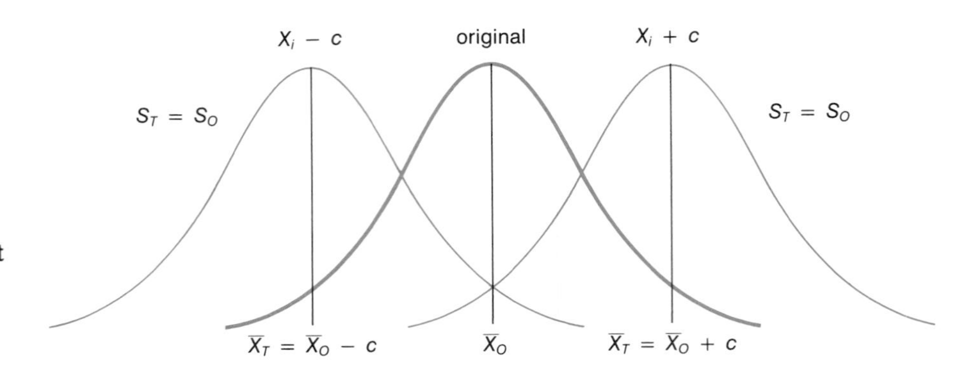

Figure 3.6

The effects of adding a constant to and subtracting a constant from each score in a normal distribution. The mean changes by the value of the constant, but the dispersion stays the same.

Table 3.7

	Original Set (X)	Addition ($X_i + c$)	Subtraction ($X_i - c$)
SS =	$172 - \frac{30^2}{6} = 22$	$406 - \frac{48^2}{6} = 22$	$46 - \frac{12^2}{6} = 22$
s^2 =	$\frac{22}{6} = 3.67$	$\frac{22}{6} = 3.67$	$\frac{22}{6} = 3.67$
s =	$\sqrt{3.67} = 1.92$	$\sqrt{3.67} = 1.92$	$\sqrt{3.67} = 1.92$

The Effect of the Addition/Subtraction Transformation upon the Measures of Dispersion. If a constant is added to every score in a distribution, the whole distribution shifts in the positive direction to a degree equal to the size of the constant, and if a constant is subtracted from every score in a distribution, the whole distribution shifts in the negative direction to a degree equal to the size of the constant. This is illustrated in figure 3.6 with a bell-shaped distribution. Although the transformations change the values within the distribution, the degree to which the scores within the distribution vary from each other does not change.

In table 3.7 the addition and subtraction transformations ($c = 3$) are applied to the same small set of scores we used above. Notice that the sum of squares (SS), of the original set 2, 3, 5, 6, 7, 7, equals the SS of both transformed sets even though the entries in the three SS formulae are quite different.

The Effect of the Multiplication and Division Transformations upon the Standard Deviation. Unlike the addition and subtraction transformations, the multiplication and division transformations do affect the measures of dispersion. We shall focus on the standard deviation.

If each original score is multiplied by a constant, the standard deviation of the transformed set will equal the original standard deviation times the constant.

$$s_T = s_O \cdot c$$

If each original score is divided by a constant, the standard deviation of the transformed set equals the original standard deviation divided by the constant.

$$s_T = s_O / c$$

For example, let us apply a multiplication transformation to the set 2, 3, 5, 6, 7, 7. If each score is doubled by multiplying each of the original scores by 2, the set becomes 4, 6, 10, 12, 14, 14. We may compute the standard deviation of this set using the following formula:

$$s = \sqrt{\frac{SS}{n}} = \sqrt{\frac{\Sigma X^2 - \frac{(\Sigma X)^2}{n}}{n}}$$

$$s = \sqrt{\frac{688 - \frac{60^2}{6}}{6}}$$

$$s = 3.83$$

As the equation predicted (allowing for some rounding error), the standard deviation of the transformed set (3.83) is twice the value of the standard deviation of the original set (1.92) that was presented in table 3.7.

Similarly, if we divide each of the original scores by 2, the original set of 2, 3, 5, 6, 7, 7 becomes 1, 1.5, 2.5, 3, 3.5, 3.5. The computation for the standard deviation of this transformed set is shown below.

$$s = \sqrt{\frac{SS}{n}} = \sqrt{\frac{\Sigma X^2 - \frac{(\Sigma X)^2}{n}}{n}}$$

$$s = \sqrt{\frac{43 - \frac{15^2}{6}}{6}}$$

$$s = 0.96$$

As predicted, the division transformation halved the standard deviation from the original 1.92 to $1.92/2 = 0.96$.

In the exercises that follow and/or with the demonstration that is run at the end of the VARSD.BAS computer tutorial, you shall have the opportunity to experiment with addition, subtraction, multiplication, and division transformations.

Summary

In this chapter you were introduced to the statistical representation of the characteristics of data. The computation and properties of the measures of central tendency (mean, median, and mode) were presented along with a comparison of these measures. Next, the computational procedures for the measures of dispersion were presented along with an analysis of the effects of transformations. With this background we are now ready to move on to some problem-solving applications in the next chapter.

Key Terms

Central Tendency
Deviation Score
Dispersion
Least Squares
Mean
Median
Mode
Overall (Weighted) Mean
Skewness
SS
Standard Deviation
Transformation
Variance
Variation (sum of squares)

Exercises

In addition to the exercises that are presented next, be sure to try a session with the VARSD.BAS computer tutorial. This will give you additional exposure to some of the material from the present chapter within a somewhat different environment. This tutorial demonstrates the computation of variation, variance, and standard deviation and then allows you to practice computations with your own data. All the steps of the computational procedure are displayed so that, should your answers not match those of the computer, you will be able to determine why.

Another objective of VARSD.BAS is to demonstrate the effects of transformations upon the measures of dispersion. You may modify a set by adding a constant to each score, subtracting a constant from each score, multiplying each score by a constant, or dividing each score by a constant. You may then compare the measures of dispersion computed on the transformed set to the original computations.

1. Given the following set of scores, give the numerical values that correspond to the listed terms.

10, 4, 3, 5, 9, 6, 12

a. ΣX^2

b. $(\Sigma X)^2$

c. $\dfrac{\Sigma X}{n}$

d. mean

e. variation

f. variance

g. standard deviation

h. median

i. $\Sigma(X - \overline{X})^2$

j. s

k. s^2

l. SS

m. Σx^2

2. Add 10 to each of the scores in the above set and recompute the:

a. mean
b. sum of squares
c. variance
d. standard deviation
e. median
f. What was the effect of the transformation on the sum of squares, variance, and standard deviation?

3. When we double each value in the original set (i.e., 20, 8, 6, 10, 18, 12, 24) what is the effect upon the original mean and standard deviation?

4. Answer question 3 for the transformation that halves each of the original scores.

5. Now, rather than going through direct computations, try answering questions 3 and 4 using the transformation formulae that were presented in the chapter. Do you get the same answers?

6. If the variance of a set of scores is 25, the standard deviation equals ________ .

7. If the mean of a normal (bell-shaped) distribution equals 40 and the standard deviation is 6, the median will equal ______ and the mode will equal ______.
8. What are the three properties of the arithmetic mean?
9. Annette, a student activist, has been very upset about what she perceived to be a problem of overcharging at the Student Union Cafeteria. She decided to collect some data on a small sample of Union Cafeteria customers and positioned herself near the exit of the cafeteria line during lunch. As the customers passed by, she asked each one the cost of their meal. Then, with her data in hand, she went to a student senate meeting to make a presentation on the issue. She will fail to make her point if she stands up and reads off the individual scores. With what you know about describing data, help Annette to prepare a brief description of the meal cost data. Here are the data.

\$3.25	\$4.10	\$2.30	\$1.95	\$2.75	\$2.80	\$3.00
\$1.85	\$2.40	\$3.10	\$5.75	\$2.10	\$2.50	\$4.15
\$3.00						

10. The expression $\Sigma(X - \overline{X})$ will always equal ______.
11. Assume the expressions $\Sigma(X - \overline{X})^2$ and $\Sigma(X - c)^2$ are computed for a particular set of scores and the mean of the set equals 3. Further, assume the value of the first expression equals 25. With this information complete the following statement. The value of the second expression will always be greater than ______ except when it is computed with the constant, c, set equal to ______.
12. If a distribution of score values is positively or negatively skewed, the ______ will give a more representative value of central tendency than the ______.
13. If the variance of an original set is 16 and this set is transformed by adding 5 to each of the original scores, the standard deviation of the transformed set will equal ______ and the variance will equal ______.
14. If the variance of an original set equals 25 and each of the original scores in the set is doubled, the standard deviation of the transformed set will equal ______ and the variance of the transformed set will equal ______.
15. Given the following set, compute the three measures of central tendency and the three measures of dispersion.

6, 4, 7, 2, 11, 10, 7, 7, 9

16. What is the range for the set in question 15?
17. In the table below examination means for four classes are displayed. What is the overall mean for the four classes combined?

Class:	I	II	III	IV
Average Grade:	75	77	72	81
Size of Class:	12	22	18	16

18. The average variation per score in a distribution is called the ______.

19. Over the course of an entire season Basketball Team A scored an average of 88 points per game. The standard deviation of the distribution of point totals is 12. Basketball Team B also scored an average of 88 points per game over the season, but the standard deviation of the distribution of points totals for Team B is only 8. If the two teams meet in postseason play, which team is more likely to score closest to its 88 average point production? Why?

20. The mode may be determined for any scale of measurement (nominal, ordinal, interval, or ratio), but the mean should be computed only if the data are on the ________ or ________ scale.

21. Each subject in a group of 50 was given a complex puzzle to assemble. Nine subjects failed to assemble the puzzle in the allotted time and were given the maximum allowable time (30 minutes) as their score. If asked to describe the group's performance in terms of the typical or average amount of time it took a subject to assemble the puzzle, which measure of central tendency would you use? Why?

22. Assume the average quiz grade of a group of 25 students was 80 and two students, the 26th and 27th members of the class, were allowed to take a makeup test. Their grades were 85 and 88. Compute a new average grade for the class with the two makeup grades included.

23. If you compute the SS, variance, or standard deviation of a set and your computations result in a negative value for any or all of these measures of dispersion, what would you conclude?

24. Six golfers from the Hiawatha Country Club played six golfers from the Battle Island Country Club in three foursomes. At the end of 18 holes all 12 scores were put up on the bulletin board. Here they are:

Hiawatha C. C.: 88, 77, 77, 78, 80, 122
Battle Island: 87, 86, 84, 78, 80, 89

Each club claimed that on the average their team was superior. How would you arbitrate this dispute?

Notes: For the interested reader, here is the proof that the deviation formula and the computational formulae are equivalent.

$$\Sigma(X - \overline{X})^2 = \Sigma(X - \overline{X})^2$$

$$= \Sigma X^2 - 2\Sigma X\overline{X} + \Sigma\overline{X}^2$$

since $\Sigma\overline{X} + n\overline{X}$,

$$= \Sigma X^2 - 2(n\overline{X})\overline{X} + n\overline{X}^2$$

$$= \Sigma X^2 - 2n\overline{X}^2 + n\overline{X}^2$$

$$= \Sigma X^2 - n\frac{(\Sigma X)^2}{n^2}$$

$$= \Sigma X^2 - \frac{n(\Sigma X)^2}{n^2}$$

$$= \Sigma X^2 - \frac{(\Sigma X)^2}{n}$$

CHAPTER 4

The z Statistic

Normal Distribution (also called the Normal Curve). A bell-shaped symmetrical curve that typifies the distributions of many behavioral (e.g., intelligence) and physical (e.g., height) variables.

There are many variables studied in the course of behavioral science research (intelligence, various performance skills, physical traits such as height and weight, etc.), which, when plotted in a graph, closely approximate the familiar bell-shaped curve that we call the **normal distribution.** The reason the graphic plots of certain variables form this distinctive shape is that the individual scores tend to bunch up in the middle around some central value. Also, the further above or below the central value we go, the fewer scores we encounter, and this trend is symmetrical for the two halves of the distribution. For example, there is a level of intelligence that is considered to be *average* (I.Q. = 100), and the intelligence of most persons is either equal to or close to this value. The further we move from the average value of intelligence, the fewer the number of persons we are likely to find that characterize those levels of intelligence. The number of persons in the extremes of the distribution, retarded persons on the low end and geniuses on the high end, is at a minimum.

Once we have data that represent a population of normally distributed scores, and once we know the mean (μ) and standard deviation (σ) of the distribution, there are several descriptive details concerning the makeup of the distribution that we may wish to know about. For example, it may be important to know what percentage of the scores in a distribution are equal to or less than a particular value. Perhaps we may wish to know how many or what percentage of the scores fall within a given range. In this chapter we shall learn to apply the z statistic to answer the whole range of such questions. Before we learn what the z statistic can do for us, let us begin with an interesting encounter.

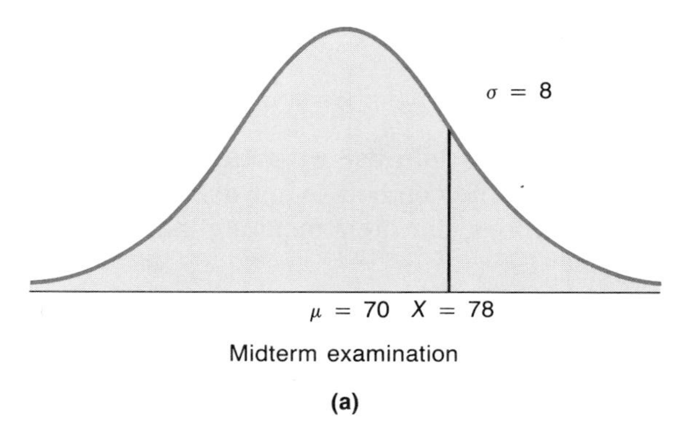

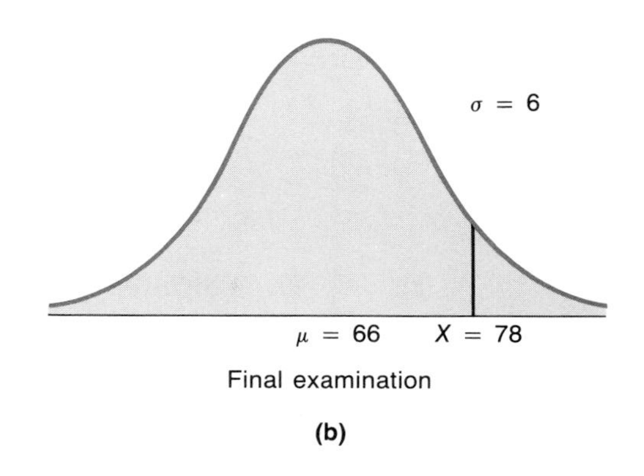

Figure 4.1

Two distributions of examination scores. The midterm scores have a mean of 70 and a standard deviation of 8. The final examination scores have a mean of 66 and a standard deviation of 6.

Bell-shaped Distribution. The characteristic shape of the distribution of a normally distributed variable. *See* Normal Distribution.

Percentile. The location of a score in a distribution in terms of the percentage of scores that equal or are less than the score value. ("Forty is on the 35th percentile.")

Percentile Rank. A value equal to the percentage of scores in a distribution that are equal to or less than a specific score value. ("The percentile rank of forty is 35.")

Kathy, a vacationing American, was traveling through Belgium by train. She noticed that the stranger seated next to her was reading a book on child rearing. Wishing to engage her fellow traveler in conversation she asked, "Do you have any children?" The reply was, "Nine." Or was it "Nein"? This one-word answer is ambiguous because it is uncertain whether the stranger spoke in the language of the questioner ("nine") or in German ("nein"), a language that is commonly spoken in Belgium. The two possible replies sound the same but have very different meanings (no children vs. nine children).

The same dilemma appears when we try to make comparisons between scores in different distributions. Consider the two normal **bell-shaped distributions** that appear in figure 4.1. Distribution (a) represents the distribution of midterm examination scores, and distribution (b) represents the final examination scores for a fictional class.

The score 78 exists in both distributions. The two 78s sound the same (sehv-en-tee-ate). But do they mean the same thing? It is apparent from inspection that a 78 on the final examination is near the top of the class, but a 78 on the midterm, although a decent score, does not represent the same high level of performance. The 78 on the midterm examination is one standard deviation above the mean ($70 + 8 = 78$). The 78 on the final examination, however, is two standard deviations above the mean ($66 + 6 + 6 = 78$). Later, you will learn to determine for yourself that the midterm 78 is in the top 16% of the test scores and the final examination 78 is in the top 2% of the scores. Put another way, approximately 84% of the midterm scores are equal to or less than 78, while approximately 98% of the final examination scores are equal to or less than 78. According to the accepted terminology, we say that the 78 on the final is on the 98th **percentile** and that the **percentile rank** of 78 is 98. Similarly, the 78 on the midterm is on the 84th percentile, and the percentile rank of 78 is 84.

Formally stated, the *percentile rank* of a specific score in a distribution is a value equal to the percentage of scores in the distribution that are equal to or less than the specific score value, and that specific score is on a *percentile* equal in value to that percentage.

COMPARING DISTRIBUTIONS

Each normally distributed array of scores with its own mean and standard deviation represents a unique language. The numbers in one distribution may sound like numbers in other distributions, but their meaning may be quite different.

How, then, do we compare scores that belong to different distributions? Let us go back to Kathy, our American tourist. She recognized that her companion's English was extremely limited, and so they conversed in French, a language common to both of them and in which both were fluent. (No, the Belgian lady did not have nine children!)

In statistics we solve a similar communication problem in the same way by agreeing to communicate in a standard language—the language of **z scores.**

z **scores.** The location of a raw score in its distribution in relation to how far from the mean of the distribution the score is in standard deviation units.

A z score is a raw score expressed in standard deviation units. The z score equivalent of a raw score tells us how many standard deviation units the raw score is from the mean of its distribution.

Using z scores we can eliminate confusion in comparing raw scores from different distributions. You saw earlier that the midterm examination score of 78 has a z value of 1.00 because it falls one **standard deviation unit** above the mean of its distribution ($70 + 8 = 78$), and the final examination score of 78 has a z value of 2.00 because it falls two standard deviation units above the mean of its distribution ($66 + 6 + 6 = 78$). Because the score of 78 on the final examination is twice as far from the mean of its distribution as is the 78 on the midterm, the 78 on the final represents the better performance of the two (*see* figure 4.1).

Standard Deviation Units. A synonym for z score units. A representation of a score in a normal distribution in terms of how far away it is from the mean.

Also, we can translate from the language of one distribution into the language of another. For example, what final examination score represents the exact same level of performance as an 82 on the midterm? The score of 82 is 12 raw score units above the mean of 70. Since the standard deviation equals 8, 82 is located 1.50 standard deviation units above the mean of 70 ($70 + 8 + 4$). We, therefore, say that 82 has a z score value of 1.50. Now we must find the final examination score that is also 1.50 standard deviation units above the mean of 66. Since the standard deviation equals 6 in this distribution, by adding $1.50 \times 6 = 9$ to the mean of 66 we get $66 + 9 = 75$. Thus, an 82 on the midterm examination represents the same level of performance as a 75 on the final examination. Both scores are 1.50 standard deviation units above the mean in their respective distributions. Although 82 sounds *better* or *more than* 75, these scores mean the same thing. They only appear to be different because they are in different languages or, in mathematical terms, on different scales.

Solving a variety of statistical problems is easier with z scores, and, as promised above, we shall deal with the whole range of such problems. First, however, you should become familiar with the z formula. Then, using the formula, we shall actually make a distribution of the z statistic so you will understand why z has certain special characteristics.

Let us begin by dissecting the formula for the z statistic:

$$z = \frac{\text{raw score} - \text{mean}}{\text{standard deviation}} = \frac{X - \mu}{\sigma}$$

Transformation. Applying the same change to each member of an original set.

If you understood from the preceding discussion that an 82 on the midterm has a z score value of 1.50, you have already been solving this formula in your head.

$$z = \frac{82 - 70}{8} = 1.50$$

This simple formula says that to convert a raw score (X) to a z score we must apply two **transformations** to the raw score. The first transformation is in the numerator ($X - \mu$) and requires us to subtract the mean of the distribution from the raw score. Let us do this transformation to each and every score in a normally distributed array of 500 scores ($\mu = 50$, $\sigma = 10$) to see what happens. The original distribution appears in figure 4.2.

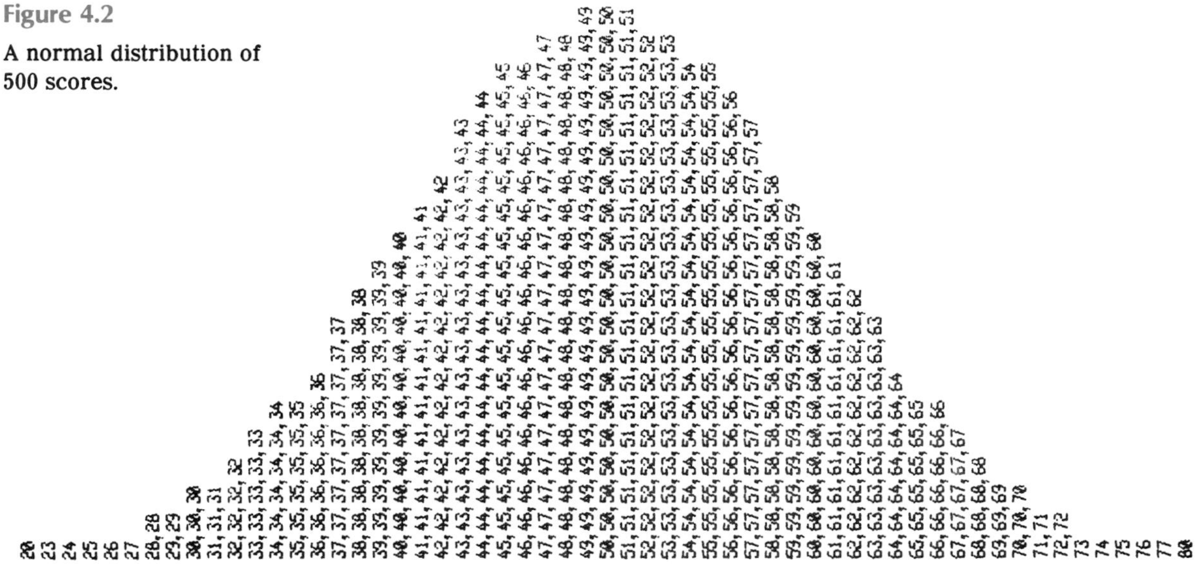

Figure 4.2

A normal distribution of 500 scores.

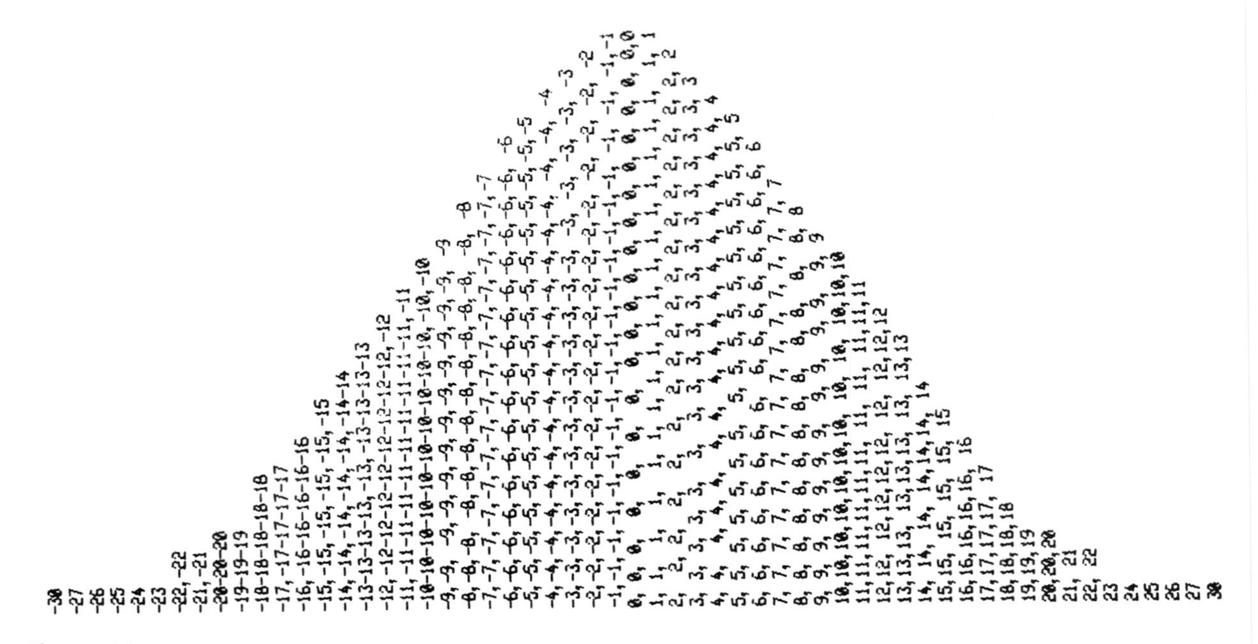

Figure 4.3

The normal distribution of 500 scores in figure 4.2 after the mean ($\mu = 50$) is subtracted from each of the 500 original scores.

If the mean of 50 is subtracted from each of the 500 scores the distribution will be changed as illustrated in figure 4.3. Notice that although the general shape of the distribution remains unchanged (i.e., the standard deviation still equals 10), the whole curve has been shifted 50 units in the negative direction. Now, the mean is zero instead of 50 and half the scores in the distribution have negative values.

That the dispersion of the scores remains unchanged from the first transformation should not be surprising. The material at the end of chapter 3 (and the last experiment in the VARSD.BAS tutorial) illustrated that adding a constant to or subtracting a constant from every score in a distribution has no effect on the dispersion of the scores.

The second transformation is to divide the first order transformation by the distribution's very own standard deviation. From chapter 3 and VARSD.BAS you learned that when each score in a distribution is divided by a constant, the standard deviation of the transformed distribution equals the original standard deviation divided by the constant.

$$\text{transformed SD} = \frac{\text{original SD}}{\text{constant}}$$

In notation:

$$s_T = s_O/c$$

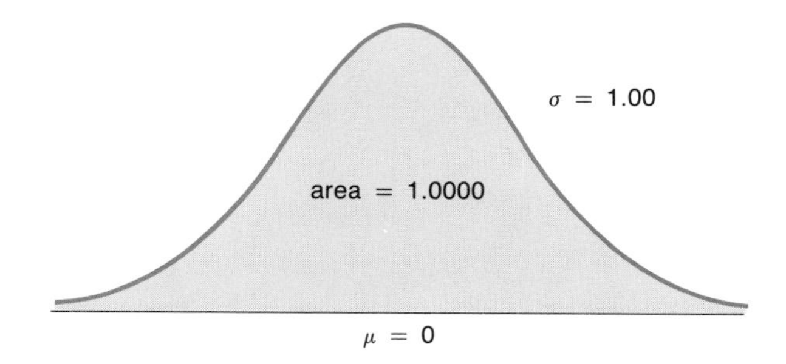

Figure 4.4
The unsegmented distribution of the z statistic.

For the distribution in figure 4.1, if the constant is set equal to the standard deviation itself, the equation becomes

$$\text{transformed SD} = \frac{\text{original SD}}{\text{original SD}} = \frac{10}{10} = 1.00$$

In notation:

$$s_T = s_O/s_O = 10/10 = 1.00$$

Thus, the effect of the second transformation is to change the standard deviation from the original 10 to 1.00. The resulting z distribution is shown in figure 4.4.

So, *the z distribution has a mean of zero and a standard deviation equal to 1.00.* But there is one other property of the z distribution that is important to know.

Unit Normal Curve (also called the Unit Normal Distribution). Another name for the distribution of the z statistic reflecting the fact that the area under the z curve is unity (1.00).

The area under the z distribution equals unity (1.00).

This is why the z distribution is also referred to as the **unit normal distribution** or the **unit normal curve.**

Proportions of Area. Using the z statistic, one can determine the proportion of the total area under any normal curve that is contained in a specific segment of the curve.

Since the area under the entire curve is 1.00, and since the distribution of the z statistic is symmetrical (one-half is the mirror image of the other half), it is only logical that the area under each half of the curve equals 0.5000 (*see* figure 4.5).

The z distribution can be further divided into segments that contain various **proportions of area.** If we move away from the mean in steps of one standard deviation we define segments of area that contain the proportions indicated in figure 4.6.

In fact, this is what makes the standard deviation "standard." Any normal distribution that is divided into segments that are one standard deviation wide as shown in figure 4.6 will be divided into the exact same proportions of area.

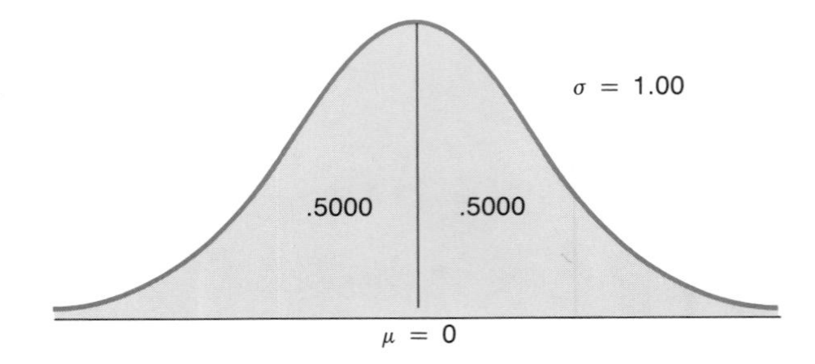

Figure 4.5

The proportion of area in the two halves of the distribution of the z statistic.

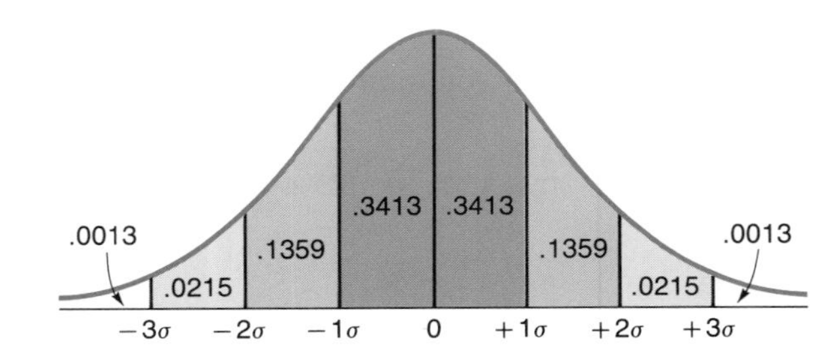

Figure 4.6

Areas under the normal curve in segments that have a width of one standard deviation unit.

The z table (*see* Appendix A) takes the subdivision of the z distribution further by progressing in steps of 0.01 standard deviation units. Column B lists the area between the mean and the z score, and column C lists the area between the score and the tail of the distribution. Since the z distribution is bilaterally symmetrical with one-half being the mirror image of the other half, only proportions of area for the positive side ($z > 0$) are listed in the z table.

For example, earlier in this chapter we converted a midterm examination score of 82 into a z score of 1.50. This told us that the 82 was located 1.50 standard deviation units ($\sigma = 8$) above the mean of its distribution (70). In the small section of the z table that is reproduced on page 77, you can see that a score that is 1.50 standard deviation units above the mean is located such that the proportion of area between it and the mean is 0.4332, and between the score and the tail of the distribution the proportion of area is 0.0668.

On the other hand, a score of 58 is also 1.50 standard deviation units away from the mean ($70 - 8 - 4 = 58$). In this case, however, the z score has a negative value,

$$z = \frac{58 - 70}{8} = -1.50$$

z Table

z	Area Between Mean and Score	Area Between Score and Tail
A	*B*	*C*
—	—	—
—	—	—
1.48	.4306	.0694
1.49	.4319	.0694
1.50	**.4332**	**.0668**
1.51	.4345	.0655
1.52	.4357	.0643
—	—	—

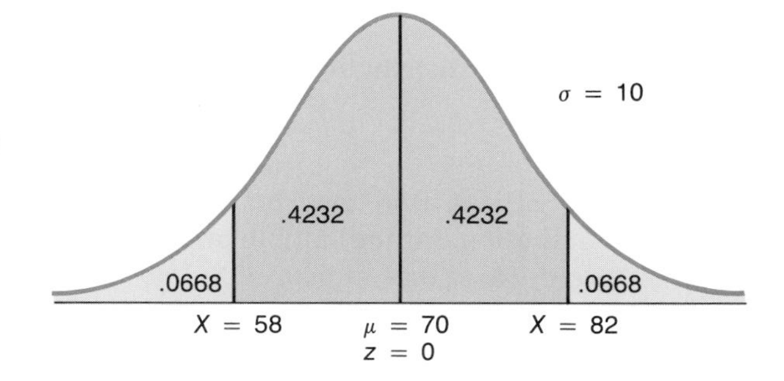

Figure 4.7

The proportions of area between the mean and score X_1 and between the tail and score X_2 for $X_1 = 58$ and $X_2 = 82$.

and because *z* is negative we know the 58 must be located below the mean as shown in figure 4.7. The scores of 82 and 58 divide their respective halves of the *z* distribution into the same proportions of area because, with the exception of the sign, their *z* score values are the same. Thus, while only positive values for *z* are listed in the table, the *z* table is used to find the proportions of area that relate to both positive and negative *z* score values.

By now you should know that:

The *z* score equivalent of the raw score *X* is the location of *X* in its distribution expressed in standard deviation units.

We can use this property of the z statistic and the accompanying z table for some practical problem-solving applications. All of the various types of problems for which we use the z statistic will be covered in the remainder of this chapter in a way that mirrors the presentation used in the ZPRAC.BAS computer tutorial. The types of problems we shall cover are listed in the following *menu* as it appears in the opening of the ZPRAC.BAS computer tutorial. To solve these kinds of problems you need to know how to use the z table and you need to apply some simple logic. So, to prepare you for the chapter exercises and/or a session with ZPRAC.BAS to practice solving these kinds of problems, let's step through an assortment of problems. Here is the menu as it appears on the computer screen:

Menu

1. What is the percentile rank of score X?
2. What score is on the nth percentile?
3. What *percentage* of scores are between (lower limit) and (upper limit)?
4. How *many* scores are between (lower limit) and (upper limit)?
5. What percentage of scores are above and below score X?
6. Select different distribution parameters, (μ, σ, and N).
7. Exit program

Although ZPRAC.BAS may be initialized with the parameters of any **normal distribution,** for the sample problems we shall use the default values of $\mu = 70$, $\sigma = 10$, and $N = 500$.

In the first type of problem the task is to determine the percentile rank of score X. As mentioned above, the percentile rank of a score is the percentage of scores in the distribution that have values equal to or less than score X. Since normal distributions are symmetrical, the mean of the distribution is on the 50th percentile. This corresponds to one definition of the median (*see* chapter 3) as the score on the 50th percentile of a distribution.

If the mean of a normal distribution is on the 50th percentile, it follows logically that any score in the distribution that is numerically lower than the mean must have a percentile rank less than 50, and any score that is larger than the mean must have a percentile rank greater than 50. This fact may seem too obvious to mention, but a carelessly omitted minus sign for the z value of a score below the mean is a common cause of errors in problems of this type. This danger will become more apparent as we tackle some specific problems.

Problem 1A. Find the percentile rank of 63. (Recall that the distribution for these problems has a mean of 70, a standard deviation of 10, and consists of 500 scores.)

The first step is to convert the X value of 63 into a z score.

$$z = \frac{X - \mu}{\sigma} = \frac{63 - 70}{10} = -0.70$$

The z score value of -0.70 tells us that 63 is 0.70 standard deviation units below the mean. If you look up the z value of 0.70 in the z table (*see* Appendix A) you will see the proportions of area that are between the score of 63 and the mean, and between 63 and the tail. The relevant section of the z table is reproduced below, and the entry for $z = 0.70$ is highlighted. Notice that there are no negative values listed in the table. Our computed z value was really -0.70, but we must use the tabled value of $+0.70$ to find the proportions of area.

To keep straight which values from the table go along with which segments of area you should make a simple sketch. The column B entry is the proportion of area between the mean and 63, and the column C entry tells us the proportion of area between 63 and the tail of the distribution.

From the sketch in figure 4.8 we can see that the proportion of area below 63 is .2420. Expressed as a percentage, 24.20% of the scores are equal to or less than 63 and, therefore, we say that 63 is on the 24.2 percentile.

***z* Table**

z *A*	Area Between Score and Mean *B*	Area Between Score and Tail *C*
0.68	.2517	.2483
0.69	.2549	.2451
0.70	**.2580**	**.2420**
0.71	.2611	.2389
0.72	.2642	.2358

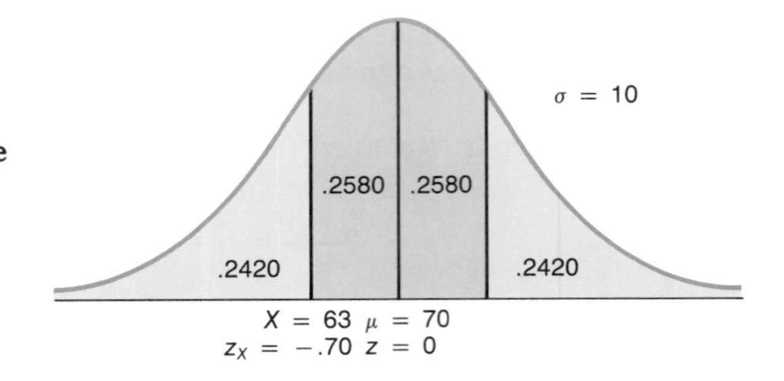

Figure 4.8
The location of 63 ($z = -.70$) and the proportions of area above and below its location.

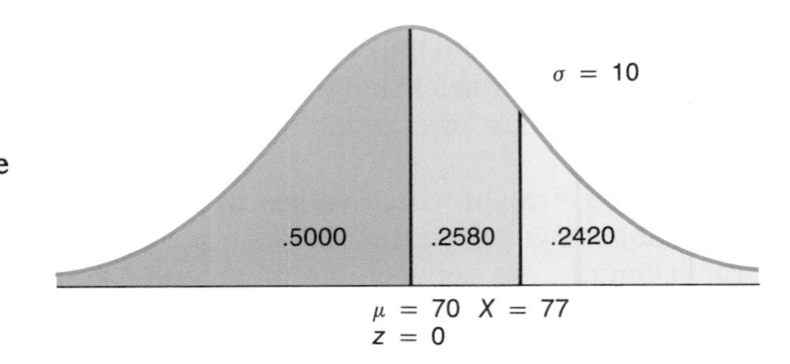

Figure 4.9
The location of 77 ($z = +.70$) and the proportions of area above and below its location.

Problem 1B. Now let's try the same type of problem for $X = 77$. If you convert 77 to a z score you will get the same answer for z that we obtained for 63, with one important exception. Instead of $z = -0.70$, now $z = +0.70$.

$$z = \frac{77 - 70}{10} = \frac{7}{10} = +0.70$$

If you make a sketch and label the segments of area (figure 4.9), you will see that 77 is on the 75.80 percentile (.5000 + .2580). In other words, 75.80 percent of the scores in the distribution are equal to or less than 77. I am sure that you now recognize the importance of keeping track of the sign of the z score. The difference between $z = -0.70$ and $z = +0.70$ is the difference between a percentile solution of 24.2 versus 75.8.

Problem 2A. In menu option 2 the problem is to find the raw score that corresponds to a given percentile. Let's find the score on the 20th percentile. We know that, by definition, score X has a proportion of area below it equal to .2000, and this can be illustrated with a sketch.

Before we use the z formula to solve for X we must determine the values for all the other entries in the formula. Since we know that the mean is 70 and the standard deviation is 10, the only remaining unknown is the value for z. To find z the first step is to look for .2000 in column C (or .3000 in column B). Why? Because we know from our sketch (figure 4.10) that the

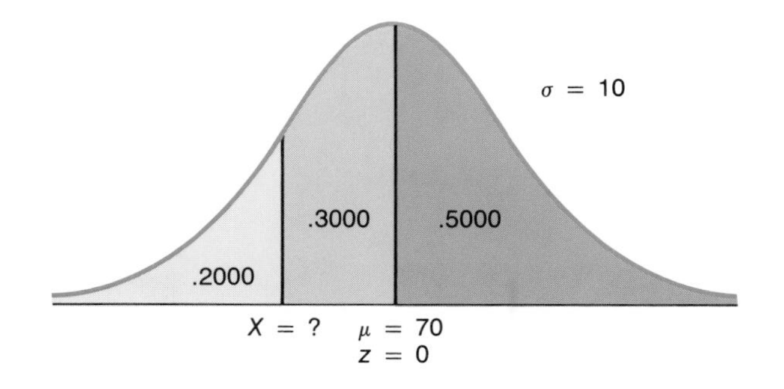

Figure 4.10

The proportions of area above and below X when X lies on the 20th percentile.

***z* Table**

z A	Area Between Score and Mean B	Area Between Score and Tail C
—	—	—
—	—	—
0.82	.2939	.2061
0.83	.2967	.2033
0.84	**.2995**	**.2005**
0.85	.3023	.1977
0.86	.3051	.1949
—	—	—
—	—	—

column C and B entries are .2000 and .3000, respectively. We may not know *what* the value of X is, but from the sketch we certainly know *where* it is.

The relevant portion of the z table is reproduced above and you can see that the exact value for which we are searching (.2000 in column C) is not in the table. The closest we can come is the .2005 entry. If you look to the left of this entry you will see that the z score that corresponds to an area between the score and the tail of .2005 is 0.84.

The z formula can now be solved for X.

$$z = \frac{X - \mu}{\sigma}$$

$$0.84 = \frac{X - 70}{10}$$

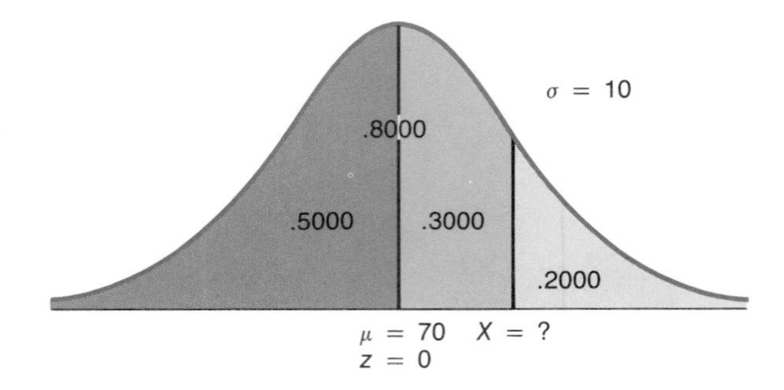

Figure 4.11
The proportions of area above and below X when X lies on the 80th percentile.

Before we solve for X, did we leave anything out? If you noticed that we forgot the minus sign for the z value you are on your toes. The z value should be -0.84, not 0.84. Remember, any score located below the mean of its distribution will have a negative z value, and our sketch showed us that any score with a percentile value less than 50 is below the mean.

Solving the corrected equation:

$$-0.84 = \frac{X - 70}{10}$$

$$-8.4 = X - 70 \qquad \text{(Multiply both sides by 10.)}$$

$$61.6 = X \qquad \text{(Add 70 to both sides.)}$$

Therefore, the score on the 20th percentile is 61.6.

Problem 2B. What score is on the 80th percentile? I'll help you with the sketch (figure 4.11), then you can do the problem yourself. You may check your work using menu option 2 in ZPRAC.BAS or consult the Answers to Selected Exercises for this chapter in Appendix D.

The problems presented in menu option 3 require us to determine the percentage of scores that exist between two points on the distribution. As shown in figure 4.12, the points may both be below the mean, both above the mean, or one may be above the mean and the other below the mean.

Problem 3A. We shall first examine the case in which both the lower limit and the upper limit of the range are above the mean. Specifically, the problem is to find the percentage of scores between 74 and 83 in a normal distribution with $\mu = 70$ and $\sigma = 10$. First we must convert 74 and 83 into z scores using the z formula.

$$z = \frac{X - \mu}{\sigma}$$

$$z = \frac{74 - 70}{10} \qquad z = \frac{83 - 70}{10}$$

$$z = 0.40 \qquad z = 1.30$$

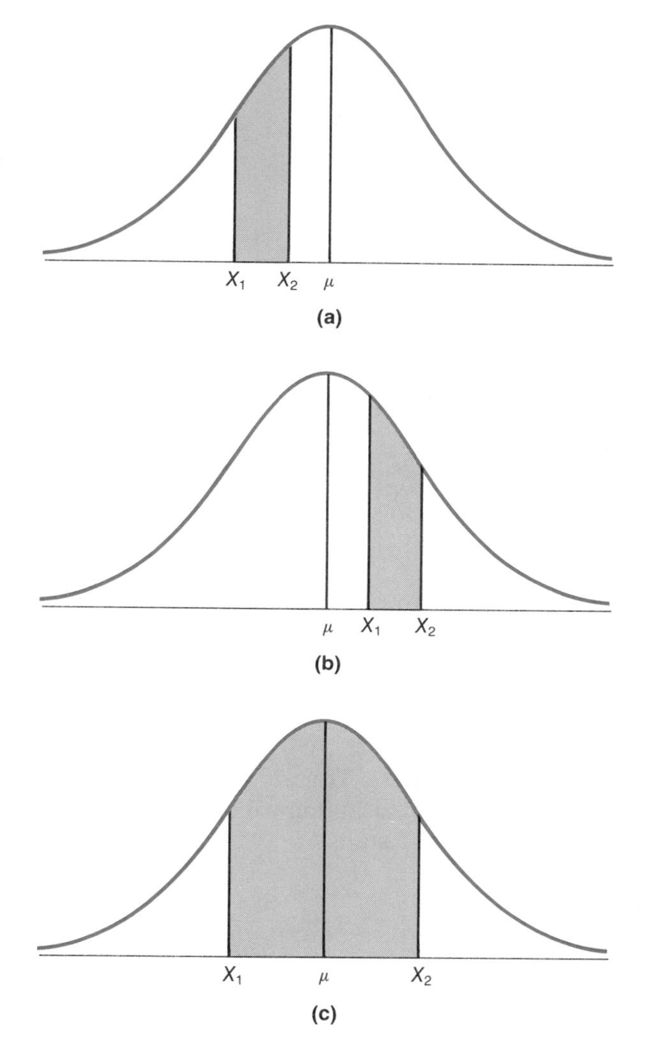

Figure 4.12

Possible positions for two score values relative to the distribution mean (a): both scores below the mean, (b): both scores above the mean, and (c): one score above and the other below.

From figure 4.13 you can see that if we first find the proportion of area between the mean and a z score of 1.30 (area = .4032), then subtract the proportion of area between the mean and a z score of .40 (area = .1554), we will be left with the answer of .2478. After converting the proportion to a percentage by multiplying by 100, we see that 24.78% of the scores are between 74 and 83.

Problem 3B. The same logic applies if both scores are below the mean. If one score is above and the other is below the mean, then we must find the area between the mean and z for both scores and simply add the proportions

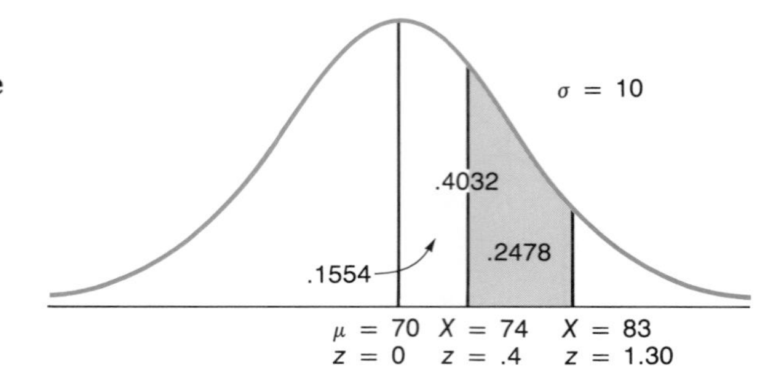

Figure 4.13

The sketch for finding the proportion of area between 74 and 83 with the subtraction method.

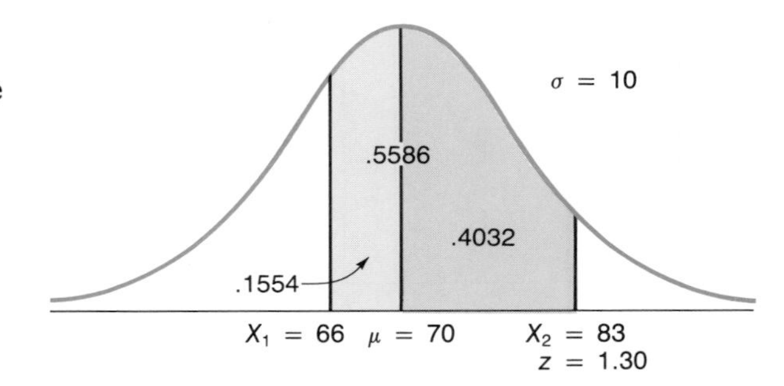

Figure 4.14

The sketch for finding the proportion of area between 66 and 83 in a distribution with a mean of 70 and a standard deviation of 10.

of area (figure 4.14). Thus, to find the percentage of scores between 66 and 83 on a normal distribution with $\mu = 70$ and $\sigma = 10$, we must first locate the scores using the z statistic.

$$z = \frac{66 - 70}{10} \qquad z = \frac{83 - 70}{10}$$

$$z = -0.40 \qquad z = 1.30$$

Then, using the table we find the proportions of area between the mean and z (table column B) when $z = -0.4$ and 1.3, respectively. After the area between 70 and 66 (.1554) is found at the z score of 0.40 and the proportion of area between 70 and 83 (.4042) is found at the z score of 1.30, these two proportions are added (.1554 + .4042 = .5586) and multiplied by 100 to get the answer of 55.86%.

Problem 4. This is really a simple extension of problem 3. To find *how many* scores in a distribution exist between two points we must first find the proportion of scores that exist between the two points. Once the proportion is known one need only multiply the proportion by the number of scores known to be in the population distribution.

Figure 4.15

The sketch for finding the proportion of area above and below 83 in a distribution with a mean of 70 and a standard deviation of 10.

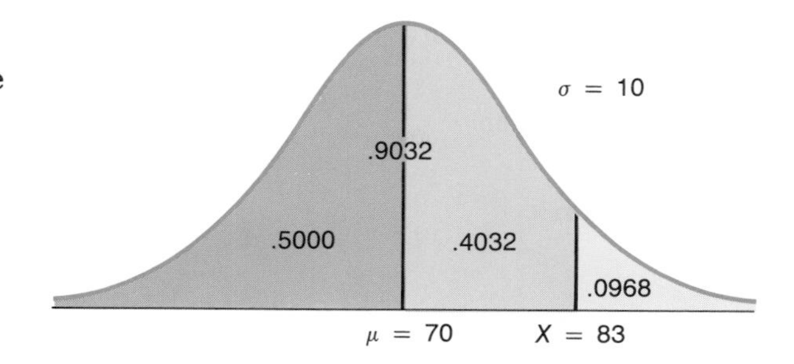

Thus, if 500 scores make up the population distribution referred to in Problems 3A and 3B, .2478 × 500 will tell us how many scores are between 74 and 83, and .5586 × 500 will tell us how many scores are between 66 and 83. The answers are 123.9 and 279.3, respectively.

Problem 5. What percentage of scores are above and below score X? Once you can do the other types of problems, this type will seem easy because there are no skills you need in addition to those you already have. For example, to find the percentage of scores above and below 83 we first convert 83 to a z score. We did this in problem 3 and the answer was 1.30. By finding 1.30 in the z table and looking in column C (the area beyond z) we get the proportion of area greater than or equal to 83, and the entry in column B (the area between the mean and z) tells us the proportion of area between 70 and 83. The proportion of area above 83 is .0968, and so we have the solution to half the problem: 9.68% of the scores are greater than or equal to 83. To find the proportion of area less than or equal to 83 we must add the area between 70 and 83 (.4032) to the area below the mean (.5000). The sum equals .9032, and so 90.32% of the scores are less than or equal to 83. The sketch for this problem may be found in figure 4.15.

Having stepped through the various kinds of problems for which we use the z statistic, you should know how to use the z table, draw an appropriate sketch, and apply some simple logic to determine the proportions of area in specific segments of a normal distribution. With these skills you should be able to tackle the exercises that follow. If you stumble, the ZPRAC.BAS computer tutorial provides a vehicle for practicing these types of problems and will show you all the steps of the solution. When your answers consistently match the computer's answers you know you have mastered this unit.

Summary

The z statistic was presented as a vehicle for extracting specific kinds of information from distributions of raw score and for making specific comparisons between different distributions. The reading of the z table was covered, and the format observed in the ZPRAC.BAS computer tutorial was presented with representative examples.

Key Terms

Bell-shaped Distribution
Normal Curve
Normal Distribution
Percentile
Percentile Rank
Proportions of Area
Standard Deviation Units
Transformation
Unit Normal Curve
***z* Scores**

Exercises

The ZPRAC.BAS computer tutorial will allow you to practice solving an infinite variety of z score problems and then check your work by calling up the step-by-step computer solution. Here are some problems of the same general type:

1. In a normal distribution with a mean of 30, a standard deviation of 4, and $N = 400$:

a. What is the percentile rank of the score 25?
b. What score is on the 80th percentile?
c. How many scores have values in the interval 25 to 34?
d. What percent of the scores are less than 32?

2. In a normal distribution with a mean of 70, a standard deviation of 6, and $N = 180$:

a. What are the limits of the middle 50% of the distribution?
b. What percent of the scores are between 75 and 85?
c. What percent of the scores are less than 66?
d. A 76 in this distribution means the same thing (i.e., is equivalent to) a score value of ______ in the distribution used in question 1.

3. In a normal distribution with a mean of 50, a standard deviation of 10, and $N = 500$:

a. What is the percentile rank of the score 55?
b. What score is on the 80th percentile?
c. How many scores have values in the interval 45 to 55?
d. What percent of the scores are less than 35?
e. What scores above and below the mean of 50 bound the middle 50% of the distribution? (i.e., What are the scores on the 25th and 75th percentiles?)

4. In a normal distribution with a mean of 50, a standard deviation of 5, and $N = 500$:

a. What is the percentile rank of the score 43?
b. What score is on the 90th percentile?
c. How many scores have values in the interval 45 to 52?
d. What percent of the scores are less than 42?

5. In a normal distribution with a mean of 60, a standard deviation of 6, and $N = 280$:
   a. What are the limits of the middle 50% of the distribution?
   b. What percent of the scores are between 65 and 75?
   c. What percent of the scores are less than 66?
   d. A 70 in this distribution means the same thing (i.e., is equivalent to) a score value of ______ in the distribution used in question 1.
6. In a normal distribution with a mean of 20, a standard deviation of 10, and $N = 500$:
   a. What is the percentile rank of the score 37?
   b. What score is on the 45th percentile?
   c. How many scores have values in the interval 16 to 30?
   d. What percent of the scores are less than 0?
   e. What scores above and below the mean of 20 bound the middle 50% of the distribution? (i.e., What are the scores on the 25th and 75th percentiles?)
7. Tom's teacher reports the results of all examinations in the form of z scores. Tom was told that he got a zero on the examination. How did Tom do on the examination relative to the rest of the students?
8. On the next examination Tom got a 1.78. What was the percentile rank of his test score?
9. If Sam, another student in Tom's class, got a raw score of 83 on both examinations, was Sam's level of performance relative to the other students necessarily equal on both tests?
10. If Sam's z score on both examinations was 1.66, was his level of performance relative to the other students necessarily equal on both tests?
11. The z formula imposes two transformations on a raw score. Explain why these transformations, if applied to every score in a normal distribution of raw scores, result in a new distribution with a mean of zero and a standard deviation of 1.00.
12. What is the area under the distribution of the z statistic?
13. What percentage of values in the distribution of the z statistic are equal to or greater than zero?
14. Explain what is *standard* about the standard deviation.
15. The z score equivalent of a raw score X is the location of X in its distribution expressed in ______________ units.

CHAPTER 5

Regression

PREDICTING POTENTIAL DATA FROM EXISTING DATA

Up to this point in the text the emphasis has been upon describing data derived from the measurement of a single variable. We described data with respect to central tendency, variability, percentile values of specific score values, etc. With regression analysis and correlation (chapter 6) our descriptive capabilities will extend to describing the relationship between two variables (correlation) and the use of one variable to predict the value of another variable (regression). (Correlation and regression analyses are also done within the context of hypothesis testing and statistical inference, but we shall defer this until chapter 11.) We shall deal first with the topic of **prediction.**

Prediction. Using the equation representing the functional relationship between two variables to predict the value of one variable with the knowledge of the other.

Statistical Prediction

As an aid to understanding the concept of statistical prediction, consider the following scenario. Francine is the personnel manager of the Acme Workshop, a half-way house that boards and employs recently released juvenile offenders. The goal of the program is to make the young men and women more employable and self-supporting through job training and counseling. Acme had just been awarded a large contract from the U.S. Department of Defense to assemble first aid kits, and Francine had the task of giving a group of new arrivals an orientation lecture.

Table 5.1

The weekly gross pay that corresponds to various levels of worker productivity.

Quantity of Assembled Kits (X)	Weekly Gross Pay (Y)
20	180
30	220
40	260
50	300
60	340
70	380
80	420

When the discussion got around to salary, Francine explained that Acme was prepared to pay the new workers $100 per week plus $4 for each kit assembled. To illustrate the relationship between worker performance and gross weekly pay, Francine used a visual aid (table 5.1). This, she believed, would drive home the message that the more units they assembled, the more money they would earn.

"Just to make sure you understand this table," Francine asked, "tell me, how much would you earn in gross pay if you assembled thirty kits in one week?" After getting the correct answer of $220, she pursued the point further by asking, "But if you really worked hard and assembled eighty units in one week, how much would you earn then?" Here, too, she got the correct answer of $420.

"But", a worker interjected, "what if I don't assemble forty or fifty or any of those numbers in the table? What if I assemble fifty-six kits? How can I use the table to predict my salary then?"

Francine was ready for this question. She placed a new transparency on the overhead projector (figure 5.1), and went on to explain how she represented each pair of X, Y coordinates with a dot and then connected the dots with a line.

"This graph," Francine explained, "represents the same data that you just saw in the table. To use this function, just find the number of kits you assembled on the X scale, go straight up until you meet the function line, then go straight over to the Y scale. The number at that point on the Y scale will be your weekly pay. In this way you can predict your gross pay fairly accurately for any number of assembled goods you may produce in any given week."

These new arrivals from juvenile detention were an unusually suspicious and surly lot. They didn't want their hard-earned salary computed by any

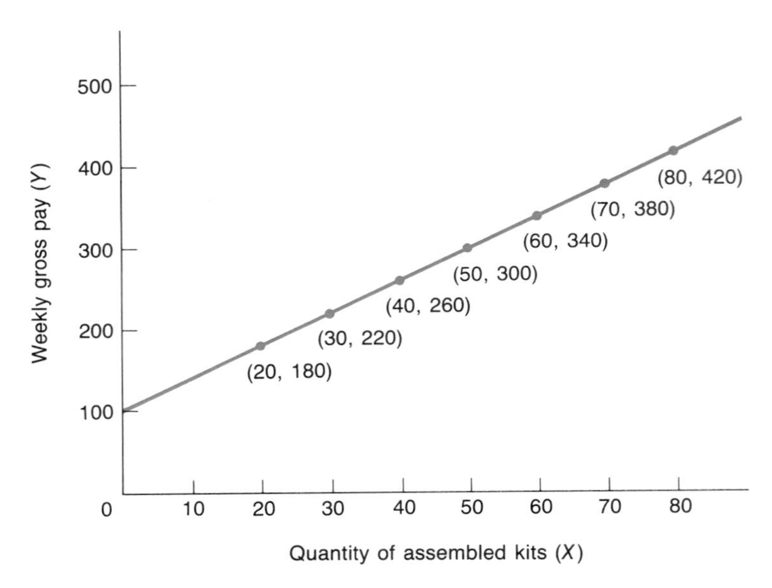

Figure 5.1

A graph of the data in table 5.1 showing the linear relationship between weekly gross pay (variable Y) and worker productivity (variable X).

hocus-pocus graph that, apparently, many did not understand. After a moment of silence, a voice from the back of the room said, "Isn't there an easier way to figure out exactly what we'll be getting for our work?"

"Well," Francine responded, "there is always this." Whereupon she changed transparencies on the overhead projector and displayed the following equation.

$$Y = 100 + 4X$$

"If you substitute the number of assembled kits for X and solve the equation for Y, this will be your gross weekly pay."

Sensing a misunderstanding and rising hostility, Francine changed the subject to recreational opportunities and living arrangements. Let us stop here and analyze what Francine attempted to communicate to the workers.

Francine tried to make the point that there is a **positive relationship** between productivity (X) and salary (Y). She could have been content to describe this positive relationship in very general terms ("The more X you do, the more Y you get."), but Francine knew, as we do, that the relationship between X and Y may be described with much greater precision. After seeing the data from table 5.1 in the form of a graph, it becomes obvious that the function relating X to Y is a straight line—a **linear function.** Using this function it is possible to predict Y values from X values. This may be stated as a general principle of prediction.

When two variables, X and Y, are functionally related, the knowledge of one variable value (X) allows one to predict the value of the other variable (Y).

Positive Relationship. A positive relationship is said to exist between X and Y when high values of variable X are paired with high values of variable Y and low values of X are paired with low values of Y. The graph of a positive linear function slopes from lower left to upper right.

Linear Function. A straight line function represented by the equation $Y = a + bX$ where a is the Y-intercept and b is the slope of the line.

Figure 5.2

A graphic illustration of the change in variable Y relative to the change in variable X.

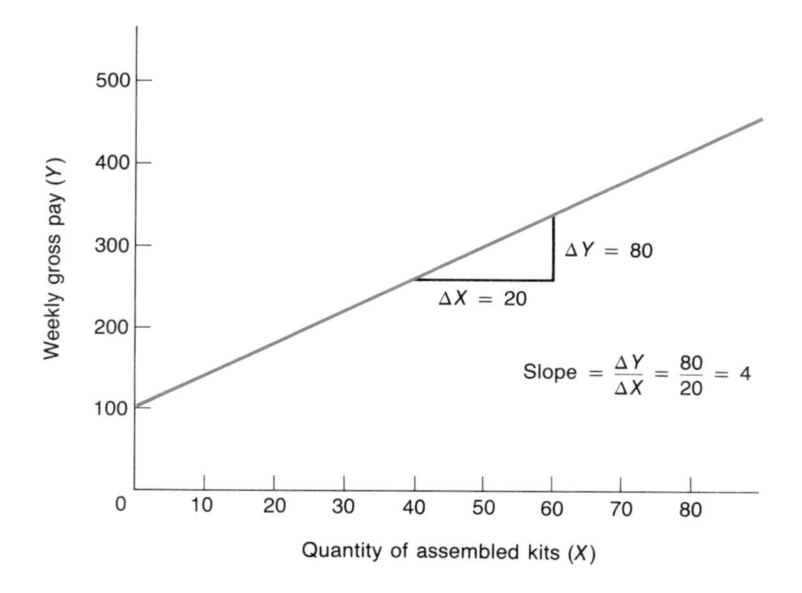

As Francine tried to explain, a more efficient way to represent the precise relationship between functionally related variables is in the form of an equation. The general form of a linear function may be written as

$$Y = a + bX$$

Y-intercept. The location on the Y-axis where the regression line for predicting Y with the knowledge of X (Y on X) crosses.

Slope. The slope of the regression (best-fit) line used for predicting Y from X is the rate of change of Y relative to X. The slope of the regression line used to predict X from Y is the rate of change of X relative to Y.

where a is the ***Y*-intercept** of the function and b is the **slope.**

The Y-intercept, the place on the Y-axis that is crossed by the linear function, is the value of Y when $X = 0$. The slope, the rate of change in Y relative to X, is computed by determining how many units Y changes for a given change in X. We can see from table 5.1 and figure 5.2 that for every eighty units Y increases, X increases twenty units. So, Y is increasing four times faster than X and, therefore, the slope is four.

$$\text{Slope} = \frac{\text{change in } Y}{\text{change in } X}$$

or, symbolically,

$$\frac{\Delta Y}{\Delta X} = \frac{80}{20} = 4$$

The small triangular symbol is the Greek *delta* and is read, "the change in (variable name)."

Table 5.2

The quantity of kits that are possible to assemble for various speeds of assembly (in minutes).

Average Kit Assembly Time (X)	Quantity of Assembled Kits (Y)
40	60
80	50
120	40
160	30
200	20
240	10

Negative Relationship. A negative relationship is said to exist between X and Y when high values of variable X tend to be paired with low values of variable Y, and low values of variable X tend to be paired with high values of variable Y. The graph of a negative linear function slopes from upper left to lower right.

The slope of a linear function need not be positive. For example in table 5.2, inspect the **negative relationship** between Quantity of Assembled Kits (Y) and Average Kit Assembly Time (X). Notice that the value of variable *Y decreases* as *X increases*. This is because the more time it takes a worker to assemble a kit (X), the fewer units (Y) that worker will be capable of assembling during a workweek. Do not be confused by the labeling of Quantity of Assembled Kits as variable X in table 5.1 and as variable Y in table 5.2. The convention is to label the variable toward which predictions are made as variable Y, the dependent variable, and to label the variable being used for making the prediction as variable X, the independent variable. The presumption is that for the data in table 5.1 we wish to predict Weekly Gross Pay from knowledge of how many kits a worker assembled, and for the data in table 5.2 the presumption is that we wish to predict the quantity of kits a worker is able to assemble from knowledge of how fast the person works.

For the data in table 5.2 the slope may be computed as follows:

$$\text{slope} = \frac{\text{change in variable } Y}{\text{change in variable } X} = \frac{+10}{-40} = -0.25$$

Thus, for every forty-minute decrease in average assembly time, a worker is able to increase his/her production by ten more units per week.

The table 5.2 data are plotted in figure 5.3.

MAKING PREDICTIONS FROM EXPERIMENTAL DATA

In the world of pure mathematics, there are graphic displays of functions that take many different shapes (parabolas, U-shaped, J-shaped, sine waves, etc.), and there are corresponding mathematical equations of varying complexity that permit the construction of such graphic displays. All of these

Figure 5.3

A scatterplot of the data in table 5.2 showing the negative linear relationship between two measures of worker productivity: average kit assembly time and the quantity of assembled kits.

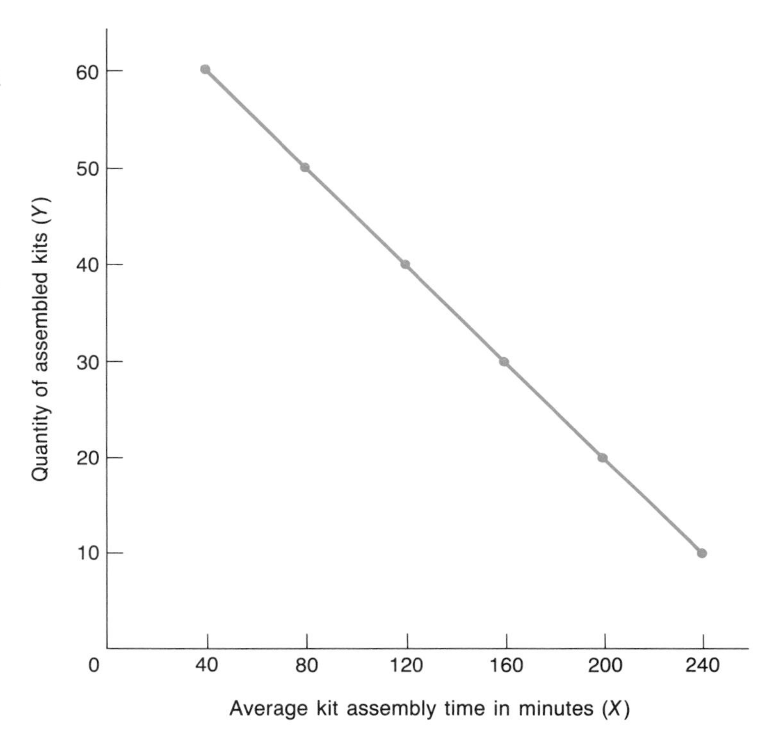

functions permit prediction of one value with the knowledge of another. Perfect functional relationships among variables, those relationships that may be precisely expressed in the form of mathematical equations, are basically nonexistent in actual experimental data. This lack of perfection, however, does not prevent us from predicting the value of one variable with the knowledge of another. If the data have a discernible trend, we can approximate or *fit* a function to the existing data. Then, this function can be used just like Francine's perfect straight-line function to predict any potential Y from any potential X. Sophisticated modeling techniques exist to fit various mathematical functions and a variety of physical shapes to experimental data, but at this introductory level the discussion will be limited to straight-line (linear) functions and their corresponding linear equations. The procedure that one must follow to fit a linear function to data is called **linear regression analysis.**

Linear Regression Analysis. Solving for the equation that best describes the linear trend between two variables.

To illustrate how this is done, consider the data in table 5.3. In this study twelve subjects were given a test for manual dexterity before their actual employment on the assembly line. This was part of an effort to develop a test instrument that would screen out applicants lacking fine-motor coordination and detect those with good productivity potential. The numbers represent the number of mistakes made within a particular time frame.

Table 5.3

Screening task errors and on-the-job assembly errors for twelve workers.

Subject	Screening Task Errors (X)	On-the-job Errors (Y)
A	2	5
B	3	2
C	5	7
D	6	5
E	7	4
F	8	10
G	8	9
H	9	12
I	10	8
J	11	13
K	11	8
L	12	10

From inspection of these data it may be apparent that low X scores tend to be paired with low Y scores ($X = 3$, $Y = 2$), high X scores tend to be paired with high Y scores ($X = 11$, $Y = 13$), and the middle values of X and Y also tend to be paired ($X = 5$, $Y = 7$). This is the same way Francine's linear function worked.

Scatterplot. A graphic display of bivariate data (i.e., two sets of measurements on a single group of subjects) in which each pair of X and Y scores is represented by a dot at the juncture of the X and Y values.

Linear Trend. The tendency of an imperfect functional relationship between two variables to resemble a straight line.

When each pair of X, Y coordinates in table 5.3 is plotted (figure 5.4), we see that, unlike Francine's data, the dots placed at each coordinate do not fall on the same straight line. Instead, we have what is called a **scatterplot.** Each X score may be paired with more than one value for Y (e.g., 8, 10 and 8, 9). Although the coordinates are not all on one line, there is, nevertheless, a **linear trend.** It becomes easier to see it if we sketch a line around the periphery of the scatterplot to form an envelope (figure 5.5). True, the shape of the envelope looks more like a cucumber than a straight line, but we say it is a positive linear trend because the general flow is from lower left to upper right, and there are no changes of direction to make the function curvilinear. Because of these characteristics, a straight line can serve as the main axis of the shape.

In figure 5.6 there is an assortment of scatterplots that illustrate positive and negative linear trends of varying strength. The more tightly clustered

Figure 5.4

A scatterplot of the data in table 5.3.

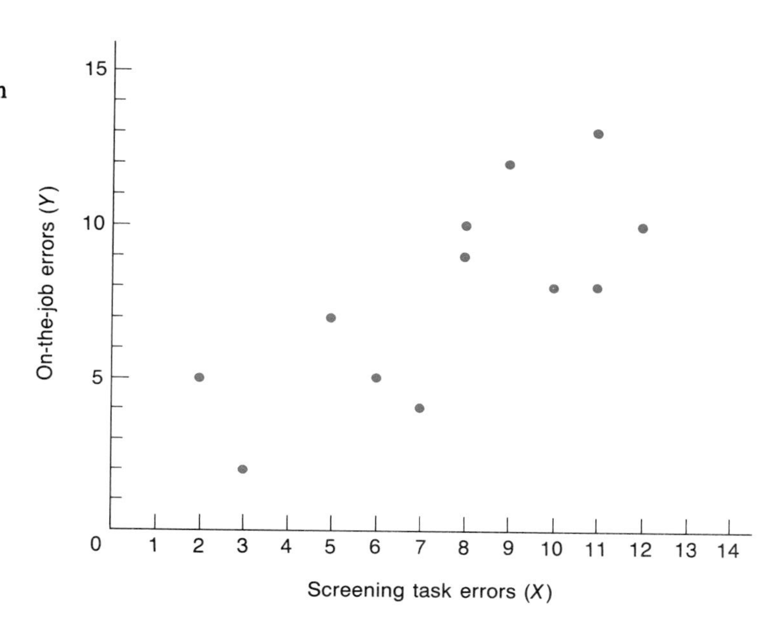

Figure 5.5

An envelope and best-fit line superimposed on the scatterplot of figure 5.3. The equation of the best-fit line appears over the envelope.

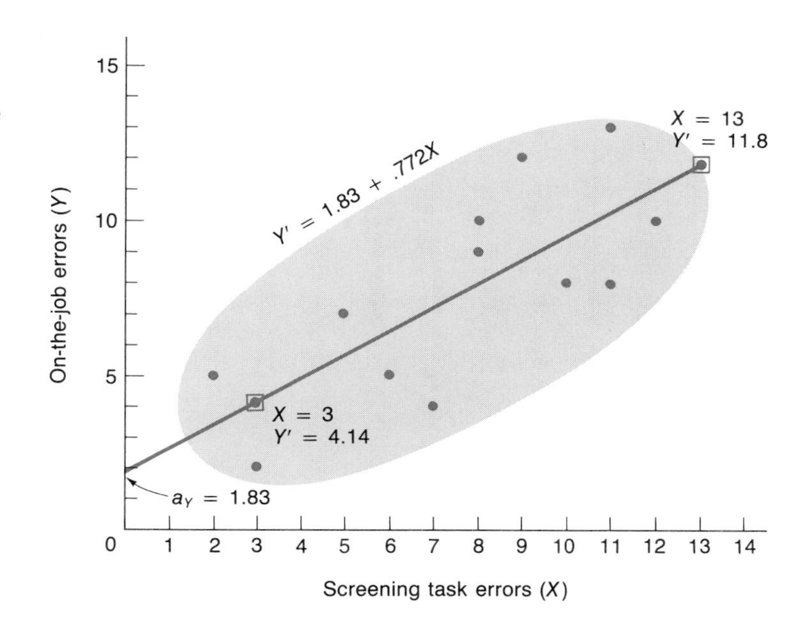

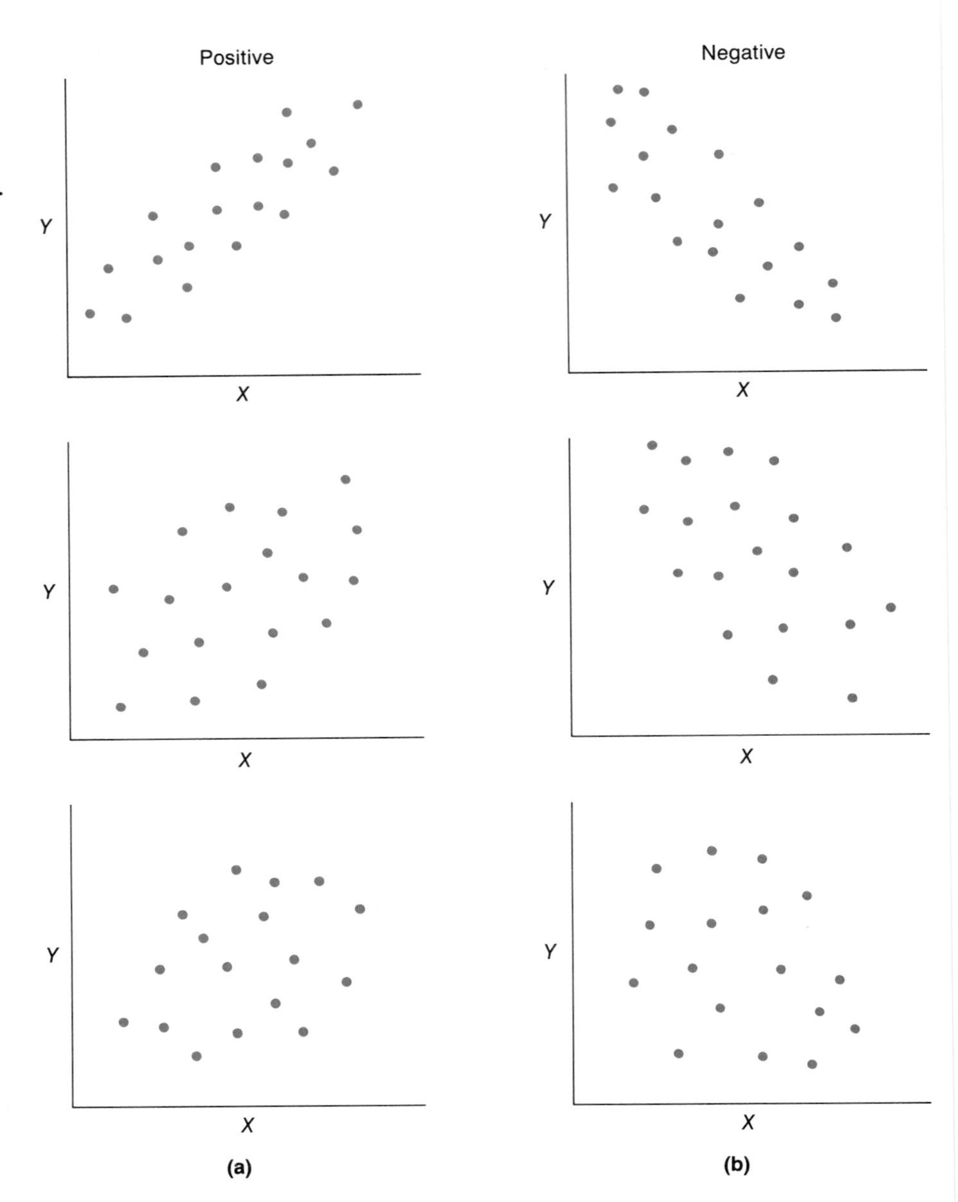

Figure 5.6

An assortment of scatterplots illustrating varying degrees of positive and linear trends.

the coordinates are about the central axis, the more the scatterplot resembles a line and, therefore, the more linear the trend is said to be.

In figure 5.6 there is an assortment of scatterplots that illustrate positive and negative linear trends of varying strength. The more tightly clustered the X, Y values (i.e., the dots in the scatterplot) are about the central axis of the general scatterplot shape, the more the shape of the scatterplot resembles a line and, therefore, the more linear the trend is said to be.

REGRESSION ANALYSIS: FINDING THE BEST-FIT LINE

At this point I hope you are thinking, "Why don't we draw a line down the axis of the scatterplot and use this line as a representative linear function the way Francine used the line in her graph? All we would have to do is find the value for X on the X-axis, move up to intersect the linear function, and read the value of Y at the point of intersection off the Y-axis. We could even find the equation for the line and use it to make predictions!" We shall do exactly that, but before we do, we must agree on what line to use. Simply looking at the general shape of a scatterplot and drawing what appears to be a representative straight line down its axis is not precise enough. Moreover, one person's impression of the **best-fit line** may not coincide with another person's impression. To arrive at as accurate a prediction scheme as possible, we need a standardized definition of the best-fit line. Once we agree on a definition of the best-fit line, we must be able to compute the slope and Y-intercept that will meet the terms of the definition. This is what linear regression analysis is: finding the slope and Y-intercept of the best-fit line so we can use these **regression constants,** a_Y and b_Y, to form the equation for the best-fit linear function:

Best-Fit Line. The linear function derived from a least squares solution that is used to represent the linear trend of a scatterplot. Each scatterplot has two best-fit lines: one for predicting Y with the knowledge of X and one for predicting X with the knowledge of Y.

Regression Constants. The slope and axis intercept of a best fit regression line.

Y'. Y prime is the predicted value of Y that is the solution of the regression equation $Y' = a_Y + b_YX$.

$$Y' = a_Y + b_YX$$

Notice that the predicted score is shown as $\boldsymbol{Y'}$ ("Y prime") rather than the simple Y that was used earlier in the equation for a perfect linear function. The prime label for Y and the Y subscripts for the Y-intercept (a) and slope (b) designate the equation as a product of regression analysis. The distinction is important. A linear function of abstract mathematical purity represents a perfect and unchanging linear relationship between variables and always results in accurate predictions of Y from X or X from Y. On the other hand, the equation of the best-fit line that results from a regression analysis of scattered data (e.g., figure 5.4), and the predictions made from that equation, do carry a potential for inaccuracy. Every dot in the scatterplot that does not fall on the best-fit line represents an error in prediction, as you shall see in the following discussion of the best-fit line.

THE BEST-FIT LINE AS A MEAN

The definition of the best-fit line that is used by statisticians is very similar to the definition of the mean of a distribution. In chapter 3 you learned that one definition of the mean is that score or potential score in a distribution about which the sum of the deviation scores is zero. It was proven (pp. 47–48) that

$$\Sigma(X - \overline{X}) = 0$$

Figure 5.7

The deviation between a predicted score value ($Y^1 = 4.9$) and the actual Y score value ($Y = 8$) when variable $X = 4$.

Raw Data

Subject	X score	Y score
A	2	1
B	4	8
C	8	7
D	9	10

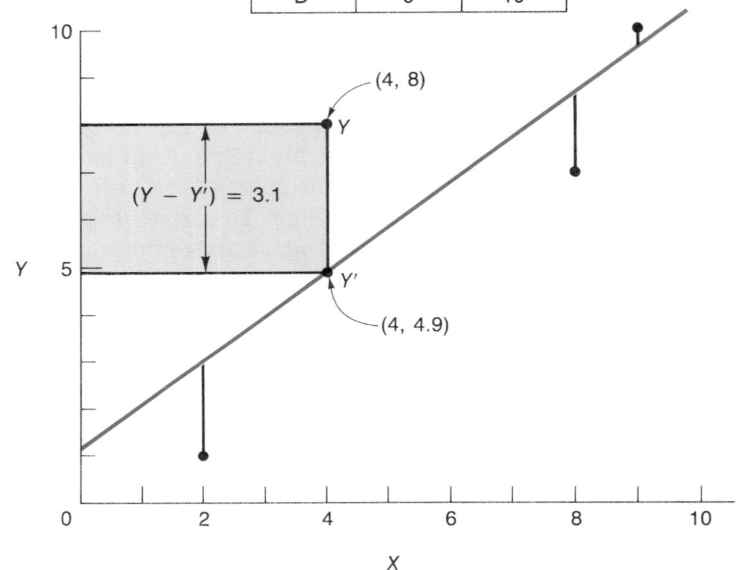

Similarly, the best-fit line for a scatterplot is the line about which the sum of the deviations is zero. Let us consult figure 5.7 so you can see what deviations are being referred to in this definition. For the sake of simplicity, the scatterplot in figure 5.7 shows the points for only four pairs of X, Y coordinates.

For each of the four values for X, there are four corresponding Y values. As with the figures we studied earlier, each dot on the scatterplot represents a pair of X, Y coordinates. In addition, in figure 5.7 the distance between each dot and the best-fit line is indicated with a line segment. The magnitude of the line segments are the deviations referred to above, and these deviations represent errors in prediction. They are errors because the actual Y scores that are paired with the X scores do not equal the predicted Y scores. They appear on the graph (figure 5.7) as dots that are either above or below the best-fit line. Sometimes, as you saw earlier in figure 5.4 and in table 5.3, a given X value ($X = 11$) is paired with more than one Y score ($Y = 8$ and $Y = 13$). The prediction line in figure 5.4 passes below one value ($Y = 13$) and above the other value ($Y = 8$).

If the axis line in figure 5.7 is indeed the best-fit line for the scatterplot, the sum of the deviations should be zero. The value of each of the four deviation scores may be determined by taking the actual Y score that corresponds to a particular X score and subtracting the predicted Y score $(Y - Y')$. One of these computations is illustrated in figure 5.7 for the X_2, Y_2 coordinates. The complete computation for all four sets of coordinates is shown below.

	Y	Y'	$(Y - Y')$
X_1	1	3.0	−2
X_2	8	4.9	+3.1
X_3	7	8.6	−1.6
X_4	10	9.5	+0.5
			$\Sigma(Y - Y') = 0$

Since the sum of the deviations does sum to zero, the line satisfies the definition of the best-fit line.

Residual Variation. The portion of the total variation of variable Y that is unpredictable with the knowledge of X or the portion of the total variation of variable X that is unpredictable with the knowledge of Y.

You may recall that another definition of the mean is that score or potential score in a distribution about which the sum of the squared deviations is a minimum. Let us add a column to the above table to compute the sum of the squared deviations that, in the context of linear regression analysis, is called **residual variation.**

	Y	Y'	$(Y - Y')$	$(Y - Y')^2$
X_1	1	3.0	−2.0	4.00
X_2	8	4.9	+3.1	9.61
X_3	7	8.6	−1.6	2.56
X_4	10	9.5	+0.5	0.25
				$\Sigma(Y - Y')^2 = 16.42$

When we say that the value 16.42 is a minimum it means that if the position of the line were changed at all (different slope, different Y-intercept, or both), the quantity $\Sigma(Y - Y')^2$ would always be greater than 16.42. There is one and only one line that will allow the sum of the deviations to be zero and the sum of the squared deviations (i.e., residual variation) to be a minimum.

COMPUTING THE REGRESSION CONSTANTS

Now that you know what conditions a line must satisfy to be the best-fit line, the next task is to learn how to determine the values for the slope and Y-intercept that will allow you to define such a line for any scatterplot with a linear trend.

To find the Y-intercept alone would not be sufficient, because any number of lines can originate from a point on the Y-axis, as shown in figure 5.8. Also, any number of lines can have a constant value for the slope. Only when both values are specified is one line, and only one line, defined.

The computational procedure for regression analysis will be illustrated using the data in table 5.3. Even if you never intend to do a regression analysis with a hand calculator, preferring to use a computer program such as CORREG.BAS, this section should still be studied carefully. Working through the steps will not only make you aware of all the work the computer is saving you, it will also give you the knowledge to make more sense of the computer output.

Here is the regression equation for Y on X. Y on X means that we want to be able to predict Y with the knowledge of X, as in the case of predicting the quality of worker performance (Y = on-the-job errors) from screening task data (X = screening task errors).

$$Y' = a_Y + b_Y X$$

The first step is to solve for the slope of Y on X. Here is the formula:

$$b_Y = \frac{\Sigma XY - \dfrac{(\Sigma X)(\Sigma Y)}{N}}{\Sigma X^2 - \dfrac{(\Sigma X)^2}{N}}$$

The denominator should look familiar. It is the computational formula for the variation of the X scores as presented in chapter 3 and in the VARSD.BAS computer tutorial. You should recall that another name for variation is *sum of squares*, which is commonly abbreviated SS.

The numerator, however, has one term you have not seen since the chapter 1 exercises: ΣXY. XY is called a cross product, and one cross product is computed for each XY pair. Each X score is multiplied by its corresponding Y score. Once this is done for each pair, all the products (there will be N products for N pairs of scores) are added. See table 5.2 for an example of this.

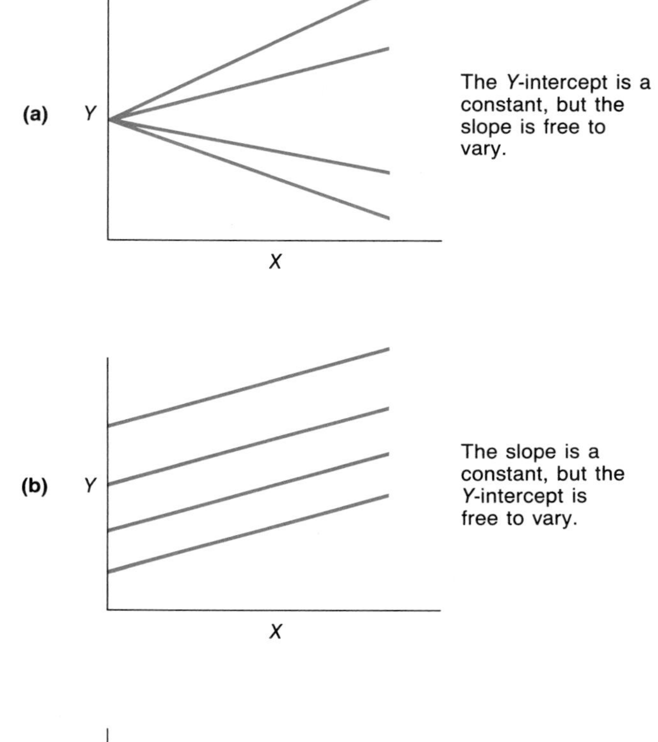

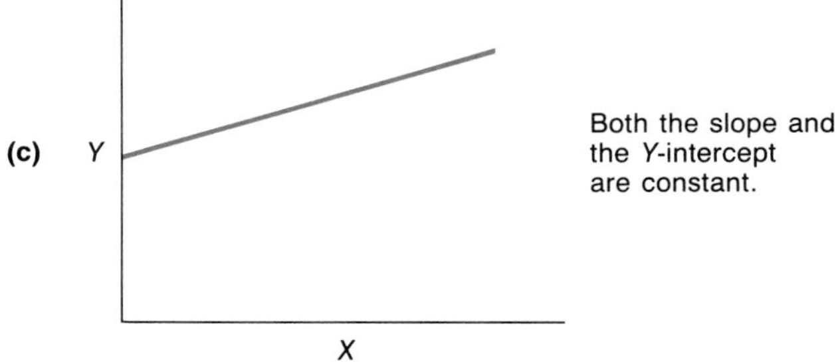

Figure 5.8

An illustration showing that specifying the slope and Y-intercept of a linear function defines one, and only one, linear function.

Like the denominator, the numerator also has a special name. It is called *covariation* or the *sum of products*. This is abbreviated SP. So, the slope for Y on X may be expressed as follows:

$$b_Y = \frac{SP_{XY}}{SS_X}$$

For the data in table 5.3 the filled-in formula for the slope of Y on X is

$$b_Y = \frac{800 - \dfrac{(92)(93)}{12}}{818 - \dfrac{(92)^2}{12}}$$

$$b_Y = \frac{87}{112.67} = 0.772$$

With the value of the slope known, the next step is to compute the Y-intercept of the best-fit line for Y on X. Here is the formula:

$$a_Y = \overline{Y} - b_Y\overline{X}$$

For the data in our sample problem,

$$a_Y = 7.75 - (0.772)(7.667)$$
$$a_Y = 1.83$$

The regression equation for Y on X for these data is

$$Y' = 1.83 + 0.772\ X$$

To plot the best-fit line for predicting Y with the knowledge of X, simply substitute an arbitrary, relatively low value for X in the regression equation and solve for Y'. Put a dot at the location of this pair of X, Y' coordinates on the scatterplot. Then do the same thing for a relatively high value for X, and connect the two dots. This is shown in figure 5.5 for $X = 3$ and $X = 13$. Specifically, the coordinates are 3, 4.14 and 13, 11.86. The X values of 3 and 13 were selected arbitrarily, and the Y values of 4.14 and 11.86 are solutions to the regression equation when $X = 3$ and $X = 13$, respectively. Notice that the best-fit linear function intersects the Y-axis at the computed value for the Y-intercept ($a_Y = 1.83$).

Standard Error of Estimate. A measure of the dispersal of the dots in a scatterplot about the best-fit line.

THE STANDARD ERROR OF ESTIMATE

Since the best-fit line has properties that are very similar to the arithmetic mean of a distribution, you may be wondering if there is an analogue in regression analysis to the standard deviation of a distribution. There is, and it is called the **standard error of estimate** ($s_{est\ Y}$). It is a measure of the dispersal of the X, Y points about the best-fit line.

When the linear function is perfect (figures 5.1 and 5.3), the standard error of estimate is zero. There is no dispersal of coordinates about the regression line because, in a perfect linear relationship, all the X, Y points are on the same straight line. This is analogous to computing the standard deviation for the set of constants

$$(7, 7, 7, \ldots 7, \ldots 7)$$

that must, of course, be zero.

When, however, the linear function is not perfect (figure 5.2 or 5.4), the standard error of estimate will be greater than zero. This is analogous to computing the standard deviation for a set in which the scores vary from each other. The presence of some variation about the mean insures a standard deviation value greater than zero just as the presence of X, Y points off the regression line will insure a standard error of estimate greater than zero.

Even the interpretation of these statistics is similar. Just as the range between one standard deviation unit above and below the mean will enclose 68% of the scores in a normal distribution (figure 4.6), a range of one standard error of estimate unit above and below the regression line will enclose 68% of the X, Y points (figure 5.9).

Notice in figure 5.9 that of the twelve X, Y points in the scatterplot, eight are enclosed within the range of plus and minus one standard error of estimate unit from the regression line. This is 67% of the X, Y points, which, with only twelve points in the scatterplot, is as close as we can come to the theoretically expected value of 68%.

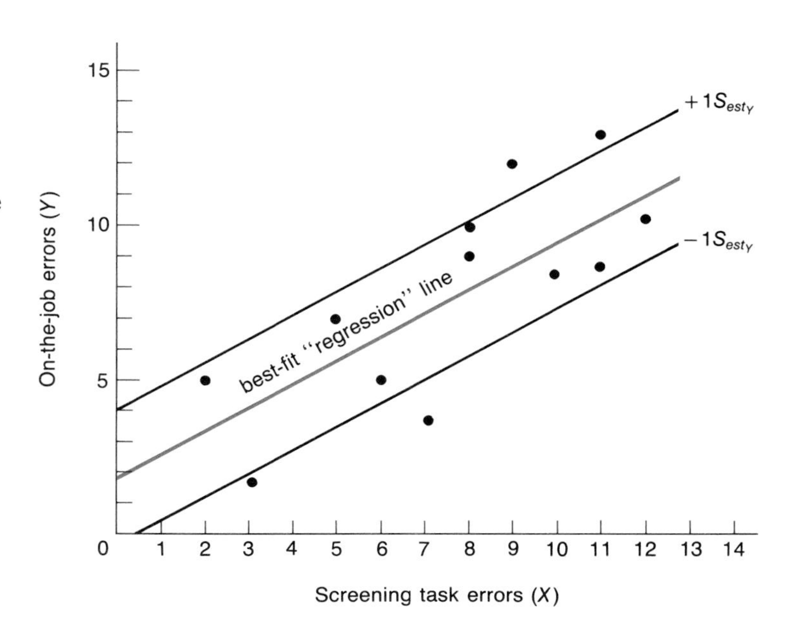

Figure 5.9

A plot of the Y on X regression line enclosed by parallel lines that are plus and minus one standard error of estimate unit from the regression line. $s_{est\ Y} = 2.30$. Approximately 68% (8 of 12 coordinates) are enclosed.

The definitional formula for the standard error of estimate is

$$s_{est\ Y} = \sqrt{\frac{\Sigma(Y - Y')^2}{N - 2}}$$

But actually to compute $s_{est\ Y}$ we use a computational formula:

$$s_{est\ Y} = \sqrt{\frac{SS_Y - \frac{SP^2{}_{XY}}{SS_X}}{N - 2}}$$

The SP_{XY} and SS_X terms are the same as those used to compute the slope, and SS_Y is the variation of the Y scores.

For the data in table 5.3 the solution is as follows:

$$s_{est\ Y} = \sqrt{\frac{120.25 - \frac{87^2}{112.67}}{12 - 2}}$$

$$s_{est\ Y} = 2.30$$

Predicting *X* from *Y* instead of *Y* from *X*

One may use a perfect linear function (figure 5.1) not only to predict Y from X, but also X from Y. If Francine (remember her?) knew the amount of a worker's gross weekly pay and wanted to determine the amount of first aid kits put together by that worker, she would locate the salary on the Y scale, move over to the function line, and then move straight down to the X scale. In this situation there is only one regression line and one set of regression constants (slope and Y-intercept) for both Y on X and X on Y.

On the other hand, when a linear relationship is less than perfect, the scatterplot will have two regression lines. One is used for predicting Y with the knowledge of X (Y on X), and the other is used for predicting X with the knowledge of Y (X on Y). The concept behind construction of the ***X* on *Y* regression line** is the same as the more familiar ***Y* on *X* regression line,** except that the variable that we have been using for prediction (X) and the variable that we have been predicting (Y) are used in the reverse way. In solving for the best-fit regression line for predicting X with the knowledge of Y, the deviations that must sum to zero and the squared deviations that must sum to a minimum are in reference to the X-axis rather than the Y-axis (figure 5.10).

Regression of *X* on *Y*. Predicting X from Y using the X on Y regression constants ($X' = a_X + b_X Y$).

Regression of *Y* on *X*. Predicting Y from X using the Y on X regression constants ($Y' = a_Y + b_Y X$).

Figure 5.11 is figure 5.4 redrawn to display these data with both regression lines, Y on X and X on Y. Notice that the two regression lines cross at the point $\overline{X}, \overline{Y}$.

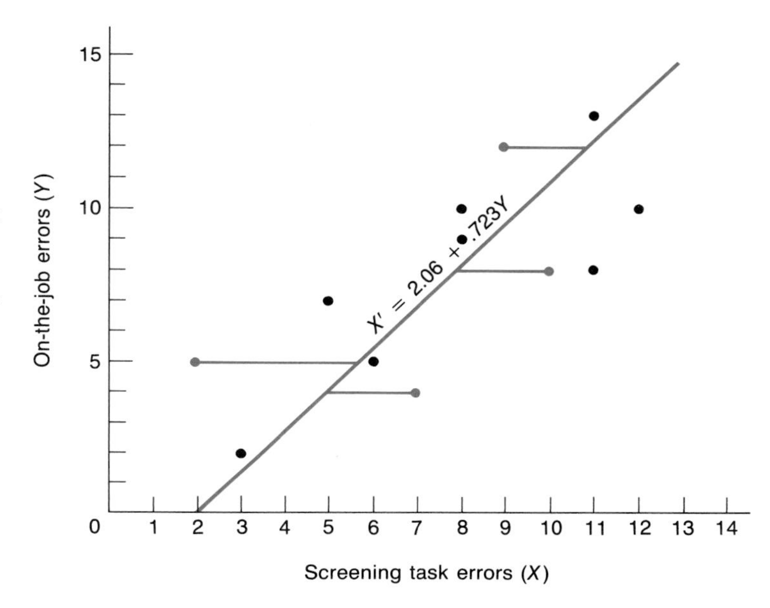

Figure 5.10

The regression line for predicting X with the knowledge of Y ("X on Y") minimizes the squared deviations along the X-axis. The scatterplot is shown together with four such deviations. The X-intercept is 2.06 and the slope is 0.723.

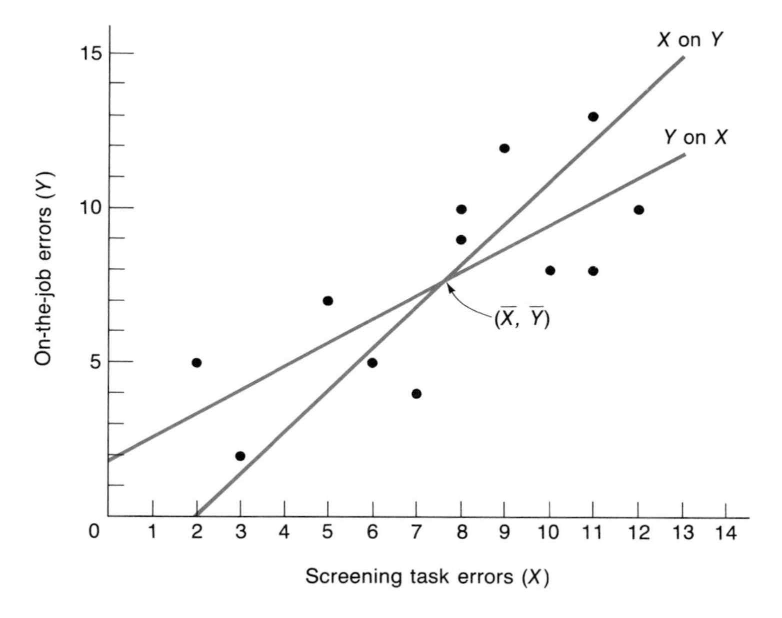

Figure 5.11

The scatterplot of the screening task and on-the-job error data with the regression lines for Y on X and X on Y.

The relative position of the two regression lines in a scatterplot is a function of the strength of the linear relationship that is present (figure 5.12). Think of it this way. In a perfect linear relationship there are really two regression lines. It only seems as if there is one line because the Y on X line is directly on top of the X on Y line. The less linear trend that is present in a scatterplot, the more the two regression lines rotate away from each other,

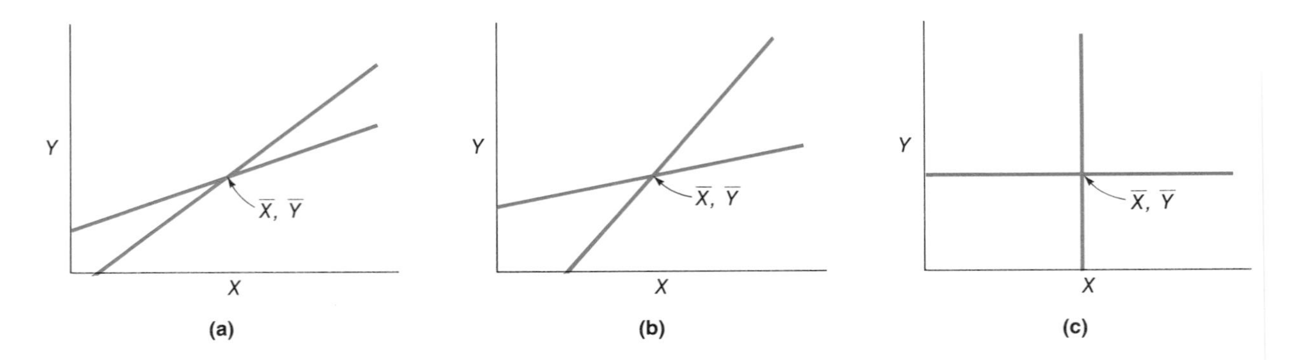

Figure 5.12

The Y on X and X on Y regression lines when a strong (a), moderate (b), or no linear trend is evident in the scatterplot. The regression lines cross at $\overline{X}$, $\overline{Y}$.

and the less accurate predictions will be. When there is no linear trend whatsoever in a scatterplot, the two regression lines are perpendicular to each other. In this situation, neither variable has any predictive power. No matter what value for X is selected, the prediction will always be the mean of the Y distribution, and no matter what value of Y is selected the prediction will always be the mean of the X distribution. This is essentially the same scenario that was described in chapter 3 (p. 61) in the discussion of the standard deviation as a measure of the precision of prediction.

In case describing a linear trend as "strong" or "moderate" (figure 5.12 legend) seems vague, be patient. In the next chapter you shall learn how to quantify the strength of a linear relationship using a statistic called the Pearson *r*. Also, you shall learn how to quantify predictive power using a statistic called the coefficient of determination.

Computing the Regression Constants for *X* on *Y*

The following formulae will allow you to find the regression constants for X on Y:

$$X' = a_X + b_X Y,$$

where

$$b_X = \frac{SP_{XY}}{SS_Y} = \frac{\Sigma XY - \dfrac{(\Sigma X)(\Sigma Y)}{N}}{\Sigma Y^2 - \dfrac{(\Sigma Y)^2}{N}}$$

and

$$a_X = \overline{X} - b_X \overline{Y}$$

and

$$s_{est\ X} = \sqrt{\frac{SS_X - \dfrac{SP^2_{XY}}{SS_Y}}{N - 2}}$$

In practice, however, especially when using a computer for regression analysis, these formulae for predicting X with the knowledge of Y are seldom used. Instead, it is easier to relabel the variables, designate the variable being used for prediction as X and the variable that is being predicted as Y.

For example, with reference to the data in table 5.3, if you wished to determine the regression equation for predicting screening test scores (X) from on-the-job scores (Y), the easiest approach would be to switch X and Y labels. Input the screening test scores on the computer as Y values and the on-the-job scores as X values, and the regression equation in the computer output will be appropriate for predicting screening test scores (Y) from on-the-job scores (X).

You are now ready to try doing and interpreting some analyses of regression. You can do the analyses for the chapter exercises, which follow, using a hand calculator and, in fact, you should do at least one regression analysis by hand to check your understanding of the computational procedure. Then do the same analysis on the computer using CORREG.BAS. It's easier, faster, and, assuming you entered the values properly, the answers provided by the microcomputer will be free of computational errors. To make sure that you are using CORREG.BAS properly, it would be a good idea to enter the data in table 5.3 and compare your results to the computations for those data that are presented in this chapter. Also, take note that CORREG.BAS does both a correlation analysis, which we have not yet covered, and a regression analysis. At this point just ignore the computer output that you don't need.

After you have done some practice exercises in regression analysis you may wish to run ZEEREG.BAS. (Refer to the *Manual for Stat/Tutor* for details on this program.) ZEEREG.BAS covers a kind of descriptive data analysis that often follows an analysis of regression, but this topic is usually considered optional in an elementary statistics course.

Summary

We discussed the concept of prediction within the context of linear functions and learned a method called regression analysis that allows us to fit a linear function to available data. We used the linear function that is fit to the data to make predictions in the same way that any perfect linear function is used to predict Y from X. We determined from the data that the best-fit line is conceptually similar to the arithmetic mean, and the dispersal of the data points about the best-fit line may be quantified by a statistic, the standard error of estimate, that is conceptually similar to the standard deviation.

Key Terms

Best-Fit Line
Linear Function
Linear Regression Analysis
Linear Trend
Negative Relationship
Positive Relationship
Prediction
Regression Constants
Regression of *X* on *Y*
Regression of *Y* on *X*
Residual Variation
Scatterplot
Slope
Standard Error of Estimate
***Y*-intercept**
***Y′* (predicted *Y* value)**

Exercises

1. The Sooni tribe lives on an island in the South Pacific, and their main source of food and income is from their fishing industry. Traditionally, the Sooni have had problems filling their nets because the fish are difficult to find. On some days the fish are found far out to sea, whereas on other days they tend to swim closer to shore.

A Peace Corps volunteer living with the Sooni knew from her diving experiences that water temperature at the bottom of the island's central lagoon fluctuated with the level of undersea volcanic activity in the area. She also knew that fish prefer a narrow range of water temperature. Perhaps, she reasoned, water temperature at sea fluctuates concurrently with lagoon temperature. If this were the case, the location of the fish could be predicted from the lagoon temperature. Specifically, when the level of volcanic activity near the island was high, the increase in water temperature should drive the fish off to more serene and cooler environs. They would be expected to return to feed near the coral reef only after the temperature dropped to an acceptable level.

Over a period of several days careful measurements were taken of both lagoon water temperature (X) and the distance from shore at which the fish were found (Y). (The scores are in malliks, a Sooni measure of distance.)

Here are the data:

Day	Temperature °F	Distance
1	68	32
2	60	27
3	54	9
4	69	44
5	60	12
6	62	29
7	56	16
8	74	38
9	74	47
10	58	15
11	69	37
12	52	9
13	63	21
14	76	54
15	64	29

   a. Prepare a scatterplot of these data.
   b. Solve the regression equation for predicting distance from shore where the fish are likely to be found from water temperature.
   c. Using the regression equation, fit a best-fit line to the scatterplot.
   d. Determine the value of the standard error of estimate and plot $\pm$ 1 standard error of estimate units above and below the best-fit line.
   e. If the lagoon water temperature on a given day is 65° F, how far from shore is the predicted location of the fish?
   f. If the lagoon water temperature on a given day is 73° F, how far from shore is the predicted location of the fish?

2. What are the characteristics of the best-fit line?
3. Explain why a given slope and a given Y-intercept define one, and only one, straight line function.
4. Why does the standard error of estimate equal zero when the relationship between X and Y is perfectly linear?
5. After completing her final grades, a teacher of Social Studies II wished to evaluate the functional relationship between the final Social Studies I grades her students were given at the end of the previous academic year and the Social Studies II grades for the current year. Here are the data:

Student	Social Studies I	Social Studies II
A	86	90
B	75	80
C	72	70
D	93	89
E	68	71
F	74	71
G	95	92
H	83	77
I	92	86
J	65	75

   a. Prepare a scatterplot of these data.
   b. Solve the regression equation for predicting Social Studies II grades from Social Studies I grades.
   c. Using the regression equation, fit a best-fit line to the scatterplot.
   d. Determine the value of the standard error of estimate and plot $\pm$ 1 standard error of estimate units above and below the best-fit line.
   e. A student who received an 85 in Social Studies I would, on the basis of these data, be predicted to obtain an ____ on Social Studies II.

6. Briefly describe the pairs of X and Y variables you could study using the tool of regression analysis that might enable you to predict:
   a. academic achievement among college students
   b. adult intelligence
   c. physical health
   d. annual salary ten years after college graduation
   e. vulnerability to becoming a drug addict

7. Explain the conceptual kinship between the properties of the arithmetic mean and the properties of the best-fit regression line.

8. Explain the conceptual kinship between the standard deviation of a set of scores and the standard error of estimate of a scatterplot.

9. Explain the difference between determining the regression of X on Y versus determining the regression of Y on X.

10. A trained observer behind a one-way mirror counted the number of times each of 10 subjects exhibited a behavioral sign of stress (biting nails, chewing pencils, grimacing, etc.) while they were taking a midterm examination. After the tests were graded the stress data were matched to the test scores. The data are presented in the following table:

Subject	Stress Data	Test Scores
A	18	84
B	31	67
C	25	63
D	29	89
E	21	93
F	32	63
G	40	55
H	36	70
I	35	53
J	27	77

a. Construct a scatterplot of these data.

b. Describe the general trend of the relationship revealed in the scatterplot that exists between exhibition of stress symptoms and test performance.

c. Do a regression analysis on these data and, using the regression equation, fit a best-fit line to the scatterplot.

d. If another squad of subjects were run in this experiment and you found out that a subject got a stress count of twenty, what would your prediction be for the test performance of that subject?

e. Reverse the assignments of independent and dependent variables and do the regression analysis for predicting a subject's stress count from knowledge of the subject's test score.

CHAPTER 6

Correlation

Correlation. A statistic that quantifies the extent of positive or negative linear trend that exists in the relationship between two variables.

Pearson *r*. A statistic that describes the extent of the linear relationship between variable X and variable Y on a scale of 0 to 1.00 or 0 to -1.00.

Spearman rho. The correlation coefficient computed on ranked data.

In the last chapter you were promised a way to quantify the extent of the linear relationship between two variables to replace vague and useless designations such as "strongly" linear, "moderately" linear, "barely" linear, etc. The quantification of linear trend is called **correlation,** and it is reflected in the value of a statistic called the *Pearson product moment correlation coefficient*, or, more commonly, the **Pearson *r*.**

There are several different ways of expressing the kind of information provided by the Pearson r statistic, and some of these are important for the beginning student to grasp. For example, r may be regarded as an index of the degree of linear relationship that is present in a scatterplot, or as an index of the accuracy with which we can predict Y with the knowledge of X, etc. In this chapter we shall explore those aspects of the Pearson r statistic that are the most relevant to our applied emphasis. Also included is an alternative correlation statistic (**Spearman rho**) that is used when certain characteristics of the data preclude the legitimate use of the Pearson r.

The Pearson r is written as r_{XY} or r_{12} and is read as "the correlation between variables X and Y" or "the correlation between variables 1 and 2." It is common for the correlation statistic to be reported along with an analysis of regression, because it provides an extra dimension of descriptive power regarding the strength of the functional relationship between variables X and Y. In fact, the correlation analysis is usually done first because it makes sense to see first if there is any relationship between two variables before one tries to use this relationship for prediction purposes. (Both analyses, correlation and regression, are computed in the CORREG.BAS computer program in *Stat/Tutor.*)

In the beginning of this chapter various aspects of the Pearson r will be discussed so you can develop an understanding of its descriptive power and theoretical underpinnings. Then, later in this chapter, you will gain knowledge of certain pitfalls to avoid and assumptions underlying the r statistic that must be met.

Let us begin with a look at the computational formula for r_{XY}.

$$r_{XY} = \frac{\Sigma XY - \dfrac{(\Sigma X)(\Sigma Y)}{N}}{\sqrt{\left[\Sigma X^2 - \dfrac{(\Sigma X)^2}{N}\right] \cdot \left[\Sigma Y^2 - \dfrac{(\Sigma Y)^2}{N}\right]}}$$

As you inspect the formula, the individual terms should look familiar. There is nothing here you have not already seen. The numerator is the sum of products or *covariation*, the same term we saw in the last chapter as the numerator in the formula for the slope of the best-fit line. The terms in the denominator that are enclosed in parentheses should also look familiar. On the left is the variation of variable X (SS_X), and on the right is the variation of variable Y (SS_Y).

Using the latter abbreviations, we can rewrite the correlation formula as

$$r_{XY} = \frac{SP_{XY}}{\sqrt{SS_X \cdot SS_Y}}$$

Let us use this formula for Pearson r (the same one displayed in CORREG.BAS) to see how specific characteristics of the data are reflected in the value of the correlation coefficient, r_{XY}.

For the first illustration, let us compute the Pearson r for the following identical sets of X and Y scores.

Data Set 1

X	Y
3	3
5	5
8	8
11	11
13	13

Here is the computational formula with all the values filled in:

$$r_{XY} = \frac{388 - \dfrac{(40)(40)}{5}}{\sqrt{\left[388 - \dfrac{40^2}{5}\right] \cdot \left[388 - \dfrac{40^2}{5}\right]}}$$

$$r_{XY} = \frac{68}{\sqrt{68 \cdot 68}} = 1.00$$

Since the relationship of any set with itself is perfect, and since the Pearson r statistic reflects the degree of linear relationship that is present, it follows that an r value of 1.00 is indicative of a perfect linear relationship between X and Y. The linear relationship may also be represented graphically as in the Data Set 1 section of figure 6.1.

The relationship of a set of scores with itself becomes even more obvious if we change the entries in the correlation formula to reflect the fact that set X and set Y are identical.

Here is the original formula:

$$r_{XY} = \frac{\Sigma XY - \dfrac{(\Sigma X)\ (\Sigma Y)}{N}}{\sqrt{\left[\Sigma X^2 - \dfrac{(\Sigma X)^2}{N}\right] \cdot \left[\Sigma Y^2 - \dfrac{(\Sigma Y)^2}{N}\right]}}$$

And here is the revised formula when X and Y are identical for each pair of coordinates:

$$r_{XY} = \frac{\Sigma XX - \dfrac{(\Sigma X)\ (\Sigma X)}{N}}{\sqrt{\left[\Sigma X^2 - \dfrac{(\Sigma X)^2}{N}\right] \cdot \left[\Sigma X^2 - \dfrac{(\Sigma X)^2}{N}\right]}}$$

$$r_{XY} = \frac{\Sigma X^2 - \dfrac{(\Sigma X)^2}{N}}{\Sigma X^2 - \dfrac{(\Sigma X)^2}{N}}$$

$$r_{XY} = 1.00$$

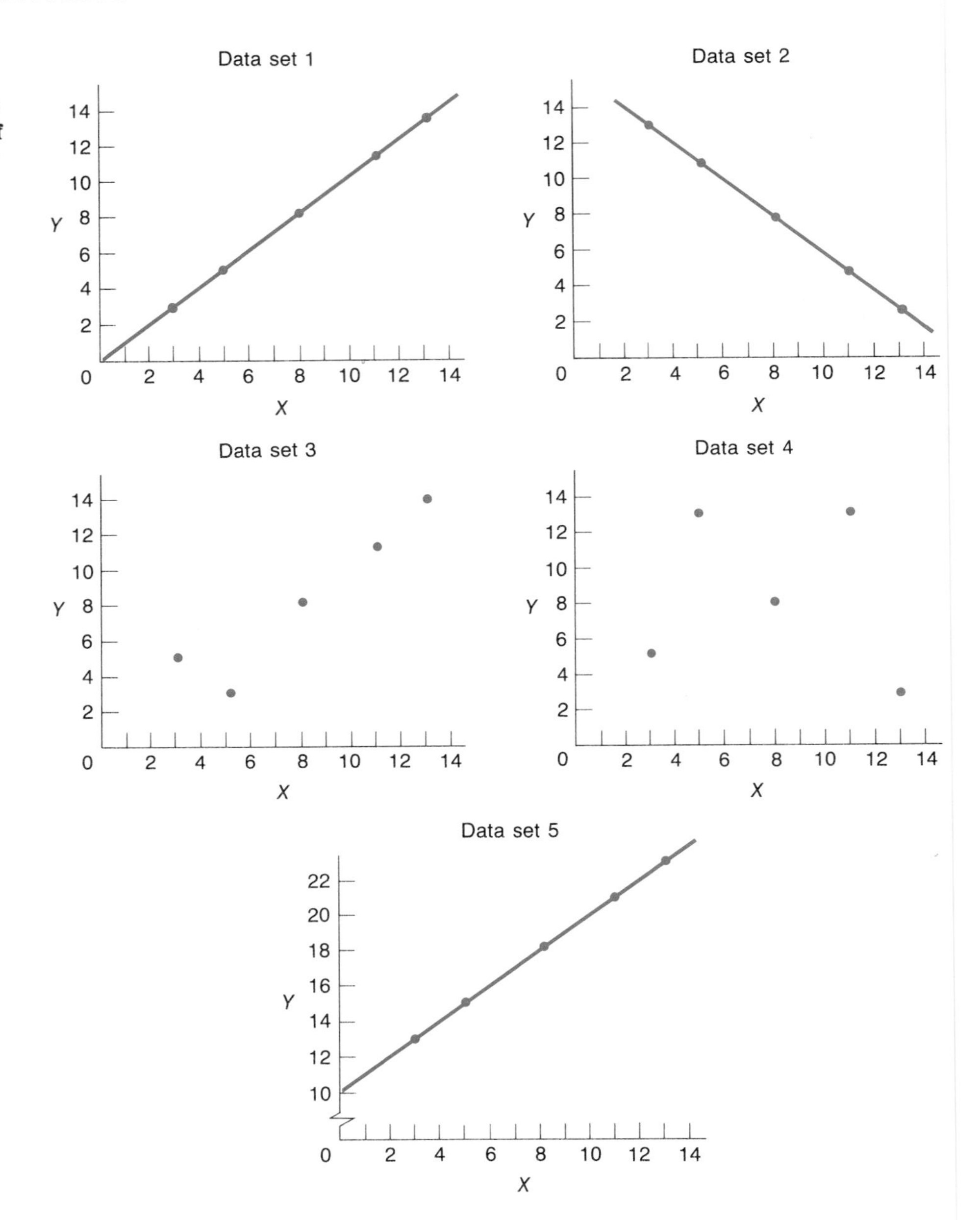

Figure 6.1

Scatterplots for data sets 1,2,3,4, and 5. The plot of sets 1,2, and 5 are linear functions.

Notice that the numerator in the original formula, the term we know as covariation, has changed to the formula for variation.

As you can see from inspecting Data Set 1, any set must covary with itself perfectly. That is, for every change in the value of X, there is an exactly corresponding change in Y. Since, in the equation on page 113, we have shown that perfect covariation between sets yields an r of 1.00, we may also regard the Pearson r as an index of the extent to which two sets covary.

Now, as shown in Data Set 2, let us invert set Y while leaving X alone and repeat the analysis:

Data Set 2

X	Y
3	13
5	11
8	8
11	5
13	3

Here is the computational formula with all the values filled in:

$$r_{XY} = \frac{252 - \dfrac{(40)(40)}{5}}{\sqrt{\left[388 - \dfrac{40^2}{5}\right] \cdot \left[388 - \dfrac{40^2}{5}\right]}}$$

$$r_{XY} = \frac{-68}{\sqrt{68 \cdot 68}} = -1.00$$

Now the result is a negative 1.00. If these data were plotted, the function would be a straight line that moves from upper left to lower right (i.e., a line with a negative slope as shown in figure 6.1). Thus, it is apparent that a perfect negative linear relationship between X and Y is reflected in an r value of -1.00. If you do this on a calculator (or with CORREG.BAS) and compare the output to the results you got for Data Set 1, you will see that the entries in the formula are the same for both analyses. The only element that changes is the sign of the numerator. If we consider that a perfectly linear positive functional relationship is the inverse of (i.e., the opposite extreme of) a perfectly linear negative functional relationship, it makes sense that the Pearson *r* has a potential range of -1.00 (perfectly linear negative relationship) to $+1.00$ (perfectly linear positive relationship).

We can easily leave the extremes and go within the -1.00 to $+1.00$ range by disrupting the perfection of the linear relationship in our demonstration data set. Let us compute the Pearson *r* for Data Set 3. Note that the numbers are the same as those used for the above demonstrations (Data Set 1 and Data Set 2), except that the first two *Y* values have been exchanged.

Data Set 3

X	Y
3	5←
5	3←
8	8
11	11
13	13

Here is the computational formula with all the values filled in:

$$r_{XY} = \frac{384 - \frac{(40)\,(40)}{5}}{\sqrt{\left[388 - \frac{40^2}{5}\right] \cdot \left[388 - \frac{40^2}{5}\right]}}$$

$$r_{XY} = \frac{64}{\sqrt{68 \cdot 68}} = .94$$

The Pearson *r* now equals .94. The perfect linear relationship between *X* and *Y* is gone. Now, in Data Set 4, let's really scramble the *Y* scores to destroy any semblance of a linear relationship and recompute the Pearson *r*.

Data Set 4

X	Y
3	5
5	11
8	8
11	13
13	3

Here is the computational formula with all the values filled in:

$$r_{XY} = \frac{316 - \dfrac{(40)(40)}{5}}{\sqrt{\left[388 - \dfrac{40^2}{5}\right] \cdot \left[388 - \dfrac{40^2}{5}\right]}}$$

$$r_{XY} = \frac{-4}{\sqrt{68 \cdot 68}} = -.06$$

For these pairs of X, Y coordinates, the Pearson r equals $-.06$. One look at the scatterplot for these data (Data Set 4 and figure 6.1) will illustrate how far we have come from the straight line relationship that was present in the original pairs. The r value of $-.06$ is barely larger than zero, and so there appears to be no linear relationship of any consequence between variable X and variable Y. This is a result of disrupting the covariation that originally existed between the two sets. The numbers within the sets are the same, but the patterns we saw earlier in the coordinates are missing for both a positive relationship (high values of X and Y paired together and low values of X and Y paired together) and a negative relationship (low values of X paired with high values of Y and high values of X paired with low values of Y).

Now let us go back to the two identical sets (Data Set 1) and apply a simple transformation to the set of Y scores by adding a constant to each score. Adding a constant 10.00 to all the original Y scores will result in the following data:

Data Set 5

X	Y
3	13
5	15
8	18
11	21
13	23

Here is the computational formula with all the values filled in:

$$r_{XY} = \frac{788 - \dfrac{(40)\ (90)}{5}}{\sqrt{\left[388 - \dfrac{40^2}{5}\right] \cdot \left[1688 - \dfrac{90^2}{5}\right]}}$$

$$r_{XY} = \frac{68}{\sqrt{68 \cdot 68}} = 1.00$$

As you can see, if we recompute the Pearson r using the transformed Y set, the solution of the formula does not change. The Pearson r still equals 1.00, and a scatterplot of the two sets of coordinates (figure 6.1) still shows that the relationship between X and Y is perfectly linear. Even the slope of the regression line is the same. The only value that changes is the Y-intercept, which moves from zero to ten, the magnitude of the transformation.

Why didn't adding a constant to all the Y scores affect the value of the correlation coefficient? If we convert all the X and Y scores to z scores, the reason for the latter result becomes apparent. Although the raw score values for X and Y do not correspond exactly, the z score values *do* correspond exactly. Each X and its corresponding Y occupy the same relative position in their respective distributions.

Data Set 5 with z Scores

X	z_X	Y	z_Y
3	−1.36	13	−1.36
5	−0.81	15	−0.81
8	0.00	18	0.00
11	+0.81	21	+0.81
13	+1.36	23	+1.36

If we reproduce Data Set 4 with z scores, the same set of X and Y scores that we determined earlier had a near zero linear relationship, we see a different picture: the z scores for numerically identical X and Y scores are not equal.

Data Set 4 with z Scores

X	z_X	Y	z_Y
3	−1.36	5	−0.81
5	−0.81	11	+0.81
8	0.00	8	0.00
11	+0.81	13	+1.36
13	+1.36	3	−1.36

This leads to yet another definition of the Pearson r as an index of the extent to which corresponding X and Y scores occupy the same relative positions in their respective distributions. If the z score transformations of the X and Y scores are numerically equal in both sign and value, as is the case with Data Set 5, the Pearson r will be +1.00. If the z scores are numerically equal but opposite in sign, as is the case for Data Set 2, the Pearson r will be −1.00. Notice that this very relationship of numerically equal z scores that are opposite in sign exists in Data Set 4 for the $X = 5$, $Y = 11$ pair and the $X = 13$, $Y = 3$ pair. If this pattern had held true for the other X, Y pairs, the Pearson r would have been perfect (-1.00) instead of near zero ($-.06$).

The relationship between the Pearson r and z scores is also evident in the following formula for the Pearson r:

$$r_{XY} = \frac{\Sigma z_X z_Y}{N}$$

Substituting from the Data Set 5 z scores:

$$r_{XY} = \frac{(-1.36)(-1.36) + (-0.81)(-0.81) + 0 + (0.81)(0.81) + (1.36)(1.36)}{5}$$

$$r_{XY} = \frac{5}{5} = 1.00$$

This is the same result we got from the computational formula. Similarly, if we enter the z score data for Data Set 2 (numerically equal raw scores have the same value z score, but they are opposite in sign), the result is

$$r_{XY} = \frac{(1.36)(-1.36) + (0.81)(-0.81) + 0 + (-0.81)(0.81) + (-1.36)(1.36)}{5}$$

$$r_{XY} = \frac{-5}{5}$$

$$r_{XY} = -1.00$$

CORRELATION AND PREDICTION

Yet another way of thinking of correlation is as an index of the accuracy with which X may be used to predict Y. If you inspect figure 6.2, you will see that in an imperfect linear relationship a value of X corresponds not to one Y score but to a potential range of Y scores. The predicted value for Y (the one on the best-fit line that is found by solving the $Y' = a_Y + b_Y X$ equation) will, on the average, be located in the middle of this range. The narrower the potential range, the narrower the scatterplot becomes, the more linear its shape becomes, and the closer the predicted value for Y will be to the obtained Y scores.

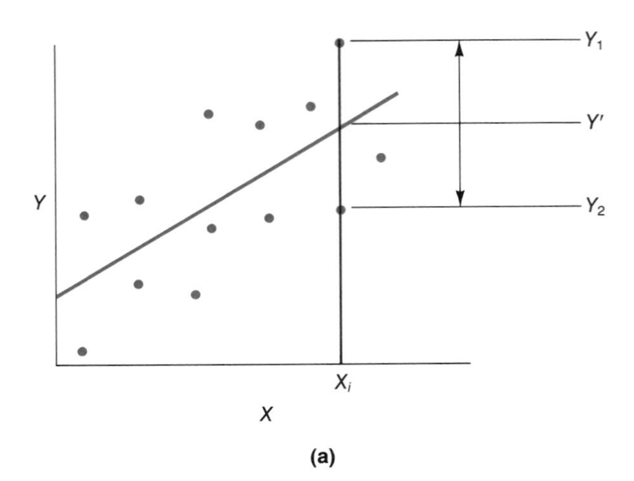

(a)

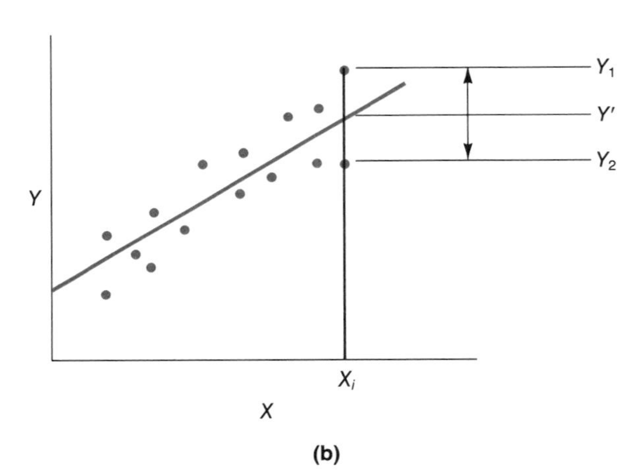

(b)

Figure 6.2
These two scatterplots have identical regression lines and identical predicted Y values for X_i, but the prediction is more precise (i.e., less subject to error) in scatterplot (b), the more compact of the two.

Specifically, as $s_{\text{est } Y} \longrightarrow 0$, $r_{XY} \longrightarrow 1.00$. (This reads, "As the standard error of estimate for the regression of Y on X approaches zero, the correlation between variables X and Y approaches 1.00.") An example of the reciprocal relationship between the standard error of estimate and the correlation coefficient can be seen by examining Data Sets 1 and 4. The standard error of estimate for Data Set 1 above is zero when $r = 1.00$. By contrast, in Data Set 4 the standard error of estimate equals 4.75 when $r = -.06$.

An even more precise relationship between the magnitude of the Pearson r and the strength of prediction is embodied in the following equation:

$$z_{Y'} = r_{XY} \cdot z_X$$

Figure 6.3

The effect of different degrees of relationship between X and Y upon the predictions of Y' from various values of X.

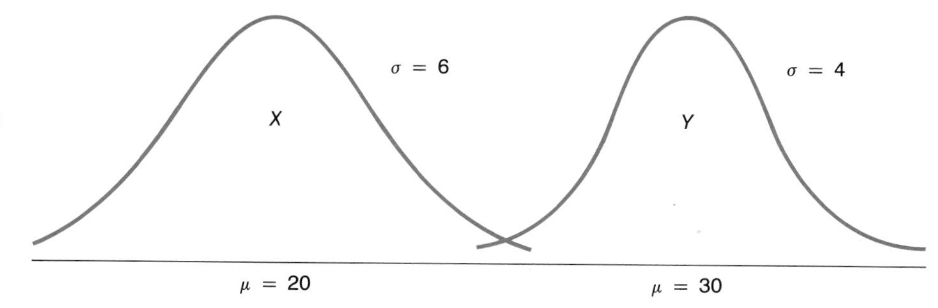

	$r = +1.00$	$r = +.80$	$r = +.60$	$r = 0.00$
X	Y'	Y'	Y'	Y'
14	26	26.8	27.6	30
17	28	28.4	28.8	30
26	34	33.2	32.4	30
29	36	34.8	33.6	30

	$r = -1.00$	$r = -.80$	$r = -.60$	$r = 0.00$
X	Y'	Y'	Y'	Y'
14	34	33.2	32.4	30
17	32	31.6	31.2	30
26	26	26.8	27.6	30
29	24	25.2	26.4	30

This equation has a much more simple message than its appearance would suggest. All it really means is that the position the Y score is *predicted* to occupy in the distribution of Y scores equals the correlation coefficient times the position the X score is *known* to occupy in the distribution of X scores. This equation is read, "The z score of the predicted Y score equals the correlation between X and Y times the z score equivalent of raw score X."

Let us make the abstract relationship represented by this equation more concrete and understandable by applying it to some actual data. Two distributions of scores, one for variable X and one for variable Y, are depicted in figure 6.3. Using the equation, predictions are made from X to Y assuming varying degrees of relationship ($r_{XY} = 1.00$, $r_{XY} = .80$, $r_{XY} = .60$, and $r_{XY} = 0.00$), and the results of these computations are included with figure 6.3.

Notice that when $r_{XY} = 1.00$, the location of the predicted Y score in its distribution equals exactly the location of X in its distribution. For example, an X score equal to 26 is one standard deviation unit above the mean ($\mu_X = 20$, $\sigma_X = 6$, $X = 20 + 6 = 26$), so we say 26 has a z score value of $+1.00$ ($z_x = +1.00$). Here is the formula:

$$z_{Y'} = r_{XY} \cdot z_X$$

Substituting for r_{XY} and z_X:

$$z_{y'} = (1.00) \cdot (1.00)$$

$$z_{y'} = 1.00$$

To change the z score value for the predicted Y to a raw score value we must substitute in the z formula:

$$z_Y = \frac{Y - \mu}{\sigma_Y}$$

For the Y distribution, $\mu_Y = 30$, $\sigma_Y = 4$, so

$$1.00 = \frac{Y - 30}{4}$$

$$34 = Y$$

As you can see, both the X score (26) and the Y score that is predicted when X equals 26 ($Y' = 34$) occupy the same position in their respective distributions ($z = +1.00$ for both $X = 26$ and $Y' = 34$).

If we change the sign of r from $+1.00$ to -1.00 in the latter example, an X score of 26 would predict a Y score of 26. The value of z_X is still $+1.00$, but z_Y equals -1.00. The X score of 26 is one standard deviation above the mean in the X distribution ($20 + 6 = 26$), but the predicted Y score is one standard deviation *below* the mean of the Y distribution ($30 - 4 = 26$) because of the negative sign.

$$z_{Y'} = \frac{Y - \mu_Y}{\sigma_Y}$$

$$-1.00 = \frac{Y - 30}{4}$$

$$26 = Y$$

Other entries in figure 6.3 illustrate what happens as r approaches zero. For example, when $r_{XY} = 1.00$ and $X = 29$, $Y' = 36$, but as r_{XY} gets closer to zero, the computed value of Y' drops down to 34.8 ($r_{XY} = .80$), then to 32.4

(r_{XY} = .60), and finally, when $r_{XY} = 0$, any X will result in a prediction of the mean of the Y distribution (30). The predicted Y value moves toward or regresses to the mean of the Y distribution as the correlation between X and Y shrinks. Also, notice in figure 6.3 that as the correlation between X and Y approaches zero from the negative side, the regression toward the mean is equally apparent in the predicted Y' scores.

Partitioning Variation. Partitioning the total variation in a predicted variable (usually Y) into predictable (explained) and unpredictable (unexplained) variation.

PARTITIONING THE TOTAL VARIATION IN VARIABLE *Y*

Figures 6.4 and 6.5 are two ways of representing the **partitioning of total variation** in variable Y into predictable (regression) and unpredictable (residual) components. Let us start with figure 6.4.

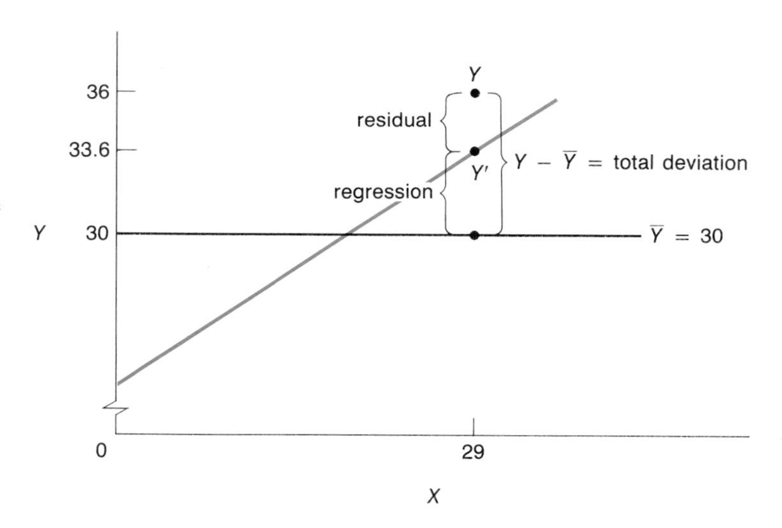

Figure 6.4

This illustration shows the difference between the actual Y score (36) and the predicted Y score (33.8) when $X = 29$. The 3.8 units between Y' and $\overline{Y}$ is the predictable variation. The 2.2 units between Y and Y' ($Y - Y' = 2.2$) is the error or "residual" in prediction.

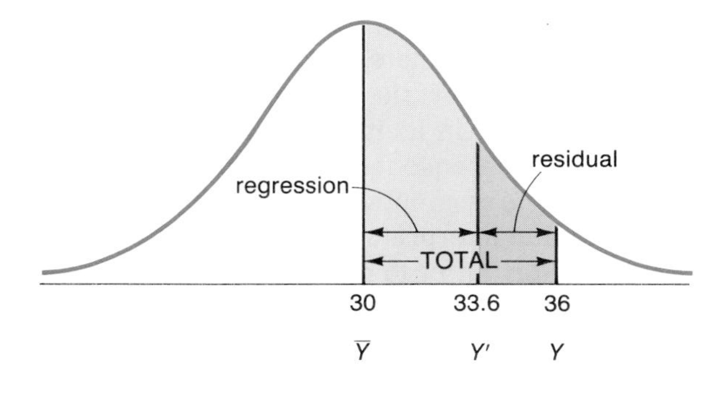

Figure 6.5

The predictable (regression) and unpredictable (residual) parts of the deviation of Y from $\overline{Y}$ when $r = +.60$ and $X = 29$. The distributions of the X and Y variables are shown in figure 6.3.

The $(Y - \bar{Y})$ value of 6 (i.e., 36 − 30) is the total deviation of Y from the mean of the Y distribution. This may be broken down into a predictable portion,

$$(Y' - \bar{Y}) = 33.6 - 30 = 3.6,$$

and an unpredictable portion,

$$(Y - Y') = 36 - 33.6 = 2.4$$

If such deviation scores were computed for every point in the scatterplot and if they were squared as follows:

$$\Sigma(Y - \bar{Y})^2, \quad \Sigma(Y' - \bar{Y})^2, \quad \Sigma(Y - Y')^2,$$

you would find that

$$\Sigma(Y - \bar{Y})^2 = \Sigma(Y' - \bar{Y})^2 + \Sigma(Y - Y')^2$$

or

$$SS_{total} = SS_{regression} + SS_{residual}$$

Predictable Variation (also called explained variation). The variation of a variable (usually Y) that is predictable with the knowledge of a predictor (usually X).

Nonpredictable Variation (also called unexplained variation). The variation of a variable (usually Y) that is not predictable with the knowledge of a predictor (usually X).

In words, we say that the total variation in variable Y equals the **predictable variation ($SS_{regression}$)** plus the **nonpredictable variation ($SS_{residual}$)**.

In figure 6.5 there is another representation of partitioning using the same data. Of the 6 units that separate the obtained Y score of 36 from 30, the mean of the Y distribution, 3.6 of the 6 units are predictable with the knowledge of X (i.e., $Y' - \bar{Y} = 33.6$), and the rest of the $Y - \bar{Y}$ deviation, from 33.6 to 36, is unpredictable.

THE ASSUMPTIONS OF THE PEARSON *r*

All statistics have certain elements in common, and the Pearson *r* is no exception. Like the others, there is a set of assumptions about the data that, if violated, can distort the meaning of its computed value, and there are cautions to observe in its interpretation. By doing controlled sampling experiments, the consequences of various assumption violations can be easily observed. The assumptions themselves and the effects of their violation upon the value and interpretation of the Pearson *r* will be discussed briefly. If you are using *Stat/Tutor* to run some sampling experiments and view the effects of various assumptions about the data upon the Pearson *r*, you should run RDIST.BAS and read the RDIST.BAS section of the *Manual for Stat/Tutor.*

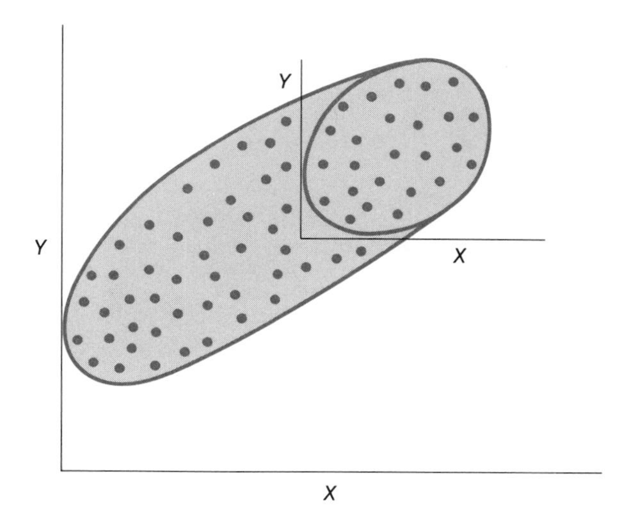

Figure 6.6

A comparison of scatterplot shapes when the ranges of variable X and variable Y are normal (larger envelope) and truncated (smaller, shaded envelope).

Homoscedasticity. One underlying assumption of the Pearson r statistic stating that the scatterplot must have a uniform cross-sectional width along its length.

Homoscedasticity. This mouthful is the assumption that the dispersion of variable Y remains essentially the same across the range of the X scores. In figure 6.7 there are illustrations of some of the patterns of scatterplots that are extreme violations of **homoscedasticity.** For each scatterplot two shapes are sketched. One shape is drawn around the entire scatterplot to include all the X, Y values represented therein, and the second shape is drawn around only the dominant cluster(s) of dots. These shapes are called *envelopes*. The smaller envelope paints the truer picture of the functional relationship between X and Y, while the larger envelope represents a distortion of the true degree of relationship between X and Y that is caused by the violation of the assumption of homoscedasticity. As a student once put it, "You mean the formula *thinks* it's working with data that look like the large envelope and it's being fooled into thinking there's more of a linear trend than there really is?" What could I say? The answer is yes. Put another way, the Pearson r that is computed when there is an absence of homoscedasticity is likely to reflect a greater degree of relationship than truly exists between the variables. A few stray, atypical values or clusters that are separated by empty space can seriously misrepresent the nature and extent of the relationship between the variables.

In figure 6.7(a) the pattern is one of a circular cluster with two stray points with high X and Y values. The small envelope has no apparent linear trend, but when combined with the stray points into a larger envelope, there is an apparent linear trend. In figure 6.7(b) there are two clusters, neither one of which suggests any linear trend. As before, the larger envelope makes something out of nothing by combining the two clusters. In figure 6.7(c) there is a central cluster with a couple of low X, Y pairs and a couple of high X, Y pairs. Again, including these errant values exaggerates the extent of the linear relationship between X and Y.

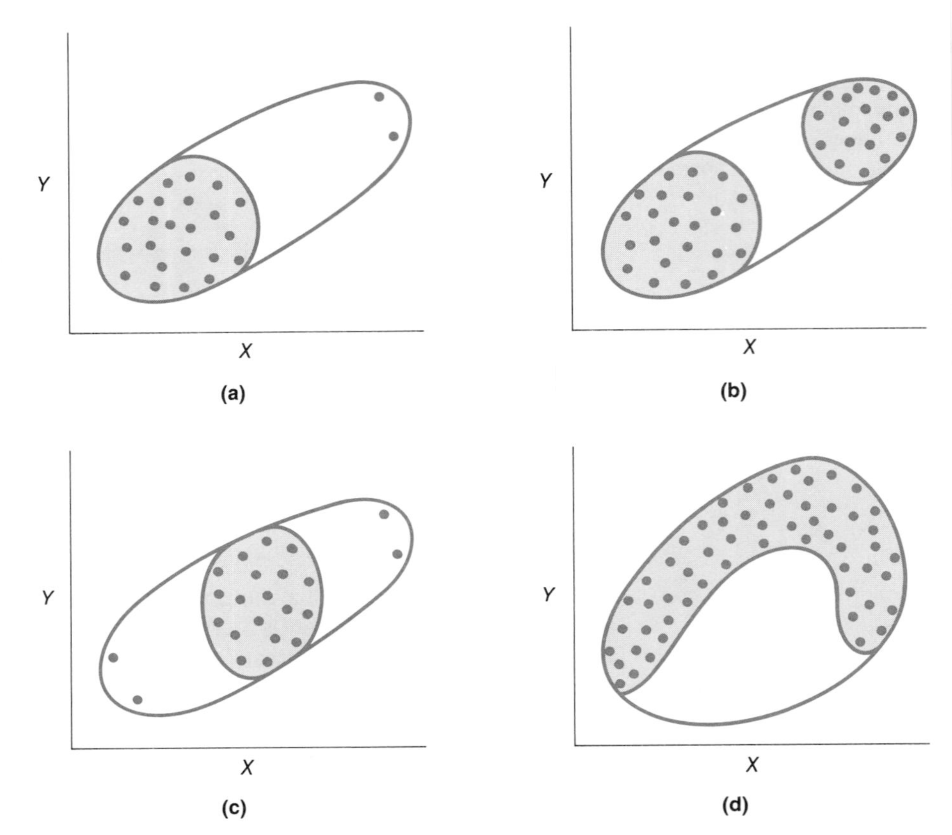

Figure 6.7

Some violations of the homoscedasticity (parts a, b, and c) and linearity (part d) assumptions. The larger envelopes reflect the degree of linear trend reflected in the Pearson *r*. The smaller (shaded) envelopes reflect the true trend of the relationship between *X* and *Y*.

Nonlinear Relationships. Functional relationships that do not plot as a straight line.

Linear versus Nonlinear Relationships. The Pearson *r* is an index of the extent of the linear relationship that exists between variable *X* and variable *Y*. **Nonlinear relationships,** even very strong ones, will not be reflected as a high value in the computation of the Pearson *r*. In the illustration in figure 6.7(d), there is a strong nonlinear relationship between *X* and *Y*, but the outer envelope, which is the one described by the Pearson *r*, shows little linear trend. This would be reflected in a low value for the Pearson *r* and could lead to an incorrect conclusion that there is little or no relationship between variable *X* and variable *Y*. There is a relationship, but it's *curvilinear* rather than linear.

Truncated Range. A condition in which the range of a variable in a set of sample data is less than the range found in the population.

Truncated Range. When the range of one or both of the variables is **truncated** (i.e., cut off) the degree of relationship indicated by the size of the computed Pearson *r* is likely to underestimate the true degree of relationship between the variables. For example, many persons were disturbed some years back by the low reported correlation between the Scholastic Aptitude Test scores of college bound high school students and the final grade point average these same students achieved upon graduation from college. If the relationship was so low, why bother to use S.A.T. scores as a predictor of success in college?

Actually, this result was inevitable. To get a more accurate picture of the relationship that is likely to exist betwen S.A.T. scores and final grade point average at the time of college graduation let us do an imaginary experiment. All high school students in a representative sample of high school students from across the country would have to take the S.A.T. and all would have to attend four years of college, regardless of their previous level of academic achievement or personal preferences on higher education. Of course, in reality the students who scored extremely low on the S.A.T. would not be admitted to a college, and even if they did gain admission with very low S.A.T. scores, there is a strong likelihood, if the S.A.T. does indeed reflect scholastic aptitude, that they would fail and have to drop out.

In the real world, however, the selection procedure for getting into college and the normal drop-out rate from college guarantee that the lower end of both variables (S.A.T. total below 850 and G.P.A. below 2.0) will be cut from the set of potentially available data. Notice the effect of this truncation upon the shape of the envelope in figure 6.6. The larger scatterplot represents the projected results of our imaginary experiment, while the segment in the upper right portion of the scatterplot depicts a scatterplot after the lower ends of both variables have been truncated. Notice how the imaginary results appear to have more of a linear trend than is present in the truncated scatterplot. Thus, there may be a strong linear trend in the relationship between two variables, but if the range of one or both variables is truncated, the strength of the linear trend may not be reflected in the magnitude of the correlation coefficient.

THE COEFFICIENT OF DETERMINATION

In the earlier section on partitioning variation you saw that the total variation in variable Y could be divided into the portion that was predictable with the knowledge of X and the portion that was not predictable. Here are the same equations you saw earlier:

$$\Sigma(Y - \overline{Y})^2 = \Sigma(Y' - \overline{Y})^2 + \Sigma(Y - Y')^2$$

or

$$SS_{total} = SS_{regression} + SS_{residual}$$

The proportion of the total variation in variable Y that is predictable with the knowledge of X is computed by dividing the $SS_{regression}$ by the SS_{total} as shown below.

$$\frac{SS_{regression}}{SS_{total}} = \text{the coefficient of determination}$$

Coefficient of Determination. The proportion of variation in the values of a variable (usually Y) that is predictable (explained) from the value of a predictor (usually X).

This proportion, called the **coefficient of determination** is used as a measure of the relative strength of relationships. For example, if the analysis of one set of data yielded a proportion of .6 and for another set of data the proportion was .2, it would be correct to say that the relationship between X and Y in the first analysis was three times stronger than in the second.

Actually, it is unnecessary to compute the coefficient of determination using the above formula. By simply squaring the Pearson correlation coefficient, we get the same value:

$$r^2 = \text{the coefficient of determination}$$

THE COEFFICIENT OF ALIENATION

Coefficient of Alienation. The proportion of variation in the values of a variable (usually Y) that is not predictable (unexplained) from the value of a predictor (usually X).

A companion to the coefficient of determination is the **coefficient of alienation,** the proportion of *un*explained variation.

$$\frac{SS_{residual}}{SS_{total}} = \text{the coefficient of alienation}$$

We can get the same proportion using the following:

$$1 - r^2 = \text{the coefficient of alienation}$$

Remember, the r statistic itself does not reflect the proportion (or percentage) of variation in Y that is predictable with the knowledge of X. Only r^2 yields descriptive information about predictable versus nonpredictable variation. For example, if, in two separate analyses, we compute correlation coefficients or $r = .4$ and $r = .8$, the relationship in the latter ($r = .8$) is *not* twice as strong as the relationship in the former ($r = .4$). It is four times stronger because $.8^2 = .64$ is four times larger than $.4^2 = .16$.

Using the coefficients of determination and alienation there is yet another way to represent the partitioning of variation in regression analysis. Here is the formula you saw earlier:

$$SS_{total} = SS_{regression} + SS_{residual}$$

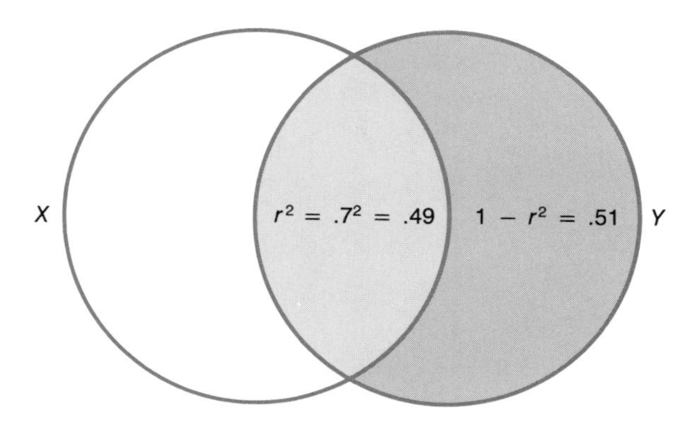

Figure 6.8

The proportions of explained (r^2) and unexplained ($1-r^2$) variation in the regression of Y on X when $r_{XY} = .70$.

Here is the same partition using r^2 and $1 - r^2$:

$$SS_{total} = r^2(SS_{total}) + (1 - r)^2(SS_{total})$$
$$SS_{total} = SS_{regression} + SS_{residual}$$

Multiplying the SS_{total} by the proportions of explained variation (r^2) and unexplained variation ($1 - r^2$) enables us to partition the total variation into its explained (regression) and unexplained (residual) components with a minimum of computation. The proportions of explained and unexplained variation are illustrated in figure 6.8 for the regression of Y on X when the correlation between the X and Y variables has been determined to be $r = .70$. In this case roughly half of the variability in Y is explained with the knowledge of X (49%), and roughly half remains unexplained (51%).

THE SPEARMAN RHO

Monotonicity. A pattern observed in some functions in which, in a positive function, successively greater X values are always paired with successively greater Y values and, in a negative function, successively greater X values are always paired with successively smaller Y values.

The **Spearman rho** statistic, also called the Spearman rank order correlation coefficient, permits an assessment of the degree of relationship between variables X and Y when certain assumptions for the use of the Pearson r have not been met. Strictly speaking, the characteristic in the data that is reflected in the value of the Spearman rho is not the degree of linear relationship. It is a property called **monotonicity.** In a positive monotonic function, as the X variable consistently increases in magnitude, so does the Y variable. In a negative monotonic function, as the X variable consistently increases in magnitude, the Y variable consistently decreases in magnitude. Some monotonic functions are shown in figure 6.9 and, of course, linear functions are included because they are monotonic. In short, because linear functions are monotonic and the Spearman rho measures monotonicity, the Spearman rho may be regarded as an indirect measure of linearity.

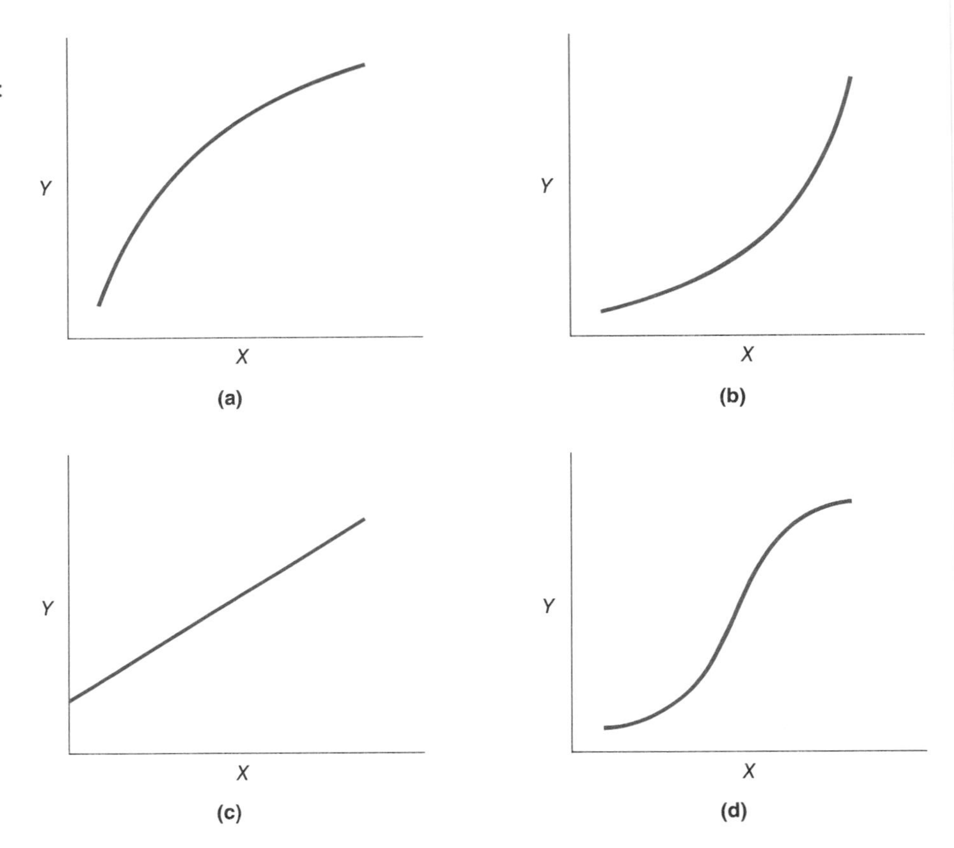

Figure 6.9
Four monotonic functions: negatively accelerating (a), positively accelerating (b), linear (c), and ogive (d).

The Pearson *r* Compared to the Spearman rho

Before using the Pearson *r* one should ascertain that the data are in the interval scale and that the scatterplot conforms to the assumption of homoscedasticity. (Various scatterplot patterns that fail to meet the assumption of homoscedasticity were discussed earlier in this chapter and are displayed in the RDIST.BAS computer tutorial.) It is not required that these assumptions be met in order to use the Spearman rho. The trend of relationship between X and Y as revealed in the scatterplot must still be linear, and the scaling of one or both variables must be at least ordinal, but the other restrictions do not apply.

Like the Pearson *r*, the Spearman rho ranges between -1.00 and $+1.00$. In fact, the Spearman rho is really just a Pearson *r* computed on ranked data. Before computing the Spearman rho we must assign a number (i.e., a rank) to each X score that reflects its magnitude relative to all the other X scores. Likewise, we must also rank all the Y scores according to their relative magnitudes. Thus, although we may use the same computational formula to compute the Spearman rho that we have been using to compute the Pearson *r*, some preparation is necessary. In assigning the ranks it really does not matter whether the numerically low scores or numerically high scores get the low ranks (1, 2, etc.). The magnitude of the Spearman rho will be unaffected (although, as you shall see, the *sign* of the correlation coefficient will be affected).

The Spearman rho: Example 1

On the basis of some diagnostic tests, twelve men were ranked in terms of their cardiovascular fitness. Without being told the results of their medical tests, their self-perception of their general level of fitness was assessed by means of a questionnaire. In table 6.1 we see the twelve men listed (variable *Y*) from the most medically fit (1) to the least fit (12), and beside each man's medical fitness rank is his self-perception score (variable *X*). Low scores from the questionnaire indicate a self-perception of being in poor physical condition and the high scores indicate a self-perception of being in good physical condition.

The first step in the data analysis is to rank the *X* scores and the *Y* scores. The medical fitness scores (variable *Y*) are already in the form of ranks, and, because we need not process these data further, the ranks column for variable *Y* is identical to the original variable *Y* data.

Table 6.1
The data for Example 1

	Fitness on the Basis of:			
	Self-Perception (*X*)		Medical Tests (*Y*)	
Men	*Data*	*Rank*	*Data*	*Rank*
A	82	9	1	1
B	85	10	2	2
C	91	12	3	3
D	86	11	4	4
E	75	7	5	5
F	80	8	6	6
G	67	6	7	7
H	53	5	8	8
I	40	3	9	9
J	45	4	10	10
K	30	2	11	11
L	20	1	12	12

The questionnaire data (variable X) are not yet ranked, and this must be done before we can enter the data into the correlation formula. Let us rank the questionnaire data by arbitrarily giving the numerically low scores the low ranks. As you can see in table 6.1, the values in the rank column for the X variable were assigned according to the relative magnitude of the questionnaire scores. The smallest questionnaire score (20) was assigned the rank of one, 30 was second lowest, then 40, etc.

Putting the X and Y ranks into the Pearson r formula gives the following results:

$$r_{XY} = \frac{375 - \frac{(78)(78)}{12}}{\sqrt{\left[650 - \frac{78^2}{12}\right] \cdot \left[650 - \frac{78^2}{12}\right]}}$$

$$r_{XY} = \frac{-132}{\sqrt{(143) \cdot (143)}} = -.923$$

We can see from this analysis that the degree of relationship between one's medically determined level of fitness and one's self-perception of fitness is rather high. But is the relationship really negative? If it were truly negative it would mean that the most medically fit persons tend to think of themselves as being in terrible shape, while the least medically fit persons tend to think of themselves as being in excellent shape.

In fact, the negative sign of the Spearman rho is a product of the arbitrary ranking procedure we used. Had we given the numerically high questionnaire scores the low ranks instead of the high ranks we would obtain the same magnitude for the Spearman rho ($-.923$), but the sign would be positive instead of negative. To avoid incorrect interpretations of the Spearman rho analysis, we must evaluate the sign of the Spearman rho statistic within the context of the experimental data. If the sign of the rho statistic does not make sense within the context of the problem, chances are that the sign is a consequence of an inverted ranking procedure. In practice, there is no need to redo the analysis because the absolute value of rho is unaffected by how one ranks the numerically high versus low X and Y scores. If you have determined, as we just did, that the sign of the result makes no sense, simply change the sign. For Example 1, rho $= +.923$. Thus, with the proper sign assigned to the rho statistic, we can see that an individual's self-assessment of fitness tends to agree with the results of objective medical tests.

Ranking Tied Data

Ranking. Arranging a set in order of the numerical value of the scores.

Sometimes the **ranking** of the data is complicated by the presence of ties—two or more X scores or two or more Y scores with the same numerical value. Consider the following set:

$$4, 3, 7, 5, 1, 11, 7, 3, 12, 16, 7, 21$$

After sorting the set, it becomes

1, 3, 3, 4, 5, 7, 7, 7, 11, 12, 16, 21

Notice that there are two scores with a value of three and three scores with a value of seven. The rule for resolving ties is to give each score involved in a tie the average of the tied positions. This average becomes its rank for analysis purposes.

Raw score set: 1, 3, 3, 4, 5, 7, 7, 7, 11, 12, 16, 21
Position: 1, 2, 3, 4, 5, 6, 7, 8, 9, 10, 11, 12
Rank of Score: 1, 2.5, 4, 5, 7, 9, 10, 11, 12

Both threes get the rank of 2.5, and all three sevens get a rank of 7. The ranked set would therefore be

1, 2.5, 2.5, 4, 5, 7, 7, 7, 9, 10, 11, 12

Spearman rho: Example 2

Let us do a Spearman rho analysis on the same data presented in table 5.2 of the last chapter. In table 6.2 both the original and ranked versions of these data are displayed. Notice the presence of ties in the actual *X* and *Y* scores and how the principles presented above were applied to rank the tied score values.

Table 6.2

The data for Example 2 (from table 5.2).

X Score	Rank *X*	*Y* Score	Rank *Y*
2	1	5	3.5
8	6.5	9	8
9	8	12	11
5	3	7	5
7	5	4	2
3	2	2	1
11	10.5	13	12
10	9	8	6.5
8	6.5	10	9.5
6	4	5	3.5
11	10.5	8	6.5
12	12	10	9.5

Putting the X and Y ranks into the Pearson r formula gives the following results:

$$r_{XY} = \frac{613 - \dfrac{(78)(78)}{12}}{\sqrt{\left[649 - \dfrac{78^2}{12}\right] \cdot \left[648.5 - \dfrac{78^2}{12}\right]}}$$

$$r_{XY} = \frac{106}{\sqrt{(142) \cdot (141.5)}} = .7478$$

An Alternative Computational Method for Spearman rho

There is an alternative computational method for computing the Spearman rho, and this is the one presented in the SPEAR.BAS computer program. If there are no (or very few) ties in the ranked version of the data, the value of the Spearman rho computed using the Pearson r formula with the X, Y ranks will be very close to the value computed using the alternative method. (Some slight discrepancy may also arise due to rounding error.) The more tied ranks there are among the X and/or Y data, the less likely one is to see a close correspondence in the two correlation values.

Here is the formula for the alternative computational method:

$$\text{rho} = 1 - \frac{6\Sigma D_i^2}{N^3 - N}$$

Sometimes the formula is written:

$$\text{rho} = 1 - \frac{6\Sigma D_i^2}{N(N^2 - 1)}$$

with a different representation of the denominator, but the two are algebraically equivalent.

For demonstration purposes, the two Spearman rho analyses we did above will be redone using this alternative formula just as they would appear in the output of SPEAR.BAS. To prepare for making the appropriate substitutions in this formula we must compute the difference between the X and Y ranks for each row. The difference score for each pair of X, Y ranks is then entered in the D column of the table. Then each difference score is squared, and the results are entered in the D^2 column. Next, the column of squared difference scores is summed to get the ΣD^2 term for the Spearman rho formula. The SPEAR.BAS program in *Stat/Tutor* does the Spearman rho using this method, and using the SPEAR.BAS program you will be able to run a variety of problems with your data to see detailed examples of this computational method.

Table 6.3

The Spearman rho analysis of the Example 1 data repeated using an alternative computational method.

	Fitness on the Basis of:					
	Self-Perception (X)		Medical Tests (Y)			
Men	*Data*	*Rank*	*Data*	*Rank*	D	D^2
A	82	9	1	1	8	64
B	85	10	2	2	8	64
C	91	12	3	3	9	81
D	86	11	4	4	7	49
E	75	7	5	5	2	4
F	80	8	6	6	2	4
G	67	6	7	7	−1	1
H	53	5	8	8	−3	9
I	40	3	9	9	−6	36
J	45	4	10	10	−6	36
K	30	2	11	11	−9	81
L	20	1	12	12	−11	121
						$\Sigma D^2 = 550$

Example 1 Repeated. In table 6.3 the original data from table 6.1 are shown along with the extra columns in the table that are used for the computation of the sum of the squared difference scores.

$\Sigma D^2 = 550$ and $N = 12$. Substituting

$$\text{rho} = 1 - \frac{6\Sigma D_i^2}{N^3 - N}$$

$$\text{rho} = 1 - \frac{6 \cdot 550}{1728 - 12}$$

$$\text{rho} = 1 - 1.92308$$

$$\text{rho} = -.923$$

Notice that this is exactly the same answer that we obtained when we substituted the X and Y ranks of the Example 1 data into the computational formula for the Pearson r.

BOX 6.1

A Research Scenario

Now that we have covered both regression and correlation, let us put all this information to work for us within the context of a research example.

Rats prefer to avoid open well-lit spaces, and when placed in an open arena called an *open field*, they exhibit two types of behavior. If they tend to have a high level of emotionality they will freeze in place for several minutes. On the other hand, if they tend to have a low level of emotionality they do not react to the stress of being in the open field in as extreme a fashion, and will become active and explore the apparatus. The data are collected by counting units of activity as the animal moves around the open field.

One disadvantage of this testing procedure is that the experimenter must catch the rat in its cage and physically place the animal in the open field. Sometimes, especially in the case of animals that are difficult to catch, the capture procedure introduces stress into the testing situation over and above the mild stress of being in the open field.

A researcher devised a new testing procedure for measuring emotionality in laboratory rats following the introduction of mild stress that did not require removing the rat from its home cage. To evaluate the relationship between the measures provided by the two different tests, a small pilot study was carried out with ten animals. Each subject was tested in both situations. Using the data that follows, let us analyze the relationship between the two sets of test results.

Subject	Cage Test (X)	*Open Field* (Y)
1	32	20
2	57	31
3	35	24
4	43	27
5	9	14
6	21	19
7	50	41
8	6	22
9	25	20
10	13	18

To solve for the Pearson r we must process the data using the following formula:

$$r_{XY} = \frac{\Sigma XY - \dfrac{(\Sigma X)(\Sigma Y)}{N}}{\sqrt{\left[\Sigma X^2 - \dfrac{(\Sigma X)^2}{N}\right]\left[\Sigma Y^2 - \dfrac{(\Sigma Y)^2}{N}\right]}}$$

$$r_{XY} = \frac{7{,}849 - \dfrac{(291)(236)}{10}}{\sqrt{\left[11{,}199 - \dfrac{291^2}{10}\right]\left[6{,}112 - \dfrac{236^2}{10}\right]}}$$

$$r_{XY} = \frac{981.4}{\sqrt{(2{,}730.9) \cdot (542.4)}} = .81$$

Therefore, on a scale of 0.00 to 1.00, the extent of the linear relationship between the open-field test scores and the cage test scores is 0.81.

The coefficient of determination, r^2_{XY} equals $.81^2 = .66$, and so we can say that 66% of the variability in the open-field scores is predictable with the knowledge of the cage test scores.

The slope of the best-fit line is found by the following formulae:

$$b_Y = \frac{SP_{XY}}{SS_X} = \frac{981.40}{2{,}730.90} = 0.36$$

The Y-intercept is found by the formula:

$$a_Y = \overline{Y} - b_Y \cdot \overline{X}$$

$$a_Y = 23.6 - 0.36 \cdot 29.1$$

$$a_Y = 13.14$$

Therefore, the equation for the best-fit line is

$$Y' = a_Y + b_Y \cdot X$$

$$Y' = 13.14 + 0.36 \cdot X$$

Using this equation, we may substitute an activity score obtained using the cage test and predict an animal's performance in the open-field test. For example, an animal that obtained an activity score of 40 on the cage test would have a predicted open-field score of $13.14 + .36 \cdot 40 = 27.8$. We may say, "On the average, animals that score 40 on the cage test will score 27.8 in the open-field test."

The standard error of estimate of the best-fit linear function is found by the following formula:

$$s_{est\ Y} = \sqrt{\frac{SS_Y - \dfrac{SP^2_{XY}}{SS_X}}{N - 2}}$$

$$s_{est\ Y} = \sqrt{\frac{542.4. - \dfrac{981.4^2}{2{,}730.9}}{10 - 2}}$$

$$s_{est\ Y} = 4.86$$

If we take the predicted Y' score of 27.8, which we just computed by substituting $X = 40$ in the regression equation, and go above and below that predicted Y value by one standard error of estimate unit (27.8 ± 4.86), we define an interval 22.9 to 32.66. We can then say, "When $X = 40$, 68% of the time the Y score will fall between 22.9 and 32.66." As discussed earlier, this is similar to determining the mean of a distribution and defining an interval around that mean plus and minus one standard deviation unit. Just as we know from our study of the z statistic that such an interval encloses the middle 68% of the distribution, so likewise does the interval $Y' \pm 1\ s_{est\ Y}$ unit enclose 68% of the actual Y scores.

Table 6.4

The Spearman rho analysis of the Example 2 data repeated using the alternative computational method.

X Score	Rank X	Y Score	Rank Y	D	D^2
2	1	5	3.5	−2.5	6.25
8	6.5	9	8	−1.5	2.25
9	8	12	11	−3	9
5	3	7	5	−2	4
7	5	4	2	3	9
3	2	2	1	1	1
11	10.5	13	12	−1.5	2.25
10	9	8	6.5	2.5	6.25
8	6.5	10	9.5	−3	9
6	4	5	3.5	.5	.25
11	10.5	8	6.5	4	16
12	12	10	9.5	2.5	6.25
					$\Sigma D^2 = 71.5$

Example 2 Repeated. One distinguishing feature of the data that we used in Example 2 was the presence of tied ranks. Let us see if we still get the same answer with both formulae when there are tied ranks. The preliminary computations are in table 6.4.

$$\text{rho} = 1 - \frac{6\Sigma D_i^2}{N^3 - N}$$

$$\text{rho} = 1 - \frac{6 \cdot 71.5}{1728 - 12}$$

$$\text{rho} = 1 - .25$$

$$\text{rho} = .75$$

Notice that the Spearman rho of .75 is slightly different from the .7478 we computed earlier with these same data. As mentioned earlier, when ties are present in the data the two computational methods will not yield exactly the same result, but, as you can see, with only a few ties, the discrepancy is minimal.

CORRELATION AND CAUSALITY

Causality. Causality exists between variables X and Y when changes in the value of variable X are the direct cause of changes in the value of variable Y. All causally related variables are also functionally related, but functionally related variables are not necessarily causally related.

In an earlier section of this chapter, r^2, the coefficient of determination, was presented as a statistic that enables us to partition the total variation in the predicted variable (usually Y) into explained and unexplained variation. When we encounter information presented as an explanation, we expect information that, according to The American Heritage Dictionary, will "offer reasons for or a cause of" an event. So, when we see the word *explained* used within the context of a correlation analysis, it may seem reasonable to attribute the existence of a functional relationship between variables to causal factors or **causality**. Sometimes this attribution is correct and can be supported with carefully collected experimental data. By itself, however, correlation analysis tells us nothing about the fundamental cause of a functional relationship; it only tells us how strong the linear trend in the relationship is.

Early reports hypothesizing a relationship between smoking cigarettes and disease were correlational. As the habits of cancer patients were studied to reveal possible risk factors, it became apparent that the stronger an individual's smoking habit was, the greater risk that individual ran for contracting lung cancer, stroke, and heart disease. Tobacco industry spokespersons argued, quite correctly, that the existence of such a functional relationship does not provide convincing evidence of a causal connection between smoking and health. Perhaps, they argued, the stress factors that cause one to light up that relaxing cigarette also promote the increased incidence of disease among smokers. Heavy smoking and resistance to disease may both be manifestations of a third variable: an individual's inability to handle stress, the true culprit.

If you ran the first sampling experiment in RDIST.BAS, you know that it is possible to get a relatively high correlation coefficient even when the data are randomly paired scores. It is rare, but it can happen. So, some persons reasoned, maybe early indications of a relationship between smoking and disease were spurious. Maybe the data were not truly representative of the relationship between smoking and disease. As the data base grew and this chance explanation for the apparent relationship between smoking and disease became less tenable, it was quickly abandoned by all but the most zealous tobacco boosters.

It wasn't until very large numbers of smokers and nonsmokers were identified and followed clinically for many years that the data base was appropriate for drawing a causal connection between smoking and disease.

Nevertheless, some purists maintain that a critical experiment linking smoking to disease has not, and because of ethical considerations, never will be run. Such an experiment would, for example, involve randomly selecting a sample of children from a cross section of ethnic origins, household and neighborhood environments, etc. Each child would then be designated as a nonsmoker, light smoker, moderate smoker, or heavy smoker. Beginning at a certain age, say 16 years, participants would begin consuming designated cigarette dosages. Examination and analysis of lifetime health records would provide the kind of experimental evidence that is necessary to label tobacco as a causal factor in disease.

In actual practice great numbers of individuals have been followed in this manner, but the random sampling and random group assignment that are fundamentals of good research design obviously had to be omitted. By working with large numbers of subjects and amassing a very large data base, researchers think that possible bias in the subject selection process ceases to be a viable explanation of the results. They are probably correct. As much as researchers want the best data possible upon which to base their conclusions, a theory that a causal relationship is at the root of a demonstrated functional relationship is not always directly testable.

Summary

We examined the computation and interpretation of the Pearson *r*, the coefficient of determination, and the Spearman rho. We also discussed the underlying assumptions of these statistics and the relationship of correlation to some aspects of *z* scores and regression analysis. We concluded the chapter with a discussion of correlation and causality.

Key Terms

Causality
Coefficient of Alienation
Coefficient of Determination
Correlation
Homoscedasticity
Monotonicity
Nonlinear Relationships
Partitioning Variation (Predictable vs. Nonpredictable)
Pearson *r*
Ranking
Spearman rho
$SS_{regression}$
$SS_{residual}$
Truncated Range

Exercises

Here are some problems that involve the computation of the Pearson *r* and the Spearman rho. If you decide to try hand calculation, you may check your work by running the data through CORREG.BAS or SPEAR.BAS, whichever is appropriate.

1. Researchers from the Department of Agriculture collected data on a random sample of fifteen El Grande households in an attempt to understand the risk factors that play a role in the recent citywide infestation of Moroccan dust mites.

The measures taken at each household included the density of mite infestation (mites per unit area), dust level (dust per unit area), and a general cleanliness rating on a scale from 1 to 100. The data are as follows:

Household	Dust score	Density score	Cleanliness rating
A	10	20	94
B	35	40	47
C	55	40	45
D	15	35	75
E	20	30	80
F	30	25	65
G	75	65	25
H	60	60	25
I	45	30	50
J	30	45	55
K	10	25	85
L	40	50	25
M	65	45	30
N	65	55	20
O	50	55	40

a. Prepare a neat and well-proportioned scatterplot of the dust and density scores of the fifteen households.

b. Using these data determine the correlation between the dust level variable and the mite density level. Present your answer by filling in all the values in the appropriate computational formula and solving the equation.

c. Determine the regression equation that would allow one to predict the level of mite infestation from the knowledge of a house's dust level. Show the equations for the slope and Y-intercept with the appropriate entries.

d. Determine the extent of the relationship that exists between the cleanliness rating and the level of mite infestation. Show all relevant formulae and entries.

e. Determine the extent of the relationship between cleanliness rating and dust level.

f. If your friend lives in the same city in which this study took place and her house was found to have a dust level of 37, what level (density) of mite infestation would you predict for her house?

g. Fill in the blanks in the following statement. "Sixty-eight percent of the homes with a dust level of 25 would be predicted to have a level of mite infestation between ________ and ________."

h. The regression line for predicting mite density from dust level and the regression line for predicting dust level from mite density cross at the coordinates $X =$ ________ , $Y =$ ________ .

i. ________ percent of the variability in mite density is predictable with the knowledge of dust level.

2. The teacher of the Physics Honors Class at Coal Creek Central High School ran a correlation between the I.Q. of her students and their performance in her class. She was shocked to find that the correlation was very low. What assumption violation could account for this result?

3. Explain the statement, "The correlation coefficient is an index of the extent to which two sets of scores occupy the same positions in their respective distributions."
4. If X_i is one standard deviation above the mean of the X scores and the correlation between X and Y is -1.00, where would the predicted Y score be located on the distribution of Y scores?
5. What happens to the accuracy of predictions as the correlation between X and Y
   a. approaches zero?
   b. approaches 1.00 or -1.00?
6. Explain why a correlation between variables does not necessarily indicate that a causal relationship exists.
7. Return to Exercise 1 in chapter 5. Compute a correlation coefficient that describes the relationship between lagoon temperature and the distance from shore where the fishing is best.
8. A researcher investigated the relationship between the average daily consumption of cigarettes and the number of office visits to a physician that were necessary over the course of one year. A group of twelve males employed by a small electronics firm participated in the experiment. Here are the data:

Subject	Cigarette Consumption	Office Visits
1	39	14
2	48	8
3	50	12
4	35	11
5	32	8
6	26	4
7	23	9
8	0	3
9	18	5
10	0	1
11	0	7
12	10	3

   a. Construct a scatterplot for these data.
   b. Compute the Pearson r for these data.
   c. What percentage of the variability in the office visits variable is accounted for by the daily consumption of cigarettes?
9. An industrial psychologist has obtained a test that is supposed to predict an employee's ability to maintain productivity when the task to be performed is repetitive and boring. If the test works it would make it possible to screen the employees for their ability to tolerate such work assignments. To evaluate the rest, ten employees were given the test and were then assigned to perform a repetitive and boring task. After two weeks the average daily productivity scores for the employees were computed. The test scores and the productivity scores are presented in the following table.

Employee	Test Score	Productivity
1	10	30
2	12	35
3	18	35
4	21	55
5	27	52
6	35	67
7	42	70
8	42	67
9	34	62
10	51	66

a. What is the extent of the relationship between the test and productivity variables?
b. Determine the regression equation for predicting productivity from test scores.
c. What percentage of the variability in the productivity scores is predictable with the knowledge of the test scores?

10. The Jervis Advertising Agency has decided to assess the relationship between advertising dollars spent by their customers and the growth in gross receipts following the conclusion of an advertising campaign. They are doing this in an attempt to collect data that will convince the business community that advertising dollars are well-spent. Below is a list of eight companies together with their expenses for the advertising of an established product and the post-campaign growth in gross receipts from the sale of that product.

Company	Advertising Expenses (in 1000s)	Growth in Gross Receipts (in 1000s)
1	12	22
2	10	34
3	17	36
4	23	49
5	17	42
6	28	57
7	27	82
8	34	62

a. Draw a well-proportioned scatterplot for these data.
b. Compute the Pearson r statistic for these data.
c. What percentage of the increase in gross receipts is accounted for by the knowledge of advertising expenditures?
d. What general statement characterizes the relationship between advertising expenditures and growth in gross receipts?
e. If a company similar to those studied in this experiment budgeted $30,000 for advertising to boost sales of an established product, what would be the predicted growth in gross receipts?

PART II

INFERENTIAL STATISTICS

CHAPTER 7

Probability

Up to this point, the text has been concerned primarily with descriptive techniques that reveal the information in a data set. By now you know that description is accomplished by recasting original data into graphic, tabular, and statistical representations, and the use of these descriptive tools enables you to make decisions with as much relevant information as possible. A typical situation could involve a company executive faced with making a tough decision. The executive would surely collect all the important data that relate to the pending decision, and with important descriptive information about the data at her disposal (e.g., central tendency, variability, percentile values of scores, etc.), she would presumably be able to make an informed and intelligent decision.

In the following chapters, rather than subjecting experimental data to descriptive analysis simply to wring out all the information the data contain, the focus shall be to use the information produced by the analysis of sample data to reveal characteristics of the population from which the sample data were presumably selected.

For example, let us say a medical researcher wishes to do a simple evaluation of the appetite-suppressing potency of an experimental drug. One approach would be for him to set up two groups of obese individuals (say, 50 per group) to be the subjects in the experiment. One group would receive a daily dosage of a placebo (a tablet with no active ingredient), while the other group would receive a daily dosage of the experimental drug. When the data are evaluated to compare the degree of weight loss for the two groups, the researcher would be interested in more than the behavior of the 100 subjects who actually participated in the experiment. Assuming the design of the experiment is sound and the assignment of subjects to the experimental and control groups was properly handled, the researcher may legitimately infer that the general population of overweight human adults would respond to the appetite suppressant in a manner similar to the experimental subjects. This is the *inferential* aspect of inferential statistics. If we assume that the sample of subjects that actually participates in a study is a representative cross section of the general population, the information derived from the analysis of sample data may be used, by logical inference, to shed light on the characteristics of the general population.

In the chapters that follow, we shall analyze samples that are selected from a variety of different kinds of populations. In some populations only two values will exist (e.g., heads and tails, male and female, etc.), and so samples from these populations can take on only two values. In other populations a wide range of potential values may exist (e.g., measurements of performance skill, the strength of a physiological or behavioral response to a drug, intelligence test scores, etc.), and sample scores selected from these populations may exist within a relatively broad range of values.

IS THIS REALLY NECESSARY?

Under the general heading of statistical inference we shall be examining some fundamentals of experimental design, hypothesis testing, and estimation of population parameters from sample data, and this shall be done within the context of many different experimental scenarios. But if you are to realize the principal objective of the remainder of the text, which is to prepare you both to do and to understand the statistical analysis of experimental data, some preparation is necessary. You must first become familiar with random sampling and the basics of probability theory because an understanding of these topics is essential to understand the logic and procedures that are used in inferential statistics. The very language that is used to set up, execute, and interpret the results of a statistical test is, to a large extent, grounded in the fundamentals of probability.*

INDEPENDENCE AND RANDOMNESS

Before we get into the fundamentals of probability theory there are a few terms that you should be familiar with. The first of these is *independence*.

*Because of the applied emphasis of this text, a great deal of probability theory is beyond our present needs. Perhaps it would be more accurate to call the material in this chapter the basics of the basics.

Independent. When the occurrence or nonoccurrence of one event in no way influences the occurrence or nonoccurrence of another event, the events are independent.

When the occurrence of event A is in no way related to the occurrence of event B, and the occurrence of event B is in no way related to the occurrence of event A, events A and B are said to be **independent.** Symbolically, this may be expressed as

$$P(A/B) = P(A)$$

or

$$P(B/A) = P(B)$$

The top equation is read, "The probability of A occurring, given B has already occurred, equals the probability of A." The bottom equation is read, "The probability of B occurring, given A has already occurred, equals the probability of B." Thus, whether or not B occurs has no effect on whether A will or will not occur, and whether or not B occurs has no effect on whether A will or will not occur.

For example, the outcomes of successive flips of a fair coin are independent from each other because the outcome of one flip has no effect on the outcome of any other flip. Therefore, if you should flip a run of five heads in a row with a fair coin, the probability of a head or tail on the next toss is still .50. The outcomes do not influence each other, and so, after a run of several heads, you are not due for a tail. Failure to understand this is called the *gambler's fallacy*. This is the notion that, after repeatedly sampling *one* possible outcome (say, five heads) when *two* outcomes are supposed to have an equal chance of occurring, you are due for a different outcome (a tail). In fact, if the coin is fair you are no more due a tail than you are due another head.

Similarly, if we assume that a child has an equal chance of being born a male or a female, a woman in her sixth pregnancy who has already given birth to five girls is no more likely to have a boy for her sixth child than she is to have another girl. This is because the determination of the sex of any one child is independent of the determination of the sex of any other child.

Let us use this concept of independence in the definition of another concept, a random sample or **random sampling.**

Random Sampling. Sampling so that each element or group of elements has an equal chance of being included in the sample.

A sample is random only if it is independent from other possible samples and if it is equally likely to be selected.

or, said another way,

A sample from a population is random if every element or group of elements has an equal chance to be included in the sample.

Chances are you were already somewhat familiar with the concept of randomness before reading these formal definitions. State lotteries, games of chance (e.g., roulette), and drawings for door prizes at social gatherings all involve random sampling.

In the conduct of research, the reason that subjects must be assigned randomly to the various groups of an experiment is to avoid bias that may doom the experiment before it is even begun. To illustrate, I'll tell you about Sasha, a laboratory assistant who unintentionally botched a sampling procedure.

Sasha was preparing to do a simple pilot study to test the effects of early rearing environment on adult aggressive behavior among laboratory mice. The first phase of the experiment called for having one group of pregnant female mice give birth in isolation in a small nesting chamber, while a second group would give birth in a much larger and perceptually more complex social chamber together with other mouse "families."

Sasha's job was to divide a group of ten pregnant female mice into the five that would give birth in the isolation chamber and the five that would give birth in the social chamber. Since the animals were already being temporarily housed in the large social chamber, Sasha decided to save himself some work. He caught and removed five relatively docile animals for placement in the isolation condition, and then simply let the five females that managed to avoid capture remain in the social chamber.

Careful consideration of Sasha's work-saving shortcut will reveal that his sampling procedure was not random. Each mouse (or group of mice) did not have an equally likely chance of being assigned to a particular birthing environment. The mice that were relatively easy to catch were assigned to the isolation condition, and the mice that escaped capture were, by default, assigned to the social condition. Had this error not been caught, the potential for bias would have been quite high. For example, whatever traits enabled some females to elude capture (speed, strength, emotionality, intelligence, etc.) could possibly be passed on to their offspring, enabling them to be relatively more successful in aggressive encounters. Thus, the socially reared mice could be more aggressive than the isolation reared mice quite apart from any influence of the rearing environment. One way to assure that the mice would be assigned to the groups in a random manner would be to place their identification codes (usually a tattoo or pattern of ear notches) on slips of paper and randomly draw the ten slips from a container ("One control, one placebo, one control, etc.").

MUTUALLY EXCLUSIVE EVENTS

Mutually Exclusive. If events are related such that the occurrence of one event denies the possibility of the occurrence of the other, the events are mutually exclusive.

When the occurrence of one event denies the possibility of the occurrence of another event, the events are **mutually exclusive.** This may be expressed symbolically:

$$P(A/B) = P(B/A) = 0$$

"The probability of A given B has occurred (or the probability of B given A has occurred) equals zero."

Mutually exclusive events are never independent, since the occurrence or nonoccurrence of one event will enable one to know whether the other event has or has not occurred. For example, when tossing a coin the outcomes heads and tails are mutually exclusive. Both events cannot occur together and, if one outcome occurs, you know the other cannot have occurred. In fact, not only are heads and tails mutually exclusive, they are also exhaustive. If we exclude the remote possibility that the coin will balance on its edge, no other outcome is possible when flipping a coin. Thus, if a coin was tossed and you were told that the outcome was *not* a head, you would, of course, know that it must be a tail. Similarly, when the mother of five girls gave birth to her sixth child and heard her doctor say, "Well, for once it's not a girl!" she knew immediately she had finally given birth to a boy.

Some other mutually exclusive and exhaustive categories include true/false, on/off, locked/unlocked, present/absent, alive/dead, etc.

Having defined the terms independent, random, and mutually exclusive, we are ready to move on to the computation of probability.

PROBABILITY

Probability. The proportion of all possible events that are considered successes:

$$P(\text{success}) = \frac{\text{successes}}{\text{successes} + \text{failures}}$$

Probability, in its most simple representation, can be expressed as follows:

$$\text{Probability} = \frac{\text{the number of favorable outcomes}}{\text{the total number of possible outcomes}}$$

or

$$\text{Probability} = \frac{\text{successes}}{\text{successes} + \text{failures}}$$

From the above you should be able to recognize that probability has a lower limit of zero (when there are no successes) and an upper limit of 1.00 (when all events are successes).* This is because the numerator can equal, but never exceed, the denominator. As an example of these two extremes consider the following.

The Basket

Pretend we have a basket of 100 Ping-Pong balls containing 20 red balls, 30 white balls, and 50 blue balls. In addition to being colored red, white, or blue, each ball in the basket is labelled with a number. Balls 1 to 20 are red, 21 to 50 are white, and 51 to 100 are blue. This basket (hereafter called *the basket*) will be used throughout the chapter as a sampling population for examples. This will prepare you for your encounter with the computer tutorial, PROBGEN.BAS, which has the same format.

If we compute the probability of randomly selecting a black ball from the basket, it must be zero, since the basket contains no black balls. If we compute the probability of selecting a nonblack ball, it must be 1.00, since all the balls in the basket are nonblack. If, instead, we compute the probability of selecting a red ball, we know it must be .20, since, of the 100 balls available for selection, 20 are red and 80 are nonred. The equation becomes

$$P(\text{red}) = \frac{20}{20 + 80} = 0.20$$

Similarly, the probability of selecting a white ball at random is .30 and the probability of selecting a blue ball is .50. Notice that these probability values rest on the assumption that the sampling was random. Any **bias** (inadequate mixing of the balls, peeking in the basket to choose a particular color, etc.) would invalidate these probability values.

Bias. A factor (or factors), other than chance or experimentally controlled variables, capable of influencing the results of an experiment.

Sample Sizes Greater than One

Sampling with versus without Replacement. In the above example only one sample was selected from a population. Often, however, sampling experiments involve taking several samples from a population. When the sample

*Because probability ranges only between 0 and 1.00, it is possible to lose a great deal of precision if probability computations are rounded too severely. When rounding is necessary, it is common to report answers out to four decimal places.

size is greater than one it is important to specify whether the first sample is replaced so that it will be eligible for further selection or whether it will be held apart from the remaining pool of elements. For example, if the question were, "What is the probability of selecting two red balls?" it must be made clear whether the first red ball is to be retained or replaced in the basket before making the second selection. Sampling *with replacement* means that individual samples are restored to the pool of elements eligible for selection. Sampling *without replacement* means that, once selected, samples remain out of the pool. In some types of sampling experiments (e.g., coin flipping and rolling dice) sampling is always with replacement since the same outcomes are always available with each flip of the coin or roll of the dice.

In the above example with the basket of colored balls only one color of the three present in the basket was considered a success. When there is more than one event that is considered a success, when a particular combination of events must occur for a success to be scored, or when the sample size is greater than one, the computation of probability becomes more complex. As pointed out earlier, we shall not get into comprehensive coverage of probability theory in this chapter. We shall, however, deal with the concepts and computational skills you should understand before going on to the topic of hypothesis testing, and these are expressed in the form of rules.

THE ADDITION RULE

If A and B are mutually exclusive events, the probability of obtaining either of them is equal to the probability of A plus the probability of B.

$$P(A \text{ or } B) = P(A) + P(B)$$

If A and B are not mutually exclusive, the probability of obtaining A or B is equal to the probability of A plus the probability of B, minus the probability of their joint occurrence.

$$P(A \text{ or } B) = P(A) + P(B) - P(A + B)$$

The reason for the absence of the "$P(A + B)$" term when A and B are mutually exclusive is that A and B, by definition, cannot occur together if they are mutually exclusive. Some examples using the basket will clarify these rules.

Addition Rule. For mutually exclusive events:

$P(A \text{ or } B) = P(A) + P(B)$.

For nonmutually exclusive events:

$P(A \text{ or } B) = P(A) + P(B) - P(A + B)$.

Notice that the conjunction *or* in the sample questions below is a cue that the **addition rule** should be applied.

Example 1. What is the probability of selecting either a red ball (event A) *or* a white ball (event B) in a single selection from the basket? A and B are mutually exclusive since no ball in the basket is both red and white. Therefore, the computation is

$$\begin{aligned} P(A \text{ or } B) &= P(A) + P(B) \\ &= \frac{20}{100} + \frac{30}{100} \\ &= .50 \end{aligned}$$

Therefore, if this experiment were repeated several times with a full basket of 100 balls (i.e., after a ball is sampled it is put back in the basket and the balls are mixed before the next selection), we would predict that on one-half of the occasions, the ball selected would be red or white.

Example 2. What is the probability of selecting either a red ball *or* a ball labeled with an odd number? If you remember that the 20 red balls were labeled with numbers 1 to 20, you should see that the quality of redness and being labeled with an odd number are *not* mutually exclusive. It is possible for one ball to have both characteristics. (In fact, balls 1, 3, 5, 7, 9, 11, 13, 15, 17, and 19 have both qualities.) Therefore, the computation should be done using the addition rule for nonmutually exclusive events.

$$\begin{aligned} P(A \text{ or } B) &= P(A) + P(B) - P(A + B) \\ &= \frac{20}{100} + \frac{50}{100} - \frac{10}{100} \\ &= .60 \end{aligned}$$

There are 20 red balls (A), 50 balls labeled with an odd number (B), and 10 balls that are both red and labeled with an odd number. If the "$- P(A + B)$" term was not included, the odd-numbered red balls would be counted twice: once as red balls and again as odd-numbered balls. The subtraction enables us to compute the correct number of possible successes (60 out of 100) rather than the 70 out of 100 that would be computed if the lack of mutual exclusivity were not taken into account.

THE MULTIPLICATION RULE

Multiplication Rule. For independent events:

$P(A \text{ and } B) = P(A) \cdot P(B)$.

For nonindependent events:

$P(A \text{ and } B) = P(A) \cdot P(A/B)$.

Just as the conjunction *or* indicated that the addition rule should be applied, the conjunction *and* indicates that the **multiplication rule** should be applied. There are two versions of the multiplication rule. One applies to the case in which A and B are independent, and the other applies to the case in which A and B are not independent.

> **If A and B are independent events, the probability of obtaining both A and B jointly is the product of their probabilities.**

Expressed symbolically,

$$P(A \text{ and } B) = P(A) \cdot P(B)$$

Example 3. What is the probability of selecting two balls from the basket (with replacement) so that the first will be blue and the second will be red? The sampling procedure is to select a ball, record its color, replace the ball in the basket, mix the balls, and select another ball. Since the color of the first ball selected does not influence the possible color of the second ball in any way, the events are independent, and the multiplication rule for independent events should be applied.

$$\begin{aligned} P(A \text{ and } B) &= P(A) \cdot P(B) \\ &= \frac{50}{100} \cdot \frac{20}{100} \\ &= .10 \end{aligned}$$

Therefore, only ten times in 100 tries would one expect to select a blue ball and then a red ball from the basket. Let's apply a very slight rewording to this example in the next problem.

Example 4. What is the probability of selecting a red ball and a blue ball in two selections (with replacement) from the basket? Here, no order is being specified. The red-blue sequence and the blue-red sequence are equally successful outcomes. This must be taken into account in solving the problem.

This problem actually requires the application of both the addition rule and the multiplication rule, and this becomes more obvious if the problem is restated.

In two samples from the basket, what is the probability of selecting a blue ball *and* a red ball *or* selecting a red ball *and* a blue ball? (Assume sampling with replacement.)

The answer may be computed in the following manner:

$$\begin{aligned} P\{(A \text{ and } B) \text{ or } (B \text{ and } A)\} &= P(A \text{ and } B) + P(B \text{ and } A) \\ &= .10 + .10 \\ &= .20 \end{aligned}$$

As you shall see in running PROBGEN.BAS, it is quite common for problems to involve the application of both rules, especially in the highest difficulty level.

Now let us examine the application of the multiplication rule when A and B are not independent. The definition may sound confusing to you, but once we do an example or two you shall see that it isn't nearly as complicated as it may appear. Here is the rule.

> **If *A* and *B* are not independent, the probability of obtaining both *A* and *B* jointly is the product of the probability of obtaining one of these events times the conditional probability of obtaining one event, given that the other event has occurred.**

Symbolically,

$$P(A + B) = P(A) \cdot P(B/A)$$

or

$$P(A + B) = P(B) \cdot P(A/B)$$

Let's apply this rule to a basket sampling problem.

Example 5. What is the probability of selecting two balls from the basket (without replacement) both of which are red? The two events of selecting a red ball are not independent because the probability of selecting the second red ball is influenced by what happens on the first selection. If a red ball is selected in the first sampling attempt, only 19 will remain for the second sampling attempt. The probability of the first red ball would be 20/100, but the probability of the second red ball (given that the first one was red) would be 19/99. As you can see, because we sampled *without* replacement rather than with replacement, the procedure for the solution became more complex.

The solution may be written as follows:

$$P(A \text{ and } B) = P(A) \cdot P(B/A)$$

$$P(A \text{ and } B) = \frac{20}{100} \cdot \frac{19}{99}$$

$$= .0384$$

With this introduction you should be prepared to polish your skills in applying the multiplication and addition rules using PROBGEN.BAS. If you make a mistake you should be able to track it down because the computer will present a step-by-step solution for each problem. After your session within the rather abstract scenario of colored Ping-Pong balls, try the more realistic problems at the end of the chapter. But before you do that, there is one last topic of great importance that relates to probability.

PROBABILITY AND THE NORMAL CURVE

This is really not a new topic because you already know how to answer a great variety of questions about probability and the normal curve. For example, let us say that the piecework production scores of 500 workers at a clothing factory are normally distributed. The average production of the 500 workers is 70 garments per week and the standard deviation of the distribution of production scores is 10. If you select one worker at random out of the 500 employees, what is the probability of choosing a worker that is capable of sewing 85 or more complete garments per week?

You say you haven't learned how to do that yet? If the question is changed somewhat you will recognize the similarity of this question to the kinds of questions you dealt with in chapter 4.

> "What percentage of scores are greater than or equal to 85 in a normal distribution with a mean of 70 and a standard deviation of 10?"

Sound familiar? Some questions we dealt with (as listed in the menu of ZPRAC.BAS) request percentages of area in specific segments of a normal distribution. The proportions upon which these percentages are based may also be regarded as probabilities. Just as probability ranges from zero to 1.00, the proportions of area in various segments of the normal curve can approach zero or 1.00. Because the area under the z distribution equals unity (1.00), and because the proportions listed in the z table can be regarded as probabilities, the techniques for determining proportions of area that you learned with ZPRAC.BAS can be applied to the determination of probabilities. To give another example, the question, "What percentage of the scores in the distribution fall between 60 and 75?" can be changed to, "What is the probability of selecting a score at random from the distribution that will have a value between 60 and 75?"

The more interesting questions, and the ones that relate more specifically to the pending topic of hypothesis testing, combine the rules covered earlier in the chapter with probabilities that are determined with the z statistic. For example, "What is the probability of selecting a sample from the distribution (mean = 70, SD = 10) that is either greater than 89.6 or less than 50.4?"

To solve this problem we must know the proportion of area that exists between the score of 89.6 and the right tail of the distribution, and between the score of 50.4 and the left tail of the distribution (figure 7.1). ZPRAC.BAS (or your hand calculations and z table) will tell you that $z = +1.96$ and $z = -1.96$ for the raw score values of 89.6 and 50.4, and that the proportion of area beyond each of these two values equals .0250.

To get the solution we must apply the addition rule for mutually exclusive events (A score cannot at the same time be less than 50.4 and greater than 89.6.):

$$\begin{aligned} P(A \text{ or } B) &= P(A) + P(B) \\ &= .0250 + .0250 \\ &= .0500 \end{aligned}$$

Thus, the probability is .05 of randomly selecting a score from a normal distribution that is greater than or equal to 1.96 z score units from the mean.

Another possible phrasing of this same question is important for you to understand because of its relevance to the forthcoming topic of hypothesis testing. "What is the probability of selecting a score from the distribution that is as rare or rarer than 50.4?" The key to setting up a solution to this form of the question is recognizing that the score of 89.6 is just as rare as 50.4. The probability of randomly selecting a score equal to or greater than 89.6 equals the probability of randomly selecting a score equal to or less than 50.4 ($P = .0250$).

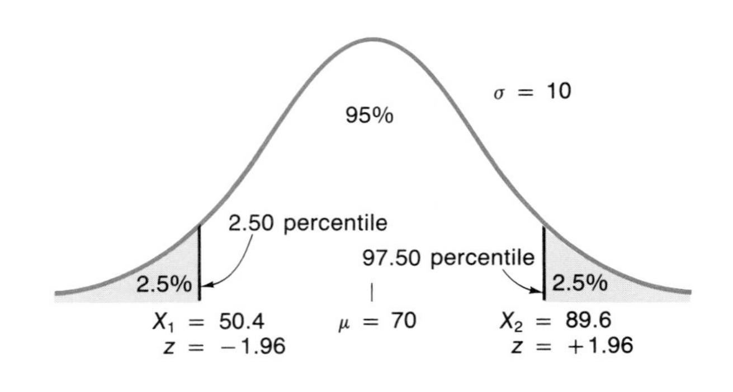

Figure 7.1

The middle 95% of a normal distribution ($\mu = 70$, $\sigma = 10$) is defined by score values that are ± 1.96 standard deviation units from the mean.

Again, as preparation for hypothesis testing, consider these questions: "What are the scores on the high and low end of the distribution beyond which 5% of the area falls?" or, said another way, "How far toward the extremes of the distribution must we go before the scores have a probability of 5% or less of being randomly selected from the distribution?" As shown in figure 7.1, these are the scores on the 2.5 and 97.5 percentiles. The answer, as we know from the earlier example, is 50.4 and 89.6 or, in standard deviation (z score) units, -1.96 and $+1.96$.

Solving for the Probability of Selecting a Specific Value

Earlier, we dealt with the following question:

> In a distribution with a mean of 70 and a standard deviation of 10, what is the probability of selecting at random a score that is greater than or equal to 85?

We may also use the z statistic to solve for the probability of selecting one specific value, such as in the question:

> In a distribution with a mean of 70 and a standard deviation of 10, what is the probability of selecting at random a score that is exactly equal to 85?

To solve this type of problem we must determine the proportion of area within the real limits of the score value. To do this:

1. Determine the limits of the score value.
2. Convert each limit to a z score.
3. Look up each z value in the z table and record the entry in column B. This will be the area between the mean and z for each limit.
4. Subtract the smaller area from the larger area. This yields a segment of area under the curve that is bounded by the real limits of the score value. The area of the segment is the same as the probability of obtaining the score value in a random selection from the distribution.

Let us use this approach to answer the question posed above. For 85 the real limits are 84.5 and 85.5. As shown below, the z score transformations of 84.5 and 85.5 equal 1.45 and 1.55.

$$z = \frac{X - \mu}{\sigma}$$

$$z = \frac{84.5 - 70}{10} \qquad z = \frac{85.5 - 70}{10}$$

$$z = 1.45 \qquad z = 1.55$$

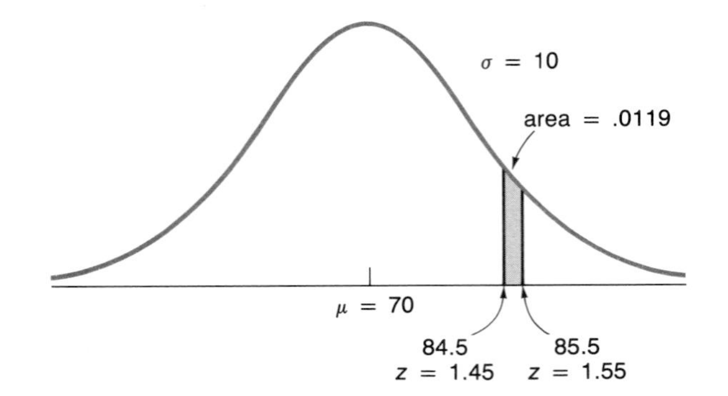

Figure 7.2
The probability of randomly selecting a score from a normal distribution with a mean of 70 and a standard deviation of 10 is the proportion of area between the true limits of the score value. The illustration is for $X = 85$.

From the z table, the column B areas for these z scores are .4265 and .4384. Subtracting the smaller area from the larger area yields a segment with an area of .0119 (figure 7.2). Therefore, the probability of selecting a single score from a distribution with $\mu = 70$ and $\sigma = 10$ that will equal 85 is .0119.

Summary

We learned the concepts of independence, random sampling, and mutually exclusive events and then related these to two basic rules in probability theory: the addition rule and the multiplication rule. We finished the chapter by applying the skills learned earlier in the chapter on the z statistic to the solution of problems of probability that relate to normally distributed variables.

Key Terms

Addition Rule
Bias
Independent
Multiplication Rule
Mutually Exclusive
Probability
Random Sampling

Exercises

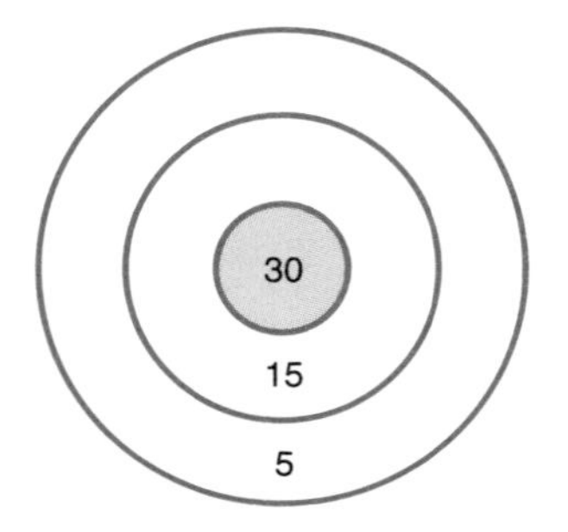

1. A quality control technician with the U.S. Army was assigned to test a shipment of .223 cal. rifle cartridges. Fifty rounds were randomly selected and fired 300 yards from a securely anchored machine-rest test barrel. The results of the test revealed that all fifty shots hit the test target. Thirty hit the target within one inch of dead center, fifteen hit the target outside of one inch but within two inches of dead center, and five shots hit outside of two inches from the center of the target. If another lot of ammunition were manufactured to the exact same specifications as the tested lot and four cartridges were randomly selected and fired, what is the probability that:
   - **a.** all four would strike within one inch of dead center?
   - **b.** at least three out of four would strike within one inch of dead center?
   - **c.** exactly two would strike outside of two inches from dead center?
   - **d.** all four would strike within two inches from dead center?

e. none would strike within one inch of the target center?
f. two would be within one inch, and two would be outside of one inch from the center?
g. at least one shot would be outside of one inch from the center?

2. Sarah has a box containing twenty cookies in a random arrangement. Five of the cookies are chocolate chip and the rest are oatmeal. What is the probability that:
(Hint: sampling is without replacement.)
   a. the first two cookies selected will both be chocolate chip?
   b. either the first cookie or the second (but not both) will be chocolate chip?
   c. at least one of the first three cookies selected will be chocolate chip?
   d. the first three cookies selected will be oatmeal?
3. A basket contains 20 red balls, 15 white balls, and 25 blue balls. If sampling is done with replacement, what is the probability that:
   a. if three balls are selected at least one will be red and none will be white?
   b. if two balls are selected neither will be blue?
   c. if three balls are selected exactly two out of three will be blue?
   d. if three balls are selected at least two will be blue and none will be white?
4. Ralph has twenty tickets to the fourth game of the World Series to give to some of his customers. Four of the seats are top-notch box seats, and the other sixteen are in the grandstand. Ralph decided to invite his twenty best customers to a drawing so that the ticket assignment to each customer will be purely random. Under these circumstances what is the probability that: (Hint: sampling is without replacement.)
   a. the first two tickets selected will both be box seats?
   b. either the first or the second ticket selected (but not both) will be box seats?
   c. at least one of the first three tickets selected will be a box seat?
5. A slot machine (one-armed bandit) has three windows, and the wheels behind each window contain pictures of the following fruits and vegetables: an ear of corn, a lemon, an apple, a banana, a pear, a cucumber, and a head of lettuce. If you insert a coin and pull the lever to spin the wheels, when the wheels stop spinning what is the probability that:
   a. all three wheels will stop with a lemon displayed in the windows?
   b. all the windows will contain pictures of vegetables?
   c. all the windows will contain pictures of fruits?
   d. the left window will contain a picture of a fruit and the other two windows will contain pictures of vegetables?
   e. any two windows will contain pears and the third window will contain the picture of a vegetable?
   f. at least two windows will contain pictures of fruits?
   g. at least one window will contain a picture of a vegetable?
   h. two fruits and a vegetable will appear without regard to order?
   i. at least one cucumber will appear?
   j. an ear of corn, a cucumber, and a head of lettuce will appear without regard to order?
   k. no window will contain a picture of an ear of corn?
   l. no window will contain an apple or a lemon?
   m. any one window will contain a banana and the other two will contain pictures of vegetables?

6. The expression $P(A/B) = A$ ("The probability of A given that B has occurred equals the probability of B.") means that A and B are
   a. mutually exclusive
   b. correlated
   c. independent
   d. a and c
7. The expression $P(A/B) = 0$ ("The probability of A given that B has occurred equals zero.") means that events A and B are
   a. mutually exclusive
   b. correlated
   c. independent
   d. a and c
8. When maintained under carefully controlled laboratory conditions, the average lifespan of a particular strain of mouse is 52 months. The standard deviation of the distribution of longevity scores is four. If a young mouse is selected at random from the colony, what is the probability that:
   a. it will live at least 55 months?
   b. it will die on or before it reaches the age of 50 months?
   c. it will live between 53 and 56 months before it dies?
   d. it will live at least four years?
9. If two mice are selected at random from the colony described in the preceding question, what is the probability that:
   a. both mice will live as long or longer than 54 months?
   b. neither mouse will live as long or longer than 52 months?
   c. one mouse will die on or before the age of 48 months, but the other mouse will live beyond the age of 56 months?
   d. one mouse or the other, but not both, will live to be at least 57 months old?

Supplement these exercises by working with the PROBGEN.BAS computer tutorial. To test your understanding of probability theory try your own solution to the computer-generated problems before displaying the step-by-step solution.

CHAPTER 8

The Binomial Distribution

It was easy to see on this particular Monday morning as I stood before my statistics class preparing to lecture on the binomial distribution, that Maurice was all smiles. I remember thinking at the time, "Surely his joy cannot be due to the anticipation of learning about the binomial distribution." By the end of the class Maurice was more subdued, but not because he found the lecture difficult. Here is what happened as related to me by Maurice, a so-called nontraditional student who decided to earn a B.A. degree twenty-three years following his graduation from high school.

Over the previous weekend Maurice's teenaged son, Claude, a senior in high school, was immersed in filling out applications to colleges. After careful reading of various school catalogs and reference books, he had narrowed the possible choices down to five schools. Though Claude's choices were all fine schools that had strengths well-matched to his interests, they were all relatively difficult to get into. In fact, Claude's research revealed that even for students with his above average qualifications (S.A.T. scores, high school grades, etc.) each of these high caliber schools sent letters of acceptance to only 30% of the qualified applicants.

With understandable concern, Claude asked his father, "What do you think my chances are of getting into at least one of these schools if they only take in 30% of applicants with my level of academic achievement?" A week earlier Maurice would have thought of something encouraging to say to his son, and he would have let it go at that. Now, however, Maurice knew some basic probability theory. He had just done very well on the probability examination, and he felt well-qualified to answer his son's question in a very precise manner. So, with a broad gesture and a clearing of his throat, he put down the evening paper and said, "What we have here is an application of the multiplication rule for independent events." Claude, to his credit as a respectful son, sat through the entire explanation, and now you will too.

MAURICE'S EXPLANATION

Maurice explained to his son that when you apply for admission to a college there are two possible outcomes: you can get accepted or rejected. The probability of acceptance to any one of the five schools is, according to Claude's research, .30, and the probability of rejection is .70. With this information Maurice thought he could figure out a probability for each possible outcome, from the extreme of not getting into any of the schools to getting into one, two, three, four, or all five of the colleges. Maurice's first project was to figure out the probability that Claude wouldn't get into any of the five colleges. Remember, P(acceptance) = .30 and P(rejection) = .70, so the probability of getting rejected by all five colleges, according to the multiplication rule for independent events, may be computed as follows:

$$(.7)(.7)(.7)(.7)(.7) = .1681$$

Similarly, the probability of getting into only one college is

$$(.7)(.7)(.7)(.7)(.3) = .0720$$

The probability of getting into two colleges is

$$(.7)(.7)(.7)(.3)(.3) = .0309$$

The probability of getting into three colleges is

$$(.7)(.7)(.3)(.3)(.3) = .0132$$

The probability of getting into four colleges is

$$(.7)(.3)(.3)(.3)(.3) = .0057$$

The probability of getting into all five colleges is

$$(.3)(.3)(.3)(.3)(.3) = .0024$$

Table 8.1

The five patterns that involve the outcome of one acceptance.

	Colleges				
	1	2	3	4	5
Patterns					
1	ACCEPT	reject	reject	reject	reject
2	reject	ACCEPT	reject	reject	reject
3	reject	reject	ACCEPT	reject	reject
4	reject	reject	reject	ACCEPT	reject
5	reject	reject	reject	reject	ACCEPT

Table 8.2

The thirty-two possible patterns for acceptance (A) and rejection (R) for Claude's applications to five colleges.

Acceptances					
0	1	2	3	4	5
RRRRR	ARRRR	AARRR	AAARR	AAAAR	AAAAA
	RARRR	ARARR	AARAR	AAARA	
	RRARR	ARRAR	ARAAR	AARAA	
	RRRAR	ARRRA	RAAAR	ARAAA	
	RRRRA	RAARR	AARRA	RAAAA	
		RARAR	ARARA		
		RARRA	RAARA		
		RRAAR	ARRAA		
		RRARA	RARAA		
		RRRAA	RRAAA		

Now, just to check, Maurice added up all these probabilities to make sure they summed to 1.00. They did not. They summed to .2556. He knew that unless the sum of the probabilities is 1.00, some possible results of Claude's college search were not being considered. It took Maurice a while to figure out his mistake, but he did. He eventually realized that some outcomes can occur in more than one way. For example, getting into only one of the five colleges can occur in five different ways because any one of the five colleges could be the only one that would send a letter of acceptance. The possible patterns consistent with the result of getting accepted to one college are presented in table 8.1.

Maurice systematically enumerated all the possible ways in which each of the six possible outcomes could occur and listed them by outcome just as you see in table 8.2.

At last Maurice was in good shape to compute the probabilities for all the outcomes that could occur in more than one way (1, 2, 3, and 4 acceptances). For the outcome of one acceptance he first found the probability for each individual result (say, ARRRR = $.3 \times .7 \times .7 \times .7 \times .7 = .0720$), then he correctly reasoned, using the addition rule for mutually exclusive events, that since patterns 1 (ARRRR) or 2 (RARRR) or 3 (RRARR) or 4 (RRRAR) or 5 (RRRRA) were equally successful for the outcome of one success, the probabilities should be added. Thus, the probability for one acceptance is the sum of the probabilities for each successful pattern ($.0720 + .0720 + .0720 + .0720 + .0720 = .3600$). He applied the same reasoning for the outcomes that involved 2, 3, or 4 successes and came up with the following probability distribution for Claude's inspection.

	Acceptances					
	0	1	2	3	4	5
Probability =	.1681	.3600	.3090	.1320	.0285	.0024

To Maurice's delight, these probabilities summed to 1.00, and he confidently handed Claude the distribution of probabilities for each possible outcome of the application process. He pointed out to his son that if, indeed, the probability is .30 of getting accepted to any one of the five colleges, the probability of getting into at least one college is the sum of the probabilities of all the outcomes that involve one or more acceptances:

$$.3600 + .3090 + .1320 + .0285 + .0024 = .8319.$$

Another approach would be to subtract the probability of no acceptances from 1.00. The probability of no acceptances equals .1681, and $1.00 - .1681 = .8319$.

Maurice was saving a report on his achievement for a collegiate version of show-and-tell, which often was held during the closing minutes of statistics class on Mondays. (Instructor: "If any of you have used or encountered statistics or statistical reasoning over the past week, please share your experience with the class.") By the end of the class, however, he realized that he had done a great deal of unnecessary work. Maurice learned during that class that the probability distribution he so patiently worked out can be found in seconds in a binomial table.

After we examine the basic elements of the binomial expansion and the binomial table, we will come back to this problem to appreciate how easily Maurice could have answered his son's question had he been familiar with the use of the binomial table.

THE BINOMIAL DISTRIBUTION

A binomial population exists when a sample from a population can take on only two values (on/off, right/wrong, male/female, accept/reject, etc.). In statistical terms we say that the two possible values in a binomial population are mutually exclusive and exhaustive. Sample values are mutually exclusive when they cannot coexist (e.g., A switch cannot be on and off at the same time.), and the sample values are exhaustive when no other results are possible (i.e., There is no other position for a switch besides on or off.).

Each of the two possible sample values in a binomial distribution has a probability of occurring, and the two probabilities must sum to 1.00. In Maurice's situation, if an acceptance is defined as a success and a rejection is defined as a failure, $P(\text{success}) = .3$ and $P(\text{failure}) = .7$, and, naturally, $.3 + .7 = 1.00$. In notation, the probability of a success is designated with the letter P, and the probability of a failure is designated with the letter Q. Thus, for the present example, $P = .3$ and $Q = .7$.

Coin flipping is commonly used to represent sampling from a binomial population. Only two results are possible (heads vs. tails), and the two outcomes are mutually exclusive and exhaustive. Heads cannot coexist with tails, and, if we exclude the possibility that a coin may land on its edge, no other result is possible besides heads and tails when a coin is flipped. Thus, every time we flip a fair coin and record the result we have, in effect, sampled from a binomial population for which $P(\text{Head}) = .50$ and $P(\text{Tail}) = .50$.

If we draw N samples from a binomial population (e.g., if we flip a coin N times), there are $N + 1$ outcomes that are possible and 2^N ways of getting those outcomes. This can be seen in a simple enumeration of all the possible results of flipping a coin. For example, in five flips of a coin ($N = 5$), thirty-two patterns are possible ($2^N = 32$). As shown in table 8.3, the thirty-two patterns fall into six outcome categories ($N + 1 = 6$), which are 0, 1, 2, 3, 4, or 5 heads. (The focus on heads is arbitrary. We could just as easily have focused on tails.)

Each of the six possible outcomes (no heads, 1, 2, 3, 4, or 5 heads) has a distinct probability of occurring, and, since all possible results of flipping a coin five times are included in the enumeration, the six probabilities will sum to 1.00.

To compute the probability for each of the thirty-two different result patterns, we must apply the multiplication rule for independent events. Thus, the probability for all heads is $.5 \times .5 \times .5 \times .5 \times .5 = .03125$. The probability of obtaining one head is also .03125 for each of the five different patterns that result in the occurrence of one head. Applying the addition rule for mutually exclusive events, we can add the five probabilities for each of

Table 8.3

The thirty-two possible patterns (H = heads, T = tails) when a coin is flipped five times and the number (i.e., frequency) of patterns that fall into each of the six possible outcome categories.

	Outcome					
	No Heads	1 Head	2 Heads	3 Heads	4 Heads	5 Heads
	TTTTT	HTTTT	HHTTT	HHHTT	HHHHT	HHHHH
		THTTT	HTHTT	HHTHT	HHHTH	
		TTHTT	HTTHT	HTHHT	HHTHH	
		TTTHT	HTTTH	THHHT	HTHHH	
		TTTTH	THHTT	HHTTH	THHHH	
			THTHT	HTHTH		
			THTTH	THHTH		
			TTHHT	HTTHH		
			TTHTH	THTHH		
			TTTHH	TTHHH		
Frequency	1	5	10	10	5	1

the five patterns (P(HTTTT) = .03125, P(THTTT) = .03125, etc.), and they sum to .1562. Applying the same procedure to all the patterns within each of the $N + 1$ outcomes will yield the binomial sampling distribution for $N = 5$ and $P = Q = .5$. Here it is.

no heads	0.0313
1 head	0.1562
2 heads	0.3125
3 heads	0.3125
4 heads	0.1562
5 heads	0.0313

Notice that the six individual probabilities sum to 1.00.

THE BINOMIAL TABLE

There is a way to get the same distribution of probability values without the cumbersome job of enumerating all the possible outcome patterns—by using a binomial table. This is fortunate, because even with as few as ten flips there

Table 8.4

The section of the binomial table for $N = 5$.

# P or Q Events	Probability Values for *P* or *Q*									
	.05	.10	.15	.20	.25	.30	.35	.40	.45	.50
0	.7738	.5905	.4437	.3277	.2373	.1681	.1160	.0778	.0503	.0312
1	.2036	.3280	.3915	.4096	.3955	.3602	.3124	.2592	.2059	.1562
2	.0214	.0729	.1382	.2048	.2637	.3087	.3364	.3456	.3369	.3125
3	.0011	.0081	.0244	.0512	.0879	.1323	.1811	.2304	.2757	.3125
4	.0000	.0004	.0022	.0064	.0146	.0284	.0488	.0768	.1128	.1562
5	.0000	.0000	.0001	.0003	.0010	.0024	.0053	.0102	.0185	.0312

would be 2^N or 1024 different patterns to enumerate with each pattern consisting of ten flips (e.g., HHTTHHHTHT). Needless to say, there would be mass confusion and a great deal of effort expended if the above approach were followed.

The first task in using the binomial table is to find the section of the table with the appropriate value for N. Here, for convenience, the entire section of the table for $N = 5$ is reproduced in table 8.4. (The entire binomial table up to the case for $N = 20$ may be found in Appendix A.)

The second task is to locate the appropriate column for P (the probability of a success) or Q (the probability of a failure). If P is less than or equal to .50, as it is for this problem, we must use the column in the table headed with the P value for the problem. (If the ***P* value** is greater than .5, we must use the ***Q* value,** but that type of problem will be covered later.) Here is the distribution from the table for the above coin flipping example ($P = .5$, $Q = .5$, $N = 5$).

***P* value.** The probability that the event defined as a success will occur in a sampling experiment.

***Q* value.** The probability that the event defined as a failure will occur in a sampling experiment.

# of *P* Events	***P* = .50**
0 Heads	.0312
1 Head	.1562
2 Heads	.3125
3 Heads	.3125
4 Heads	.1562
5 Heads	.0312

To find the probabilities that relate to Maurice's problem, since $P = .30$, we must use the column headed .30 in table 8.4. Comparing the tabled values to Maurice's hand computations shows them to be nearly identical. The discrepancies are due only to insignificant rounding error. Here is the distribution from the table when $P = .3$:

# of *P* Events	$P = .30$
0 Acceptances	.1681
1 Acceptance	.3602
2 Acceptances	.3087
3 Acceptances	.1323
4 Acceptances	.0284
5 Acceptances	.0024

WHERE DO THE VALUES IN THE BINOMIAL TABLE COME FROM? THE BINOMIAL EXPANSION

Binomial Expansion. The expansion of the expression $(P + Q)^N$. Each of the $N+1$ terms in the expansion yields a probability, and all the probabilities sum to 1.00.

The probability values that are listed in the binomial table are computed from a mathematical expression called the **binomial expansion.** Even though, in practice, you shall find the probabilities you need to solve a binomial problem in the binomial table rather than through hand computations, you may wish to read through the following optional section that explains the derivation of the values in the table.

To illustrate how the probabilities for 0, 1, 2, 3, 4, and 5 successes may be derived using the binomial expansion, we shall do the appropriate expansion for Maurice's problem ($N = 5$, $P = .3$, and $Q = .7$). Do not be intimidated by the appearance of the formula that follows. The expansion may appear to be complex, but once the orderliness of the computations is explained, it should make sense to you. Before we fill in the values for Maurice's problem, let us first look at the expansion for $N = 5$ in its general form.

$$(P + Q)^5 = P^5 + \frac{N}{1}P^4Q + \frac{N(N-1)}{1 \cdot 2}P^3Q^2 + \frac{N(N-1)(N-2)}{1 \cdot 2 \cdot 3}P^2Q^3 + \ldots$$

$$\ldots + \frac{N(N-1)(N-2))\,(N-3)}{1 \cdot 2 \cdot 3 \cdot 4}PQ^4 + Q^5$$

Notice that the exponent of the P term starts at N and is diminished for each term (5, 4, 3, 2, 1, 0). P raised to the zero power (P^0) is omitted from the last term of the expansion since it must equal 1.00. Similarly, the exponent on the Q term climbs from zero in the first term to five in the last term. As was true for P^0, Q^0 is omitted from the first term since it equals 1.00 and would contribute nothing to the value of the first term.

The last orderly pattern resides in the binomial coefficients. These are the terms that come before the P and Q entries. The numerator starts at N and progresses to $N(N-1)$ then to $N(N-1)(N-2)$, etc., while the denominator starts at 1, then changes to $1 \cdot 2$, $1 \cdot 2 \cdot 3$, etc. These *binomial coefficients* represent the number of patterns that can result in each of the $N+1$ outcomes. No successes and all successes will always have a coefficient of 1.00, since these patterns can occur in only one way. In this example, the solution to the coefficients is 1, 5, 10, 10, 5, 1, and they correspond to the frequencies seen in the enumeration patterns presented in table 8.3 for $N = 5$. Taken together, the sum of the coefficients will always equal 2^N. Here, 2^5 equals 32 as does $1 + 5 + 10 + 10 + 5 + 1$.

In the present example, since $N = 5$, there are $N + 1 = 6$ separate terms, and the solutions of the six expressions yield the $N + 1$ probabilities that make up the binomial distribution for specific P and Q values. Solutions of the binomial expansion for various P (or Q) values (from .05 to .50) are listed in the binomial table.

Now let us solve the expansion that relates to Maurice's problem. To do this we must substitute the values $P = .3$, $Q = .7$, and $N = 5$ in the expansion as shown in table 8.5. This expansion yields the probabilities for obtaining each one of the $N + 1 = 6$ possible outcomes, from all successes (the P^N term on the left side of the expansion) to no successes (the Q^N term on the right side of the expansion). The same six probability values for 5, 4, 3, 2, 1, or 0 successes are listed in the binomial table in the section for $N = 5$ and in the column headed $P = .3$. Once the probabilities for all six possible outcomes have been computed, the probability of getting into "at least one of the colleges" or "one or more of the colleges" may be found either by adding the probabilities of 1 acceptance, 2 acceptances, 3 acceptances, 4 acceptances, and 5 acceptances:

$$P(\text{at least 1 acceptance}) = .3602 + .3087 + .1323 + .0284 + .0024$$
$$= .8320$$

Table 8.5

This is the solution to the binomial expansion, $(P + Q)^5$, when $P = .30$ and $Q = .70$. The six values shown are the probabilities for Claude's getting accepted to 5, 4, 3, 2, 1, or no colleges if the probability of his getting accepted to any one college is .30.

Acceptances					
5	4	3	2	1	0
$.3^5 +$	$\frac{5}{1}.3^4 \cdot .7 +$	$\frac{5 \cdot 4}{1 \cdot 2}.3^3 \cdot .7^2 +$	$\frac{5 \cdot 4 \cdot 3}{1 \cdot 2 \cdot 3}.3^2 \cdot .7^3 +$	$\frac{5 \cdot 4 \cdot 3 \cdot 2}{1 \cdot 2 \cdot 3 \cdot 4}.3 \cdot .7^4 +$	$.7^5$
$.3^5 +$	$5(.3^4 \cdot .7) +$	$10(3^3 \cdot .7^2) +$	$10(.3^2 \cdot .7^3) +$	$5(.3 \cdot .7^4) +$	$.7^5$
.0024 +	.0284 +	.1323 +	.3087 +	.3602 +	.1681

Table 8.6

This is the solution to the binomial expansion, $(P + Q)^5$, when $P = Q = .50$. The $N + 1 = 6$ probabilities listed are, from left to right, for 5, 4, 3, 2, 1, or zero successes when the outcome "Heads" is defined as a success.

Heads										
5		4		3		2		1		0
$.5^5$	+	$\frac{5}{1}.5^4 \cdot .5$	+	$\frac{5 \cdot 4}{1 \cdot 2}.5^3 \cdot .5^2$	+	$\frac{5 \cdot 4 \cdot 3}{1 \cdot 2 \cdot 3}.5^2 \cdot .5^3$	+	$\frac{5 \cdot 4 \cdot 3 \cdot 2}{1 \cdot 2 \cdot 3 \cdot 4}.5 \cdot .5^4$	+	$.5^5$
$.5^5$	+	$5(.5^4 \cdot .5)$	+	$10(5^3 \cdot .5^2)$	+	$10(.5^2 \cdot .5^3)$	+	$5(.5 \cdot .5^4)$	+	$.5^5$
.0312	+	.1562	+	.3125	+	.3125	+	.1562	+	.0312

or by subtracting the one possible failure (no acceptance to any college) from 1.00:

$$
\begin{aligned}
P(\text{at least 1 acceptance}) &= 1 - P(\text{no acceptances}) \\
&= 1 - .1681 \\
&= .8319
\end{aligned}
$$

The difference in the two answers (.8320 vs. .8319) is due to slight rounding error.

Similarly, if we solve the expansion for $P = .5$, $Q = .5$, $N = 5$ to determine the probabilities that relate to the coin tossing example discussed earlier (table 8.6), we shall get the same values shown in the section of the binomial table for $N = 5$ in the column headed $P = .5$.

MAURICE: AN EPILOGUE

I guess you can appreciate now why Maurice was more subdued by the end of the class. He found out that his solution to Claude's problem involved a great deal of unnecessary work, and he interpreted this as an error on his part. Of course it might have been more elegant to use the binomial expansion or, better yet, the binomial table, but the mastery of the addition and multiplication rules that Maurice demonstrated when he initially solved the problem was impressive, especially for a student with a minimum of mathematical background.

In summary, when a probability problem involves the possible occurrence of two mutually exclusive and exhaustive events, we may solve for the probability of the occurrence of any quantity of successes (from zero to

$N + 1$) by entering the binomial table with the value for N, locating the column headed by the appropriate probability value, and finding the row(s) that equal the quantity of successes stated in the problem.

THE BINOM.BAS PROGRAM

With the BINOM.BAS computer tutorial you will have the opportunity to review much of the foregoing information using a somewhat different format, and, in the problem-solving section of the tutorial, you will be able to practice using the binomial table to solve problems. You may recall the recommendation at the end of the last chapter that you do some problems in the abstract (the Ping-Pong ball scenario) before tackling the more realistic set of problems, which follow the chapter in the exercises section. That is also the recommendation here. But before you try the tutorial, we should first step through a couple of sample problems that mimic the tutorial format.

First, as promised earlier, we shall do a problem for which P, the probability of a success, is greater than .50. The following example will acquaint you with the proper use of the binomial table in this $P > .50$ situation as well as with the Ping-Pong ball scenario used in BINOM.BAS.

BINOM.BAS Sample Problem 1.

A basket contains 20 balls, 6 of which are black and 14 of which are white.

In 5 selections from the basket (sampling with replacement) what is the probability of selecting at least 4 white balls?

Our first task is to identify the problem as one that requires the use of the binomial. Initially, the problem may not appear to relate to the binomial because there are 20 separate balls in the basket. The appearance is that there are 20 rather than two possible results in a single sample from the basket. On one level this is true, but not when we focus only on the color of the sample ball. When color alone is considered, only two mutually exclusive and exhaustive results are possible: a black ball or a white ball. $P(\text{white}) = .7$ because 14 of the 20 balls are white, and $P(\text{black}) = .3$ because 6 of the 20 balls are black. Since $N = 5$, we may use the same section of the table that was used above for Maurice's problem (*see* table 8.4).

The successes as defined in the problem are 4 white balls and 5 white balls. This is because both these outcomes satisfy the requirement of "at least 4 white balls." Notice, however, that there is no listing in the table for $P = .70$. Therefore, we must mentally turn the problem around as follows:

What is the probability of selecting one or less than one black ball?

One black ball is really the same outcome as 4 white balls, and no black balls is really the same outcome as 5 white balls. Using the column headed $Q = .30$, we can find the probabilities we need for the solution in the 0 row and the 1 row. The probabilities are .1681 (for 0 black balls) and .3602 (for 1 black ball). Since both these outcomes are successes, the addition rule mandates that they be added. The answer to the problem is .5283. This is the probability of randomly selecting 5 balls from the container of 14 white and 6 black balls (with replacement) and getting at least 4 white balls.

BINOM.BAS Sample Problem 2.

A basket contains 20 balls, 5 of which are black and 15 of which are white.

> **In 5 selections from the basket (sampling with replacement) what is the probability of selecting more than 2 black balls?**

The successes as defined in the problem are 3, 4, or 5 black balls. The outcome "2 black balls" is not a success because the problem specifically states "*more* than 2 black balls." The probability of a success (a black ball), on any single selection is found by solving the ratio of the number of possible successes to the total number of successes plus failures. There are 5 black balls (successes) and 20 total balls (successes plus failures = 5 black balls plus 15 white balls = 20 total balls). Thus, P, the probability of selecting a black ball, equals $5/20 = .25$.

Since $N = 5$, we may again use the segment of the binomial table shown in table 8.4. The probabilities for 3, 4, and 5 black balls may be found in the "# of P or Q events" rows labeled 3, 4, and 5 and in the column headed by the P value of .25. The values are .0879, .0146, and .0010. Since all three outcomes are successes, we must add these probabilities to arrive at the answer. The events are mutually exclusive because a ball cannot be both black and white at the same time, and so from the addition rule covering mutually exclusive events we see that:

$$\begin{aligned} P(A \text{ or } B \text{ or } C) &= P(A) + P(B) + P(C) \\ P(3 \text{ or } 4 \text{ or } 5 \text{ black balls}) &= .0879 + .0146 + .0010 \\ &= .1035 \end{aligned}$$

In summary, the probability of selecting more than 2 black balls (with replacement) from a basket that contains 5 black balls and 15 white balls is .1035.

THE z APPROXIMATION TO THE BINOMIAL DISTRIBUTION

Abner's Problem

Abner runs a successful flower and shrub nursery as well as a plant science consulting firm. One day, as he was preparing to sow some very expensive and exotic seed, he noticed a message printed on a package of thirty seeds that said "Notice: Only 50% Germination." For reasons having to do with cost projections and the efficient use of greenhouse space, he wanted to know the probability that eighteen or more of these seeds would germinate. His first thought was to look for the answer in the binomial table. He correctly reasoned that once he found the probabilities of eighteen or more successes in the section of the table for $N = 30$ and $P = .5$, all he would have to do is add them to get the solution. Unfortunately, Abner's table, like ours, did not go as high as $N = 30$.

The binomial distribution is appropriate for solving this problem because germination either occurs or it doesn't, and germination and the failure of germination are mutually exclusive events. But Abner knew that unless he could find a comprehensive binomial table that presented the probabilities for N as large as thirty, using a binomial table would not be an option for solving his problem. He thought of solving the binomial expansion $(P + Q)^{30}$, but immediately decided he was not that anxious to know the answer!

z approximation to the binomial distribution. The use of the z statistic to estimate proportions of area under segments of the binomial distribution. The sample size must be greater than twenty for a reasonable approximation and greater than thirty for a good approximation.

There is an approach to Abner's problem that does not require the use of a binomial table. It is called the **z approximation to the binomial distribution.** The sketch in figure 8.1 ($N = 20$, $P = Q = .5$) should help you to grasp on an intuitive level why a smooth curve such as the z distribution can be used to approximate a probability histogram. In figure 8.1 you shall notice the smooth progression of the curve connecting the midpoints of the histogram bars in comparison to the stepwise progression of the histogram bars themselves. The smooth curve does not enclose all the area bounded by the histogram bars. The outer corners of each bar are above rather than below the smooth curve, and so are left out of any calculation of area under the smooth curve.

Thus, whenever the proportion of area in a segment of a normal distribution is used to approximate the proportion of area in a segment of a histogram, some inaccuracy is inevitable. The amount of error changes with the sample size. The larger the sample size becomes, the smoother the frequency polygon becomes that connects the midpoints of the histogram bars.

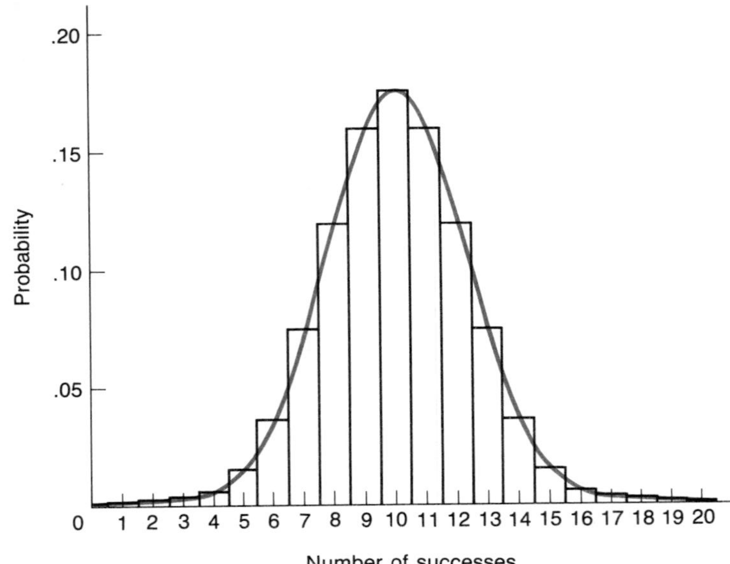

Figure 8.1

The probability histogram of the binomial expansion when $P = Q = .50$ and $N = 20$ shown together with a smooth curve approximation.

For comparison purposes, the probability histogram for a relatively small sample size is presented in figure 8.2 ($P = .5$ and $N = 5$). Notice how the change in probability values from outcome to outcome takes place in a much less gradual manner compared to figure 8.1 and how, with this relatively small sample size ($N = 5$), much more of the histogram bars are on the outside of the line connecting the midpoints of the bars than is the case for figure 8.1. For sample sizes greater than twenty, the amount of error inherent in the z approximation is tolerable, and for sample sizes greater than thirty, the amount of error is quite negligible, especially if an adjustment called the **correction for discontinuity** is incorporated into the z formula. The formula for the z approximation is

Correction for Discontinuity. A correction that is applied to improve accuracy when the distribution of the z statistic is used to approximate the distribution of the binomial.

$$z = \frac{x \pm .5 - N \cdot P}{\sqrt{N \cdot P \cdot Q}}$$

where N is the sample size, P is the probability of a success, Q is the probability of a failure, x is the outcome (i.e., the number of successes) for which the probability is sought, and plus or minus .5 is the correction for discontinuity. The .5 is *added* to x if the frequency value for x is less than the $N \cdot P$ product and .5 is *subtracted* from x if x is less than $N \cdot P$. If this formula is compared to the z formula we used in chapter 4,

$$z = \frac{X - \mu}{\sigma}$$

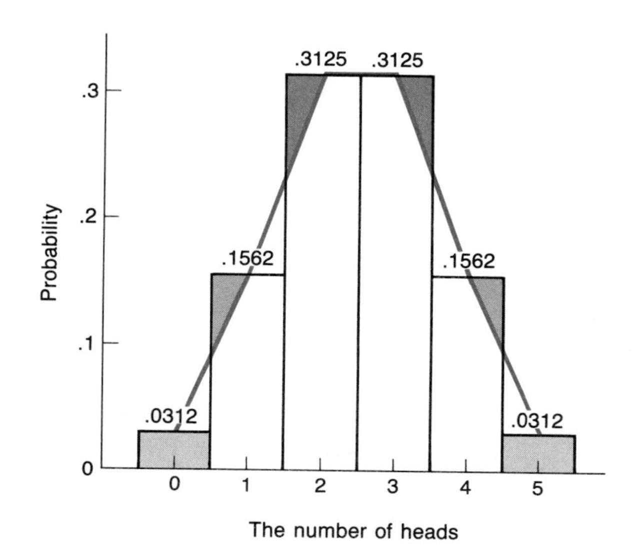

Figure 8.2

The probability histogram and approximating curve for the expansion of $(P+Q)^N$ where $P = Q = .5$ and $N = 5$. The solution of the expansion yields the probabilities for the 6 possible outcomes when a coin is tossed 5 times. The shaded areas are included in the bars but are not under the curve.

it becomes apparent that the $N \cdot P$ term is really estimating μ, and the square root of $N \cdot P \cdot Q$ is estimating σ.

Solving Abner's Problem

For the problem of seed germination, the formula would be completed as follows:

$$z = \frac{18 - .5 - (30 \cdot .5)}{\sqrt{30 \cdot .5 \cdot .5}}$$

$$z = \frac{17.5 - 15}{\sqrt{7.5}}$$

$$z = \frac{2.5}{2.74} = .91$$

The outcome of 18 successes (adjusted to 17.5 to correct for discontinuity) is then treated as a score in a normal distribution that has a mean of 15 and a standard deviation of 2.74. Once 17.5 is located in this distribution ($z = .91$), all that remains is to look up $z = .91$ in the z table and determine the proportion of area beyond z (column C).

Reference to the z table reveals that the proportion of area beyond a z value of .91 is .1814. Thus, as illustrated in figure 8.3, when P(germination) $= .50$, the approximate probability of 18 or more of the 30 seeds germinating equals .1814. This compares favorably with the exact probability of .1808 computed using the binomial expansion.

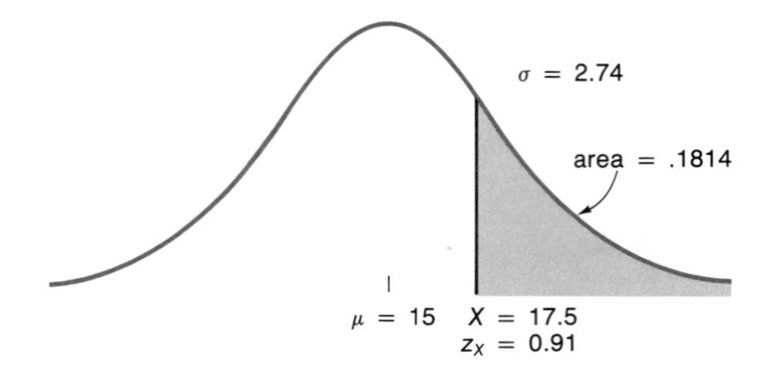

Figure 8.3

The use of the z approximation to determine the probability of 18 or more successes in a binomial sampling experiment when $N = 30$ and $P(\text{success}) = .50$. The correction for discontinuity (18 reduced to 17.5) is included.

SOLVING FOR THE PROBABILITY OF A SPECIFIC OUTCOME

Let us assume Abner wished to know the probability of *exactly* eighteen seeds germinating (rather than eighteen or more). To determine this probability we shall employ the same method discussed in chapter 7 (p. 159) that we used to determine the probability of obtaining a specific value when sampling from a normally distributed population. Using this method we computed the proportion of area under the normal curve that was located between the two real limits of a particular score value. In the present case, the score value is the outcome of eighteen successes, and the lower and upper real limits of eighteen are 17.5 and 18.5.

For estimating the probability of a specific outcome we can safely ignore the correction for discontinuity. As shown in figure 8.4, the estimation error will be minimal because the extra area that is between $x = 17.5$ and $x = 18.5$ of the smooth curve, but is not contained within the histogram bar, is just about equal to the area above the smooth curve, which is within the histogram bar but is left out of the smooth curve approximation. By substituting in the z formula we find

Lower limit:

$$z = \frac{\text{lower limit} - N \cdot P}{\sqrt{N \cdot P \cdot Q}}$$

$$z = \frac{17.5 - (30 \cdot .5)}{\sqrt{30 \cdot .5 \cdot .5}}$$

$$z = \frac{2.50}{2.74} = 0.91$$

Upper limit:

$$z = \frac{\text{upper limit} - N \cdot P}{\sqrt{N \cdot P \cdot Q}}$$

$$z = \frac{18.5 - (30 \cdot .5)}{\sqrt{30 \cdot .5 \cdot .5}}$$

$$z = \frac{3.50}{2.74} = 1.28$$

To find the area in the segment of the normal curve between $z = 0.91$ and $z = 1.28$ we shall use the same method employed earlier in chapters 4 and 7. We must subtract the proportion of area between the mean and

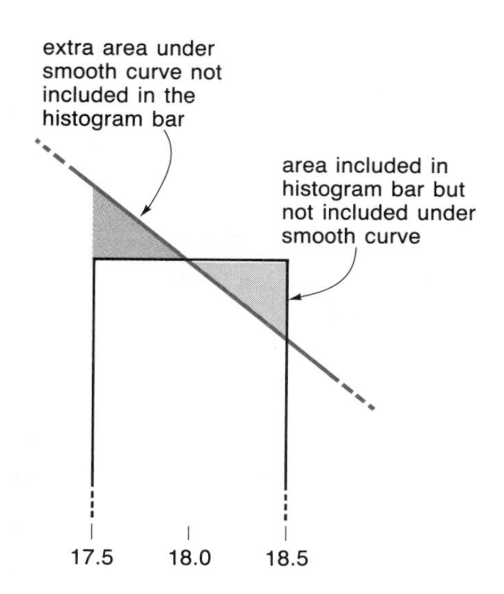

Figure 8.4

An enlarged view of the interface between the histogram bar for 18 out of 30 successes ($P = .50$) in a binomial sampling experiment and the smooth curve of the z approximation.

$z = 0.91$ from the proportion of area between the mean and $z = 1.28$. From column B of the z table, these proportions of area are .3997 when $z = 1.28$ and .3186 when $z = 0.91$.

Subtracting:

$$.3997 - .3186 = .0811$$

Thus, the approximate probability of *exactly* eighteen seeds germinating is .0811. This compares favorably to the more exact value of .0806 computed from the binomial expansion.

When P or Q Does Not Equal .50

If $P \neq .50$ the z approximation may still be used if the sample size is sufficiently large. The more the P value deviates from .50 the larger the sample size must be for the z approximation to be reasonably close. A rule of thumb when $P \neq Q$ is that $N \cdot P \cdot Q$ should be greater than or equal to nine for the approximation to be reasonably close (*See* Siegel (1956) for details.)

Summary

We learned that the binomial distribution provides a shortcut method for solving probability problems that involve two mutually exclusive and exhaustive categories, but that it is seldom necessary, or even desirable, to expand the binomial by hand. Instead, when N is less than or equal to 20, we look up probabilities in the binomial table. We consult the section of the table that corresponds to the value of N, the column that corresponds to the value of P (or Q), and the row that corresponds to the number of successes specified in the problem. When N is greater than 20 and the value of P is equal to or close to .50, the z approximation may be used.

Key Terms

Binomial Expansion
Correction for Discontinuity
***P* value**
***Q* value**
***z* approximation to the binomial distribution**

Exercises

1. In a cross between two strains of laboratory mice, twenty-five percent of the adults have kinky tails, and seventy-five percent have normal-looking straight tails. If sixteen animals are randomly selected from a very large colony of such mice, what is the probability that
   a. exactly six will have kinky tails?
   b. ten or more will have kinky tails?
   c. at least twelve will have normal tails?
   d. exactly fourteen will have normal tails?
   e. five or less will have kinky tails?
   f. eight will have normal tails and eight will have kinky tails?
2. According to statistics compiled by the Newtonian Skydiving Club, one-fourth of all novice jumpers are at risk for suffering some sort of injury (from minor scratches and bruises to broken bones) on any of the first ten jumps. (After ten jumps, if the individual is still alive and still involved in the sport, the probability of injury decreases markedly.) If Mr. Klotznik is scheduled for ten jumps:
   a. what is the probability that he will be able to perform all the jumps without any injury?
   b. what is the probability that Klotznik will be injured exactly twice?
   c. what is the probability that Klotznik will be injured on at least one jump?
   d. what is the probability that Klotznik will escape injury on all but one of the jumps?
3. The Slobovian National Bank has a coin-sorting machine into which a quantity of brovniks may be dumped and out of which come automatically wrapped packets of fourteen brovniks per packet. At the start of business on Monday, when the machine was empty, a teller dumped 210 brovniks into the hopper. Shortly thereafter another teller dumped what she thought were seventy brovniks into the hopper, but they were actually seventy American quarters. Before the error was detected, the machine mixed the quarters thoroughly with the brovniks. The teller decided to do a sampling experiment before sorting out the coins. She selected fourteen coins from the hopper, with replacement, and recorded whether each coin was a brovnik or a quarter. After each coin was selected, the machine was turned on briefly to mix the coins.

Of the fourteen randomly selected coins, what is the probability of obtaining

a. exactly five quarters?
b. exactly ten brovniks?
c. at least eleven brovniks?
d. less than two quarters?
e. more than six quarters?

4. Don't forget to try the BINOM.BAS computer tutorial. Part of the program is a review of the binomial, and this is followed by a few problems for you to solve and step-by-step solutions for you to review.

5. If a fair coin is flipped fifty times,

   a. what is the probability of obtaining thirty or more heads?
   b. what is the probability of obtaining twenty-eight or fewer tails?

6. The ammunition testing scenario that was used for the first problem in chapter 7 will be repeated for this question. Now, however, instead of determining the probabilities using the addition and multiplication rules, use the binomial table. As stated in the original problem, the specifications for the ammunition are such that thirty of fifty shots will hit the test target in the X ring (within one inch of dead center), fifteen shots will hit in the ten ring (within two inches of dead center), and five shots will hit in the nine ring (outside of two inches but within three inches of dead center).

   If ten cartridges manufactured to the above specifications are fired from the test barrel, what is the probability that

   a. five or more shots will strike the nine ring?
   b. six will strike the X ring?
   c. there will be no nines?
   d. exactly eight of the ten shots will be tens or Xs?
   e. less than five shots will fail to be a ten or an X?
   f. exactly five shots will hit the X ring and five shots will be outside the X ring?

7. A wheel of fortune has been built that has one hundred positions at which the wheel may stop. These positions are labeled 1 to 100. If the wheel is spun eight separate times, what is the probability that (use the binomial table to find the answers)

   a. the wheel will stop on an odd number on six out of the eight spins?
   b. the wheel will stop on a number that is less than or equal to forty on half the spins?
   c. on no spins of the wheel will the number be more than eighty?
   d. on all spins of the wheel the number at which the wheel stops will either be less than or equal to twenty-five or greater than or equal to seventy-six?
   e. on four out of the eight spins the wheel will stop on an even number?
   f. the wheel will always stop on a number that is greater than thirty?
   g. on half the spins the wheel will stop on a number between seventy-five and one hundred?
   h. on exactly six spins of the wheel the number at which the wheel stops will be less than or equal to twenty-five?

8. Seventy percent of a particular model of an industrial milling machine are still in service ten years after their purchase date. The same machines are still being sold. If you buy fifteen machines for your factory and assume the durability will be the same for your new machines as for those sold previously, what is the probability that
   a. after ten years at least eleven machines will still be in service?
   b. exactly four of the machines will become useless before ten years have passed?
   c. fewer than three machines will fail before ten years have passed?
   d. all the machines will still be in service after ten years?
   e. six or less will still be in service after ten years?

CHAPTER 9

Introduction To Hypothesis Testing

An experimental hypothesis is a tentative explanation that accounts for a set of facts. For example, it is a fact that individuals who are prone to have bouts of clinical depression are more likely to fall ill during late December and January. Some persons have advanced the hypothesis that this phenomenon is a psychological consequence of the holiday season. Patients think they are supposed to feel very happy and content around this time, and, when that expectation is not realized, a bout of depression is triggered. Others, noting the absence of bright light during the winter months, have hypothesized that depression is a physiologically mediated phenomenon that arises as a consequence of light deprivation.

An experimental hypothesis must be tested in order to graduate from a tentative explanation, or hunch concerning the cause(s) of a phenomenon, to an accepted fact supported by hard data. To use the light hypothesis as an example, we could compare the clinical records of those patients who live in the northern regions of the country where the loss of light during the winter is more profound, to the records of comparable patients who live in the Sunbelt. If the relationship between winter and depression is absent in the Sunbelt group, this observation would lend some support to the light hypothesis.

We could also evaluate the effects of light therapy (as in a tanning studio experience) to see if exposure to bright light on a regular basis tends to reduce vulnerability to depression during the winter. In general, to be meaningful in a scientific sense, an experimental hypothesis must be testable, and to provide a valid test of a hypothesis, an experiment must be carefully designed so that the interpretation of the results can be as unambiguous as possible. This information, when considered along with other available information, is then used to resolve the uncertainty about the accuracy of the experimental hypothesis.

Sometimes an experimental hypothesis is not testable because of the difficulty in collecting the necessary data. In many cases, however, patience is rewarded by the development of a new instrument or technique or an act of nature that finally enables the researcher to collect the data necessary to test the hypothesis. Here are a few examples. Various hypotheses about the makeup of the moons of the planet Jupiter could not be verified until the Voyager spacecraft sent back the critical data. Nature lent a hand in the testing of a previously untested element of Einstein's Theory of Relativity concerning the effect of gravity on light. The hypothesis was finally verified with hard data by measuring the bending of light as it passed by the moon during a total solar eclipse. The hypotheses on gene-splicing were only ideas before the technology necessary to test the hypotheses was developed.

Some hypotheses, however, will never be testable. Articles of religious faith ("There is life after death.") and beliefs such as, "In a previous life, I was a Viking!" are generally of the untestable variety.

LIVING WITH UNCERTAINTY

In the empirical sciences great care is taken to design experiments that will allow the researcher to decide which of several possible explanations truly accounts for a phenomenon. But no matter how much effort is expended to weed out incorrect explanations of a phenomenon, no matter how expertly an experiment is carried out, the information that is supposed to reflect on the veracity of an experimental hypothesis is usually somewhat ambiguous. This does not mean that we are doomed to be indecisive about the truth of a hypothesis, but it does mean that we shall have to tolerate making decisions in the face of some uncertainty.

Statistical analysis is a tool that enables us to make decisions in the face of uncertainty. Rules, conventions, fixed procedures, and rituals are used for processing the data of experiments and arriving at decisions about the accuracy of an experimental hypothesis. The particular statistical analysis that is used may vary as a function of the kind of data that is collected, one statistic may be preferred over another because of the type(s) of question(s) that is(are) being asked, but the format of hypothesis testing and the sequence of steps that are followed to test the hypothesis do not change. No matter what kind of data are collected to test an experimental hypothesis, no matter what statistical analysis is employed to process the data, the underlying logic and procedures of hypothesis testing remain the same.

HYPOTHESIS TESTING WITH THE BINOMIAL DISTRIBUTION

Thus far in the text we have dealt with only two statistical distributions: the z distribution and the binomial distribution. In this chapter we shall begin the topic of hypothesis testing with an illustration that applies to the binomial distribution.

Let me tell you about Scott, a student with a rather common problem. He was having trouble deciding whether or not to take a break from his studies to go home for the weekend. He really wanted to get home to Mom's cooking and his "significant other," but midterm examinations were on the horizon. The idea of tossing a coin occurred to him, so he dug out his lucky antique Spanish coin. (This is the one he recovered while scuba diving on the ocean floor off the coast of Bermuda.) Scott decided that if he tossed tails he would stay on campus and hit the books. He was just about to flip the coin when he paused to think.

He really wanted to use his lucky coin for the flip, but he was worried that, being handcrafted and somewhat irregular in shape, it may favor one side over the other. So, before he flipped the coin to determine whether or not he would go home, he decided to do a test to see if it was a fair and unbiased coin that would come up heads just as often as it would come up tails. In doing this, Scott entered the domain of hypothesis testing. He was about to do research within the context of a binomial sampling experiment. (It is binomial because there are only two possible sample values, and each sample value (heads vs. tails) is mutually exclusive from the other.)

SETTING UP THE TEST OF AN EXPERIMENTAL HYPOTHESIS: THE NULL HYPOTHESIS, ALTERNATIVE HYPOTHESIS, AND DECISION RULE

Before an experimental hypothesis can be tested, it must be formally stated. Also, we must state specifically the standard that will be applied in deciding whether or not the experimental data support the experimental hypothesis. These formal statements precede the actual test of the experimental hypothesis, and they involve important and somewhat subtle concepts that form the logical foundation of hypothesis testing. Here, and in the computer tutorials, these preliminary statements are said to make up the *format* of hypothesis testing.

So, before we accompany Scott on his adventure in hypothesis testing, we must first learn how to set up the test of a hypothesis. Toward this end, here is a story about a local character.

Simon the Fisherman

Simon (we always called him "Simple Simon") was a slow-witted chap who could never seem to hold down a job. One day he was wandering through the countryside with his fishing pole over his shoulder when he spotted a very promising pond on some private property. He walked to the residence to ask permission to fish in the pond, and this permission was granted—with an important proviso. Simon could keep any fish he caught except for the rainbow trout. The owner wanted to save those for himself. This was a problem for Simon because, although he liked to eat fish, he didn't bother learning the names of the different species. "A fish is a fish is a fish" was his approach to the sport. After Simon confessed his dilemma, the property owner handed him *The Pictorial Encyclopedia of Fish*. With this reference book Simon could identify any fish he should happen to catch.

As luck would have it, he caught a fish immediately. With the fish flopping on the bank, Simon began leafing through the book: Albacore, bass, carp, . . . haddock . . . pike . . . salmon . . . TROUT!! Finally, Simon found the picture of the fish he had caught. Of course, by this time the poor creature had expired.

Had Simon been a little more astute, he would have approached this problem differently. He would have assumed that every fish caught was a trout. Then, leaving the book open to the picture of the trout, he could accept or reject this working assumption after comparing the markings and shape shown in the picture to those of his live specimen. This is a **null hypothesis** or a formally stated assumption that the one way something could happen is in fact the way it did happen. There is only one way to catch a trout, but there are essentially an infinite number of nontrouts that could also be caught.

Null Hypothesis. In the context of chapter 9, the null hypothesis is best described as a statement that the probability of a success equals a specific value. For example, if the null hypothesis in a coin flipping experiment is that $P(\text{Head}) = .5$, this states that only chance will influence the results of the experiment. In general, the null hypothesis is a working assumption that always states an equality.

The same logic that Simon should have used to label his catch as trout versus nontrout pertains to a legal proceeding. There is only one way a person can retain his/her status of innocence—by not breaking any law. On the other hand, there is a staggering variety of laws in the criminal code that an individual can break to lose his/her status of innocence. So, by following the procedure of formulating a null hypothesis around the assumption that the one way an event could happen is indeed the way it did happen, a defendant in a court proceeding is presumed to be innocent unless and until the weight of evidence causes the initial working assumption of innocence to be rejected.

Scott's Null Hypothesis and Alternative Hypothesis

In Scott's situation the same logic applies. There is only one way the coin can be perfectly fair (the probability of a head equals the probability of a tail equals .50), but there are many degrees of bias that could affect the coin.

The coin could be only slightly biased, yielding an almost but not quite even split of heads and tails, or it could be so biased that it would yield a heads outcome virtually every time. Since there is only one way a coin can be fair (P (head) = P (tail) = .5) and a great number of nonfair biases (e.g., P (head) = .35, P (head) = .40, etc.), the null hypothesis is that the coin is fair.

Alternative or Experimental Hypothesis. A logical state contradictory to the equality that is formally stated in the null hypothesis. For example, if the null hypothesis in a coin flipping experiment is that P(Head) = .5 ("The coin is fair."), the alternative hypothesis will be $P \neq .5$. ("The coin is not fair.") The alternative hypothesis states that nonchance factors will influence the results of the sampling experiment.

H_0, read "H naught," is used as a symbol to represent the null hypothesis, and H_1 is used to represent the **alternative or experimental hypothesis.** Formally stated for Scott's problem:

$$H_0\text{: } P \text{ (Heads)} = P \text{ (Tails)} = .50$$
$$H_1\text{: } P \text{ (Heads)} \neq P \text{ (Tails)} \neq .50$$

Notice that the null hypothesis describes a scenario in which only chance is operating. Stating that the probability of obtaining a head on the flip of a coin equals .5 is the same as saying that nothing other than chance is going to affect the outcome of the coin flip. In other words, the null hypothesis assumes the absence of any bias favoring heads or tails.

In a typical scientific experiment, the null hypothesis serves the same function as in the present coin flipping example: to state a working assumption that only chance is affecting the values of the experimental data. For example, a physical rehabilitation therapist wanted to compare progress in two groups of amputees as a function of two different approaches to rehabilitation. Both groups received the same excellent medical care, but one group met regularly with a psychologist to air frustrations, to develop coping skills, self-confidence, etc., while the second group received only informal support from family and friends. The null hypothesis for this experiment is simply that the group psychotherapy will have no effect on the speed of the rehabilitative process. There is only one logical state of "no effect," and this is stated as a null hypothesis.

H_0: Group psychotherapy has no effect on the progress of rehabilitation, and any difference between the groups that appears to exist is due only to chance factors and not the experimental variable (psychotherapy vs. no psychotherapy).

The alternative (experimental) hypothesis is that the group psychotherapy did have an effect. Notice that there are many logical states of some effect: the effect of psychotherapy on the rehabilitative process could be slight, profound, or any degree in between. In formal terms:

H_1: The rehabilitation of group 1 proceeded at a rate different from the rehabilitation of group 2. The difference between the groups is too large to be caused by chance alone. It is caused by the experimental variable.

THE DECISION RULE

Decision Rule. A statement of the standard that will be applied in deciding whether to reject or fail to reject the null hypothesis.

The issue every researcher must confront is, How inconsistent with the null hypothesis must the experimental result be before we reject the null hypothesis assumption that chance alone is responsible for the pattern of experimental results? In evaluating whether or not the null hypothesis should or should not be rejected, a standard based upon probability is applied. This is the **decision rule.** In hypothesis testing we first assume that the null hypothesis is true and only chance is operating in the experimental situation. Then, while maintaining this assumption, we determine statistically the probability of getting the obtained experimental result. If the probability of getting the obtained result is less than .05, we reject the null hypothesis and default to a nonchance explanation of the experimental results. (A more stringent probability standard of .01 is also used in hypothesis testing and, near the end of this chapter, the considerations that apply to the selection of .05 versus .01 will be discussed.)

The Concept of Indirect Proof

The underlying logic of hypothesis testing is described as *indirect* because the truth of the alternative (experimental) hypothesis is agreed to only by default if, and only if, the null hypothesis is rejected. *The experimental hypothesis itself is never tested directly.* For example, if we tossed Scott's Spanish coin ten times and got ten heads in a row, this would lead us to reject the null hypothesis that the coin is fair because .001, the probability of tossing a fair coin ten heads in a row, is less than .05. But this does not mean that we have proven Scott's coin to be biased. Although it is rather rare ($P = .001$), a coin can be perfectly fair ($P(\text{head}) = .50$) and still be flipped for ten heads in a row. So, rather than regarding an extreme outcome as proof that the coin is biased, we reject instead the assumption of fairness. We might say "Ten heads in a row is so unlike the behavior of a fair coin that we must reject the assumption that the coin is fair." It is by default that we adopt the alternative hypothesis that the coin is biased.

On the other hand, if a coin yields 5 heads and 5 tails in ten tosses, we would fail to reject the null hypothesis. We might say "The behavior of the coin is so like the behavior of fair coins that we should retain (fail to reject) the null hypothesis." It is important to understand that failure to reject the null hypothesis does not mean we have proven it to be true or that we *accept* it. A coin that has been doctored to, say, come up tails an average of 8 out of 10 tosses is still capable of coming up with a 5 heads/5 tails split ($P = .0264$). We can never prove the null hypothesis. We can only fail to reject it.

The probability values of .05 (5 chances out of 100) and .01 (1 chance in 100) are agreed to by convention. This is analogous to the criterion of "beyond a reasonable doubt" that is used in the courtroom as a standard for rejecting the original assumption of innocence. Only after considerable incriminating evidence mounts up would a juror be expected to reject the original assumption of the defendant's innocence. Similarly, only after considerable statistical evidence is presented that is inconsistent with the null hypothesis would we reject the null hypothesis and default to the alternative hypothesis. How much statistical evidence is *considerable?* The juror cannot quantify considerable, but in testing statistical hypotheses, we can. The answer, as pointed out above, is a result that could occur by chance less than or equal to 5% (or 1%) of the time.

Alpha Level. The Greek α represents the level of significance that is used in a statistical test. It is also the probability of falsely rejecting the null hypothesis.

Level of Significance. The probability level (usually .05 or .01) at which we decide to reject the null hypothesis and default to the alternative hypothesis. The alpha (α) level of a test. The probability of Type I error.

"as rare or rarer than." In Step 4 of hypothesis testing, assuming the null hypothesis is true, we must determine the probability of obtaining a statistic as rare or rarer than **(as extreme or even more extreme than)** the computed value.

In statistics the .05 or .01 probability value is called the **alpha level** or **level of significance** of the test. It is a statement of how inconsistent with the null hypothesis the experimental data have to be before the null hypothesis is rejected. For example, when a coin is tossed ten times we expect five heads and five tails. This is the most frequent result. But if the split is 6/4 or 7/3 we don't immediately declare the coin to be biased. We know that, with only chance operating, these outcomes are not unusual. Deviations from even splits can occur from chance alone. But, the more extreme the split becomes (8/2, 9/1, 10/0), the less likely we are to continue to go along with the assumption that only chance is operating. If you refer back to the binomial table you will see that an event **as rare or rarer than** a 9/1 split has a probability of $.0010 + .0098 + .0098 + .0010 = .0216$. Thus, if we use the .05 convention, when a coin is tossed 10 times, only a split **as extreme or even more extreme** than 9/1 or 10/0 will cause us to reject the assumption that the coin is fair. If we used the more stringent .01 standard, with a 9/1 split we would still retain the assumption that the coin is fair ($.0216 > .01$). Using the .01 standard it would take a 10/0 split to cause us to reject the null hypothesis that the coin is fair ($.0010 + .0010 = .0020$, and $.0020 < .01$). Even though we know that results as extreme as 9/1 and 10/0 splits are possible with perfectly fair coins, they are so unusual in their frequency of occurrence that, if we are forced to make a decision as to whether a coin is fair or not, a very extreme outcome will lead us to reject the null hypothesis that the coin is fair. How extreme does the outcome have to be before this happens? According to convention, "beyond a reasonable doubt" in statistical hypothesis testing is reached when the probability of the computed statistic is less than or equal to .05 or, sometimes, .01. In general, the decision rule takes the following form:

> "Reject the null hypothesis if the probability of obtaining a statistic with the computed value is less than or equal to .05."

or,

> "Reject the null hypothesis if the probability of obtaining a statistic with the computed value is less than or equal to .01."

Scott's decision rule employs the .05 alpha level and may be written as follows:

> Decision Rule: Reject H_0: if the probability of a split as rare or rarer than a 7/3 split is less than or equal to .05.

Testing an Experimental Hypothesis: The Formal Steps

The Steps of Hypothesis Testing. The representation of the data analysis phase of all hypothesis testing, no matter which statistical procedure is employed, as a uniform series of five steps. See the text for details.

Now that the null hypothesis, alternative hypothesis, and decision rule have been formally stated, we can go through the actual hypothesis testing phase. But before going through **the steps of hypothesis testing,** I wish you to know that in formal research a great deal of thought and preparation must precede the phase of data collection. The steps of hypothesis testing as presented here are meant to refer only to the data collection and statistical analysis that is done within the larger framework of a total research effort.

Here are the steps of hypothesis testing that Scott followed to evaluate the fairness of his coin.

Step 1. *Collect a sample from a population.* To test a hypothesis, we must collect data that can provide information about the accuracy of the hypothesis. In the present context, we need to know about the behavior of Scott's coin. The population from which Scott sampled to get this information, the population of flipping outcomes, is a binomial population because only two values exist: heads and tails. Each time Scott flipped the coin, he was, in effect, sampling from a binomial population. So, to complete the first step Scott knew he had to toss the coin a specified number of times and record the occurrence of a head or tail for each toss.

Scott decided to do an experiment consisting of ten flips of the coin. In other words, he set N, the sample size, equal to ten.

Step 2. *Compute a statistic from the sample data.* In this set of circumstances the statistic Scott needed was a simple frequency. He didn't need any complicated formula to compute it. He simply counted the number of heads and tails that occurred in ten tosses of the coin. In ten tosses Scott obtained seven tails and three heads.

Step 3. *Locate the statistic computed in Step 2 on its theoretical sampling distribution.* You know what a statistic is and you have had experience with one kind of sampling distribution (the binomial), but the concept of a sampling distribution has not been formally presented. An understanding of this very important concept is critical for an understanding of the steps of hypothesis testing, so read the following description of a sampling distribution very carefully.

> **If the sample values produced by a hypothetical sampling experiment are determined by chance alone, and a statistic is computed from each set of sample data, the theoretical sampling distribution of the statistic will display all possible values the statistic can equal and the probability of obtaining each value.**

The word *hypothetical* means that we don't really have to do the experiment to know what would happen if we did. This is because the characteristics of various sampling distributions can be derived mathematically, as we saw in the last chapter with the binomial expansion. The word *theoretical* is a disclaimer. It means that if you really did decide to do a particular sampling experiment and it didn't work out empirically exactly as the mathematics predict, you should not be unduly surprised. In the real world, because of chance factors, predictions from abstract mathematical theory do not always match physical reality.

To help drive home the concept of a sampling distribution, Scott ran a simulated coin-flipping experiment on his microcomputer. The experiment was based on an important assumption: that all sampling in the experiment would be purely random. In other words, chance and chance alone would determine a head or a tail outcome. This may be expressed symbolically as $P(\text{Head}) = P(\text{Tail}) = .5$. In other words, the probability of a head equals the probability of a tail equals .5.

Now for the experiment. In Scott's computer simulation the coin was flipped 10 times for each experiment and the head/tail split was recorded. This flipping and recording of results (5 heads/5 tails, 6 heads/4 tails, 2 heads/8 tails, etc.) was repeated 10,000 times. (You can try this yourself by running FLIPS.BAS on *Stat/Tutor*.) As he examined the results from the 10,000 experiments Scott noticed:

1. Out of the ten thousand experiments that were performed, only eleven different outcomes occurred: 0, 1, 2, 3, 4, 5, 6, 7, 8, 9, or 10 heads. (This conforms with what you learned earlier when you studied the binomial distribution: there are $N+1$ possible outcomes in any binomial sampling experiment.)

2. Some of the eleven possible outcomes were more frequent than others. For example, the 10 heads/0 tails outcome occurred only 10 times in 10,000 experiments, but 5 heads/5 tails occurred 2,461 times. By dividing the frequency of each of the eleven outcomes by 10,000, Scott knew that the probability for each of the eleven possible outcomes could be determined. When he compared the probability values computed from his simulation data to

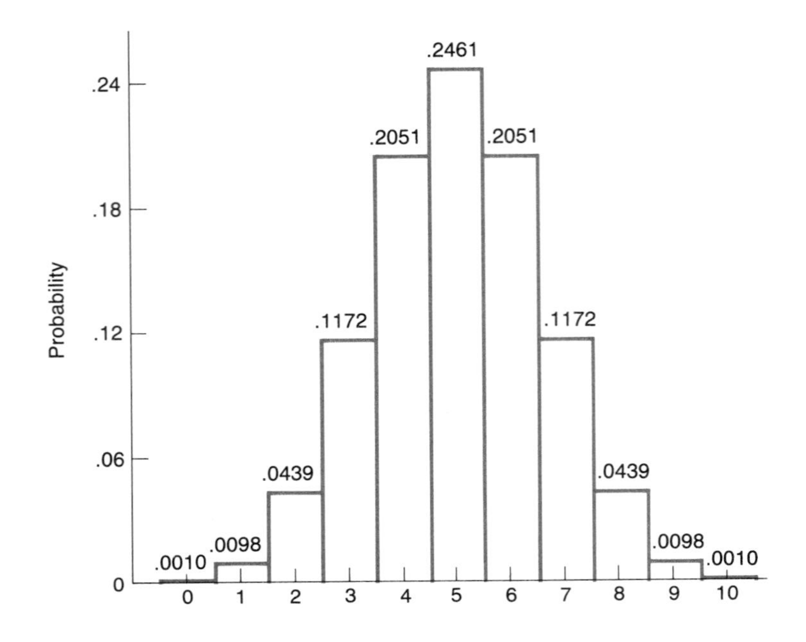

Figure 9.1
The probability histogram for the binomial expansion, $(P+Q)^N$, when $P = Q = .5$ and $N = 10$.

the theoretically expected values listed in the binomial table for $N = 10$ and $P = .50$, he noticed that the probabilities listed for each outcome were *almost* the same.

3. Scott saw that the distribution of the eleven probabilities could be represented in a graph as a histogram and he could locate the bar in the histogram that represents the 7 head/3 tail outcome (figure 9.1).

Having had some experience with the binomial sampling distribution, you are probably aware that Scott did not have to do a real or simulated sampling experiment to construct the binomial sampling distribution that he needed to complete Step 3. One option was to compute the theoretical sampling distribution using the binomial expansion, but Scott saved himself the work and looked up the distribution in the binomial table with $N = 10$ and $P = .50$ (table 9.1). Notice, as specified in the above description of a theoretical sampling distribution, all the $N + 1$ possible outcomes, from no heads to all ten heads, are represented, and a probability is assigned to each outcome.

By using table 9.1, it was an easy matter for Scott to locate the obtained outcome of 7 heads and 3 tails on the binomial sampling distribution for which $P = .5$ and $N = 10$. With the necessary information from the sampling distribution in hand, Scott was ready for Step 4.

Table 9.1

The section of the binomial table for which $N = 10$. The probabilities that relate to Scott's coin tossing experiment ($P = .5$) are in bold type in the column on the far right.

		P or *Q*									
N		.05	.10	.15	.20	.25	.30	.35	.40	.45	**.50**
10	0	.5987	.3487	.1969	.1074	.0563	.0282	.0135	.0060	.0025	**.0010**
	1	.3151	.3874	.3474	.2684	.1877	.1211	.0725	.0403	.0207	**.0098**
	2	.0746	.1937	.2759	.3020	.2816	.2335	.1757	.1209	.0763	**.0439**
	3	.0105	.0574	.1298	.2013	.2503	.2668	.2522	.2150	.1665	**.1172**
	4	.0010	.0112	.0401	.0881	.1460	.2001	.2377	.2508	.2384	**.2051**
	5	.0001	.0015	.0085	.0264	.0584	.1029	.1536	.2007	.2340	**.2461**
	6	.0000	.0001	.0012	.0055	.0162	.0368	.0689	.1115	.1596	**.2051**
	7	.0000	.0000	.0001	.0008	.0031	.0090	.0212	.0425	.0746	**.1172**
	8	.0000	.0000	.0000	.0001	.0004	.0014	.0043	.0106	.0229	**.0439**
	9	.0000	.0000	.0000	.0000	.0000	.0001	.0005	.0016	.0042	**.0098**
	10	.0000	.0000	.0000	.0000	.0000	.0000	.0000	.0001	.0003	**.0010**

Step 4. *Determine the probability of obtaining a statistic with a value as rare or rarer than the computed value.* (You may have noticed that Scott really didn't "compute" the probability of a 7 head/3 tail split using the binomial expansion. He took the easy way out and looked up the value of .1172 in a binomial table similar to table 9.1. In other kinds of hypothesis testing more computation will be involved.)

To complete Step 4 Scott had to determine the probability of any outcome as rare or rarer than a 7 tail/3 head outcome. These outcomes are highlighted in table 9.1. They include any table entry with a value less than or equal to .1172, the probability of obtaining 7 tails and 3 heads. Scott added the probabilities that are highlighted and got a sum of .3438. Is this value of .3438 consistent with the position that the coin is fair, or should we reject that assumption? To answer this question Scott had to complete the fifth and last step of hypothesis testing.

Step 5. *Compare the probability value computed in Step 4 to the critical value stated in the decision rule.* The "computed" probability from Step 4 was .3438. Since this value is clearly much greater than .05, Scott failed to reject the null hypothesis: he retains the assumption that the coin is fair. The difference between the theoretically expected outcome (a 5/5 split) and the obtained outcome (a 7/3 split) is not large enough to cause rejection of the null hypothesis assumption that $P = .5$. Thus, the difference between the expected and obtained outcomes is regarded as having arisen solely from random factors.

Once a statistical analysis is complete, the researcher must interpret the results within the context of the research problem. In Scott's case the meaning of the analysis was clear: the coin was fair and could be used to make a yes/no decision on a purely random basis. ("Heads I go home, tails I don't.") As you progress to more complex analyses in the coming chapters within more complex research scenarios, and as you become more exposed to real research results in more advanced courses, you shall see that interpretations of statistical analyses are not always so clear-cut. Results are very often open to a wide variety of interpretations, and disagreement regarding the interpretation of research results, even after exhaustive statistical analysis, is a fact of life in the scientific community.

DECISION ERRORS

At the completion of a trial, a verdict is rendered of the guilt or innocence of the defendant. As we all know too well, sometimes mistakes are made. Innocent persons are sent to jail and the guilty go free. For example, take the case of Maxwell.

Max was involved in a barroom brawl with a close acquaintance of his on a Friday night. Early Saturday morning the person was found dead near his apartment from a blow to the head. The police were given an anonymous tip concerning the quarrel between Maxwell and the victim, and Max was picked up for questioning.

He was in real trouble. Not only was he placed near the scene of the crime, not only was a motive established, but he also had blood stains of the victim's type on his clothing and was found to be carrying property on his person (a knife) that was identified as having belonged to the victim.

Max was tried and convicted of first degree murder. He was, however, innocent. He got the victim's blood on his clothing during and after the fight. Max felt terrible about the whole incident and went to his friend's apartment shortly after being thrown out of the bar. They resolved their differences verbally, and Max helped the victim to clean and bandage a hard-to-reach cut behind his left shoulder. After using the victim's knife to cut the gauze bandage, Max absentmindedly put the knife in his pocket. It wasn't until the murder weapon (a piece of pipe) was found with somebody else's fingerprints on it that Max was vindicated and released. The fingerprints belonged to a career criminal with a long arrest record for violent crime, but without evidence in addition to the fingerprints, the district attorney could not convince the jury to vote for conviction. The guilty party was never sent to jail for this offense.

Type I Error. Rejecting the null hypothesis when it should not have been rejected.

Type I Error

In the terminology used in hypothesis testing, a **Type I error** is the mistake of rejecting the null hypothesis when the null hypothesis is true. Maxwell's conviction for murder was a Type I error. The jury rejected the assumption of innocence following the presentation of very convincing evidence pointing toward Max's guilt, but he was really innocent. The jury made a mistake.

In a research setting a Type I error usually involves invoking a nonchance explanation for the observed results when, in fact, only chance was operating. For example, a medical instrument salesperson claimed that in a one hour workshop he could train a technician how to administer and interpret the ultrasound examinations that are often given to pregnant women. A technician was trained by the salesperson and, of sixteen women he examined, the newly trained technician judged that thirteen women were carrying male fetuses.

The technician's assessment of a 13 male/3 female sex ratio is different from the 8 male/8 female sex ratio that would be expected if only chance were operating. That is, in determining the sex of fetuses carried by a random sample of 16 pregnant women, you would expect an 8/8 sex ratio to occur more than any other. (In the binomial table in the section for $N = 16$ and $P = .5$, the entry for an 8/8 split is .1964, higher than for any other possible split.) Is there a nonchance explanation for the relatively rare 13/3 outcome? Is the technician inept at reading the ultrasound images? Are the women among a group of patients that have undergone special procedures to select the sex of their offspring? Did the supervising physician purposely send more women carrying male fetuses to the technician to make the test more difficult?

The salesperson who was told the results of the ultrasound examinations was suspicious of the unusual 13/3 sex ratio, so he subjected these data to a formal binomial test. He found that an event as rare or rarer than a 13/3 split when an 8/8 split is expected equals 0.021. (Look in the section of the binomial table for $N = 16$, $P = .5$, and in the rows labelled 0, 1, 2, 3, and 13, 14, 15, 16. The values $0 + .0002 + .0018 + .0085 + .0085 + .0018 + .0002 + 0 = .021$.) Since $0.021 < .05$ he rejected the null hypothesis that only chance was operating and decided to look for a nonchance explanation for the 13/3 split.

As it turned out, no nonchance explanation was ever found. The technician's readings were verified, the women were not following any regimen in an attempt to select the sex of their offspring, and there was no attempt by the supervising physician to send a disproportionate number of women whom he knew were carrying male fetuses. Apparently, through chance alone, 13 of the 16 women happened to be expecting sons. By rejecting the null hypothesis and invoking a nonchance explanation for the statistically rare 13/3 split, the salesperson made a Type I error.

Type I Error and Alpha. The conventional probability value (alpha) of .05 that forms the basis of the decision rule is really the same as the probability of Type I error. By using the .05 level of significance in the test of a hypothesis we, in effect, recognize that the probability is .05 of rejecting the null hypothesis when it should not be rejected. Thus, researchers who analyze their data using the .05 standard run a 5% risk of rejecting H_0 and invoking a nonchance explanation of their experimental results when, in fact, only chance was operating.

How can we be sure that when we reject a null hypothesis that we are doing so correctly? Short of replicating the experiment to increase our confidence in the result, we can never really be sure. Thus, even though statistical tests exist to allow us to make decisions in the face of uncertainty, some uncertainty as to the accuracy of those decisions will always remain.

Alpha = .05 versus Alpha = .01. Sometimes the level of significance for testing a hypothesis is set at .01 rather than .05. This is done in situations for which the cost of incorrectly rejecting the null hypothesis is considered to be too high to accept a .05 probability of making a Type I error. This concept can be explained by extending the courtroom analogy. For example, assume you are serving on a jury and are hearing evidence regarding the commission of a particularly heinous crime. If a prominent and respected member of the community is accused of the crime, the cost of an incorrect guilty verdict would be the destruction of a productive and well-liked citizen. You may, therefore, have to be convinced beyond any shadow of a doubt (a higher standard than beyond a "reasonable" doubt) before voting guilty. On the other hand, if the man on trial is known to be a member of a notorious gang and comes across as a menacing scoundrel, you might be less likely to agonize excessively about the possibility of rendering an incorrect guilty verdict. (Everyone is supposed to be equal in the eyes of the law and presumed innocent at the beginning of a trial, but sometimes jurors are influenced by facts not contained in the formal trial record.)

The same concept relates to the testing of research results. Let us say that two new drugs are being evaluated for their therapeutic effect. One drug is very expensive to manufacture, while the other may be made quite cheaply. It would be reasonable to evaluate experimentally the response of subjects to the expensive drug using a .01 rather than a .05 significance level. This is because you would want an extra degree of confidence that the hypothesized therapeutic action was genuine before making the financial commitment to produce an expensive product. With the inexpensively produced drug the financial risks would not be as great, and you could tolerate a greater chance for making a Type I error (i.e., judging the drug to be effective when it actually is not).

Type II Error

Type II Error. Failing to reject the null hypothesis when it should have been rejected.

The other possible error, called **Type II error,** occurs when we fail to reject the null hypothesis when it should have been rejected. Perhaps Scott's antique Spanish coin really is biased and his experiment was not powerful enough to detect the bias. Perhaps if he did an experiment with 100 tosses ($N = 100$) the extra information provided by the increased sample size would reveal some degree of bias. If the null hypothesis really should be rejected but we fail to do so because of an insufficient amount of information pointing to that decision, we commit a Type II error.

The analogy to the courtroom is the jury decision to set the guilty party free due to lack of evidence. This is what happened to the real perpetrator of the crime for which Maxwell was convicted. Also, a jury may have heard very convincing evidence of guilt only to be told by the judge that they must "disregard" the evidence. Perhaps testimony was stricken from the record when a revelation came in midtrial that physically abusive interrogation methods were used to extract a confession. In any event, if the weight of allowable evidence is not strong enough to cause the jury to reject the assumption of innocence and enough doubt of guilt still remains to vote for acquittal, a guilty person may be found "not guilty." The *decision matrix* that summarizes the relationship between jury decisions and Type I and Type II error is shown below.

	The State of Reality	
Jury Decision	**Defendant Innocent (H_0 True)**	**Defendant Guilty (H_0 False)**
Guilty (Reject H_0)	Type I error	correct decision
Not Guilty (Fail to reject H_0)	correct decision	Type II error

Notice the term "not guilty" is used rather than "innocent." The jury doesn't declare the innocence of a defendant; the twelve men and women simply declare insufficient evidence has been presented for them to reject the assumption of innocence. This is an important distinction because in hypothesis testing the null hypothesis is not considered provable. Failing to reject the null hypothesis is not considered to be equivalent to declaring its truth, or, as is sometimes incorrectly stated, "accepting" it. If you recall the test of Scott's Spanish coin, Scott didn't prove his coin was unbiased. He just failed to reject the null hypothesis that it was fair. Scott simply retained the assumption that the coin is fair. When jury members can't vote for conviction because of insufficient evidence, they retain the original presumption that the defendant is not guilty. This does *not* mean they believe 100% in the innocence of the defendant. It *does* mean that they don't believe enough (beyond a reasonable doubt) in the defendant's guilt to reject the assumption of innocence.

Another short problem for which the binomial is appropriate is presented in *Stat/Tutor* along with a step-by-step solution. Working through this program (HYPTST.BAS) will give you additional exposure to the important concepts that were discussed above. This mastery is especially important since the remainder of this text is devoted to hypothesis testing in one form or another.

Summary

We examined the underlying principles of hypothesis testing within the context of an example, and we tested hypotheses as presented in a formal step-by-step process. After setting up the test with a statement of the null hypothesis, alternative hypothesis, and decision rule, we processed the data according to the five steps.

Key Terms

Alpha Level
Alternative Hypothesis
"as extreme or even more extreme"
"as rare or rarer than"
Decision Rule
Level of Significance
Null Hypothesis
The Steps of Hypothesis Testing
Type I Error
Type II Error

Exercises

In doing these problems be sure to state the null hypothesis, alternative hypothesis, a decision rule, and a statement of conclusion.

1. Juvenile male and female ring doves look so much alike that, from appearance alone, it is virtually impossible to tell them apart from casual inspection. If a research project demands accurate sex identification, a surgical procedure must be done.

   A young technician, Lazar Fogelman, claimed that he could make this discrimination without resorting to surgery. To test his ability, his supervisor selected a dozen birds for Lazar to segregate by sex. Afterwards, for verification, the sex was determined surgically. If Lazar selected the sex correctly for ten of the twelve birds, do you believe he can indeed tell the sex without surgery, or was he just lucky? Test the hypothesis using the .05 level of significance.

2. The director of a metropolitan basketball conference heard a rumor that Lewis "Hot Rod" Epstein, star guard on the first place team, was seen with a notorious gambler. Hot Rod was rumored to be part of a point-shaving scheme and was supposedly planning to affect the point spread by purposely missing some foul shots in the next conference game.

Hot Rod's usual percentage from the foul line is 85%. In the game in question he sank eight foul shots out of thirteen attempts. Was his foul shot success rate significantly below his typical performance? What do you conclude about the allegation that Hot Rod was part of a point-shaving scheme? (Use $\alpha = .05$.)

3. Sid claims his Ouija board enables him to consult the spirits to help him answer questions on objective tests. On a fifteen item true/false test he scored eleven out of fifteen correct without even reading the questions. He relied solely on the Ouija board. Do these data support Sid's claim that his success rate is better than would be the case if only chance were in operation? (Use $\alpha = .05$.)
4. Marion claims that when her arthritis begins to bother her after a pain-free interval, it will rain within twenty-four hours. Marion claims her forecasting system is 90% accurate. If Marion accurately predicted the last fifteen out of twenty rainy periods, does this support her contention that her pain can predict rain with a 90% accuracy rate? (Use $\alpha = .05$.)
5. An investor in real estate is expressing interest in some rural property that contains a large man-made pond. According to the property owner, the stocked pond contains 50% black bass and 50% other species such as carp, bluegills, etc. To verify the claim that the pond contains 50% bass, a trap was set baited with food that was equally desirable for all the species of fish. When the trap was checked there were eight bass, thirteen bluegills and five carp. Test the hypothesis that one-half of the fish in the pond are bass. (Use $\alpha = .05$.)
6. At the conclusion of marching band season the high school band director learned from interviewing parents that only twenty of his fifty band students had been practicing at home at least thirty minutes per day. At the beginning of the next season the director gave a speech to a new group of band students to address this problem. At the end of that season he determined that the number of faithfully practicing students rose to twenty-five out of fifty. Does the increase from twenty to twenty-five represent a statistically significant increase? Is there evidence that the speech affected the students' attitude toward practicing? (Use $\alpha = .05$.)
7. The rejection rate of widgets in the quality control department has been stuck on 30% for several months. Recently a change was made in the assembly procedure to address this problem. Following the change, a sample of twenty widgets was randomly selected. It was found that only three of the twenty widgets failed quality control inspection. Did the change in assembly method result in a significant change in the rejection rate? (Use $\alpha = .05$.)
8. A water witch (dowser) claims that 80% of the spots he picks for the digging of wells result in the successful location of water. It turns out that his assistant is your friend's brother-in-law, and you find out from your friend that of the last twenty spots the dowser picked for digging wells, twelve were successful. Do you accept the dowser's claim of an 80% success rate? (Use $\alpha = .05$.)
9. A genetically engineered bacteria has been developed that may be able to give tomato plants some protection from frost damage. Normally, 90% of plants of a particular variety of tomato would be expected to die after being exposed to temperatures below 30° F. Following treatment with the bacteria and exposure to temperatures below 30° F, six of twenty tested plants survived. Did treatment with the genetically engineered bacteria result in a significant reduction in plant mortality? (Use $\alpha = .05$.)

CHAPTER 10

Hypothesis Testing with the z Statistic: The Single Sample Case

Sampling Distribution. The distribution of a statistic that results from a sampling experiment. The distribution displays all possible values the statistic can equal and the probability of obtaining each value.

In the previous chapter you were introduced to the concepts of null hypothesis, alternative hypothesis, and decision rule, and were led through the five steps of hypothesis testing within the context of a specific binomial example. With this background you are well-prepared to tackle a different kind of hypothesis testing problem—a problem for which the z statistic is appropriate. But before applying the z statistic to hypothesis testing with experimental data, you must first gain an understanding of an important new concept: the theoretical **sampling distribution** of the sample mean.

To develop this understanding, the sampling experiment that provides the data for the sampling distribution of the sample mean will be described. Next, we shall cover the various theoretical characteristics of the sampling distribution of the sample mean. These are the characteristics that derive from pure mathematics. Once we know theoretically what to expect from a sampling experiment, we shall do some experiments, construct some sampling distributions from the experimental data, and take note of their characteristics relative to theoretical expectations. (Using SAMPLING.BAS you can try these experiments for yourself on a microcomputer.) After this we shall work through some "mental" experiments to introduce the application of the z statistic to hypothesis testing, and, finally, we shall use the z statistic for hypothesis testing within the context of a realistic scenario.

THE SAMPLING EXPERIMENT

In the last chapter the concept of sampling was presented within the context of the binomial: only two sample values existed in the population—heads and tails. In the present chapter the population from which we shall sample is assumed to contain many values and be normally distributed. An example of such a population distribution is presented in figure 10.1. We shall do some sampling experiments using this population of 500 scores. To understand the sampling experiment it helps to imagine the 500 score values in the population as 500 numbered slips of paper in a basket. A sample from the population is an imaginary dip into the basket to retrieve randomly a slip containing a particular score value.

Just as we saw in the case of the binomial when, on the basis of probability, we theoretically expected ten flips of the coin to yield a 5 head/5 tail split, sampling experiments done with normal distributions also have theoretical expectancies.

THEORETICAL EXPECTATIONS

In the last chapter the sampling distribution was described in the following way:

> **If the sample values produced by a hypothetical sampling experiment are determined by chance alone, and a statistic is computed from each set of sample data, the theoretical sampling distribution of the statistic will display**

Figure 10.1

A normal distribution of 500 scores.

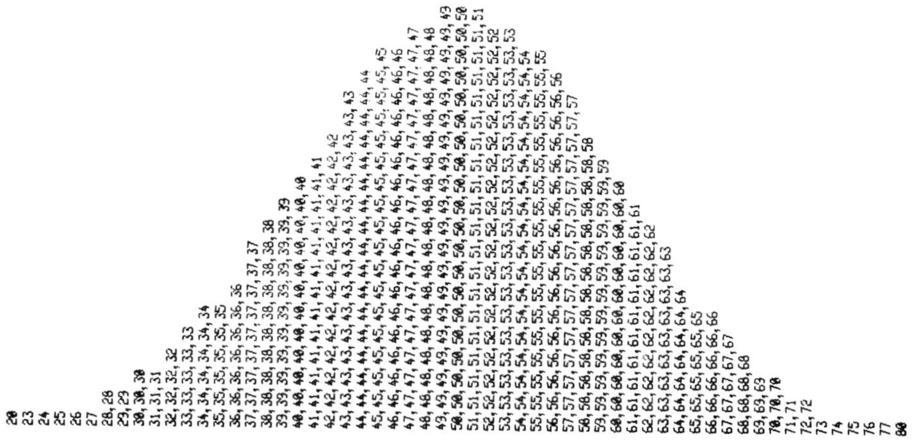

all possible values the statistic can equal and the probability of obtaining each value.

This general description of a sampling distribution also applies when samples are selected from a normal distribution. In the present context, the *population* from which the sample data are selected is a raw score population with a mean of μ and a standard deviation equal to σ. The *statistic* that is computed for each set of n sample scores is X, the sample mean. The *hypothetical sampling experiment* is to select k samples of n scores per sample from the population of raw scores and compute a mean for each sample. By plotting the resulting distribution of sample means, we get the *sampling distribution of the sample mean:* a distribution made up not of raw score values, but of sample mean values.

Central Limit Theorem. A mathematical theorem that allows one to predict the characteristics (mean and deviation measure) of the sampling distribution of the sample mean.

The Central Limit Theorem. The characteristics of the sampling distribution of the sample mean can be determined theoretically using the **central limit theorem.** A proof of this theorem is beyond the scope of the present text, but you are not asked to accept its predictions on faith. The SAMPLING.BAS computer program will allow you to conduct a variety of sampling experiments that conform to the hypothetical sampling experiment format described above. You will be able to vary the size of your sample and the number of samples selected from the population and then see for yourself how closely the empirical results conform to theoretical expectations. The results of a few runs through SAMPLING.BAS will be presented later in the chapter, but before doing that let us discuss those theoretical expectations referred to above.

Expected Value. The value that a sample statistic is theoretically expected to equal within the restraints of a given sampling experiment.

1. If a single score were randomly selected from the population depicted in figure 10.1 and you were asked to give your best guess of the score's value, your guess (most would intuitively choose the mean of 50) would be an **expected value.** But what is the expected value of the mean of several sample scores?

The mean of the distribution of all possible sample means that is generated by the hypothetical sampling experiment has an expected value equal to the mean of the raw score population.

In other words, assume we select k samples from a population of raw scores with n scores per sample and compute the mean for each of the k samples. Because the average of all the raw scores equals μ, we say that *the expected value of any individual score selected at random from a population of raw scores is μ.* If an individual score has an expected value of μ, and a sample is made up of n individual scores, *the expected value of any individual sample mean is also equal to μ.*

Even though we theoretically "expect" the sample mean to equal the population mean, if, by chance, a sample contains more scores from the higher end of the raw score population than from the lower end, the mean of that sample would tend to be greater than the mean of the raw score population. Similarly, if by chance a sample happened to contain many low scores, it would tend to have a sample mean less than the mean of the raw score population. But if we compute the mean of the entire set of k sample means, according to the central limit theorem, the mean of all the sample means will exactly equal the mean of the raw score population from which the samples were drawn. In notation:

$$\mu_{\overline{X}} = \mu_X$$

Notice that parameter notation is being used for the mean of all the sample means. This is because the hypothetical sampling experiment is assumed to generate all possible values (i.e., a population) of the sample means.

2. If we compute the standard deviation of the set of all possible sample means, the value of this parameter will equal the standard deviation of the raw score population divided by the square root of the sample size. In notation:

$$\sigma_{\overline{X}} = \frac{\sigma_X}{\sqrt{n}}$$

Standard Error. The deviation measure of a distribution of sample means, as distinguished from the standard deviation, the deviation measure of a distribution of raw scores.

As explained above, because of random chance some sample means will be less than μ and some will be greather than μ. The dispersion in the set of all possible sample means is described by a statistic called the **standard error.** By giving the standard deviation of a set of sample means a special name (standard error) we avoid confusing it with the standard deviation of a set of raw scores. As explained above for the mean, because it is assumed we are dealing with the set of all possible sample means, the standard error of the hypothetical distribution of sample means is a parameter.

3. If the hypothetical sampling experiment is carried out with a variety of sample sizes, a different distribution of all possible sample means will result for each sample size used. The sampling distribution of the sample mean is, therefore, not one distribution but, rather, a family of distributions. The mean of all possible hypothetical sampling distributions will equal μ, no matter what the sample size, but the standard error will decrease as the sample size increases. This is illustrated in figure 10.2.

4. If the population of raw scores is normally distributed, the hypothetical sampling distribution of the sample means will also be normally distributed, regardless of the sample size.

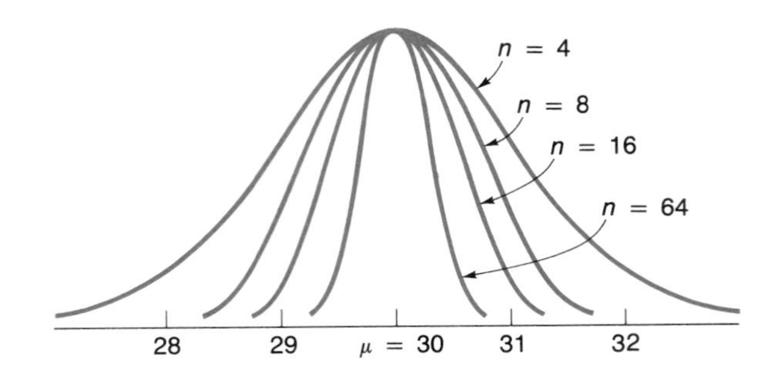

Figure 10.2

The sampling distribution of the sample mean when samples of $n = 4$, $n = 8$, $n = 16$, or $n = 64$ are taken from a population with a mean of 30 and a standard deviation of 2.00 ($\mu = 30, \sigma = 2$). The mean stays constant for the various sample sizes, but the dispersion shrinks with increasing sample size.

In the behavioral sciences, the variables studied do tend to be normally distributed. There are exceptions, such as latency scores (e.g., How long does it take the subject to give the correct response?), but the exceptions are outnumbered by the normal or near normal distributions of most measures of physical (height, weight, strength, etc.) and behavioral (intelligence, manual dexterity, temperament, etc.) characteristics.

The above not withstanding, according to the central limit theorem, even in cases where the raw score distribution is not normal, if the sample size is sufficiently large, the hypothetical sampling distribution of the means will still be normal. The less the raw score distribution conforms to the normal bell-shaped standard, the larger the sample size must be for the hypothetical distribution of sample means to be normal. If the distribution of a variable is reasonably close to being normal, and this includes most variables studied by behavioral scientists, a sample size of thirty or more is generally assumed to yield a normally shaped distribution of sample means.

From Hypothetical to Empirical: A Few Sampling Experiments

Table 10.1 is a compilation of three separate sampling experiments that were done using the SAMPLING.BAS program from *Stat/Tutor*. (A detailed description for this program is in the *Manual for Stat/Tutor*.) This program prompts the user to input the number of samples to be selected (k) and the size of each sample (n), and then runs the random sampling experiment defined by those values. The results of the sampling experiments reported in table 10.1 were all run with k set equal to 25, but the sample size (n) was either 1, 4, or 25.

Table 10.1

The results of three sampling experiments done with SAMPLING.BAS. The number of samples selected (k) for all three experiments was 25. The sample size was $n = 1$ for Experiment 1, $n = 4$ for Experiment 2, and $n = 25$ for Experiment 3.

Sample Mean	Experiment 1 ($n = 1$)	Experiment 2 ($n = 4$)	Experiment 3 ($n = 25$)
#1	52.00	45.75	52.24
#2	66.00	48.50	50.12
#3	50.00	48.75	51.80
#4	53.00	50.50	47.40
#5	80.00	51.75	49.00
#6	62.00	40.75	50.96
#7	24.00	52.00	48.92
#8	53.00	49.50	52.12
#9	37.00	51.75	51.56
#10	54.00	53.25	52.12
#11	39.00	54.75	48.80
#12	73.00	44.25	51.64
#13	47.00	59.50	49.28
#14	61.00	56.50	51.84
#15	51.00	48.75	48.36
#16	38.00	59.00	49.32
#17	42.00	56.00	54.84
#18	57.00	53.25	47.60
#19	33.00	43.00	50.92
#20	51.00	50.75	47.72
#21	71.00	46.75	49.16
#22	59.00	52.25	49.40
#23	51.00	46.75	51.20
#24	45.00	53.25	57.40
#25	48.00	48.50	51.36
Overall Mean:	51.88	50.63	50.59
Standard Error:	12.61	4.58	2.24

As you inspect table 10.1 notice the degree to which the hypothetical predictions are evident in the actual experimental data. Prediction 1 was that the mean of all the means would equal fifty, the mean of the population from which the samples were drawn. On the average, as predicted, the mean of each set of sample means came very close to matching that prediction (51.88, 50.63, and 50.59).

Prediction 2 was that the standard deviation of the set of sample means (the standard error) would equal the standard deviation of the raw score population divided by the square root of n, the sample size. When n is set equal to one, the computation of the standard error,

$$\sigma_{\overline{X}} = \frac{\sigma_X}{\sqrt{n}}$$

reduces to

$$\sigma_{\overline{X}} = \frac{\sigma_X}{1} = \frac{10}{1} = 10.00,$$

and when $n = 4$

$$\sigma_{\overline{X}} = \frac{\sigma_X}{\sqrt{4}} = \frac{10}{2} = 5.00$$

and when $n = 25$

$$\sigma_{\overline{X}} = \frac{\sigma_X}{\sqrt{25}} = \frac{10}{5} = 2.00$$

Inspection of table 10.1 shows that the standard errors that were computed for the three sets of sample means came fairly close to the predicted values (12.61 vs. 10.00, 4.58 vs. 5.00, and 2.24 vs. 2.00).

Prediction 3 was that the standard error would decrease as the sample size increased. With sample sizes of 1, 4, and 25, the standard errors were 12.61, 4.58, and 2.24, respectively, and so this prediction is also supported by the data from the sampling experiments.

Prediction 4 states that if the raw score population is normally distributed, as ours certainly is (*see* figure 10.1), the sample means will also be normally distributed regardless of the sample size. This prediction is relatively difficult to verify with so few samples, but if you look, for example, at the results of Experiment 2, you will see that of the twenty-five sample means, seventeen means fall within one standard error unit (50.63 ± 4.58) of the mean. This is 68%, exactly what one would predict for a normally distributed array of scores. (Review figure 4.6 .)

HYPOTHESIS TESTING WITH THE z STATISTIC: SOME MENTAL EXPERIMENTS IN THE DATA ROOM

To understand the Data Room, use the device mentioned at the beginning of the chapter. Imagine the distribution of 500 scores shown in figure 10.1 as numbers in a basket. The basket contains 500 uniform slips of paper on which are individually written the values of the 500 scores. The mean of the population of 500 scores is fifty ($\mu = 50$) and the standard deviation is ten ($\sigma = 10$). This special basket of scores is labelled with a big "X" and is kept in the Data Room with a very large number of other baskets which contain similar populations of scores. The only fact we know about these other populations is that some have a mean less than fifty and some have a mean greater than fifty, but *none* has a mean equal to fifty. Only basket X contains a population of scores with a mean of fifty. A sketch depicting this situation is shown in figure 10.3.

Experiment 1: $N = 1$

As we wait outside the Data Room, the Data Room Attendant gives us a single slip of paper on which is written a single score value. Our job is to decide whether the sample score was taken from population X or from one of the many other populations. If we follow the logic of the **null hypothesis,** as presented in the last chapter, our approach to the problem should be to assume the sample came from population X. There is only one way the sample could have come from population X, but there are many non-X populations.

Null Hypothesis. In the context of the z test, the null hypothesis is stated as follows: H_0: μ_0 = (value). In words, the mean of the population from which the sample was drawn equals (value).

Remember, any score selected at random from a population has an expected value equal to the mean of that population, and, of all the populations from which the score could have been sampled, only population X has a mean of fifty. Therefore, any score passed from the Data Room with a value

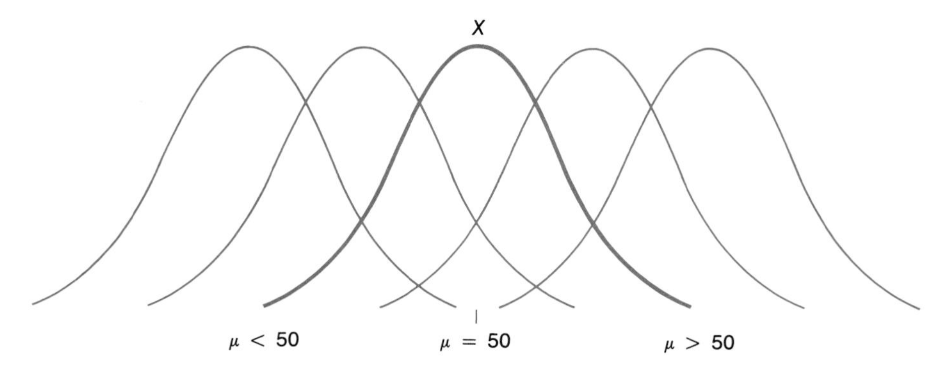

Figure 10.3

Some distributions of score values from the data room. The distribution from basket X has $\mu = 50$. The distributions from the other baskets have means that are either less than or greater than 50.

reasonably close to fifty could be regarded as coming from population X, and any score that is unreasonably far from fifty could be regarded as coming from one of the other non-X populations.

Naturally, the standards "reasonably close to fifty" and "unreasonably far from fifty" are too vague to be of much use. The answer is to standardize the decision criteria by using the 5% convention. If the probability turns out to be less than .05 that a sample came from a population with a mean equal to fifty, the sample would be regarded as having been selected from other than population X. If the probability turns out to be greater than .05, the original working assumption, the null hypothesis, would not be rejected, and the sample would be assumed to have been selected from population X.

Of course, this approach will not eliminate errors. We could decide incorrectly that a score came from population X when it really came from one of the non-X populations (**Type II error**). The possibility of Type II error exists because some of the non-X populations also have scores that are close to and even equal to fifty. This can be seen in figure 10.3 as a proximity or overlap of the tails of the right and left populations with the center of population X. Also, we could decide that a score is too far away from fifty to have come from population X when it really did (**Type I error**). This can happen because there are some rare scores in population X way out on the tails of the distribution that do have a probability of being selected that is less than .05.

Type II Error. Failing to reject the null hypothesis when it is really false. In the context of the z test, this would be the decision to retain the assumption that the sample was drawn from a population with $\mu_X =$ (value) when, in fact, it really was not.

Type I Error. Rejecting the null hypothesis when it is really true. In the context of the z test, this would be the decision that a sample was not drawn from a population with $\mu_X =$ (value) when, in fact, it really was.

The Critical Region (or Region of Rejection)

The question remains, how far from fifty must the sample score be before it is appropriate to reject the null hypothesis. To answer this question we must determine how far from fifty a score has to be before the probability of selecting it drops below .05. Since the sample value can deviate from fifty by being either too high or too low, we must split the .05 into two areas (figure 10.4) of .0250, one for each tail of the distribution.

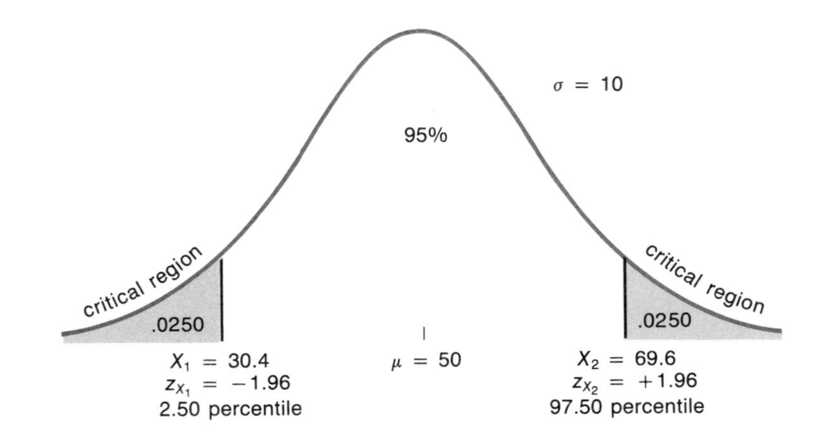

Figure 10.4

Raw score, z score, and percentile designations of the critical regions for a two-tail z test with $\alpha = .05$.

Critical Region. In the context of chapter 10, the critical regions for a two-tail test are the mirror image segments of area in the right and left tails of the z distribution that sum to alpha (.05 or .01). The borders of the critical regions are -1.96 on the left and $+1.96$ on the right when alpha equals .05 and $+2.58$, and -2.58 when alpha equals .01. For a one-tail test the critical region begins at 1.64 when alpha equals .05 and 2.33 when alpha equals .01.

Region of Rejection (also called Critical Region). If the computed value of the z statistic falls in a region of rejection we must reject the null hypothesis.

Each of these areas is called a **critical region** (or **region of rejection**). The border of the lower critical region is on the 2.5 percentile, and the border of the upper critical region is on the 97.5 percentile. Since we know the mean and standard deviation of population X, we can use the z statistic to find the scores on the 2.5 and 97.5 percentiles. As shown in figure 10.4, the z scores at these locations are -1.96 and $+1.96$, and we can solve for the raw score values at these locations using the same technique applied in chapter 4.

$$z = \frac{X - \mu}{\sigma}$$

$$-1.96 = \frac{X - 50}{10} \qquad +1.96 = \frac{X - 50}{10}$$

$$X = 30.4 \qquad X = 69.6$$

We now have specific guidelines: Reject the null hypothesis any time the value passed from the Data Room is less than or equal to 30.4 or greater than or equal to 69.6.

Experiment 2: $n = 4$

In this experiment the Data Room Attendant passes us four slips of paper at once. We are told that all four scores have been selected from the same population and we must decide which population, X or non-X, was used for the selection. This time, let us set this up as a formal hypothesis test following the same format and steps developed in the last chapter.

$$\text{null hypothesis: } H_0\text{: } \mu = 50$$
$$\text{alternative hypothesis: } H_1\text{: } \mu \neq 50$$

Decision Rule: If the probability of selecting the four scores from the null hypothesis population is less than or equal to .05, we shall reject the null hypothesis. Specifically, if $z < -1.96$ or $z > +1.96$, reject the null hypothesis.

Here are the steps of hypothesis testing as they apply to Data Room Experiment 2.

Step 1. *Collect a sample from a population.* The four scores in our sample were collected by the Data Room Attendant.

Step 2. *Compute a statistic from the sample data.* The statistic we shall compute is the sample mean. The expected value of a sample mean is the mean of the population from which the sample was drawn. Therefore, the sample mean will provide information concerning which population, X or non-X, the sample may have come from. The mean of the four scores equals sixty.

Null Hypothesis Population. The population described in the null hypothesis from which we assume the sample was drawn. This is the raw score population with $\mu_X =$ (value) and $\sigma_X =$ (value).

Step 3. *Locate the statistic on its theoretical sampling distribution.* In general, when we know the mean and standard deviation of the **null hypothesis population** (here, $\mu = 50, \sigma = 10$), we may locate a *single* raw score selected from that population using the z statistic. We did this in Experiment 1 using the following formula:

$$z = \frac{X - \mu}{\sigma}$$

Using words rather than symbols, this formula may be written:

$$z = \frac{\text{(score from a normal distribution)} - \text{(distribution mean)}}{\text{(deviation measure of the distribution)}}$$

In experiment, since our sample mean of sixty is also considered to be a single score from a normal distribution (i.e., the distribution of all possible sample means. See Theoretical Expectation 4 earlier in this chapter.), we may use the z statistic to locate sixty on its sampling distribution. According to Theoretical Expectation 1, the mean of the sampling distribution will equal the mean of the null hypothesis population, and according to Theoretical Expectation 2, the deviation measure of the sampling distribution of the sample mean will equal the standard deviation of the null hypothesis population divided by the square root of the sample size. Therefore, we may locate our sample mean of sixty as follows:

$$z = \frac{\overline{X} - \mu}{\sigma/\sqrt{n}}$$

$$z = \frac{60 - 50}{10/\sqrt{4}}$$

$$z = \frac{10}{10/2}$$

$$z = \frac{10}{5} = 2.00$$

The sample mean of sixty is located two standard error units above the sampling distribution mean of fifty.

Notice that the two z formulae for locating a raw score versus a sample mean look different from each other. The original formula we used in chapter 4 to locate a single raw score:

$$z = \frac{X - \mu}{\sigma}$$

compared to the formula for locating a sample mean,

$$z = \frac{\overline{X} - \mu}{\sigma / \sqrt{n}}$$

Actually, when we translate the symbols in these formulae into words, both say

$$z = \frac{(\text{score from a normal distribution}) - (\text{distribution mean})}{(\text{deviation measure of the distribution})}$$

Step 4. *Determine the probability of obtaining a statistic with a value as rare or rarer than the computed value.* Here, as with most hypothesis testing, the most important determination is whether or not this probability is greater than or less than .05 (or .01 if that standard is used). In our Data Room Experiment 2, it is not necessary to know the exact probability of selecting four scores with a mean of sixty from a population with a mean of fifty and a standard deviation of ten. All we have to do is compare our computed value for z (here, $z = 2.00$) to the value stated in the decision rule ($z = 1.96$) to know whether the probability of selecting the sample was less than or greater than .05. We shall do this in Step 5.

Step 5. *Compare the value computed in Step 4 to the value stated in the decision rule.* The computed value for z exceeds the value of 1.96 that is stated in the **decision rule,** and so the computed value falls in the critical region (also called the region of rejection). Therefore, we know that the probability of getting a sample of four scores from the null hypothesis population that will have a mean as extreme or even more extreme than sixty is less than .05.

Decision Rule. A statement of the standard that will be applied in deciding whether or not to reject or retain the null hypothesis.

Experiment 3: $n = 25$

In this final experiment all is the same as above except that twenty-five sample scores are passed to us by the Data Room Attendant. In this case the mean of the twenty-five sample scores equalled fifty-four. Here is the computation for the z statistic.

$$z = \frac{\overline{X} - \mu}{\sigma / \sqrt{n}}$$

$$z = \frac{54 - 50}{10 / \sqrt{25}}$$

$$z = \frac{4}{10/5}$$

$$z = 2.00$$

Notice that the sample mean of sixty in Experiment 2 and the sample mean of fifty-four in Experiment 3 are both located two standard error units (or z score units) above the mean of fifty. The reason that two different sample mean values can be in the same location in their respective sampling distributions is because the sampling distribution based on a sample size of $n = 4$ has a larger standard error than the sampling distribution based on a sample size of $n = 25$.

$$\text{For } n = 4\text{: } \sigma_{\bar{X}} = 5.00.$$
$$\text{For } n = 25\text{: } \sigma_{\bar{X}} = 2.00.$$

The test of the null hypothesis in Experiment 3 will yield the same result we obtained in Experiment 2. The location of the sample mean fifty-four ($z = 2.00$) in the critical region ($2.00 > 1.96$) means that the probability is less than or equal to .05 of selecting twenty-five scores from a population ($\mu = 50$, $\sigma = 10$) and getting a sample mean as deviant as four units away from the expected value of fifty. Therefore, we reject the null hypothesis that the values came from basket "X" ($\mu = 50$) and default to the **alternative hypothesis** that the mean of the population from which the twenty-five scores were drawn does not equal fifty.

Alternative Hypothesis. In the context of chapter 10, the alternative hypothesis is that the sample was drawn from a population with a mean unequal to the specific value for the population mean stated in the null hypothesis. In notation, H_1: $\mu \neq$ (value).

HYPOTHESIS TESTING WITH THE z STATISTIC: A REALISTIC SCENARIO

The z test is of limited use in the behavioral sciences because one almost never knows the standard deviation of the null hypothesis population, and this value is needed to compute a standard error. Nevertheless, stepping through a problem with the z test will give you further exposure to the underlying logic of hypothesis testing and will serve as important preparation for the next chapter. Notice that the values used in the following example are the same as those used in Experiment 3.

Problem 1A Careful analysis of 1988 production data of U.S. Manufacturing, Inc. revealed that the average (μ) output per factory worker was fifty completely assembled motors per week. The standard deviation (σ) of the production scores was ten. As an experiment, twenty-five randomly selected workers were given a training program in 1989 during which they were taught a somewhat different method for assembling the motors. These workers returned to their jobs and their productivity was carefully monitored. At the end of the test period the figures revealed that the retrained workers had increased their productivity from an average of fifty assembled motors per week to fifty-four motors per week.

The problem we must resolve may be stated as follows:

> Does the change from fifty to fifty-four represent a significant change in the level of productivity, or is it merely a random fluctuation in productivity that is not sufficiently large to credit to the training program?

There is only one way the training program could have *no* effect on worker performance, but there are many levels of change (from a little to a lot) that are possible if the training program did have *some* effect. The null hypothesis should be based upon the single logical state of "no change" versus the multiple states of "some change." Therefore, the null hypothesis is that the training program had no effect and that any change in the performance of the specially trained workers is due only to chance.

The null hypothesis for this problem may be written symbolically:

$$H_0\colon \mu = 50$$

The alternative hypothesis, stating that the training program did indeed have an effect, may be written as:

$$H_1\colon \mu \neq 50$$

The decision rule is to reject H_0 if the obtained outcome has less than a .05 probability of occurring by chance alone. Thus, if the difference between the obtained productivity score of fifty-four motors and the expected (according to H_0) productivity score of fifty motors is a difference that could occur by chance less than 5% of the time, then we will reject H_0 and default to the position that the training program did have an effect on worker productivity.

Because both μ and σ of the null hypothesis population are known, the z statistic is appropriate for locating the sample mean on its theoretical sampling distribution. The critical values for the z test when alpha is set to .05 are -1.96 and $+1.96$ because these are the values that enclose the middle 95% of the area under the curve. Any computed z score that is outside this range will be associated with a probability of less than .05. Therefore, we may state the decision rule using z score values rather than probability values as we did with the binomial test in the last chapter.

> **Decision Rule: reject H_0 if the computed value for z is greater than $+1.96$ or less than -1.96.**

The Steps of Hypothesis Testing

Step 1. *Collect a sample from a population.* In this problem the sample is the twenty-five productivity scores of the random sample of twenty-five workers who obtained the special training.

Step 2. *Compute a statistic from the sample data.* In this problem the statistic is the mean of the twenty-five productivity scores. This mean equals fifty-four.

Step 3. *Locate the statistic on the theoretical sampling distribution of the statistic.* This is the distribution of all possible values of the statistic if the null hypothesis is true. In this problem the theoretical sampling distribution of the sample mean of fifty-four has a $\mu = 50$ and $\sigma/\sqrt{n} = 10/\sqrt{25} = 2.00$. The location of fifty-four may be determined by solving the following equation.

$$z = \frac{\overline{X} - \mu}{\sigma/\sqrt{n}}$$

$$z = \frac{54 - 50}{10/\sqrt{25}}$$

$$z = \frac{4}{10/5}$$

$$z = 2.00$$

Step 4. *Determine the probability of obtaining a statistic with a value as rare or rarer than the computed value.* In the binomial test this step had to be completed, but in most cases of hypothesis testing it may be skipped. This is because we do not have to find the exact probability of obtaining the computed value of a statistic by chance. The important determination is whether the probability is greater than .05 or less than .05 (or $> .01$, $< .01$). To find out we compare the computed value of a statistic to the critical values stated in the decision rule, and this is done in Step 5.

Step 5. *Compare the computed value of the statistic (the location of the statistic on its theoretical sampling distribution) to the critical value(s) stated in the decision rule.* In this problem we used the z statistic with an alpha level of .05, and so the critical values are -1.96 and $+1.96$. Since the computed value of 2.00 is outside this range (i.e., it is located in the critical region), getting a sample mean of fifty-four when the null hypothesis is true would occur by chance less than 5% of the time. We must reject the null hypothesis, and by doing so we reject a chance explanation for the change in the productivity of the twenty-five workers from fifty to fifty-four motors per week. Instead, the statistically significant difference between fifty and fifty-four allows us to attribute the change in worker productivity to the worker retraining program.

THE EFFECT OF CHANGING SAMPLE SIZE

Problem 1B. Let us change the latter problem somewhat and then retest the hypothesis. The basic scenario and values from Problem 1A will remain the same except for the sample size. For this problem the sample size will be twenty instead of twenty-five. With the new sample size of twenty the z value will be different from the 2.00 we computed for Problem 1A.

$$z = \frac{\overline{X} - \mu}{\sigma / \sqrt{n}}$$

$$z = \frac{54 - 50}{10/\sqrt{20}}$$

$$z = \frac{4}{10/4.47}$$

$$z = 1.79$$

Unlike the 2.00 value computed earlier, the 1.79 value does not fall in the critical region (< -1.96 or $> +1.96$). If the same mean of fifty-four were obtained for a mean of twenty scores instead of twenty-five scores the decision would be that the training program failed to result in a significant improvement in productivity. The reason is that the standard error, the denominator of the z statistic, is smaller when $n = 25$ than when $n = 20$. This should remind you of an important fact that was discussed earlier regarding the relationship between sample size and the size of the standard error: the larger the sample size is, the smaller the standard error of the mean is.

One-Tail versus Two-Tail Tests

Even before the data collection phase of an experiment, there is sometimes an expectation about the direction of the difference that will result from an experimental treatment. In the example just presented, the project director may have expected that the special training the twenty-five workers received could only help their on-the-job efficiency. After all, the method may have had a good track record in other manufacturing environments, and, while it may be far from certain that it can result in a significant improvement in the speed of electric motor assembly, there may have been no reason to think it could possibly reduce job efficiency.

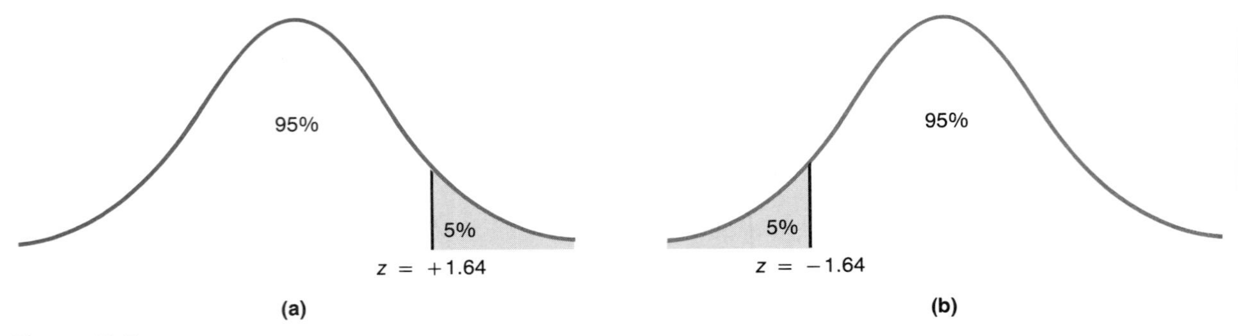

Figure 10.5

The critical regions for the one-tail z test ($\alpha = .05$). The critical region on the right is used to test H_0:$\mu_0 \leq$ [value], and the critical region on the left is used to test H_0:$\mu_0 \geq$ [value].

One-tail Test. The statistical test that is employed to test a directional hypothesis. The 5% (or 1%) of area that is enclosed in the critical region is located in either the right tail or the left tail.

When there are sound reasons for anticipating the direction of a difference an experimental treatment will produce, a **one-tail test** can be justified. Instead of locating critical regions to the right and left of the middle 95% of the area under the z distribution, one critical region is located either on the right tail of the distribution or the left tail. If the sample mean is expected to be larger than the population mean, the critical region is on the right tail, and if the sample mean is expected to be less than the population mean the critical region is on the left (*see* figure 10.5).

The critical value that is stated in the decision rule must reflect the combining of two critical regions into one, and for the z statistic the critical value stated in the decision rule is $+1.64$ or -1.64 when alpha $= .05$ and $+2.33$ or -2.33 when alpha $= .01$. To do a one-tail (alpha $= .05$) test of the hypothesis regarding the effectiveness of the special training on worker productivity, the null and alternative hypotheses would be

$$H_0\text{: } \mu \leq 50$$
$$H_1\text{: } \mu > 50$$

Decision Rule: reject H_0 if the computed value of z is greater than 1.64.

Since the computed z value of 1.79 is greater than the critical value and is located in the critical region on the right tail of the z curve, we would reject the null hypothesis and regard the improvement from an average of fifty to fifty-four motors per week to be a significant improvement in productivity.

Two-tail Test. A test of a nondirectional hypothesis. In the context of the z test, the null hypothesis is rejected if the sample mean is either significantly less than or greater than the value of the population mean specified in the null hypothesis.

Some Comments about One-Tail Tests

The decision to use a one-tail test must precede the data collection process. It would not, for example, be a valid use of the one-tail test if, after having missed significance with a **two-tail test** in the above experiment ($z = 1.79$), the experimenter decided he/she was entitled to use a one-tail test.

The second point is that even in situations where one can justify the use of a one-tail test before collecting data, it is not always used. The reason is that the two-tail test is considered to be more conservative in such instances. Conservative in this context means there is less chance of incorrectly rejecting the null hypothesis, and this happens because the computed value of z (assuming alpha = .05) must be more extreme to reject H_0 in a two-tail test (1.96) than in a one-tail test (1.64). The effect of using a two-tail test when you could justify a one-tail test is to lower the probability of incorrectly rejecting the null hypothesis (Type I error) from .05 to .025.

The third and last point regarding the use of one-tail tests may be explained within the context of the manufacturing productivity example presented above. Assume the experiment was carried out with a sample of twenty workers, and the computed z was 1.79 as in Problem 1B above. If you were the plant manager would you, on the basis of this experimental result, be willing to commit yourself to an expensive program of retraining for all the workers?

The fact that the difference was significant only when the one-tail critical value was used would be unlikely to inspire you with confidence concerning the value of the training program. The difference was significant, but your attitude may be that it "just barely made it," and you would probably be reluctant to commit yourself to the expense of retraining all the remaining workers.

Good statisticians are not supposed to think in these terms. Strictly speaking, a result either is or is not significant, and it is inappropriate to describe results as "very significant" or "barely significant." Thus, if appropriate procedures were followed and a one-tail test is justified for a research problem, one should not regard an obtained z as marginally significant just because, if a two-tail test were applied, it would have missed significance. Unfortunately, this type of thinking is more the rule than the exception among scientists. A set of significant research results submitted to a scientific journal is likely to be regarded skeptically if the statistical tests are significant only when using the critical value for a one-tail test but not when using the critical value for a two-tail test *even if the one-tail test is completely justified*. The reason for this apparent departure from statistical orthodoxy is the reluctance to commit the Type I error—representing a set of published results as significant that later cannot be replicated by other researchers.

Summary

In this chapter we examined the characteristics of the sampling distribution of the sample mean through a presentation and empirical verification of the central limit theorem. By combining this information with the information on hypothesis testing originally presented in the last chapter, we learned how to apply the z statistic to the testing of single sample hypotheses. All the general terms that relate to hypothesis testing (null hypothesis, alternative hypothesis, decision rule, Type I error, Type II error, one-tail vs. two-tail test, and critical region (or region of rejection)) were addressed within the context of the single sample z test.

Key Terms

Alternative Hypothesis
Central Limit Theorem
Critical Region
Decision Rule
Expected Value
Null Hypothesis
Null Hypothesis Population
One-tail Test
Region of Rejection
Sampling Distribution
Standard Error
Two-tail Test
Type I Error
Type II Error

Exercises

1. If twenty-five samples of 100 scores each are drawn from a population with $\mu = 40$ and $\sigma = 20$, and if a mean is computed for each sample, the mean of the twenty-five means has a theoretically expected value equal to ________ and the deviation measure of the distribution of sample means (the standard error) has a theoretically expected value equal to ________.
2. Ms. Turnbull, along with the other third grade teachers, has been using the same standardized spelling test for her class for many years. The average performance for her students over the years is eighty-two and the standard deviation of the population of test scores is ten.

   This year she made some changes in her presentation of the material and her class of twenty-five obtained an average of eighty-six. Was this a random fluctuation or does Ms. Turnbull have reason to believe that her new style of presentation significantly increased the level of student performance? Use the .05 level of significance.
3. Over many years the Peerless Hardware Co. has kept careful records concerning the defect rate of their #77 flush valve. For as long as Peerless has been making the product, the average number of valves that fail quality control inspection has averaged twenty valves for every 250 produced, and the standard deviation of the distribution of rejection scores is six.

   In January a suggestion from one of the hourly workers was put into effect and the rejection rate for the next nine weeks averaged eighteen per 250. Does this represent a significant change in the rejection rate? Use $\alpha = .05$ (two-tail).
4. The College Quarterly did an analysis of the S.A.T. scores of all entering freshmen and reported that, for the first time in Marquardt University's history, the average combined verbal/mathematics S.A.T. score for incoming freshmen topped 1300. The standard deviation of the distribution of S.A.T. scores was forty.

   There was a rumor that this claim was fabricated for publicity purposes, but when you asked for access to the data to verify the claim, your request was denied. Instead, by using the Freshman Directory, you called a random sample of sixteen freshmen and asked them to tell you their S.A.T. scores. The mean of the sixteen scores was 1280. Do you conclude that the rumor is likely to be true? Use $\alpha = .01$.

5. What is the relationship between sample size and the deviation measure (the standard error) of the sampling distribution of the sample mean?
6. If a sample is selected at random from a population, what is the expected value of the sample mean?
7. Explain the distinction between one-tail and two-tail tests. If you completed Exercise 3 by using a one-tail test, would you have arrived at a different decision regarding the change in the rejection rate?
8. Defend the use of one-tail tests for Exercises 3 and 4.
9. If you are testing a hypothesis using the z test with alpha set equal to .05, the regions of rejection will be below the ____________ percentile of the z distribution and above the ____________ percentile.
10. The characteristics of the sampling distribution of the sample mean are given by the ______________________ Theorem.
11. Depending on the outcome of the hypothesis testing you did to answer Exercises 2, 3, and 4 (reject or fail to reject H_0), invent a scenario that could account for the occurrence of a Type I error or a Type II error within the context of each problem.
12. The herpetologist at the zoo buys live rodents to feed the snakes. Records reveal that the snake colony consumes an average of fifty rodents per month, and the standard deviation of the distribution of monthly rodent consumption scores is five. Although the snakes have shown no definite symptoms of being ill, the herpetologist thinks that they did not eat normally during the previous month when they consumed only forty-one mice. Let $\alpha = .05$.
    a. Does the figure of forty-one rodents represent a significant departure from the usual average of fifty?
    b. Can you defend the use of a one-tail test for testing the experimental hypothesis that rodent consumption has decreased?
    c. Does it make a difference in the outcome of the test if a one-tail test is used instead of a two-tail test.
13. Weather records going back 100 years show that the average daily high temperature during January in Rocky Point, Arkansas is 52° F. The standard deviation of the distribution of temperature scores is three. This past January the average daily high temperature was 60°, and the weatherman declared that the greenhouse effect had arrived in Rocky Point. Was his conclusion justified? Use $\alpha = .01$.

CHAPTER 11

The Single Sample *t*-Test and Confidence Intervals

Step 3 in testing hypotheses, according to the sequence of steps used in this text and in the computer tutorials, requires locating a sample statistic on its sampling distribution. When we applied the single sample z test to experimental data in the last chapter, this step was accomplished by transforming the sample mean into a z score by using the following formula:

$$z = \frac{\overline{X} - \mu}{\sigma_{\overline{X}}}$$

To locate the sample mean, $\overline{X}$, in terms of standard error units away from μ, we must know the other two values in the formula: the mean, μ, and standard deviation, σ, of the null hypothesis population. One basic assumption (as stated in the null hypothesis) is that the mean of the population from which the sample was drawn is the same as the mean of the null hypothesis population. For example, the null hypothesis: H_0: $\mu = 50$, says, "We assume that the sample was drawn from a population with a mean of 50." A second assumption is that the standard deviation of the null hypothesis population is known. The standard error of the mean (the deviation measure of the theoretical sampling distribution of all possible sample means), is represented in the z formula as $\sigma/\sqrt{n}$, the population standard deviation divided by the square root of n, the sample size.

In the imaginary Data Room we used for some "mental" experiments, the determination of these important values was no problem, but for real experimental data in the behavioral sciences, we almost never know the value of the population standard deviation and, hence, can not know the true value of the **standard error.** This should not be surprising because, in the behavioral sciences, the populations about which we make inferences from sample data tend to be very large. In most behavioral research the population is a significant segment of the human race, and even the thought of trying to measure every member of a defined population can be overwhelming. When σ is unknown and a decision must be made whether a sample did or did not come from a specified population, the z statistic cannot be used. Without a value for σ we cannot determine the value of $\sigma/\sqrt{n}$, the formula cannot be completed, and we cannot use z to locate the sample mean in its sampling distribution.

Standard Error. The deviation measure of a distribution of sample means. To compute the t statistic we must estimate the standard error from sample data.

ESTIMATING σ

When a value of a population parameter is unknown, the most logical thing to do is to derive the best possible estimate from whatever information is available. The first thought that usually comes to mind is "Why not use the sample standard deviation as an estimate of the population standard deviation?" Unfortunately, the sample standard deviation provides a biased estimate of the population standard deviation. We say the estimate is biased because, on the average, the sample standard deviation tends to underestimate σ. (This is demonstrated in the SAMPLING.BAS computer program.)

Why Does s_x Underestimate σ_x?

If a small sample is selected from a relatively large and normally distributed population, most of the sample scores will be on or close to the mean of the population. This is because the scores with values on or near the mean are the most numerous and have the highest probability of being included in a random sample. On the other hand, scores that are relatively distant from the mean are fewer in number and, because they are less well-represented in the population, they are less likely to be selected. If the extreme scores near the tails of a large population distribution are not included in a small sample, the amount of variability among the scores in the sample will not reflect accurately the full amount of variability present among the scores of the population (figure 11.1).

Figure 11.1

The makeup of a relatively small sample (under the line) that is selected from a relatively large population; a typical outcome.

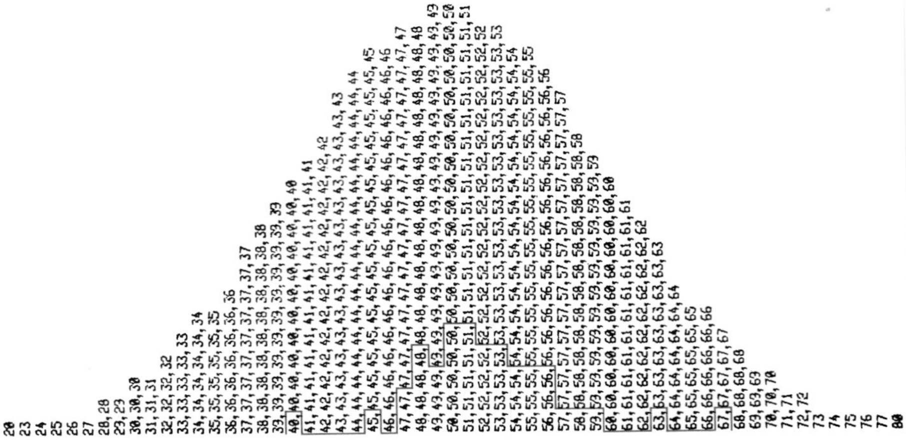

HOW CAN WE IMPROVE THE ESTIMATE OF σ?

As discussed briefly in chapter 3, when variance computed on sample data is to be used as an estimate of σ, variation must be divided by $n - 1$ instead of n. The $n - 1$ term represents the number of elements that were used to compute the variation of a set (i.e., the size of the sample) minus 1, and is called **degrees of freedom.**

Degrees of Freedom. The number of elements of data that are free to vary in calculating a statistic. In the context of the single sample *t*-test, degrees of freedom equals the sample size minus one. In notation, $df = (n - 1)$.

> **The number of degrees of freedom (*df*) for a statistic is the number of elements of data that are free to vary in calculating the statistic.**

We know from chapter 3 that the sum of the deviation scores around the mean must equal zero: $\Sigma(X - \overline{X}) = 0$. In computing the sum of squares for a set using the deviation method, we must first compute the set of deviation scores:

X	$\overline{X}$	$(X - \overline{X})$	$(X - \overline{X})^2$
1	3	−2	
2	3	−1	
3	3	0	
4	3	1	
5	3	?????	
		$\Sigma(X - \overline{X}) = 0$	$SS_X = \Sigma(X - \overline{X})^2$

For the sum of the deviation scores to equal zero, the last deviation must equal two. The last deviation score is not free to vary, and so only four out of the five $(n - 1)$ deviation scores are free to vary. In general, *the degrees of freedom associated with the computation of the variation (SS) of a set is the number of scores in the set minus one* $(n - 1)$.

Dividing variation by degrees of freedom $(n - 1)$ instead of n inflates the estimate of σ and yields an **unbiased estimate** of the population variance. It can be shown that with this correction, the expected value of $s^2 = \sigma^2$, and the expected value of $s = \sigma$. Similarly, when degrees of freedom is used in the computation of the standard error, it can be shown that the expected value of $s_{\overline{X}} = \sigma_{\overline{X}}$.

Unbiased Estimate. A sample statistic is an unbiased estimate of a population parameter if, on the average, the sample statistic equals the population parameter.

COMPARING THE t AND z STATISTICS

Let us substitute our unbiased estimate $s_{\overline{X}}$ for $\sigma_{\overline{X}}$ in the z formula:

$$\frac{\text{sample mean} - \text{population mean}}{\text{estimate of } \sigma_{\overline{X}}}$$

Unbiased estimate or not, this statistic will not be distributed as z because the denominator is a variable. The estimate of the standard error, $s_{\overline{X}}$, changes from one set of sample data to another, whereas the true standard error, $\sigma_{\overline{X}}$, is a constant.

The above statistic is not distributed as z. Instead, we say it is distributed as "t" and represent it as follows:

$$t = \frac{\overline{X} - \mu}{s_{\overline{X}}}$$

Keep in mind that what we have in the ***t* statistic** is really

$$t = \frac{\overline{X} - \mu}{\text{estimate of } \sigma_{\overline{X}}}$$

t statistic. The t statistic is a difference score (score − mean) divided by an estimate of the distribution's deviation measure. In the current context:
score $= \overline{X}$,
mean $= \mu$, and
deviation estimate $= s_{\overline{X}}$.

The estimate of the standard error, $s_{\overline{X}}$, can be too low, too high, or right on, but the accuracy of the estimate gets better as the sample size increases. In fact, the distribution of the t statistic approaches z as the sample size approaches infinity.

This relationship between the distribution of the t statistic and sample size can be seen by comparing the z and t distributions in graphic form and in tabular form. Let us first take a careful look at the t table in Appendix A.

You already know from the last chapter that the middle 95% of a normally distributed population of scores is found between -1.96 and $+1.96$ z score units from the mean of the distribution. The -1.96 and $+1.96$ limits are the critical values for a two-tail z test at the .05 level of significance. The t table shows the very same 1.96 value on the bottom row of the .05 level of significance (two-tail test) column. This is the entry for the critical value of t when the sample size is infinitely large, since s approaches σ in this case.

Notice the *df* heading of the left column. This stands for "degrees of freedom," and, as pointed out above, *df* equals one unit less than the sample size $(n - 1)$. For each value of *df*, there are specific values of t that define the limits within which the middle 95% of the area under the curve is located, and the upper and lower limits of this segment of area are the critical values for purposes of hypothesis testing.

As you examine the .05 column, you will see that as *df* decreases, the middle 95% of the t distribution is bounded by limits that progressively increase. For example, if we look in the row labeled $df = 9$, instead of -1.96 to $+1.96$, the critical values for t are -2.262 and $+2.262$. (This is shown in graphic form in figure 11.2.) Whereas the z statistic had one range of critical values to use for a test at the .05 level of significance (-1.96 to $+1.96$), the t-test uses a family of critical values. The critical value that is appropriate to use for any given t-test is a function of the sample size and, ultimately, degrees of freedom. Thus, when writing the decision rule, one must be careful to select the critical values from the table that are appropriate for the sample size.

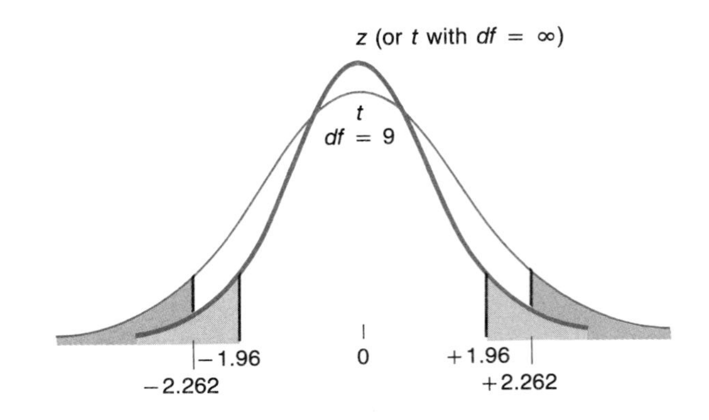

Figure 11.2

A comparison of the distributions of the z and t statistics. The curve for t assumes $df = 9$. The upper and lower limits for both t and z are on the 2.50 and 97.5 percentiles, respectively.

Computing the t Statistic

The computational formula for the t statistic is presented below.

$$t = \frac{\overline{X} - \mu}{\sqrt{\frac{SS_x}{n(n-1)}}}$$

$$\text{where } SS_x = \Sigma X^2 - \frac{(\Sigma X)^2}{n}$$

In this form you may not recognize the denominator as a standard error, but this representation is more simple to write than:

$$\frac{\sqrt{\frac{SS_x}{(n-1)}}}{\sqrt{n}} = \frac{\text{standard deviation}}{\text{square root of } n}$$

The Practical Application of the Single Sample t-Test

The microcomputer provides more flexibility than the printed page in illustrating the mechanics and application of the t statistic. In HYPTEE1.BAS, hypotheses for which the single sample t-test is appropriate are tested using the same format and steps of hypothesis testing that were used for the z statistic in the last chapter. This tutorial presents a problem scenario, generates its own data, and permits the user to select the sample size and level of significance. The t table is built-in, and at the end of the test a brief interpretation of the results is offered.

Sample Problems

Problem 1. To give you a flavor of a session with HYPTEE1.BAS (and to provide you with examples in case you do not have ready access to a microcomputer), we shall step through two problems taken from HYPTEE1.BAS. In the first problem a relatively small sample size of ten will be used, and this will be increased to thirty in the second problem.

The Scenario. Assume that you have ordered a shipment of widgets and wish to test them to be sure that they were manufactured to the desired specifications. As the engineer in charge of widget quality control, you have decided to accept some variation in overall length as long as, on the average, the widget length is 25.0 cm. To determine if the widgets have been manufactured to the proper specifications you must select and analyze a random sample from the shipment. You do so with a sample size of ten and carefully measure the widgets. Here are the length scores for the ten widgets:

24.8, 24.6, 24.0, 25.4, 26.4, 26.2, 26.0, 25.6, 26.4, 26.0

If these ten widgets belong to a population of widgets that have an average overall length of 25.0 cm, then we expect the mean of a sample drawn from such a population to have a mean of 25.0. This expectancy may be stated formally as a null hypothesis.

$H_0: \mu = 25.0$

In words, the null hypothesis is the mean of the population from which the sample was drawn that equals 25.0.

If for some reason the widgets violate the specification of having an average overall length of 25.0 cm, then the sample mean was not selected from a population with a mean of 25.0. This may be stated formally as the alternative hypothesis.

$H_1: \mu \neq 25.0$

In words, the alternative hypothesis is that the mean of the population from which the sample was drawn does not equal 25.0 cm.

Since the population standard deviation is unknown and could only be determined by measuring the many thousands of widgets in the shipment, you decide to estimate σ. Because of this you must locate the sample mean on its theoretical sampling distribution with the t statistic rather than the z statistic. The critical value for t, if you use the .05 level of significance, is given in the t table with $n - 1 = 9$ degrees of freedom. Therefore, the decision rule for this problem may be written:

Decision Rule: Reject H_0 if the computed value for t is less than -2.262 or greater than $+2.262$.

Any computed value for t that falls outside of the range -2.262 to $+2.262$ (the middle 95% of the t distribution when $df = 9$) will lead to rejection of the null hypothesis and you must regard the difference between the sample mean and the null hypothesis population mean of 25.0 cm to be significant (i.e., due to more than just chance factors).

The mean of the ten widget scores equals 25.54, and to locate that mean on its sampling distribution using the t statistic you must fill in the values in the following formula.

$$t = \frac{\overline{X} - \mu}{s_{\overline{X}}}$$

$$\text{where: } s_{\overline{X}} = \frac{s}{\sqrt{n}}$$

You know that $\overline{X} = 25.54$ and $\mu = 25$. What remains is to compute the standard error of the mean. Here is the formula for the estimate of the standard error:

$$s_{\overline{X}} = \sqrt{\frac{SS_X}{n(n-1)}}$$

$$\text{where } SS_X = \Sigma X^2 - \frac{(\Sigma X)^2}{n}$$

Substituting:

$$s_{\overline{X}} = \sqrt{\frac{6529.08 - \dfrac{255.4^2}{10}}{10(9)}}$$

$$s_{\overline{X}} = 0.2616$$

If this estimate of the standard error is substituted in the t formula:

$$t = \frac{25.54 - 25.0}{0.2616}$$

$$t = 2.064$$

Since the decision rule stated that a t value more extreme than 2.262 must be obtained before the null hypothesis can be rejected, and since the computed value for t (2.064) fails to reach that standard, you must fail to reject the null hypothesis.

AN INTERPRETATION OF THE RESULTS

What does this result mean within the context of the problem? If the null hypothesis is really true, the mean length of the sample of ten widgets should be equal to 25.0. Instead, the sample mean equals 25.54. Failure to reject the null hypothesis means that this difference of 0.54 is regarded as a consequence of unsystematic random factors as opposed to a systematic error in the widget manufacturing process.

The Effect of Larger Sample Size: Problem 2

In HYPTEE1.BAS the widget length scores have a slight bias that is applied in the data selection process. That is, the null hypothesis assumption that the widget scores are selected from a population that has a mean of 25.0 is not true. In the first problem, the statistical test failed to pick up this bias and we failed to reject the null hypothesis that the sample was selected from a population with a mean of 25.0. The difference between the sample mean of 25.54 and the mean of the null hypothesis population (25.00) was judged to be not significant. In making this decision we committed a Type II error: failing to reject the null hypothesis when it is not true.

In large part, the lack of statistical power we experienced in trying to reveal the significance of this difference was due to the relatively small sample size that was used. Now we shall repeat the experiment with a sample size of thirty. Here are the thirty widget scores from an actual run of HYPTEE1.BAS.

24.6, 25.6, 26.0, 24.6, 26.2, 25.8, 24.4, 25.8, 25.2, 24.4, 25.4, 24.6, 26.2, 24.6, 26.4, 24.4, 25.8, 24.8, 25.6, 24.8, 25.6, 25.8, 26.0, 25.6, 25.6, 26.0, 25.2, 25.2, 26.0, 26.0

This sample mean of 25.41 is closer to the null hypothesis population mean of 25.0 than the 25.54 mean for the ten widgets in the last problem. Since 25.54 versus 25.0 was not a significant difference in the last problem, why evaluate an even smaller difference? Let us proceed anyway. You may be surprised.

The null and alternative hypotheses will be the same as in the previous problem, but the decision rule must be modified to reflect the larger sample size and increased degrees of freedom. There are now $30 - 1 = 29$ degrees of freedom, and so the decision rule now reads:

Decision Rule: Reject the null hypothesis if the computed value of t is less than -2.045 or greater than $+2.045$.

Notice that the middle 95% of the t distribution with $df = 29$ is contained within the range -2.045 to $+2.045$. This is a narrower range than the -2.262 to $+2.262$ of the previous problem for which $df = 9$ and reflects the effect of the larger sample size on the sampling distribution of the t statistic.

The difference between the 2.262 and the 2.045 critical values for t may not seem to be a large difference, but, to put it in perspective, if the computed value for t in this problem turns out to be the same as the computed t of the last problem (2.064) we shall be able to reject the null hypothesis ($2.064 > 2.045$), whereas in the previous problem we could not ($2.064 < 2.262$).

In fact, using these thirty widget scores the computed t value equals 3.57 as shown in the following computation of the t formula.

$$t = \frac{25.41 - 25}{\sqrt{\frac{11.32}{(30)(29)}}}$$

$$t = 3.57$$

Interpretation of the Statistical Test

When this computed value for t is compared to the critical value as stated in the decision rule ($3.57 > 2.045$) we reject the null hypothesis. The decision is that the average widget length is greater than the specified 25.0 length to a degree greater than can be blamed on chance factors alone. Because the difference between the mean length of the thirty widgets (25.41) and the mean of the null hypothesis population (25.0) is statistically significant, in a quality control test, this would result in rejection of the shipment because of unacceptable departure from the size specification. Any sample of widgets must be regarded as having come from a population with a mean of 25.00 in order to pass inspection.

As you run HYPTEE1.BAS you should notice that the larger the sample size is that you select for the experiment, the more likely you are to detect the built-in bias ($\mu \neq 25.00$). The term that is used in describing this relationship is the **power of a test.** The larger the sample size, the more power we have to detect information that will lead to rejection of the null hypothesis if the null hypothesis is not true.

Power of a Test. The ability of a test to reject the null hypothesis when it is false and should be rejected.

Also, as you run HYPTEE1.BAS you may occasionally observe a pattern of results that is opposite to those just described. The built-in bias of the sampling procedure may sometimes be detected even with a small sample and, conversely, you may occasionally fail to detect the bias with a large sample. This is a reflection of what can happen in an actual quality control experiment. Just by chance, a large sample may contain only properly made items even when the batch as a whole is flawed. Conversely, when a batch is really within specifications, just by chance the few defective items in an otherwise perfect batch may be selected for the sample. If you are suspicious of a result, repeat the experiment—several times, if necessary.

CONFIDENCE INTERVALS

Point Estimation. Estimating a population parameter with a specific score value. For example, the value of a sample mean may be used as a point estimate of μ, the mean of the population from which the sample was drawn.

Interval Estimation. Specifying a range of values that has a certain likelihood of containing the value of a parameter (e.g., μ) as opposed to the specific value stated in a point estimate.

Point Estimation. There are two basic approaches for estimating population parameters: point estimation and interval estimation. We have already been practicing **point estimation** by using sample statistics to estimate population parameters. In the case of the mean, the expected value of the sample mean equals the population mean, and so the sample mean may be used as a point estimate of the population mean. The sample mean is an unbiased estimate of the population mean because, on the average, the sample mean equals the population mean. (This is demonstrated in SAMPLING.BAS and was discussed in the last chapter.)

Despite the fact that, on the average, the sample mean equals the population mean, you know from the last chapter that individual sample means that are computed in a sampling experiment are sometimes less than μ and sometimes greater than μ (review table 10.1), and it is unlikely that the mean of any particular random sample will exactly equal μ.

Interval Estimation. **Interval estimation** is an approach for estimating the population mean from sample data that does not tie us down to a specific value for an estimate. Instead, we determine an interval that we believe, with a specified degree of confidence (say, 95%), contains the value of the population mean. For example, with a point estimate we say, "I estimate that the mean of the population equals (*sample mean*)," but with an interval estimate we say, "I am 95% confident that the true value of the population mean is somewhere between (*lower limit*) and (*upper limit*)." Again, we do not try to assign a value to the population mean when using an interval estimate. We simply determine a range that we believe, with a specified degree of confidence, contains the population mean.

The formula for determining the upper and lower limits of such an interval is really just a rearrangement of the familiar *t*-test formula in which μ is isolated on one side of the equation.

Here is the formula for the t statistic:

$$t = \frac{\overline{X} - \mu}{s_{\overline{X}}}$$

And here is how the formula may be rearranged:

$$t \cdot s_{\overline{X}} = \overline{X} - \mu \qquad \text{(Multiply both sides by the standard error.)}$$

$$\mu = \overline{X} - t \cdot s_{\overline{X}} \qquad \text{(Isolate } \mu\text{.)}$$

When negative values are subtracted, as in the equation

$$\mu = \overline{X} - (-t) \cdot s_{\overline{X}},$$

removing parentheses requires addition, as in

$$\mu = \overline{X} + t \cdot s_{\overline{X}}$$

Since the t statistic may be either positive or negative, we may write

$$\mu = \overline{X} \pm t \cdot s_{\overline{X}}$$

In substituting values into this rearrangement of the t formula, the mean ($\overline{X}$) and the standard error ($s_{\overline{X}}$) are computed using the same formulae presented earlier.

$$\overline{X} = \frac{\Sigma X}{n}$$

and

$$s_{\overline{X}} = \sqrt{\frac{SS_X}{n(n-1)}}$$

To finish the substitutions so we can solve this equation for μ, we need the two values for the t statistic that enclose the middle 95% of the t distribution. The necessary t values are not computed from sample data but, rather, are obtained from the t table in the row labeled with degrees of freedom (df) equal to $n - 1$ and in the column labeled ".05 Two-tail Test." As you can see from figure 11.2, the t values that set off the middle 95% of the distribution are of equal value, but one t value is negative, and the other is positive. (Like the distribution of the z statistic, one-half of the distribution of t is the mirror image of the other half, and so to save space the t table only provides the absolute values. We must provide the sign, + or −, as appropriate.)

If we use the tabled (i.e., absolute) value for t, subtracting $t \cdot s_{\overline{X}}$ *from* $\overline{X}$ will give us the lower limit of the interval, while adding $t \cdot s_{\overline{X}}$ to $\overline{X}$ will give us the upper limit of the interval.

Confidence Interval. An interval of score values within which the population mean is expected to lie with a specified degree of confidence (usually 95% or 99%).

Here are the formulae for both limits of a 95% **confidence interval:**

lower limit of confidence interval:

$$\overline{X} - t_{.05} \cdot s_{\overline{X}}$$

and

upper limit of confidence interval:

$$\overline{X} + t_{.05} \cdot s_{\overline{X}}$$

When the limits are computed, they may be expressed in the following form:

$$P(\text{lower limt} \leq \mu \leq \text{upper limit}) = .95$$

This is read as, "The probability that μ is between (lower limit) and (upper limit) equals .95." (If the t value from the table is taken from the .01 column, the probability that the interval contains μ is .99.)

A SAMPLING EXPERIMENT TO VERIFY THE PRINCIPLES OF INTERVAL ESTIMATION

In theory, if 100 samples are selected from a population with a known mean and limits are computed from each set of sample data, 95 (if the 95% limits are being computed) or 99 (if the 99% limits are being computed) out of the 100 sets of limits will include μ, the mean of the population.

Of course, we do not need to estimate the mean of a population if we already know its value. The sampling experiment described in the previous paragraph, which is done by the CONFDEMO.BAS program, is meant to be an empirical demonstration of the underlying theory. In CONFDEMO.BAS one hundred samples of n scores per sample are selected from a normally distributed population of 500 scores (figure 11.1), a confidence interval is computed using the data from each sample, and it is determined whether or not the resulting interval does or does not contain the population mean of fifty.

A typical pattern of results for the limits computed from several samples is illustrated in figure 11.3. Notice that the range of some of the limits just barely contain the population mean of fifty, although for others the population mean is well within the limits. Two sets of limits, the ones that are starred, missed including μ. Again, for such a sampling experiment, there should be 95 hits and 5 misses. Try this for yourself on CONFDEMO.BAS.

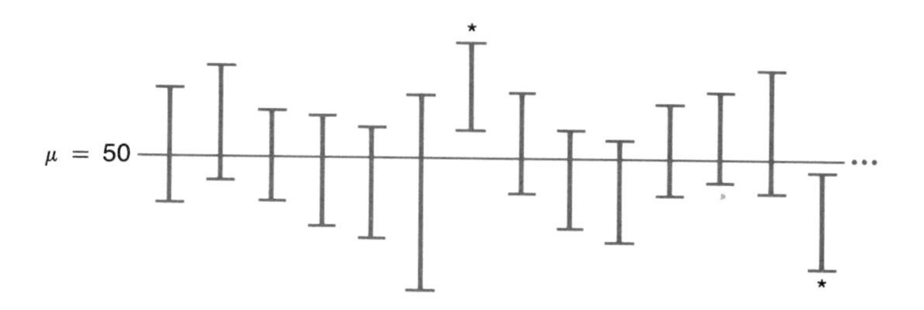

Figure 11.3

When interval estimates for μ are computed from sample data, not all the intervals will contain μ, the true population mean. Note that the starred intervals have upper and lower limits that do not contain μ. Try this with the CONFDEMO.BAS computer program.

Confidence Intervals: A Practice Example

To compute a confidence interval for your own sample data, you may use CONFINT.BAS, but first, let's work through an example.

Harold and his wife retired after long and distinguished professional careers and decided to buy a condominium in Florida. Because they would be on fixed incomes and had an expensive travel agenda, they wanted to be sure not to tie themselves down with excessive fixed costs. The agent of the condominium complex to which they were considering moving could not tell Harold the cost of the average utility bill he might expect to pay. On his own, Harold wandered around to ask residents about the monthly cost of utilities they were experiencing. Here are the data from sixteen residents that we shall assume represent a random sample of the residents:

$125, $135, $110, $95, $140, $140, $130, $95, $120, $100
$125, $140, $135, $155, $130, $125

Here are the formulae for both limits of a 95% confidence interval:

lower limit of confidence interval:

$$\overline{X} - t_{.05} \cdot s_{\overline{X}}$$

and

upper limit of confidence interval:

$$\overline{X} - t_{.05} \cdot s_{\overline{X}}$$

The t value is $t_{.05}$ with $df = 15$. From the t table, this equals 2.131. Here is the computation of the standard error:

$$s_{\overline{X}} = \sqrt{\frac{SS_X}{n(n-1)}}$$

$$\text{where } SS_X = \Sigma X^2 - \frac{(\Sigma X)^2}{n}$$

Substituting:

$$s_{\overline{X}} = \sqrt{\frac{254{,}500.00 - \frac{2{,}000^2}{16}}{16 \cdot 15}}$$

$$s_{\overline{X}} = 4.33$$

The sample mean is 2000/16 = 125. Substituting these values into the limit formulae:

$$\text{Lower Limit} = 125 - 2.131 \cdot 4.33 = 115.77$$

$$\text{Upper Limit} = 125 + 2.131 \cdot 4.33 = 134.23$$

$$\text{Thus, } P(115.77 \leq \mu \leq 134.23) = .95$$

This is read, "The probability that μ is between 115.77 and 134.23 is .95." Therefore, Harold should be 95% confident that the average monthly utility bill for the condominium residents falls between \$115.77 and \$134.23.

Correlation Revisited: Testing the Significance of the Pearson *r*

If we determined that the correlation between two variables was 0.00, we could say with great confidence that there is no linear relationship between the variables. Likewise, if the relationship was +1.00 or −1.00 we could say that there is indeed a linear relationship between the two variables (in fact, a perfect one). At what point do we say that *r* is large enough to indicate the presence of "some" linear relationship—not a perfect one, perhaps, but real nonetheless? To answer this question for a particular *r* value we must perform a test of statistical significance using the steps of hypothesis testing. First, however, it is important to understand the sampling distribution of this statistic.

The Sampling Distribution of the Pearson *r*

Consider a sampling experiment that requires us to

1. draw forty independent random samples from a population
2. randomly pair the scores ($X_1,Y_1;X_2,Y_2; \cdots X_n,Y_n$) to form twenty random pairs
3. compute r_{XY}, the Pearson *r* statistic, for the twenty *X*, *Y* pairs.

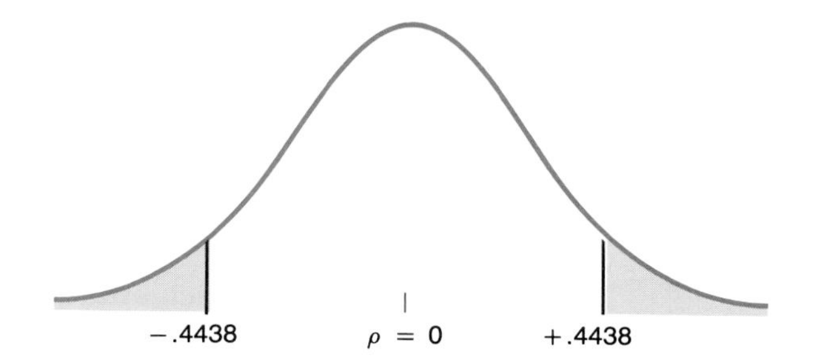

Figure 11.4

The distribution of the Pearson r statistic when $n = 20$ and $\rho = 0$. Lower case rho (ρ) is a parameter that represents the relationship between variables X and Y that is stated in the null hypothesis. The critical values are shown for $\alpha = .05$.

Such a sampling experiment is done in the RDIST.BAS computer tutorial (discussed in chapter 6). If we ran this sampling experiment 100 times and recorded the value of the r statistic for each run, we could take the set of 100 r values and form a sampling distribution similar to the one sketched in figure 11.4. An inspection of the distribution of 100 r values would reveal that most of the time the correlation between the randomly paired sets would equal or approach the theoretically expected value of zero.

Why Zero?

The size of the r statistic reflects the extent of the linear relationship between X and Y, and when variables are functionally related, the value of one variable is *dependent* upon the value of the other variable. For example, given that there is a positive functional relationship between average daily caloric intake and body weight, we can say that one's body weight is at least in part dependent upon how much one eats. ("Once on your lips, forever on your hips.")

Compare this to the random pairing of values. By definition, the procedure of randomly selecting and pairing score values guarantees that the X and Y scores will be *independent* from each other. For example, let us say we roll a pair of dice one of which is labeled with an "X" and the other with a "Y." If we roll the dice 100 times and record the X and Y values for each roll (e.g., $X = 4$, $Y = 2$; $X = 3$, $Y = 6$; etc.), it should be apparent that on any given roll a given X value is equally likely to be paired with any of the six possible Y values. If $X = 1$, the pairings 1,1; 1,2, 1,3; 1,4; 1,5, and 1,6 are equally likely. Thus, X and Y are independent of each other because on each roll of the dice the value showing on the X die is in no way influenced by the value showing on the Y die.

Of course, theoretical expectations are not always empirically verified. Even when the sampling and pairing of score values is determined by chance alone, it is possible for a pattern to emerge that suggests the presence of a significant linear relationship between the variables. For example, when running RDIST.BAS a significant positive relationship of, say, +.52 could result if, just by chance, a sampling experiment yielded many low X, Y pairings (e.g., 30,32) and high X, Y pairings (e.g., 77,79). Such a chance result creates the illusion of a functional relationship when in fact there is no "real" way a dependent relationship can exist between two sets of randomly selected and randomly paired scores.

Figure 11.4 is a sketch of the theoretical sampling distribution of the r statistic when $n = 20$. Notice that the mean of the distribution is zero and the potential range of r values approaches −1.00 on the negative (left) side and +1.00 on the positive (right) side of the curve. The r values of +.4438 and −.4438 mark the critical regions of the sampling distribution for r when $n = 20$. Like the critical values we have used for the z test (e.g., 1.96) and the t-test, these r values are on the 2.5 and 97.5 percentiles of the theoretical sampling distribution of the r statistic. They are the limits beyond which only 5% of the r values exist, and this is the value the computed r must equal or exceed in order for the relationship between X and Y to be considered significantly greater than zero (i.e., "real"). (In the RDIST.BAS tutorial .4438 was given the vague designation of "a special value" because you had not yet been introduced to the concepts of critical value and statistical significance.)

Like the t statistic, the sampling distribution of the r statistic is not one distribution but is, instead, a family of distributions. Each distribution has a mean of zero, but the dispersion present in any particular distribution is a function of the sample size that was used in deriving the sampling distribution. Also, like the t statistic, the r scores that border the middle 95% of each sampling distribution can be listed in a table (Table D in Appendix A) and used for defining the limits of the critical regions in hypothesis testing for a wide range of sample sizes.

As stated earlier, in testing the Pearson r for significance we must decide whether the obtained value for r is close enough to zero to permit retention of the null hypothesis:

H_0: The correlation between X and $Y = 0$

or whether it is far enough away from zero to reflect the existence of a true linear relationship between X and Y.

H_1: The correlation between X and $Y \neq 0$

The null and alternative hypotheses can also be represented symbolically as follows:

H_0: $\rho = 0$

and

$$H_1\colon \rho \neq 0$$

where the lower case Greek rho is the population parameter representing the true degree of relationship between the X and Y variables.

Testing the Pearson r for Significance: An Example

In the boxed example that appeared at the end of chapter 6, the correlation coefficient between the open-field scores and the cage test scores was .81. We might legitimately ask, "Is the .81 correlation coefficient significantly greater than zero? Is there a significant linear relationship between the open-field test scores and the cage test scores? Specifically, can the correlation coefficient between ten pairs of score values equal .81 by chance more than 5% of the time or less than 5% of the time?"

To determine how large a correlation based upon $n = 10$ must be before we should regard it as significant, we may do a special version of the single sample t test*. There is, however, an easier way: Table D in Appendix A shows the critical values of r for specified degrees of freedom. (In testing r for significance, $df = n - 2$.) Below is a partial reproduction of Table D.

Critical Values of the Pearson r

$df = n - 2$	Level of Significance				
	.10	*.05*	*.02*	*.01*	*.001*
—	—	—	—	—	—
—	—	—	—	—	—
—	—	—	—	—	—
6	.6215	.7067	.7887	.8343	.9249
7	.5822	.6664	.7498	.7977	.8982
8	.5494	→ .6319 ←	.7155	.7646	.8721
9	.5214	.6021	.6851	.7348	.8471
10	.4973	.5760	.6581	.7079	.8233
—	—	—	—	—	—
—	—	—	—	—	—
—	—	—	—	—	—

*This test is described in Pagano, *Understanding Statistics* (St. Paul, MN: West, 1981).

The arrows point to the .6319 table entry because with $df = 10 - 2 = 8$ and alpha set equal to .05, this is the critical value for r. This means that when only chance is operating, the probability equals .05 that the correlation between ten pairs of scores will be greater than or equal to .6319 or less than or equal to $-.6319$. If the computed value for r is less extreme than .6319 we regard r as nonsignificant and, for all practical purposes, equal to zero. But if the computed r is more extreme than the critical value of .6319, we say that r is significant. Since $r = .81$ is further from zero than the critical value of .6319, we say that the correlation between the open-field scores and the cage test scores is significant.

It is quite common to evaluate the Pearson r for significance before doing a regression analysis on the data. The reason is quite logical: why try to use an apparent functional relationship for prediction purposes if it may not be significant.

Testing the Significance of the Spearman rho. We may follow essentially the same procedure for testing the significance of the Spearman rho statistic that was described above for testing the significance of the Pearson r. The Spearman rho statistic, to refresh your memory, is the correlation coefficient we used (chapter 6) to describe the relationship between two variables when, after inspecting the data, we decided that one or more assumptions of the Pearson r (interval/ratio scaling, homoscedasticity, etc.) appeared to be violated. (Analyzing data that are in the form of ranks is the most common application of the Spearman rho.)

To evaluate the computed value of the Spearman rho statistic for significance, just as we did with the Pearson r, we must compare it to the critical value from a statistical table. The table we use for this is Table E (Appendix A).

We do not, however, find the critical value of the Spearman rho in Table E in exactly the same way we found the critical value of the Pearson r in Table D. In using Table E it is important to keep in mind that you must enter the table in the row that corresponds to the number of *pairs* (n) included in the Spearman rho analysis. This is different from how we used Table D, which was entered with the row corresponding to the *degrees of freedom* ($n - 2$) of the Pearson r.

Summary

We examined the t-test as a method for deciding whether or not a single sample is likely to have come from a specified population. We used it as an alternative to the z statistic when σ is unknown and must be estimated from sample data. Using the problem scenario from the HYPTEE1.BAS computer tutorial as a model, we did some t-test analyses and followed with interpretations of results. Next, we discussed point estimation and interval estimation of a population mean along with the description of a sampling experiment (CONFDEMO.BAS) that illustrates an important principle of interval estimation. We did a sample problem on interval estimation, and for the final topic, we tested the significance of the Pearson r and Spearman rho statistics.

Key Terms

Confidence Interval
Degrees of Freedom
Interval Estimation
Point Estimation
Power of a Test
Standard Error
***t* statistic**
Unbiased Estimate

Exercises

1. Developmental data on a species of South American catfish indicate that the four-month-old fingerling is usually about 10 cm long. An aquarium containing sixteen newly hatched fish was maintained with a greater than normal water temperature, and after four months all the fish were measured. Did the elevated water temperature result in supernormal growth? Use $\alpha = .05$.

   Scores: 10.7, 11.1, 9.8, 10.1, 10.8, 9.5, 10.4, 9.5, 10.8, 9.6, 10.1, 12.0, 10.6, 11.5, 11.4, 10.6

2. Regard the sixteen length scores in question 1 as a random sample of sixteen scores from a population of catfish. Construct an interval estimate of the mean length of this population.

3. Ever since its development, the seed yield of a particular variety of sunflower has been twenty bushels per acre. Recently, an agronomist has developed a new fertilizer that, if applied at the appropriate time in the growth cycle, should result in a significant increase in seed yield.

   An experimental plot of sixteen acres was planted with the new hybrid and the plants were fed at the appropriate time with the new experimental fertilizer. The table below lists the yield per acre for each of the sixteen plots.

Plot	Yield
1	22
2	21
3	20
4	24
5	19
6	23
7	20
8	18
9	23
10	19
11	20
12	24
13	25
14	22
15	24
16	20

   Did the fertilizer result in a yield that was significantly different from twenty bushels per acre? Do a two-tail test with α equal to .05.

4. At a recent P.T.A. meeting Mrs. Anderson voiced a complant that the school children spend too much time on school buses, and she demanded that more buses and shorter routes be provided. The representative from the Board of Education responded that, on the average, a school child spends only thirty minutes per day on the bus.

Mrs. Anderson decided to do some research to evaluate the veracity of this claim. She selected ten names at random from the student body and had those students keep careful records of the amount of time they spent on the bus on a randomly selected day in a randomly selected week in April. The scores are given below. Do you believe that the students spend about thirty minutes per day on the bus as claimed by the Board of Education representative to the P.T.A., or do the data indicate otherwise? Set $\alpha = .05$.

Student	Time on Bus (minutes)
1	32
2	28
3	38
4	35
5	35
6	29
7	31
8	37
9	40
10	27

5. Regard the bus data above as a random sample of scores from a population. Construct an interval estimate of the mean of the population.
6. Why does the distribution of the t statistic tend to be more dispersed than the distribution of the z statistic?
7. Why is SS divided by $n - 1$ rather than n in computing the estimate of σ?
8. Which of the following expressions represent the standard error?

   a. $\sqrt{\dfrac{SS_X}{n(n-1)}}$

   b. $\sqrt{\dfrac{\dfrac{SS_X}{(n-1)}}{n}}$

   c. $\sqrt{\dfrac{\dfrac{SS_X}{n}}{(n-1)}}$

9. Review the Pearson r and Spearman rho values you computed for the exercises at the end of chapter 6 and evaluate them for statistical significance.
10. Explain the difference between a point estimate and an interval estimate.
11. Why does increasing the size of a sample increase the power of the t-test?
12. A sample of 25 scores has a mean of 70 and a standard deviation of 5. Using $\alpha = .05$, test the null hypothesis that the sample was drawn from a population with a mean of:

    a. 68
    b. 72
    c. 72.5
    d. 73

13. A sample of 16 scores has a mean of 70 and a standard deviation of 5. Test the null hypothesis that the sample was drawn from a population with a mean of:

a. 68
b. 72
c. 72.5
d. 73

14. Compare the results of the hypothesis testing for exercises 12 and 13. The values for the mean and standard deviation of the sample and the population means were the same, so what accounts for the different decisions of rejecting or failing to reject the null hypothesis?

15. Several years ago a study of the health records of graduating seniors at Fallbrook College revealed that students were graduating an average of nine pounds over the "normal" weight listed in reference tables. Lately, students have been complaining that the diet provided by the residence halls has become even more starchy and high in calories. This prompted a replication of the earlier study. Based upon the weight scores of twelve randomly selected graduating seniors, have the students tended to become even more overweight than nine pounds? Use $\alpha = .05$, one-tail test.

weight scores: 11, 8, 12, 14, 9, 10, 11, 14, 18, 12, 13, 7

16. A life insurance salesperson has been trying to sell Max a new policy, claiming that he is underinsured. Max decided to poll his friends who compare closely to him (about his age, married with children, similar income, etc.) to see how much life insurance they carry. Here are the figures for ten of Max's friends (in thousands).

insurance: 20, 15, 15, 35, 50, 25, 10, 50, 100, 40

Construct a 95% confidence interval estimate of the average amount of life insurance held by Max's peers.

17. The HYPTEE1.BAS computer tutorial performs an interactive demonstration of the single sample t-test with computer-generated data. The steps of hypothesis testing are presented within the context of the problem scenario and all computations and conclusions are presented in great detail. Try several runs through this program with different sample sizes and alpha levels.

18. CONFDEMO.BAS is a demonstration program showing that 95 (or 99) out of 100 intervals computed from 100 sets of sample data are likely to contain the population mean. See the *Manual for Stat/Tutor* for details.

19. TEETEST1.BAS is a data analysis program that you may use to test the accuracy of your computations for the single sample t-tests required by several of the above exercise questions. All computational steps are presented in great detail for your reference.

CHAPTER 12

The Two-Sample *t*-Test

THE TWO-TREATMENT EXPERIMENT

Experimental Group. The group in an experiment that is randomly designated to receive the experimental treatment.

Control Group. A group that is as similar as possible to the experimental group in composition and experience except for exposure to the experimental treatment.

Repeated Measures Design. Each subject is tested under both the control and experimental conditions. The before and after design is one type of repeated measures design.

One of the most basic experimental designs used in behavioral science research is the two-treatment experiment. In the independent groups version of the two-treatment experiment, subjects are randomly selected from a large group of potential subjects and are randomly assigned to one of two-treatment conditions. Sometimes the subjects in one group (the **experimental group**) receive exposure to an experimental treatment while the subjects in the other group (the **control group**) remain untreated and provide a baseline against which the experimental data may be compared. ("Did the group that received the medication recover faster than the group that received no medication at all?") In another version of the two group experiment both groups may receive a treatment. ("Did the use of reinforcer A result in faster learning than the use of reinforcer B?")

In the correlated version of the two-treatment experiment, both the control and experimental conditions apply to the same set of subjects (**repeated measures design**) or to two matched groups of subjects (**matched pairs design**).

For example, if several sets of identical twins were divided into two groups with one twin from each set receiving Treatment 1 and the other receiving Treatment 2, we would have what could be considered the ultimate matched pairs design. Since several matched pairs of subjects form two matched groups, the matched pairs design is also called the **correlated groups design** or, sometimes, the matched groups design. In contrast, when data are collected from the same subjects under both treatment conditions (e.g., Treatment 1—rest period—Treatment 2) we have a repeated measures design. In one version of the **correlated experimental design** called the **before and after design,** control data are collected on all subjects to serve as a baseline (the "before" condition), then the experimental treatment is administered to the same (or matched) subjects and additional data are collected to reflect the effect of the experimental treatment (the "after" condition).

Correlated Experimental Designs. There are two types of correlated experimental designs. In the matched pairs or correlated groups design, before the experiment is begun, each subject that is assigned to the control condition is matched in some way (or ways) to a subject in the experimental condition. In the repeated measures design the same subject is tested under both experimental and control conditions.

Before and After Design. A type of repeated measures experimental design. A single group of subjects is tested before and after exposure to the experimental treatment.

In the two-treatment independent groups design just described, random assignment of subjects to the control and experimental conditions helps to insure that the two groups are as identical as possible in their performance potential before the experiment begins. Also, care must be taken during the course of the experiment to treat the two groups exactly alike except for the presence or absence of the experimental treatment. If we carry out an experiment and assume that random assignment of subjects and carefully thought out experimental procedures have been successful in eliminating all sources of bias, it is natural to conclude that any difference in the data collected under the control and experimental conditions is caused by the experimental treatment. Many times this is indeed the case, but there is another reason why data collected under the control and experimental conditions may differ: random unsystematic variation that has nothing to do with systematic sampling bias or sloppy procedures in running the experiment.

The function of statistical analysis is to enable the researcher to decide on the basis of probability considerations whether any quantitative difference between the data of the control and experimental conditions is because of an experimental effect or because of insignificant random factors. This decision-making process is carried out by using the same steps of hypothesis testing that were used earlier for the single sample t-test. In the two-sample case, however, the statistic that is computed, the theoretical sampling distribution on which the statistic must be located in step 3 of hypothesis testing, and the formulae that are used to accomplish this analysis are different from any you have yet encountered.

A New Sampling Distribution

Difference Score. The difference score is the difference in value between the control score and the experimental score for each subject in a repeated measures design (or matched pair of subjects in a matched groups design).

One statistic that we may use to compare two samples (e.g., control data vs. experimental data) is called a **difference score** and its sampling distribution is called the *distribution of difference scores*. These two terms will first be explained on an abstract level within the context of a sampling experiment. Then we shall apply our knowledge of the sampling distribution of all possible difference scores to the procedures of hypothesis testing.

The Sampling Experiment

Let us begin as we did in chapter 10 with a general description of a sampling distribution.

> **If the sample values produced by a hypothetical sampling experiment are determined by chance alone and a statistic is computed from each set of sample data, the theoretical sampling distribution of the statistic will display all possible values the statistic can equal and the probability of obtaining each value.**

The particular set of sampling experiments presented below was done by the SERDIF.BAS demonstration program. A random sample of *n* scores was selected from a normally distributed population of 500 scores that has a mean of fifty and a standard deviation equal to ten (*see* figure 10.1). Once the sample scores were selected, a sample mean was computed. This was done a second time, and the mean of the second sample was subtracted from the mean of the first sample to yield a *difference score*, $\overline{X}_1 - \overline{X}_2$. This was repeated fifteen times to yield a set of fifteen difference scores. In theory, we could run this experiment a very large number of times until, eventually, we would have a distribution of all possible values of such difference scores for every possible pair of sample sizes.

Let us first discuss the mean of the sampling distribution of all possible difference score values. It will be the same, no matter what the sample size is. Theoretically, as discussed in chapter 10, each individual mean has an expected value equal to μ, the mean of the population from which the sample was drawn. Therefore, the difference between any two sample means has an expected value of zero (i.e., if $\overline{X}_1 = \mu$ and $\overline{X}_2 = \mu$, then $\overline{X}_1 - \overline{X}_2 = 0$).

This theoretical expectation may be empirically verified using the SERDIF.BAS computer demonstration. Here are the results of three runs through this program with three different sample sizes. (As mentioned above, variable k, the number of pairs of samples to be generated, was held constant at fifteen.)

Experiment 1. Here are the difference scores for fifteen pairs of sample means with ten scores per sample:

+7.10	+7.90	+5.40	−4.30	+2.70	−3.30	+5.00
−4.40	−1.00	+5.80	+1.50	−3.60	+6.30	−1.20
−8.00						

The average of these difference scores is +1.06. The standard deviation of these difference scores is 5.08.

Experiment 2. Here are the difference scores for fifteen pairs of sample means with twenty scores per sample:

−4.00	+4.00	+3.60	−2.95	−1.25	−0.40	−0.90
−1.20	+5.05	−0.50	−4.35	−0.80	+2.75	+3.95
−3.20						

The average of these difference scores is +0.38 The standard deviation of these difference scores is 3.10.

Experiment 3. Here are the difference scores for fifteen pairs of sample means with forty scores per sample:

−1.075	+4.35	+2.575	+0.775	−2.60	+2.675	−1.45
−2.075	+4.30	+2.30	+1.40	−1.725	−2.65	+2.30
+0.675						

The average of these difference scores is +0.07. The standard deviation of these difference scores is 2.52.

As you can see from these actual runs through SERDIF.BAS, the mean of the difference scores came close to the theoretically expected value of zero, and the larger the sample size was (10, 20, or 40), the closer this expectation came to being realized (1.06, 0.38, and 0.07, respectively). Also, the larger the sample size used (10, 20, or 40), the smaller was the standard deviation of the set of difference scores (5.08, 3.10, and 2.52, respectively).

THE STANDARD ERROR OF THE DIFFERENCE

Standard Error of the Difference. The deviation measure of a distribution of difference scores.

The standard deviation of a set of difference scores is given a special name. It is called **the standard error of the difference.** This is so we can avoid confusing it with the *standard deviation* of a set of raw scores or the *standard error* of a set of sample means. In the sampling experiments described above, because we know the standard deviation of the population equals ten ($\sigma = 10$), we can determine the value of the theoretically expected standard error of the difference. Here is the formula:

$$\sigma_{\bar{X}_1 - \bar{X}_2} = \sqrt{\frac{\sigma_1^2}{n_1} + \frac{\sigma_2^2}{n_2}}$$

This formula directs us to divide the variance of the population from which the first sample was drawn by n_1 (n_1 = the size of the first sample), divide the variance of the population from which the second sample was drawn by n_2, (n_2 = the size of the second sample), add the two quantities, and take the square root of the total. In our case this is simplified by the fact that both samples in each of the three experiments are based upon the same sample size ($n_1 = n_2$) and all samples were selected from the same population. The variance of the population, σ^2, is simply the square of the standard deviation, σ, which was given as ten, and so $\sigma^2 = 100$.

If we solve this expression for the three sample sizes (10, 20, and 40) we get

$$n_1 = n_2 = 10 \qquad \sigma_{\bar{X}_1 - \bar{X}_2} = \sqrt{\frac{100}{10} + \frac{100}{10}}$$

$$\sigma_{\bar{X}_1 - \bar{X}_2} = 4.47$$

and

$$n_1 = n_2 = 20 \qquad \sigma_{\bar{X}_1 - \bar{X}_2} = \sqrt{\frac{100}{20} + \frac{100}{20}}$$

$$\sigma_{\bar{X}_1 - \bar{X}_2} = 3.16$$

and

$$n_1 = n_2 = 40 \qquad \sigma_{\bar{X}_1 - \bar{X}_2} = \sqrt{\frac{100}{40} + \frac{100}{40}}$$

$$\sigma_{\bar{X}_1 - \bar{X}_2} = 2.23$$

These values (4.47, 3.16, and 2.23) are parameters. They are the standard error of the difference values of the distributions of all possible difference scores when $n = 10$, 20, or 40, respectively. Notice in the following chart how close these theoretically expected values are to the deviation measures computed from the difference scores in the sampling experiments.

Standard Error of the Difference

	Theoretical Value	Empirical Value
$n_1 = n_2 = 10$	4.47	5.08
$n_1 = n_2 = 20$	3.16	3.10
$n_1 = n_2 = 40$	2.23	2.52

In the preceding sampling experiments we were able to compute the standard error of the difference because we knew the standard deviation of the population from which the samples were drawn. In most applications of statistical analyses to research data, it is most unlikely that this value will be known, and so the standard error of the difference must be estimated from the sample data just as, in the single sample *t*-test, we had to estimate the standard error from sample data. In the next section we shall estimate the standard error of the difference from sample data within the context of the independent groups two-sample *t*-test.

ANOTHER MENTAL EXPERIMENT IN THE DATA ROOM

The Data Room is still crammed with baskets containing normal distributions of scores. Unlike our first encounter with the Data Room, there is no information available concerning the mean or standard deviation of any of the distributions contained therein.

Selecting Two Independent Random Samples

The Data Room Attendant passes us two samples of ten scores, each with instructions to decide whether the two samples were selected from the same population of scores or from different populations.

Here are the two sets of sample data from the Data Room.

Set 1	Set 2
48	41
49	41
51	43
54	49
55	51
56	52
58	52
60	54
62	54
62	64

To minimize error in making this decision we shall follow the standard format of setting up a null hypothesis, alternative hypothesis, and decision rule, and then apply the five steps of hypothesis testing to the data.

The Null and Alternative Hypotheses. To state the null hypothesis we must apply the standard developed earlier in the "Introduction to Hypothesis Testing" in chapter 9. (Remember "Simple Simon?") Let us briefly review the underlying logic of the null hypothesis and apply it to the present example. The logical relation of sameness ("That is a picture of me!" or "That face = my face.") can occur only one way, but the logical relationship of difference ("That is *not* a picture of me!" or "That face ≠ my face.") can occur in essentially infinite variety. There is only one you, and a very large number of "non-you" persons that exist.

Similarly, there is only one way the two samples could have been drawn from the same population or from identical populations (population 1 is *identical* to population 2) and essentially an infinite number of ways they could have been drawn from two different populations (population 1 is *different* from population 2). In describing two populations as "different," the difference can be a little to a lot or anywhere in between, but in describing two populations as "identical," no logical states are allowed that would violate the "identical" specification. There is only one way X can be absolutely identical to Y.

For reasons of efficiency in decision making that were developed in chapter 9, when we formulate a null hypothesis, we must assume that the one way an event could happen is in fact the way it did happen. In the present example, therefore, the null hypothesis must be that both samples were drawn from the same population distribution.

Null Hypothesis: $H_0: \mu_1 = \mu_2$ **or** $\mu_1 - \mu_2 = 0$
Alternative: $H_1: \mu_1 \neq \mu_2$ **or** $\mu_1 - \mu_2 \neq 0$

The Decision Rule. To state the decision rule we must know the values that define the critical region. As we did for the single sample t-test, we look up these values in the t table. In the independent groups t-test we must combine the degrees of freedom from the two groups: $(n_1 - 1) + (n_2 - 1)$ or, written another way, $n_1 + n_2 - 2$. The df value for our analysis equals 18 $(10 + 10 - 2 = 18)$. If the .05 level of significance is used, the critical value that appears in the t table for $df = 18$ equals 2.101. Here is the formal statement of the decision rule.

Decision Rule: Reject the null hypothesis if the computed value of t is greater than or equal to 2.101 or less than or equal to −2.101.

The Steps of Hypothesis Testing

Step 1. The first step of hypothesis testing says to collect sample data. The scores on page 248 are the sample data from the Data Room.

Step 2. The second step requires the computation of a statistic from the sample data. The statistic that is relevant for answering the question at hand ("Did the samples come from the same or from different populations?") is the difference between the two sample means, $\overline{X}_1 - \overline{X}_2$.

The logic for using the statistic $\overline{X}_1 - \overline{X}_2$ is really quite simple. If the sample means are identical $(\overline{X}_1 - \overline{X}_2 = 0)$, there is no problem accepting the idea that they were both drawn from the same population. If they were drawn from two different populations with very different means, the difference between them will likely be quite far from zero. The difference between the two sample means is, therefore, a reflection of whether or not the samples were drawn from the same population or from different populations. The mean of the first sample is 55.5, the mean of the second sample is 50.1, and so the difference between the two sample means is 5.4. Using the t-test we shall decide whether this difference of 5.4 units is or is not significant.

Step 3. To complete the third step we must locate the sample statistic on the theoretical sampling distribution of the statistic. This is the distribution of all possible values of the statistic if the null hypothesis is true.

In our coverage of the central limit theorem you learned that the expected value of any individual sample mean is the mean of the population from which the sample is drawn. If, in the present example, the null hypothesis is true and both independent random samples were drawn from the same population, both sample means would be expected to have the same value (μ). Chance, however, results in individual sample means that are sometimes above and sometimes below the population mean. This causes some difference scores to be greater than zero and some to be less than zero (see the data from SERDIF.BAS discussed earlier in this chapter). In fact, the difference scores are distributed around the expected value of zero in a bell-shaped curve. The standard deviation of the distribution of difference scores (the standard error of the difference) must be estimated from sample data using the expression that appears below as the denominator in the t formula. Once this measure is known, our one difference score ($\overline{X}_1 - \overline{X}_2 = 5.4$) can be located on the theoretical distribution of all possible difference scores that exists when n_1 and $n_2 = 10$.

$$t = \frac{(\overline{X}_1 - \overline{X}_2) - (\mu_1 - \mu_2)}{\sqrt{\left[\frac{SS_1 + SS_2}{n_1 + n_2 - 2}\right] \cdot \left[\frac{1}{n_1} + \frac{1}{n_2}\right]}}$$

where $SS = \Sigma X^2 - \frac{(\Sigma X)^2}{n}$.

The SS is computed separately for the group 1 data and the group 2 data and is then substituted in the t formula.

Notice that although this formula for t appears to be quite different from the formula that was used for the single sample t-test, it follows the general form of the earlier t formula.

$$t = \frac{\text{(score in a distribution)} - \text{(mean of the distribution)}}{\text{estimate of the deviation measure of the distribution}}$$

The "score in a distribution" is a difference score $(\overline{X}_1 - \overline{X}_2)$, the "mean of the distribution" (assuming the null hypothesis is true and both samples were drawn from the same population) is represented by $(\mu_1 - \mu_2)$, which equals zero, and the "estimate of the deviation measure of the distribution" is the standard error of the difference.

Step 4. In certain situations (e.g., hypothesis testing with the binomial) step 4 requires us to determine the exact probability of obtaining a statistic with a value as rare or rarer than the computed value. When we were testing hypotheses using probabilities from the binomial table, this information was available. For the t-test, however, we do not need to know the exact probability of obtaining a difference score of $(\overline{X}_1 - \overline{X}_2)$. Because we are only interested in determining whether the probability of obtaining a statistic with the computed value (5.4) is less than or equal to .05, all we need to know are the values that define the critical region. These were stated in the decision rule as ± 2.101.

Step 5. Once the difference score of 5.4 is located in t score units on its theoretical sampling distribution (the location in t units is the solution to the t formula), and once the critical value for t has been determined from the t table, all that remains is to compare the computed value of t to the critical value from the table. This is done using the decision rule.

SOLVING FOR THE VALUE OF THE t STATISTIC

To solve for t we must find the sum of squares (SS) for both the Set 1 and Set 2 data using the familiar computational formula for sum of squares (SS) shown below. These values are substituted in the denominator along with the values for the two sample sizes n_1 and n_2. Notice that $\mu_1 - \mu_2 = 0$ because this is the assumption stated in the null hypothesis.

Here is the t formula and solution for the independent groups analysis as it appears in TEETWO.BAS:

$$t = \frac{(\overline{X}_1 - \overline{X}_2) - (\mu_1 - \mu_2)}{\sqrt{\left[\frac{SS_1 + SS_2}{n_1 + n_2 - 2}\right] \cdot \left[\frac{1}{n_1} + \frac{1}{n_2}\right]}}$$

Where $SS = \Sigma X^2 - \frac{(\Sigma X)^2}{n}$

$$t = \frac{(55.5 - 50.1) - (0)}{\sqrt{\left[\frac{448.9 + 232.5}{10 + 10 - 2}\right] \cdot \left[\frac{1}{10} + \frac{1}{10}\right]}}$$

$$t = \frac{5.4}{2.75} = 1.96$$

Since the value of the t statistic is not extreme enough to fall in the critical region, we fail to reject the null hypothesis and, instead, take the position that the samples were drawn from the same population. Had the t value been more extreme than 2.101 in either the positive or negative direction (say, 2.23 or -2.19), we would have rejected the null hypothesis. Maybe that devious old Data Room Attendant thought he could trick us by rigging the outcome to equal 1.96, the critical value for the z statistic. If we had used the critical value from the z table to evaluate the null hypothesis, we would have incorrectly rejected H_0.

FROM THE DATA ROOM TO REAL RESEARCH

When the t statistic was applied to the two samples from the Data Room and the decision was made that both independent random samples were drawn from the same population, the 5.4 unit difference between the sample means was considered to have arisen from chance factors (i.e., was not judged to be significant). In an experimental context this would be a failure to demonstrate an experimental effect.

A result that is opposite to the one we got in the latter example is obtaining a computed value of t that is located in the critical region. When that happens it indicates that the obtained difference between the sample means could have arisen by chance 5 or fewer times in 100 random sample pairings ($p < 0.05$), and so the difference is regarded as statistically significant. Within the context of the two-treatment experiment, statistical significance means that the difference in the performance of the two-treatment groups is attributed to a treatment effect rather than to chance factors.

TYPE I AND TYPE II ERRORS

As in any test of a hypothesis that is made on the basis of probability, there is always the chance of an incorrect decision. If the means of 100 pairs of samples are computed from scores randomly selected from the same population, five of those 100 pairs of sample means will be different enough from each other *just by chance* to cause rejection of the null hypothesis. In such an instance, on the basis of the .05 standard, we would decide that the samples had been drawn from different populations when, in fact, they had been drawn from the same population. As you may remember from our discussion of this concept in the earlier single sample context, this kind of error is called Type I error.

Power and Type II Error

Conversely, it is possible to miss the fact that scores were selected from two different populations (i.e., fail to reject the null hypothesis when it should have been rejected). In the Data Room scenario, because of a relatively small sample size or a great degree of overlap between two different population distributions, the t-test may not have the power to reveal the fact that two samples were drawn from different populations. If there truly is an experimental effect and we fail to detect it, this is a Type II error. In a research context, the more subtle the experimental effect is, the more power we need to detect the difference. In practical terms, additional power is usually achieved by increasing the sample size and/or by reducing error variability through refinements of the experimental method.

For example, let us say you and I are doing a two group experiment that involves testing animals in the open-field apparatus described at the end of chapter 6. Without realizing it, we have substantially different approaches for getting the rat from its home cage into the apparatus. You pick up the animals with a minimum of fuss and place them in the apparatus, but I, ever worried about being bitten, make tentative and abrupt movements to capture the test subjects and wind up with very upset rats. Since the open-field test measures the behavioral response of rats to the mild stress of being in an open well-lit arena, and since my rats are stressed before being placed in the test apparatus although yours are not, this is going to increase the variability of our test results and make it more difficult to detect any difference when we compare the behavior of the two treatment groups. If we standardized the capture procedure (e.g., you do all the testing) this extra source of variability would be minimized, the estimate of the standard error of the difference would be smaller than it otherwise would be, the computed value for t would be larger than it otherwise would be, and t would more likely be large enough to fall in the region of rejection (critical region). In summary, nonexperimental variables that increase variability in the data erode the power of the test, and minimizing such nonexperimental sources of variation improves the power of a test.

HYPTEE2.BAS: A PREVIEW OF THE INDEPENDENT GROUPS SCENARIO

A description of HYPTEE2.BAS is in the *Manual for Stat/Tutor.* This demonstration program is written in a style similar to the earlier HYPTEE1.BAS program. After presenting the problem scenario and generating its own data, it does a complete step-by-step t-test analysis for both independent and correlated groups designs. To introduce you to HYPTEE2.BAS and to provide an example of the application of the t-test within a research scenario, the results of one run through the program will be partially reproduced here.

Independent Groups Design. In one kind of two-group experiment, one group is randomly designated as the control group, and the other group is the experimental group.

Here is a problem scenario for the **independent groups design.** Two groups of adult male laboratory rats have been randomly selected from a large colony and have been randomly assigned either to a control or experimental condition. The animals in the control condition were fed their normal diet while the animals in the experimental condition were fed a diet with a special additive. As a test of general health and vigor, all animals were tested for general activity in a running wheel apparatus after being on the diet for one month.

Three options are available with regard to data selection: no treatment effect, a slight treatment effect, or a strong treatment effect. The data on the next page were generated from the "slight treatment effect" data selection routine. Thus, the null hypothesis really is not true in this experiment. Let us see if the t-test analysis on these sample data can detect the difference in activity level between the two groups with the level of significance set at .05.

Since the experimental design and the sample sizes are the same as for the previous Data Room example, the null hypothesis, alternative hypothesis, decision rule, and steps of hypothesis testing will be basically the same as given previously for the analysis of those data. Review this presentation as necessary.

Here are the running wheel data from HYPTEE2.BAS along with the final phase of the independent groups *t*-test analysis:

	Control Group	Experimental Group
	73	66
	57	69
	45	46
	40	51
	50	67
	51	59
	32	43
	20	51
	45	39
	52	75
Means:	46.5	56.6

$$t = \frac{(\overline{X}_1 - \overline{X}_2) - (\mu_1 - \mu_2)}{\sqrt{\left[\frac{SS_1 + SS_2}{n_1 + n_2 - 2}\right] \cdot \left[\frac{1}{n_1} + \frac{1}{n_2}\right]}}$$

$$t = \frac{(46.5 - 56.6) - (0)}{\sqrt{\left[\frac{1834.5 + 1364.4}{10 + 10 - 2}\right] \cdot \left[\frac{1}{10} + \frac{1}{10}\right]}}$$

$$t = \frac{-10.1}{5.96} = -1.69$$

Since the computed *t* value is not in the critical region (greater than or equal to 2.101 or less than or equal to −2.101), we fail to reject the null hypothesis and fail to demonstrate that the food additive led to a change in general activity level. The *t*-test lacked the power with a sample size of only ten to detect the slight treatment effect built into the data selection routine, and so this analysis leads to a Type II error. If this were a real experiment instead of a demonstration that we know has a built-in bias, a reasonable conclusion would be that the differences among the activity scores are due only to random, unsystematic (i.e., not caused by a treatment effect) variation. When you run HYPTEE2.BAS with the "slight treatment effect" option, you should notice that with increased sample sizes you will be less likely to fail to detect the difference between the groups.

HYPTEE2.BAS: A PREVIEW OF THE "BEFORE AND AFTER" CORRELATED GROUPS SCENARIO

In the previous section of this chapter headed "Power and Type II Error" an example was discussed regarding the effect of extraneous sources of variation upon the power of a test. Because the rats were handled differently by two experimenters attempting to collect data, differences in test performance could arise from the handling factor rather than for reasons having to do with the experimental treatment. This extra variability, in turn, erodes the power of the test to detect experimentally induced differences in test performance.

The question arises, "What if every aspect of the experiment were under precise control and every animal experienced the exact same testing procedure? Would the test scores still vary from each other?" They would, and the catchall phrase that describes this unsystematic source of variation is called *individual differences*. Because no two living creatures are exactly alike (even "identical" twins), we cannot expect identical behavior from different subjects even if it were possible to present explicitly uniform testing conditions.

While we cannot control variation from individual differences by tightening up the experimental procedure as we did in the open-field example, we may accomplish a statistical or methodological control of individual differences by means of a correlated type experimental design. The two correlated designs are the repeated measures design and the matched pairs design. As mentioned earlier in the repeated measures design, each subject is tested under both the control and experimental conditions and serves as his/her/its own control. In the matched groups design, pairs of subjects are matched along some dimension (I.Q., size, strength, athletic ability, some personality dimension, etc.), and then one member of each pair is randomly assigned to one treatment condition and the other is assigned to the other treatment condition. In these designs, as we shall see, the extent of the variation due to individual differences can be assessed and removed from the estimate of error that is due to truly random causes. The data analysis for both the two treatment repeated measures design and the matched pairs design is the same. In the next section this type of t-test analysis will be demonstrated for the repeated measures design.

Here is the scenario as described in HYPTEE2.BAS that is suitable for analysis with the correlated version of the t-test. The research problem is the same as described earlier, but the experimental design is different. A group of adult male laboratory rats was randomly selected from a large colony. While on their normal diet they were tested in a running apparatus to get a baseline activity level. Then a special additive was put into their food. After one month on the special diet all the animals were retested in the running wheel. Did the animals exhibit a change in activity level after eating the special diet?

Let us first set up the test of this hypothesis with a statement of the null hypothesis, alternative hypothesis, and decision rule, and then we shall work through the five steps of hypothesis testing.

The Null Hypothesis and Alternative Hypothesis. The null hypothesis and alternative hypothesis for this version of the two-treatment experiment is the same as for the independent groups version. In the present context it is appropriate to assume no difference between the performance of the animals in the control versus experimental conditions (H_0). In the alternative or "experimental" hypothesis it is appropriate to assume that there will be a difference in performance. Symbolically:

$$H_0: \mu_1 - \mu_2 = 0$$
$$H_1: \mu_1 - \mu_2 \neq 0$$

The Effect of the Experimental Design on the Degrees of Freedom and Power

The critical value that is stated in the decision rule is found in the t table in the column headed by the selected level of significance (.05 or .01) and in the row labeled with the appropriate degrees of freedom. Before determining the critical values of t from the t table, we must discuss an important difference between the computation of degrees of freedom for the correlated type t-test analysis versus the independent groups analysis. In the independent groups analysis $df = n - 1$ for group 1 and $n - 1$ for group 2 for a combined $df = n_1 + n_2 - 2$. In the correlated groups analysis $df = n - 1$ where n is the number of *pairs* of scores. This means that for the same number of observations the degrees of freedom in the independent groups analysis will be double the degrees of freedom in the correlated groups analysis. For example, two independent groups of ten scores each or two correlated groups of ten scores each both have twenty data points, but the *df* for the independent groups analysis is $n_1 + n_2 - 2 = 18$, whereas the *df* for the correlated groups analysis is $df = n - 1 = 9$. The practical result of this is that the critical value of t for a given number of data points will be greater for the correlated groups t-test analysis ($df = 9$, $t_{crit} = 2.262$) than for the independent groups t-test analysis ($df = 18$, $t_{crit} = 2.101$).

The potential gain in sensitivity and power one might expect from a correlated groups design, because each subject is serving as its own control, is partly offset by the higher critical value for t that appears in the decision rule. Simply put, if two analyses have equal sample sizes, to achieve statistical significance, the computed t from the correlated analysis must be more extreme than the computed t from the independent groups analysis. (This will be illustrated when we compare the independent groups analysis to the correlated groups example that follows.)

Sometimes a researcher *must* design an experiment as an independent groups experiment. For example, some medical experiments involve sacrificing the subjects as part of the data gathering procedure. One could not, therefore, collect data under, say, the control condition, bring the animal back to life, restore the integrity of its internal parts, and retest the animal under the experimental condition. In such a case we would say that the nature of the experiment precludes using subjects as their own control. When, however, there is a choice, as in the research scenario presented in HYPTEE2.BAS, one must weigh the potential gain in precision that is often a feature of correlated experimental designs against the loss of degrees of freedom. If the variable under study is known to present itself with wide individual differences in the population (e.g., body weight), it is to your advantage to use a correlated groups design. This is because the systematic individual differences component will not contribute to the size of the standard error of the difference as it does in the independent groups design. If, on the other hand, the variable under study is not typically found in the population with great individual differences (e.g., blood sugar level) the lack of individual differences among the subjects will, because of the restricted range of the data, result in a minimal increase in precision and statistical power. In such a case, the increase, if any, in power would not be worth the loss of degrees of freedom.

The Decision Rule. For this run through the HYPTEE2.BAS repeated measures scenario we again have ten scores per group, but because this is a correlated experimental design, there are $n - 1 = 9$ degrees of freedom.

The Decision Rule is: Reject H_0 if the computed value for t is less than or equal to −2.262 or greater than or equal to +2.262.

Here are the data:

Subject	Control Group	Experimental Group
A	73	66
B	57	69
C	45	46
D	40	51
E	50	67
F	51	59
G	32	43
H	20	51
I	45	39
J	52	75
Means:	46.5	56.6

You may have noticed that the scores are the same as those we analyzed for the independent groups example. These data were "rigged" in this way to facilitate comparing the two analyses later.

The Steps of Hypothesis Testing

Step 1. *Collect the sample data from a population.* The experimental data in our two samples were, if the null hypothesis is true, sampled from the same population (or from two identical populations).

Step 2. *Compute a statistic from the sample data.* The relevant statistic is the difference between the two sample means. Here, that difference equals −10.1.

Step 3. *Locate the statistic on its theoretical sampling distribution.* As demonstrated earlier with sampling experiments, the theoretical sampling distribution of all possible difference scores has a mean of zero and a deviation measure equal to the standard error of the difference.

We shall use the t statistic to locate our difference score of −10.1 on its sampling distribution but, as you will notice from the analysis that follows, the computational procedure is different from the one we used for the independent groups analysis. Let us first do the necessary computations for the correlated version of the t-test, then we shall discuss why it is necessary to have a different computational procedure for correlated data.

Direct Difference Method. The computational method for the correlated groups or repeated measures t-test.

To compute the t statistic for correlated data we shall use the **direct difference method.** The first step is to add two columns to the data table. The D column lists the differences between the pairs of scores. Thus, to compute the D values simply subtract the subject's experimental score from the control score. These differences are squared in the D^2 column. Here are the data as they would be presented as the results of a correlated groups experiment (and as they appear in HYPTEE2.BAS and TEETWO.BAS).

Subject Number	Control Group	Experimental Group	D	D^2
1	73	66	7	49
2	57	69	−12	144
3	45	46	−1	1
4	40	51	−11	121
5	50	67	−17	289
6	51	59	−8	64
7	32	43	−11	121
8	20	51	−31	961
9	45	39	6	36
10	52	75	−23	529
			$\Sigma D = -101$	$\Sigma D^2 = 2315$

Here is the formula for the correlated t-test:

$$t = \frac{\overline{D} - (\mu_1 - \mu_2)}{\sqrt{\dfrac{\Sigma d^2}{n(n-1)}}}$$

where

$$\Sigma d^2 = \Sigma D^2 - \frac{(\Sigma D)^2}{n} = 2315 - \frac{-101^2}{10} = 1294.9$$

and $\overline{D}$ is the average of the difference scores (−10.1).

$$t = \frac{-10.1 - 0}{\sqrt{\dfrac{1294.9}{90}}}$$

$$t = \frac{-10.1}{3.79}$$

$$t = -2.66$$

Step 4. *Determine the probability of obtaining a statistic with a value as rare or rarer than the computed value.* As pointed out in chapter 10, in most cases we do not need to know the exact probability but, rather, whether that probability is greater or less than .05 (or .01). This is accomplished in step 5.

Step 5. *Compare the value computed in step 4 to the value stated in the decision rule.* The critical value for t at the .05 level of significance with $df = 9$ is 2.262. Since the computed value for t is more extreme than the critical value, we conclude that the difference between the means of the two groups is significant.

Why Two Different Formulae for $s_{\bar{X}_1 - \bar{X}_2}$?

The numerator of both independent and correlated groups t-test formulae are the same for the two HYPTEE2.BAS problems we did, but the denominators, the estimating formulae for the standard error of the difference, are not the same. As a first step in understanding why there must be two approaches to computing the standard error of the difference, inspect the general formula for the standard error of the difference as it appears next. Even though we will not discuss the derivation of this formula or ever use it in this form for computational purposes, taking note of certain general features will make it possible to illustrate two important points.

$$s_{\bar{X}_1 - \bar{X}_2} = \sqrt{s_{\bar{X}_1}^2 + s_{\bar{X}_2}^2 - 2r_{12}s_{\bar{X}_1}s_{\bar{X}_2}}$$

First, notice that the standard error of the difference is a pooled error term. The plus sign tells us that information regarding the dispersion of scores in Sets 1 and 2 that is attributable to random error is added together ("pooled") to compute the estimate of the standard error of the difference. (By pooling the information on dispersion from both sets we can arrive at a more accurate estimate of population variance.) The second point is that a term that contains r, the correlation coefficient between the Set 1 and Set 2 data, is subtracted from the pooled dispersion measures.

In the independent groups analysis the correlation between the two sets of scores must be assumed to be zero. This is because "independent" is really a synonym for uncorrelated. As presented in the first experiment in RDIST.BAS, when the pairing of scores on any given row of a $2 \times N$ data table is random, the expected value for r is zero. If the correlation between the two groups equals zero, the term on the right side of the general formula that contains r will equal zero because zero times anything equals zero. With this expression assumed to equal zero, the remaining formula for the standard error of the difference will be

$$s_{\bar{X}_1 - \bar{X}_2} = \sqrt{s_{\bar{X}_1}^2 + s_{\bar{X}_2}^2}$$

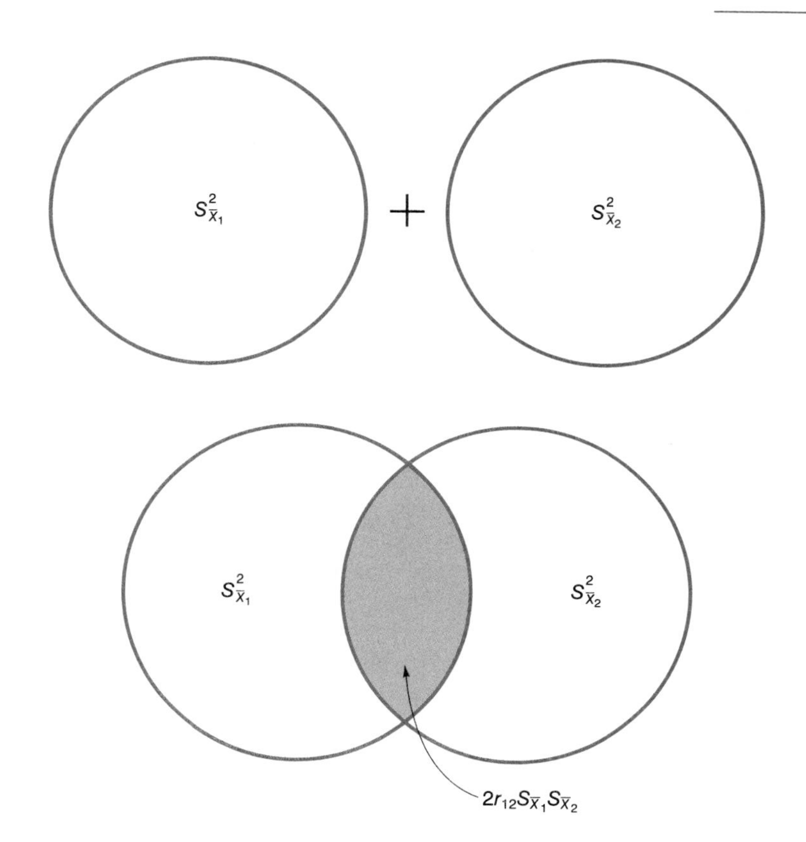

Figure 12.1
Venn diagrams representing the pooling of two independent measures of dispersion.

Figure 12.2
Venn diagrams representing the covariance (area of overlap) between two measures of dispersion.

The addition or pooling of the dispersion measures for the independent groups design may be represented with Venn diagrams as shown in figure 12.1.

In a correlated groups design we have two measures on the same subject (or matched pair), and so a correlation is assumed to exist. For the correlated HYPTEE2.BAS data we analyzed previously, $r = 0.60$. When the value of r is greater than zero, the term on the right, $-2r_{12}s_{\bar{X}}s_{\bar{X}}$, will be greater than zero and must be subtracted from the sum of the two terms to its left, $s^2_{\bar{X}} + s^2_{\bar{X}}$, in computing the standard error of the difference.

$$s_{\bar{X}_1 - \bar{X}_2} = \sqrt{s^2_{\bar{X}_1} + s^2_{\bar{X}_2} - 2r_{12}s_{\bar{X}_1}s_{\bar{X}_2}}$$

Now compare a diagrammatic representation of the preceding formula that reflects the existence of correlation (figure 12.2). The term on the right that contains r will be reflected in the Venn diagram as an area of overlap. This area of overlap is the extent to which the n pairs of scores covary or occupy the same relative positions in their respective distributions.

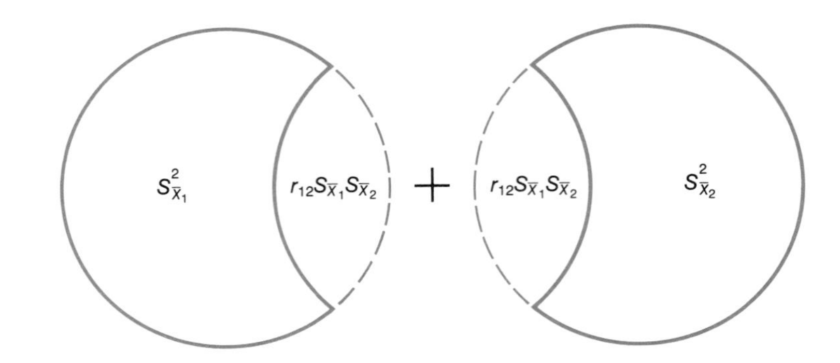

Figure 12.3
Venn diagrams representing the pooling of two measures of dispersion that partially covary. The pooling does not include the covariance ($r_{12}s_{\overline{X}_1}s_{\overline{X}_2}$).

The covariation is a contaminant in the estimation process. It reflects *systematic* individual differences. It is, therefore, nonrandom and has no place in the computation of an estimate of random error. To get rid of the covariation, the pooling must take the form illustrated in figure 12.3. Notice that the area of covariation has been excised twice, once from each group's dispersion measure. This is consistent with the formula that indicates that two times the covariation ($-2r_{12}s_{\overline{X}_1}s_{\overline{X}_2}$) must be subtracted from the pooled measures of dispersion to get a correct estimate of the standard error of the difference. This feature is "built-in" to the direct difference computational method we just applied to the correlated data.

If data from a correlated experimental design were somehow incorrectly analyzed as an independent groups design, the estimate of the standard error of the difference would include the contaminant of covariation and would be overestimated. On the other hand, if data from an independent groups design were incorrectly analyzed as a correlated design and if, just by chance, the random pairings in the data table resulted in a nonzero correlation coefficient, some error variation would be inappropriately subtracted from the estimate of error, and the standard error of estimate would be underestimated. Because both HYPTEE2.BAS scenarios that were just presented were demonstrated using the exact same data, we can compare the two estimates of the standard error of the difference. In the independent groups analysis the standard error of the difference was 5.96, while in the correlated analysis of the same twenty scores the standard error of the difference was a smaller 3.79.

Because of these different values for $s_{\overline{X}_1 - \overline{X}_2}$, the correlated t-test revealed a significant difference where the independent t analysis did not. This happened because the correlation that exists between the two sets ($r = .60$) was incorporated into the computation of the standard error of the difference in the correlated t analysis, but not in the independent groups analysis.

To prove to yourself how important the presence or absence of correlation between the sets is in the computation of the t statistic, randomly reposition the scores within the two groups and recompute the two t-test analyses using TEETWO.BAS or your hand calculator. The independent analysis will be unchanged, but the correlated analysis will be greatly affected.

Assumptions for the *t*-Test

The underlying assumptions that must be met for the *t*-test to be used legitimately are a matter of some debate. The more traditional members of the statistical community take the position that to render a meaningful interpretation of the results of a *t*-test analysis, the variable represented in the data must be of interval or ratio scaling and be normally distributed and continuous. Also, the variances of the two groups of data must be of relatively uniform size. This condition is called homogeneity of variance.

Other less traditional statisticians say, in effect, that numbers are numbers, and the solution of a formula is only a function of the numbers that are plugged in. Since the scaling of the variable will not affect the numerical value of the computed result, they say the result is interpretable.

For at least two reasons this controversy does not present serious problems and will receive little attention here. First, if data appear not to meet the orthodox assumptions underlying the *t*-test, there are other tests that may be used as alternatives to the *t*-test that do not have such assumptions. These tests will be covered in the next chapter. The second reason is that t is a robust test. This means that the *t*-test is relatively insensitive to violation of its assumptions, and this is especially so if the groups have thirty or more scores and are equal or near equal in size.

There is a rule of thumb regarding the homogeneity of variance assumption. Don't be concerned about meeting the assumption of homogeneity of variance unless the ratio of the two group variances (larger divided by smaller) is greater than 3:1 for $n = 10$ per group, 2.5:1 for $n = 15$ per group, or 2:1 for larger group sizes.

Although the *t*-test may be robust to violations of the assumption of homogeneity of variance, it can be a mistake for a researcher to ignore such a violation. Some experimental treatments may exert their effect not by causing a general increase or decrease in mean performance, but by increasing the variability that is present. For example, changes in the workplace may decrease the productivity of some workers who cannot adjust to the new system, increase the productivity of those workers who can adjust, and leave the productivity of others unchanged. Rather than write off the changes as ineffective, focusing on the increased variability in job performance would likely prompt a search for the factor(s) that enhance or inhibit adjustment to the changes. Thus, ignoring extreme variability in a group's performance can blind us to some important considerations that influence the impact of the experimental treatment.

Summary

We studied the underlying concepts and the practical application of the t statistic to two types of two-group experimental designs (independent and correlated) within both abstract and realistic scenarios. We were introduced to the computer programs, TEETWO.BAS, HYPTEE2.BAS, RDIST.BAS, and SERDIF.BAS, that illustrate the concepts and methods covered in this unit.

Key Terms

Before and After Design
Control Group
Correlated Experimental Designs
Correlated Groups Design
Difference Score
Direct Difference Method
Experimental Group
Independent Groups Design
Matched Pairs Design
Repeated Measures Design
Standard Error of the Difference

Exercises

If you do the following problems with a hand calculator, be sure to run the data through TEETWO.BAS to check your work. Don't forget to state H_0, H_1, and a decision rule. Then state your conclusion of the meaning of the analysis within the context of the problem.

1. A researcher for a nationally known drug company is examining the tranquilizing properties of a new experimental drug on a group of laboratory rats. The measure she is using to reflect the tranquilizing potency of the compound is spontaneous activity in an activity wheel following treatment. Both pretreatment baseline scores and post-treatment scores are presented below. The numbers represent the number of revolutions of the activity wheel during the test period. Did the drug have an effect upon activity level? Use $\alpha = .05$.

Subject	Pretreatment Baseline Activity	Post-treatment Activity
1	87	63
2	66	71
3	92	70
4	73	59
5	113	88
6	49	57
7	89	69
8	76	68
9	101	80
10	95	73
11	80	63
12	99	76

2. The owner of a chain of eleven retail stores wished to compare the number of shoplifter apprehensions in his stores for a one-month period prior to the installation of a new security system to the number of apprehensions in the same stores for a one-month period after the security system was in place. The data are in the following table. Did the new security system result in a different level of shoplifter detection? Use $\alpha = .05$.

Store	Old Security System	New Security System
1	26	24
2	18	19
3	19	18
4	26	24
5	30	26
6	17	14
7	34	26
8	28	25
9	24	21
10	27	24
11	22	24

3. A group of twenty-two female infants was randomly divided into two groups. The mothers of group A agreed to use Method A for toilet training their children, and the mothers of group B agreed to use Method B. The data below represent the number of months of age it took to achieve one "accident free" week. Did one method achieve earlier toilet training than the other? Use $\alpha = .05$.

Method A	Method B
26	24
18	19
19	18
26	24
30	26
17	14
34	26
28	25
24	21
27	24
22	24

4. The data for Problems 2 and 3 are identical. What accounts for the different values of the t statistic? (If you enter these data into TEETWO.BAS you will have the option of seeing both independent groups and correlated groups analyses. You will be prompted for the option to see the alternative ("wrong") analysis following the data analysis section of the program.)
5. Explain why there must be two versions of the two-group t-test—one for independent groups and one for correlated groups or repeated measures.
6. Identify Type I error and Type II error within the context of Problems 1, 2, and 3 above.
7. Explain the relationship between sample size and the power of the t-test.

8. Explain how refining experimental methodology can increase the power to detect an experimental effect.
9. What are the considerations one must keep in mind when designing an independent groups versus a correlated groups experiment?
10. An experimental psychologist wished to assess the effectiveness of two schedules of reinforcement in teaching an obedience skill to dogs. Ten dogs were taught a skill using Reinforcement Schedule A, and another group of twelve dogs were taught the skill using Reinforcement Schedule B. The data represent the number of trials it took the animals to learn the correct response and to meet a criterion of five correct responses in a row. Was there a difference in acquisition of the response for the two groups? Use $\alpha = .05$.

    Schedule A: 26, 23, 21, 18, 19, 31, 33, 28, 19, 12
    Schedule B: 9, 22, 16, 20, 25, 18, 29, 33, 16, 18, 26, 20

11. Mr. Allen was assured by his principal that students were assigned to the two senior Spanish II classes purely at random, but he has the nagging suspicion that Miss Standish got most of the bright students and that most of the under-achievers were assigned to his class. To test this hypothesis, he obtained the averages all the seniors earned in Spanish I and compared his students to Miss Standish's. If the comparison were made using $\alpha = .05$ with a two-tail test, what is the appropriate conclusion?

Mr. Allen	Miss Standish
84	82
73	65
85	78
71	66
83	87
94	83
87	81
75	72
84	91
72	81
84	68
75	84
88	82
93	85
86	78
78	84
85	82
73	80
75	68
95	83

12. An athletic director hired a new coach in midseason for the basketball team. At the end of the season he decided to compare the average point production per player during the first-half of the season to the average point production during the second-half of the season under the new coach. The data are in the following table. Was there a significant change in the player's ability to score under the new coach? Make the comparison using $\alpha = .05$.

Player	Average Point Production 1st-Half	Average Point Production 2d-Half
1	18	23
2	21	20
3	12	15
4	8	10
5	22	26
6	18	16
7	11	19
8	14	17
9	23	30
10	6	6
11	4	8
12	12	22

13. Twenty-four arthritis sufferers were randomly divided into two groups of twelve. One group was given the standard medication to control pain with instructions to use the medication only when the pain became very uncomfortable. The second group was given the same medication and instructions but, in addition, they were taught some self-hypnosis skills to help them manage the pain of their disease. The data below represent the number of pain tablets consumed by the patients over a one-week period. Did the group that was taught the self-hypnosis skills consume less painkilling medication? Use the $\alpha = .05$.

Use of Self-hypnosis: Yes	Use of Self-hypnosis: No
17	15
14	10
20	23
27	18
23	16
22	11
19	22
36	9
16	27
31	6
21	30
18	14

14. What circumstances could be responsible for the commission of a Type II error in the conclusion drawn from the analysis in question 13? If you believe the data represent a trend toward significance (the difference is, in fact significant if a one-tail test were applied), what steps could you take in your planned replication of the experiment to make a more convincing case for the effectiveness of self-hypnosis?
15. Explain how you could have set up an experiment to evaluate the effectiveness of self-hypnosis in helping patients to cut down on pain medication using a correlated groups design.
16. HYPTEE2.BAS is a demonstration program that generates its own data within an independent groups or correlated groups scenario. The program follows the steps of hypothesis testing, presents the details of the computational procedures, and offers a conclusion based upon the results of the t-test. Because the user selects the sample sizes to be used, the program provides a good demonstration of the role of sample size in the power of a test. Read about HYPTEE2.BAS in the *Manual for Stat/Tutor* and run through a few demonstrations of independent groups and correlated groups t-tests.
17. Hypothesis testing with the two-sample t-test was done in the preceding exercises using $\alpha = .05$. Would any of your conclusions have been different if $\alpha = .01$ were used? Can you justify the use of a one-tail test for any of these problems?

CHAPTER 13

Nonparametric Two-Group Tests

Hypothesis testing has been presented in the earlier chapters as an orderly and logical set of statistical procedures. First we set up the hypothesis test with a statement of the null hypothesis, alternative hypothesis, and decision rule, then we apply the five steps of hypothesis testing to the data. When we are done we interpret the results and make a decision based upon that interpretation. Having covered several different statistical inference tests up to this point (binomial, z, single sample t-test, and independent and correlated two-sample t-tests), you no doubt have an appreciation for the fact that the attributes of the data and the type of experimental question that is being asked determine the selection of the test that is used for statistical decision-making.

Since the two-sample t-test is appropriate for analyzing the data of some very basic research designs (e.g., the control group vs. experimental group design), it is a particularly useful and widely applied statistical test. It cannot, however, be applied indiscriminately to the data of all two-group experiments. Underlying the t-test is a set of assumptions having to do with the scaling of the data (interval), the shape of the population distribution from which the samples were hypothetically drawn (normal), and the uniform size of the variances of the two null hypothesis populations (i.e., the assumption of homogeneity of variance). Even though, as explained in the last chapter, the t-test tends to be robust to violations of its assumptions when the sample sizes are equal or near equal, substantial violations can distort the distribution of the t statistic. If a t-test is applied under questionable circumstances and the results are reported in the scientific literature, critics will raise questions in the research community about the validity of the test and the interpretation of its results.

ALTERNATIVES TO THE TWO-SAMPLE *t*-TEST

Wilcoxon *T*-Test. This nonparametric test may be regarded as an enhancement of the sign test. Both the sign of the difference score and the magnitude of the difference score influence the value of the Wilcoxon *T* statistic.

Sign Test. A nonparametric substitute for the correlated *t*-test. This relatively weak test is really a binomial test that is done on the frequencies of plus and minus difference scores.

Nonparametric Statistics (also called "distribution free" statistics). Statistical procedures for hypothesis testing that do not require the estimation of population parameters and, in general, do not require meeting many of the assumptions that must be met for legitimate use of the parametric tests.

If a researcher is concerned enough about assumption violations to reject the use of the *t*-test, there are alternative procedures available for data analysis. For the independent groups *t*-test the alternative is the Mann-Whitney U-test, and for the correlated groups *t*-test the alternatives are the **sign test** and the **Wilcoxon *T*-Test,** the full name of which is the Wilcoxon matched pairs signed-ranks test. Unlike the *t*-test, these tests have relatively few assumptions that must be met to apply them legitimately to data analysis. The scaling of the data need only be nominal (sign test) or ordinal (Wilcoxon and Mann-Whitney) rather than interval. There is no requirement regarding homogeneity of variance, and the null hypothesis populations (the populations from which the two samples are presumably drawn) need not be normally distributed.

Because the values of population parameters and other population characteristics (e.g., skewness) are irrelevant to the legitimate application of these inference tests, they are called **nonparametric statistics** or, sometimes, **distribution free statistics.** The tests that will be presented in this chapter are only three of a large group of such nonparametric tests that are applied to many different kinds of data. More nonparametric statistics will be presented in a later chapter on the analysis of nominal data. Many other nonparametric tests, some of which are seldom applied in the behavioral sciences, are beyond the scope of this text and will not be covered.*

Nonparametric statistics are generally easy to compute, and they can be applied to the data of two-group experiments even when the assumptions of the *t* statistic have not been violated. Generally, however, parametric tests are preferred over nonparametric tests because they are more powerful and can be applied to a greater variety of experimental situations. Of the three two-group tests presented in this chapter, one is rather weak (the sign test), one is moderately powerful (the Wilcoxon), and one, the Mann-Whitney *U*-test, is about as powerful as its parametric cousin, the independent groups *t*-test.

THE SIGN TEST

The sign test is little more than a binomial test. The same general procedures that Scott had to use to determine the fairness of his antique Spanish coin (chapter 9) are used in the sign test. The following example will illustrate the application of this test to experimental data.

*For detailed discussions of many other nonparametric tests consult S. Siegel *Nonparametric Statistics for the Behavioral Sciences* (New York: McGraw-Hill, 1956) or W. Daniel, *Applied Nonparametric Statistics* (Boston: Houghton-Mifflin, 1978).

Sign Test Example. An advertisement appeared in a nationally circulated tabloid praising the virtues of a new allergy remedy. The claim was that an herbal tea concocted with a secret plant extract would provide miraculous relief from the symptoms of hay fever if taken during the early stages of an allergy attack.

A physician decided to test this therapy with twelve patient volunteers who suffer from an allergy to pollen. The patients were each given two tea bags with coded labels. Both tea bags contained the herbal tea, but only one had the secret plant extract. The patients did not know that the two tea bags they were given were different or that any special additive had been included.

The physician instructed all twelve volunteers not to take any of their usual allergy medication at the start of their next attack. Instead, they were to brew a cup of tea with one of the bags and drink it. One-half hour later they were instructed to record the code printed on the tea bag label along with a rating of the relief they felt on a scale of 0 (no relief) to 100 (complete relief). If necessary, they could then supplement the tea therapy with their usual medication. On the occurrence of their next attack the procedure was to be repeated with the remaining tea bag. After all the responses were turned in, they were recorded in tabular form as shown in table 13.1.

The choice of the sign test to analyze these data hinges on two observations. First, the experiment uses repeated measures, a type of *correlated experimental design*. In repeated measures experiments each participating subject contributes data to both the control and experimental conditions. The second observation is that the data are ordinal. Any time numbers reflect subjectively determined ratings or rankings, they should be considered as

Table 13.1

The raw data (degree of relief from allergy symptoms on a rating scale of 0 to 100) of twelve patients in the correlated groups herbal tea study.

Subject	Normal Tea	Tea w/Extract
1	20	40
2	15	45
3	16	33
4	30	48
5	10	35
6	0	45
7	40	68
8	34	10
9	5	60
10	30	11
11	25	28
12	22	22

ordinal data. For reasons explained in chapter 2, regarding numbers that stem from subjective impressions as interval or ratio data is very difficult to defend.

The first step in doing the sign test is to decide what to do with tied scores, if there are any in the data. If there are very few ties compared to the total number of pairs they may be discarded. In the present example the twelfth pair is a tie, and so this pair of scores may be discarded. (If there had been more than a few ties, we would retain them for the analysis and treat them according to a method to be described below.) The second step is to add a column to the original table of data to record the difference score that results from subtracting each second column entry from each first column entry. For example, the first person rated the relief from her normal tea to be only 20, while she rated the relief from the special tea at 40. The difference is −20, so this value is recorded in the difference column.

The next step is to count the number of difference scores that are positive and the number of difference scores that are negative. As you can see in table 13.2, two of the differences are positive and nine are negative.

When there are many ties in the data it is acceptable to credit one-half of the ties to the plus tally and one-half to the minus tally. If the number of ties is odd, throw one away to make it even. This method has the merit of never throwing out more than one pair of scores, maximizing power by retaining a larger sample size, and avoiding a distorted view of the experimental results that can result whenever data are discarded.

The 2/9 plus/minus split is the obtained statistical result. Let's apply the sign test to the experimental data by following the steps of hypothesis testing.

Step 1. *Collect the sample data.* The data are the two groups of scores.

Table 13.2

The data of the repeated measures herbal tea study with signed difference values.

Subject	Normal Tea	Tea w/Extract	Difference
1	20	40	−20
2	15	45	−30
3	16	33	−17
4	30	48	−18
5	10	35	−25
6	0	45	−45
7	40	68	−28
8	34	10	+24
9	5	60	−55
10	30	11	+19
11	25	28	−3

Step 2. *Compute a statistic from the sample data.* Here, the statistic is the ratio of plus to minus (or minus to plus) relationships. For the allergy relief data, the ratio is 9:2.

Step 3. *Locate the statistic on its theoretical sampling distribution,* the distribution of the sample statistic if the null hypothesis is true. For this experiment the sampling distribution is the binomial with $P = Q = .5$.

The population is binomial because the sign of the relationship between pairs of scores (+ or −) is mutually exclusive and exhaustive. The location of the 9/2 split is the third term in the $(P + Q)^{11}$ binomial expansion (i.e., 9 successes/2 failures).

The Null and Alternative Hypotheses. For this experiment, the null hypothesis would be that the special extract did not enhance the therapeutic value of drinking hot tea to alleviate allergy symptoms. If the experimental treatment had no effect on the ratings, only chance is determining whether the experimental score is higher or lower than the control score. Therefore, a plus sign is as likely to occur in the difference column as a minus sign. The null and alternative hypotheses may be formally stated as:

$$H_0: P(+) = P(-) = .50$$
$$H_1: P(+) \neq P(-) \neq .50$$

Step 4. *Determine the probability of obtaining a statistic as rare or rarer than the computed value.* Here, this probability will be the sum of the probabilities for the following possible splits: 9/2, 10/1, 11/0, 2/9, 1/10, and 0/11. To get these probabilities we must consult the binomial table for $N = 11$ and $P = .50$. The probabilities are, respectively, .0269, .0054, .0005, .0269, .0054, and .0005. They sum to .0656.

Step 5. *Compare the probability computed in step 4 to the decision rule.* The decision rule in the binomial test is very direct. It says to reject the null hypothesis if the probability computed in step 4 is less than .05 (or .01, depending on the level of significance being used). Since the computed probability equals .0656, we fail to reject the null hypothesis and conclude that the special extract did not enhance the therapeutic value of the tea.

If you inspected table 13.2 before doing the sign test you may have expected a different outcome. After all, nine out of eleven subjects reported an improved therapeutic effect from the experimental treatment, and some of the levels of improvement were quite dramatic (e.g., subject 6 went from a rating of 0 to 45). The sign test, however, is a weak test. Its lack of statistical power is one result of the potentially important information that we discard when we do a sign test: only the sign of the difference, not the magnitude of the difference, is considered. Notice, for example, that the slight difference in the evaluations of subject 11 ($25 - 28 = -3$) is given the same weight as the relatively large difference in the evaluations of subject 6 (0 − 45 = −45). Both differences are scored only as a minus sign. In the Wilcoxon matched pairs signed-ranks test, as you shall see, the magnitude of the difference scores is taken into account.

THE WILCOXON MATCHED PAIRS SIGNED-RANKS TEST

The Wilcoxon T-test is set up in the same way as the sign test, but the analysis is carried further to take the magnitude of the difference scores into account. In table 13.3 we see the same data that were displayed in table 13.2 but with two added columns: the rank of the difference scores and the ranks with the smaller sum. (Table 13.3 appears exactly as it will on your computer screen when you use WILCOX.BAS to analyze your own data.) To rank the difference scores give the difference score with the smallest absolute value the rank of one, and work your way up to the numerically highest score. In our example, the difference score of 3 gets the rank of one, 17 gets the rank of two, and so on up to 45, which gets the rank of ten. Notice that the sign of the difference score is ignored for ranking purposes but is retained for reference purposes in parentheses next to the rank. Next, all the ranks with minus signs are added (sum = 56) and all the ranks with plus signs are added (sum = 10). The smaller sum of ranks equals the Wilcoxon T statistic. Here, $T = 10$. (Notice that the Wilcoxon T is capitalized, but the parametric t-test is referred to with a lower case t.)

Table 13.3

The table for computing a Wilcoxon signed-ranks test on the data of the correlated groups herbal tea study.

Subject	Cont.	Exper.	Diff.	Signed-Rank of Difference	Ranks (+/−) with Smaller Sum
1	20	40	−20	(−)5	
2	15	45	−30	(−)9	
3	16	33	−17	(−)2	
4	30	48	−18	(−)3	
5	10	35	−25	(−)7	
6	0	45	−45	(−)10	
7	40	68	−28	(−)8	
8	34	10	+24	(+)6	6
9	5	60	−55	(−)11	
10	30	11	+19	(+)4	4
11	25	28	−3	(−)1	
					$T = 10$

To evaluate the T value of 10 for significance we must compare the computed value of T to the tabled value for $N = 11$. According to the Wilcoxon table in Appendix A, the critical value of T at the .05 level of significance with eleven pairs of scores is 10. If the computed T is less than or equal to the tabled value of T the difference between the two groups is considered to be significant. Notice the departure from the way we have been using the statistical tables. For the t and z tests significance was achieved if the computed value was *greater than* or equal to the tabled value. The Wilcoxon T is somewhat unusual because the computed value must be *less than* or equal to the tabled value.

It becomes apparent in comparing the sign test and Wilcoxon T analyses that taking the magnitude of the difference scores into account resulted in a test of greater power. The Wilcoxon test resulted in rejection of the null hypothesis, but the sign test did not. The Wilcoxon is more powerful than the sign test, but it has one more underlying assumption. To use the Wilcoxon T statistic the difference scores have ordinal scaling. This assumption is satisfied if it makes sense for you to say that the larger a person's difference score is, the greater the difference is between a person's control versus experimental performance. In practice, for most kinds of data this assumption is easy to satisfy.

The Power of T versus t

Let us pretend that the ordinally scaled control and experimental data in table 13.3 are interval or ratio data from a different experiment and meet all the assumptions for the t-test that were discussed in chapter 12. For example, let us assume that the data are the correct responses on a learning task under a control versus an experimental condition. If we analyze these data using the correlated t-test, then $t = -2.49$. The critical value of the t statistic for this analysis is -2.228 at the .05 level of significance (two-tail test). (If you are using the *Stat/Tutor* software, you may do this analysis by using the TEETWO.BAS program.) So, because -2.49 is more extreme than -2.228 (by 0.262 units), we would reject the null hypothesis and conclude that subjects in the experimental group completed significantly more correct responses than the control group.

By contrast, if you recall the Wilcoxon T analysis we completed above using these same table 13.3 data, the computed value of the Wilcoxon T exactly equalled the critical value ($T = 10$). Had the computed value for T been any greater than 10 (say, $T = 11$) we would not have been able to reject the null hypothesis.

If we relax for a moment and use forbidden terminology (*see* page 217), we might say the Wilcoxon T was "just barely" small enough to achieve statistical significance, whereas the correlated t-test was significant "with room to spare" (0.262 units). In an informal way, the relative ease with which the t statistic was significant compared to the Wilcoxon T when both analyses were done using the same data is empirical support that the parametric *t*-test is more powerful than the nonparametric Wilcoxon *T*-test. This difference in power stems partly from the fact that the Wilcoxon *T* is computed using the rank order of the difference scores, and information is lost when data are ranked (e.g., the sets 2, 7, 8 and 2, 11, 27 both yield the ranks 1, 2, 3 despite differences in the raw score magnitudes). By comparison, the *t*-test is computed using the actual score magnitudes and no information is lost.

THE MANN-WHITNEY *U*-TEST

Mann-Whitney *U*-Test. A nonparametric test that may be used as a substitute for the independent groups *t*-test. The statistical power of the Mann-Whitney *U*-test is comparable to that of the *t*-test.

The **Mann-Whitney *U*-test** is a nonparametric alternative to the independent groups *t*-test. Unlike the nonparametric alternatives to the correlated *t*-test (the sign test and the Wilcoxon *T*-test), the Mann-Whitney has power comparable to the *t*-test.

There is a rather tedious and error prone method for computing the Mann-Whitney *U* statistic that is virtually never used in actual data analysis. Nevertheless, this counting method will give you a firmer grasp on the concept of the sampling distribution of the *U* statistic. So, before presenting an example with the easy-to-use formula, let us briefly work through the counting method. Consider the following experimental (*E*) and control (*C*) data:

C: **14 20 33 50 60**
E: **9 10 16 29 45**

If the data are put in rank order and labeled as to which group they came from, they look like this:

Rank	Score	Group
1	9	*E*
2	10	*E*
3	14	*C*
4	16	*E*
5	20	*C*
6	29	*E*
7	33	*C*
8	45	*E*
9	50	*C*
10	60	*C*

The next step is to count the number of *C*s that are preceded by each E. An *E* score is said to precede a *C* score if it has a lower rank. For the actual data, the *E* in position 1 precedes all five *C*s in the rankings. The same is true for the *E* score in position 2. The next *E* score in the ranking is in position 4 and it precedes four *C*s. The *E* in position 6 precedes three *C*s, and the *E* in position 8 precedes two *C*s. The total of the five counts is $5 + 5 + 4 + 3 + 2 = 19$. If we had counted the numbers of *E*s that are preceded by each *C*, the count would have been $3 + 2 + 1 + 0 + 0 = 6$. The smaller of the two counts is arbitrarily designated as the *U* statistic. The larger of the two counts is the U' statistic. Thus, for these data, $U = 6$ and $U' = 19$.

To grasp what these numbers 6 and 19 mean it is helpful to look at two extreme situations. For the outcome *EEEEECCCCC* in which all the *E* scores are ranked lower than the *C* scores, *U* and U' would equal 0 and 25, respectively. But for an outcome with extensive overlap among the ranks such as *ECCEECCECE*, $U = 12$ and $U' = 13$. The closer *U* and U' are to each other, the more likely it is that only chance factors are operating to cause the outcome pattern.

Think of it this way. If you had a basket that contained five *E*s and five *C*s and drew them out randomly one by one without replacement, you should expect extensive mingling of *E*s and *C*s (e.g., *ECECECECEC*, *CECECECECE*, *ECCEECCECE*, etc.). The reason for this rests on simple probability theory. If the first selection is an *E*, there would be five *C*s and only four *E*s remaining in the basket. Therefore, on the next selection an outcome of *C* is favored. On the next selection there are four *E*s and four *C*s from which to choose, so neither is favored. However, as soon as the selection is made (say, a *C*), four *E*s and only three *C*s remain, so *E* has the edge on the next selection. The more overlap there is between *E*s and *C*s, the closer the *U* and U' values tend to be to each other. The less overlap there is the farther apart *U* is from U'.

In order to derive the sampling distribution of the *U* and U' statistics, values for *U* and U' must be computed using the counting procedure illustrated above for each and every possible pattern configuration. With this sampling distribution in hand, we could determine the values of *U* and U' that would be so extreme they would only occur 5% or less of the time. To provide a useful reference for hypothesis testing purposes, this would have to be done for a great number of sample size combinations.

All this work has already been done and is available in the Mann-Whitney table. By finding the column labeled n_1 and moving to the row labeled n_2, we can find the *U* and U' values that are the critical values for purposes of hypothesis testing. If the computed *U* is less than or equal to the lower of the two values, or if U' is equal to or higher than the higher of the two values, the null hypothesis is rejected. If, on the other hand, the computed values for *U* and U' fall within the range of the two tabled values, we fail to reject the null hypothesis. The entry in the Mann-Whitney U table (alpha = .05 for a two-tail test) that pertains to the present example is reproduced below.

	n_1	5 . . . .
n_2		.
.		.
.		.
.		.
.		.
.		.
.		.
5		2 23

For the ten E and C scores above, $U = 6$ and $U' = 19$. The tabled values with n_1 and $n_2 = 5$ and alpha set at .05 are 2 and 23. Since 6 and 19 fall between 2 and 23, we would fail to reject the null hypothesis if these were real experimental data.

THE COMPUTATION OF U AND U'

As mentioned above, the counting method is not practical for actual data. Instead, U and U' are found using the simple formula shown below:

$$U = n_1 n_2 + \frac{n_1(n_1 + 1)}{2} - R_1$$

or

$$U' = n_1 n_2 + \frac{n_2(n_2 + 1)}{2} - R_2$$

Let us use these equations to compute U and U' for the same experimental and control data we used to step through the counting method. The n_1 and n_2 terms are simply the sample sizes for groups 1 and 2. Here, $n_1 = 5$ and $n_2 = 5$. To get the R_1 and R_2 values we must regard all the scores as members of a single set, as we did in the counting method, and we must rank all the scores. Then the ranks are summed for each group as shown next. R_1 is the sum of the ranks for group 1 and R_2 is the sum of the ranks for group 2.

Group 1		Group 2	
Control	Rank	Experimental	Rank
14	3	9	1
20	5	10	2
33	7	16	4
50	9	29	6
60	10	45	8
	$R_1 = 34$		$R_2 = 21$

Inserting the values from the above table into the U formula yields

$$U = 5 \cdot 5 + \frac{5(5 + 1)}{2} - 34$$
$$U = 25 + 15 - 34$$
$$U = 6$$

If the U' formula is used:

$$U' = 5 \cdot 5 + \frac{5(5 + 1)}{2} - 21$$
$$U' = 25 + 15 - 21$$
$$U' = 19$$

As you can see, $U = 6$ and $U' = 19$, the same result we obtained with these data when we used the counting method.

A Research Scenario

Let us apply this computational method to some experimental data. In another version of the correlated groups herbal tea experiment that was presented previously, two groups of allergy sufferers were randomly designated as control subjects or experimental subjects. The control subjects were given tea bags with ordinary herbal tea, whereas the experimental subjects were given the tea containing the special extract. The patients were unaware of which group they were in and knew of no special additive to the tea. As before, the patients were to rate the degree of relief from their symptoms one-half hour after drinking the tea. The scaling of the data is ordinal as it was for the correlated groups experiment, but the groups are independent, and so the Mann-Whitney is the statistic of choice to test the difference between the groups for significance.

Table 13.4

The raw data and ranks for the Mann-Whitney analysis of the independent groups herbal tea study

Control	Rank	Experimental	Rank
30	6	37	9
24	2	25	3
27	4	46	13
44	12	33	8
32	7	54	18
39	11	49	16
59	19	50	17
19	1	48	14.5
29	5	61	20
38	10	48	14.5
		63	21
	$R_1 = 77$		$R_2 = 154$

The data and computations we need to fill in the Mann-Whitney formula are in table 13.4. As discussed previously, the n_1 and n_2 terms are the sample sizes for groups 1 and 2 and R_1 and R_2 are the sums of the ranks for the respective groups. (The table of raw data and ranks, and the computations of U and U' are presented here in essentially the same way as they appear on the computer monitor when you run MANNWHIT.BAS.) Notice that tied ranks are handled in a way identical to the procedure we used in computing the Spearman rho statistic (page 132).

Inserting the values from table 13.4 into the U formula yields

$$U = 10 \times 11 + \frac{10(10 + 1)}{2} - 77$$

$$U = 110 + 55 - 77$$

$$U = 88$$

If the U' formula is used:

$$U' = 10 \times 11 + \frac{11(11 + 1)}{2} - 154$$

$$U' = 110 + 66 - 154$$

$$U' = 22$$

You may have noticed that these results are not consistent with an earlier statement that U is arbitrarily designated as the lower of the two possible U values, and U' is the larger of the two. This sometimes happens when computing the Mann-Whitney U, but the apparent inconsistency will have no impact upon the accurate testing of the hypothesis. If the experimental group data were switched to the left column and the control group data were in the right column, U would have been 22 and U' would have been 88. The important consideration, regardless of whether U or U' has been computed, is to compare the computed value to the range given in the Mann-Whitney table. If the computed value is outside the tabled range, U (or U') is significant.

If the test were carried out at the .05 level of significance, the tabled range of U and U' values for $n_1 = 10$ and $n_2 = 11$ is 26 to 84. Since the computed U and U' values fall *outside* that range (22 is less than 26 and 88 is more than 84), the difference between the groups is regarded as significant. If, however, the test were carried out at the .01 level of significance, the tabled range of U and U' values is 18 to 92. Since U and U' both fall *within* this range, the difference would not be significant at the .01 level of significance.

Notice that the decisions made using U or U' are always consistent. Both are either inside or outside the tabled range. If, for example, U falls within the tabled range and U' is outside the tabled range, look for a computational error. Another check on your computations can be done using the following relationship:

$$U + U' = n_1 n_2$$

$$22 + 88 = 10 \times 11$$

$$110 = 110$$

This relationship tends to break down if there are excessive numbers of tied ranks, but in most cases it provides a quick check of computations.

A COMPARISON WITH THE *t*-TEST

The Mann-Whitney test is regarded to be about as powerful as the *t*-test. For the data presented in table 13.4, the Mann-Whitney revealed a statistically significant difference if the .05 level were used, but not if the .01 level were used. Interestingly, this is the same pattern that results if the *t*-test were applied to these data. The computation of *t* as presented in TEETWO.BAS shows that $t = -2.53$. This is well above the critical value of 2.093 ($df = 19$) at the .05 level of significance, but falls short of the 2.861 needed for significance at the .01 level. This similar pattern supports the notion of comparable power for these tests.

The Mann-Whitney table is quite extensive and is not built into the MANNWHIT.BAS program as the t table is built into the TEETWO.BAS program. It is important that you read the table headings carefully so you will be sure to look up the critical values for the designated level of significance.

Summary

We extended our study of data analysis within the context of two-group experimental designs to include data for which the t-test is inappropriate. We learned that the sign test and Wilcoxon matched pairs signed-ranks test are alternatives to the correlated t-test, and the Mann-Whitney test is an alternative to the independent groups t-test. We finished the chapter with a comparison of the relative power of these nonparametric tests to the independent and correlated t-tests.

Key Terms

Mann-Whitney *U*-Test
Nonparametric Statistics
Sign Test
Wilcoxon *T*-Test

Exercises

These problems are appropriately analyzed using either the Wilcoxon test or the Mann-Whitney test. If you do them by hand, check your work with WILCOX.BAS and MANNWHIT.BAS. Don't forget to follow the usual steps of hypothesis testing along with a statement of conclusion.

1. A new food additive has been discovered that, according to its manufacturer, will make the fur of ranch mink thicker and softer. To evaluate this claim, the Mink Ranchers Association arranged for an experiment to be done with twenty juvenile minks. The group of animals was divided randomly into two groups of ten each. Ten animals were raised with the special food additive and ten were fed the normal diet. A panel of independent experts rated the pelts on a scale of 0 to 100 after they were harvested and processed. Did the additive result in a difference in fur quality? Use $\alpha = .05$.

Treatment	
Additive	*No Additive*
81	63
73	89
98	52
44	92
79	83
68	71
88	77
62	91
87	81
91	88

2. The makers of a complex piece of laboratory equipment could not decide how to word the explanation of a particularly critical phase of operation in their instruction manual. To compare the effectiveness of two different sets of instructions, nine randomly selected technicians were taught how to use the apparatus by using instruction set *A*, and a second group of nine technicians was taught with instruction set *B*. The numbers below represent error scores for each of the eighteen technicians during a test run of the equipment. Was there a difference in the performance of the two groups? Use $\alpha = .05$.

Error Scores	
Set A	*Set B*
4	9
11	2
12	7
8	10
13	5
15	9
6	7
3	7
14	1

3. A group of parents of high school athletes was concerned about apparent differences in standards of excellence used by judges from two different school districts in the county Water Sports Olympics. They compared the average ratings (on a scale of 0 to 10) that judges from two different school districts gave a group of ten divers, all of whom did the same compulsory dive. Was there a difference in the ratings of the two sets of judges? Use $\alpha = .05$.

	Diving Judges	
Diver	*District A*	*District B*
1	8	9
2	7	9
3	9	9.5
4	7.9	8.5
5	6	7
6	9	8.5
7	8	9.5
8	7.5	7.5
9	9.5	9.5
10	8.5	9.5

4. A physical therapist decided to compare recovery speed following two different kinds of treatment for deep muscle injury. Thirteen matched pairs of persons with close to the same type and severity of injury were assigned to treatment groups. One member of each matched pair received diathermy and the other member received hydrotherapy. Recovery was rated by a panel of physicians who had access to the medical records of the subjects, but had no knowledge of the type of therapy that was used to treat the injury. Was there a difference in the effectiveness of the therapies? Use $\alpha = .05$.

	Recovery Scores	
Pair	*Diathermy*	*Hydrotherapy*
1	120	114
2	121	118
3	117	103
4	137	122
5	115	127
6	122	106
7	130	125
8	116	113
9	121	109
10	130	112
11	92	100
12	140	120
13	88	79

5. Why does the Wilcoxon test have more power than the sign test?

6. Generate some data on HYPTEE2.BAS for both the independent groups and repeated measures scenarios. Make a record of the data and *t*-test analyses using a "screen dump" to a printer or by copying the screen output by hand. (If you are fortunate enough to have a microcomputer laboratory, you may do this with two computers side by side.) Then, using MANNWHIT.BAS and WILCOX.BAS, compare the *t*-test analyses on these data to the Mann-Whitney and Wilcoxon analyses. Are the results similar? Does an increase in sample size have an equivalent impact on the power of the parametric versus the nonparametric tests? Are the parametric and nonparametric tests equally able to detect a slight treatment effect?

7. Two strains of white laboratory rats were tested to see if they differed in their ability to tolerate handling. A technician was not told which animals belonged to which strain. He caught and held each animal for five seconds and then rated the animal on a scale of 0 to 25 in terms of its acceptance of handling. A 0 would indicate complete docility, but a 25 would indicate constant and violent resistance to being held, attempts to bite, etc. On the basis of the technician's ratings do you conclude that there is a difference in the ability to tolerate handling across the two strains of laboratory rats? Use $\alpha = .05$.

Strain 1	Strain 2
14	20
8	22
18	15
10	19
20	15
10	16
6	22
13	16

8. Two strains of laboratory rats were bred to enlarge the colony. The number of pups born to each animal was recorded. Did one strain tend to have larger litters than the other? Use a Mann-Whitney test with $\alpha = .05$.

The Number of Pups per Litter	
Strain A	*Strain B*
8	11
12	15
7	10
10	12
14	12
15	9
8	9
6	11
9	14
12	10

9. Mothers in stressful situations because of incessantly crying infants and other family problems have a high potential for child abuse. One social worker in a county agency has been working with mothers in crisis situations to teach them stress management skills. A second group of mothers was identified as being in

crisis, but they were not taught the stress management skills. One month into the program the mothers in both groups were asked to rate their perceived level of stress on a scale of 1 to 10. Did the mothers who received instruction on stress management report a lower level of perceived stress? Use $\alpha = .05$ with a one-tail test.

Received Instruction on Stress Management	
Yes	*No*
5	8
4	9
8	7
3	10
2	6
5	7
1	4
6	9

10. A group of newly hired salespersons did some role-playing during which they tried to sell a stubborn client some company products. Their effectiveness and composure in the face of a very resistant and rude client was rated on a scale of 0 to 100 by observers who sat behind a one-way mirror. Then, the new staff attended a special two-week school on sales techniques after which they were rated once again by the same observers in a similar selling scenario. Did their experience in the two-week training session result in a change in their rated performance? Use $\alpha = .01$.

	Performance Ratings (0–100)	
Employee	*Before*	*After*
A	40	65
B	50	80
C	23	50
D	74	91
E	40	37
F	60	88
G	35	61
H	27	45
I	60	75
J	77	70
K	60	65

11. Proper humidification of air in the home is supposed to affect comfort. In a very dry home the temperature must be maintained at a relatively high level for persons to feel comfortable during the cold winter months. Conversely, in a properly humidified home, the temperature may be set lower for the same degree of comfort. An environmental psychologist decided to investigate this phenomenon in a controlled laboratory environment. A chamber was maintained either at 68° F and 10% relative humidity or 68° F and 60% relative humidity. One-half of a group of subjects experienced the high humidity condition first and the other half experienced the low humidity condition first. In the second exposure, one week later, the treatments were reversed so that all subjects experienced both conditions. After each session in the chamber the subjects reported a comfort rating on a scale of 0 to 100. Did the raised humidity affect the perceived comfort at 68° F? Use $\alpha = .05$.

	Comfort Ratings	
Subject	*Low Humidity*	*High Humidity*
A	50	75
B	57	80
C	28	50
D	44	71
E	50	67
F	60	88
G	45	83
H	27	45
I	65	75
J	37	70
K	70	75
L	20	80

CHAPTER 14

Chi-Square

The chi-square test, like all statistical tests, allows us to evaluate the likelihood that differences between observed and theoretically expected outcomes are due to chance alone. If that likelihood is very small, chance alone is rejected as an explanation, and we defer to a nonchance explanation (the alternative hypothesis, H_1). The determining factor that dictates the use of the chi-square statistic for this decision-making process is usually the nominal scaling of the data. When the recording of data includes keeping a frequency count in various categories, the data are nominal. (You may wish to review a discussion of this issue in chapter 1.). Both the one variable and two variable chi-square tests are covered in this chapter within the context of typical experimental applications of this very useful statistic. Julius, a student summer intern at the Acme Advertising Agency, related the following account of the Sunbelt Market taco shell study, and we shall use his experience as a typical application of the one-variable chi-square statistic.

The Diego Brand Taco Shell Study

The Acme Advertising Agency was hired to redesign the packaging for Diego Brand Taco Shells. In an effort to evaluate the attractiveness of some prospective designs, the same Diego Brand Taco Shells were prepared for sale in four different types of packages and were displayed side by side on the shelves of all the Sunbelt Markets in a large southwestern city. Each package design was printed with a distinctive bar code so the laser scanners at the checkout counters could feed the computer a complete record of how many boxes of each design were sold.

An advertising campaign in the test market city ("Look for the same fresh product in the colorful new boxes!") alerted consumers to the fact that all the packages contained the usual taco shells. Assuming this fact was effectively communicated, differences in consumer preference for some package (or packages) over others could be assumed to be a function of the attractiveness of the package and not to differences in the product within the packages.

Certain precautions were followed to insure that each consumer "voted" only once. If any shopper purchased more than one box and the boxes were not all of the same package design, no record of the transaction was kept for the experiment. If two or more boxes were purchased and all the boxes were of the same design, only the first box through the scanner was registered in the tally. The final precaution was to limit the test period to one week under the assumption that shoppers would be unlikely to buy taco shells more than once in a given week.

Table 14.1 gives the combined sales data for all the markets in the test market city.

Inspection of these results reveals that there are differences in the numbers of purchases recorded for each type of package, and Design 3 was selected by more consumers than any of the other three designs. Do the observed differences in buying behavior reflect only chance or do they reflect a real preference for one type of packaging? If one design is identified as having significantly greater appeal than the others, using such an appealing package could give the Diego Company an edge over its competition. As with any situation requiring a decision from data, chance alone may be disregarded as an explanation for experimental results only after the appropriate statistical analysis has been done.

The project supervisor, a competent statistician and researcher, knew before the data were collected that chi-square would be the statistic of choice to analyze these data. This is as it should be. To collect data without knowing in advance how they are to be evaluated is very unwise. It may turn out

Table 14.1

Package Design	# of Purchases
1	514
2	498
3	604
4	528

that there is no way to get the information you want from the kind of data you collected. A more in-depth discussion of this point will be saved for chapter 19.

You, the reader, also know that the correct choice is the chi-square statistic. You know this not because you spent your semester break reading ahead to become familiar with the computation and application of the chi-square statistic, but because this is the chi-square chapter. This is an artificial situation that is inherent in a formal academic course. Obviously, the problems that are posed within and at the end of a chapter pertain to the type of analysis covered in that chapter. Julius, however, didn't know what statistic should be applied to the data and, as part of his learning experience, he was given the task of determining the correct analysis. His supervisor wanted to give him a taste of the real world where any statistical test is a possible choice for data analysis until ruled out, and only one choice of statistical analysis is likely to be 100% correct. (Your turn for this type of experience will take place in the last chapter, so learn from Julius' errors.)

THE SCALING OF THE DATA

Julius knew that to choose the correct statistical test for the analysis of experimental data it is very important to identify correctly the scaling of the data. His first impression was that they were ratio and that one of the parametric statistical analyses would be appropriate. The scores appeared to fit the description of a variable with a true zero point because it was theoretically possible for a particular package design to be chosen by the consumers zero times. If one design happened to be chosen 100 times and another happened to be chosen 200 times, it would be quite accurate to say that twice as many chose the latter design over the former. This type of ratio statement, Julius knew, was only valid for ratio-scaled variables. Even if the data were not ratio, Julius thought they would be at least interval since the difference in frequencies between 50 and, say, 100 is the same magnitude of difference that exists between 100 and 150. If equal intervals on a scale mean the same thing, the data must be at least interval.

"No, Julius! You're way off!" the supervisor abruptly intoned, and so Julius was sent back to reexamine the data. This time he was sure he had the answer. Since 604 is more than 528, and 528 is more than 514, and 514 is more than 498, the data must be ordinal. Unfortunately, the supervisor again did not agree. He told Julius since there was only one scale left, the nominal scale, he was bound to be correct on the next try, but just saying "nominal" would not earn him any points. Julius had to explain *why* the data were nominal.

Frequency Data. A synonym for nominal or categorical data.

Categorical Data. A synonym for nominal or frequency data. Data typically take the form of tallies in discrete categories.

Tallies (also called "ticks" or "hash marks".) Tallies are used to record frequency counts of events.

After consulting his statistics notes and his old text, Julius remembered that one must consider the nature of a single data point to avoid confusing nominal data with other scaling. Data in a nominal scale (also called **frequency data** and **categorical data**) are simple **tallies.** Responses are assigned to categories, and no numbers are assigned to individual data entries. Clearly, the taco shell sales data fit this description. Each purchase is categorized as a type 1, 2, 3, or 4 package design. The purchase decision of each customer is recorded as a simple tally in the appropriate category. Even though at the end of the data collection phase it is the sum of the tallies within the four categories to which the statistical analysis is applied, and even though these sums appear to take on the characteristics of ratio data, you must be careful to remember that it is the nature of a single data point (i.e., a simple tally) that reveals the nominal scaling of these data.

Goodness of Fit between Observed and Expected Frequencies

Expected Frequencies. The frequencies that each cell would be expected to have if the null hypothesis were true.

Observed Frequencies. The actual frequency data upon which the chi-square analysis is performed.

In a sense, the chi-square test is an extension of the binomial test. Both statistics serve to evaluate the "goodness of fit" between **expected frequencies** and **observed frequencies,** and both require that the frequencies be independently assigned to mutually exclusive categories. But, whereas the binomial test can only handle two categories at a time, the chi-square test may be applied to any number of independent categories.

The Computation of the Chi-Square Test for Goodness of Fit

The supervisor was pleased and gave Julius the job of doing the chi-square analysis. After some review, Julius found that the first step in the computation of the chi-square statistic is to determine the expected frequencies for each category or *cell.* Since the null hypothesis in this study is that there is no preference for any one package design over another, our working assumption is that the cell frequencies should be equal. That is, any differences in the frequency totals of the cells are assumed to be due to chance alone. If f = cell frequency, then the null and alternative hypotheses are

$$H_0: f_1 = f_2 = f_3 = f_4$$
$$H_1: \text{not } H_0$$

Julius computed the expected frequencies assuming the null hypothesis was true. All he had to do was take the total frequency across all categories and divide by k, the number of categories. Here, $k = 4$ and the total $f = 2144$. The expected frequency for each cell is therefore $2144/4 = 536$. With the expected frequencies included, the data now is given in Table 14.2.

Table 14.2

Package Design	# of Purchases	Expected *f*
1	514	536
2	498	536
3	604	536
4	528	536

Chi-square is computed by squaring the difference between the observed frequency and the expected frequency of each cell and dividing the resulting product by the expected frequency. By squaring the difference, the size of chi-square is independent of whether the observed frequency is greater than or less than the expected frequency, and, unlike t or z, the value of chi-square is always positive and the test is always nondirectional.

The computation is represented in the following formula. The f_o in the formula equals the observed frequency for a cell, f_e equals the expected frequency, and the Σ directs us to add the results of the computations across all cells.

$$\chi^2 = \Sigma\frac{(f_o - f_e)^2}{f_e}$$

For the taco shell sales data, the computations take the following form:

$$\chi^2 = \frac{(514 - 536)^2}{536} + \frac{(498 - 536)^2}{536} + \frac{(604 - 536)^2}{536} + \frac{(528 - 536)^2}{536}$$

$$\chi^2 = 12.33$$

The computed value of the chi-square statistic equals 12.33. Now this value must be located on the theoretical sampling distribution of the chi-square statistic with reference to the critical value. If the computed chi-square is greater than the critical value from the chi-square table, then we know that the probability of obtaining a chi-square of the computed magnitude just by chance is less than .05 (or .01, depending upon the level of significance being used). If the computed chi-square is less than the critical value, then it has a probability of more than .05 (or .01), and the difference between the observed frequencies and the expected frequencies is not statistically significant.

The sampling distribution of the chi-square statistic takes on a wide variety of shapes depending upon the number of degrees of freedom that are present. The number of degrees of freedom is simply the number of categories (cells) minus one. If you look at figure 14.1 you will see a sampling

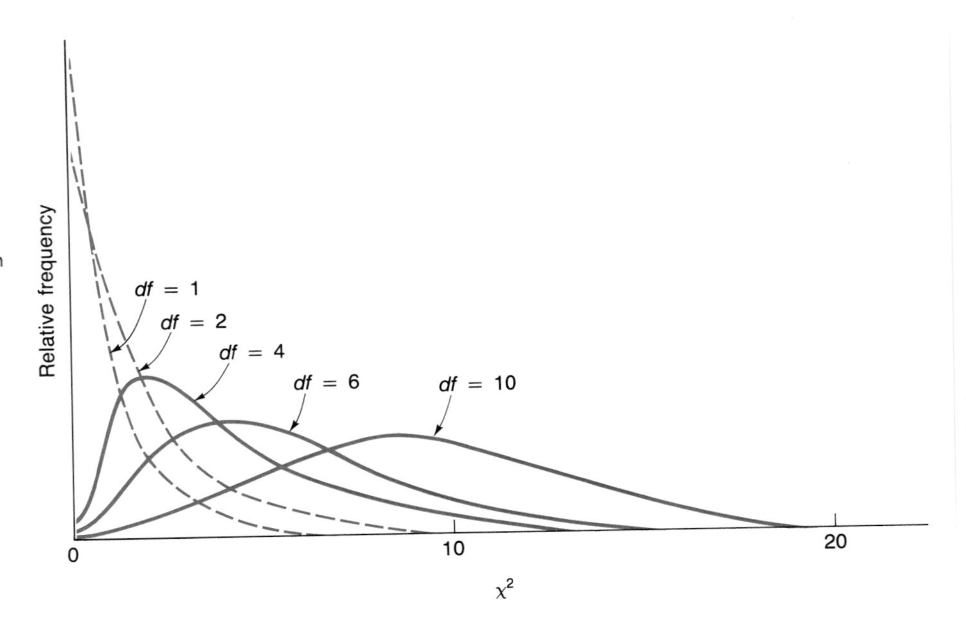

Figure 14.1

Distribution of χ^2 for various degrees of freedom.

Lindquist, E. F., *Design and Analysis of Experiments in Psychology and Education*. Copyright © 1953 by Houghton Mifflin Company. Used with permission.

Degrees of Freedom. In the context of the chi-square statistic, degrees of freedom in the one-variable ("goodness of fit") case equals $k - 1$. In the two-variable case (the chi-square test of independence), $df = (r - 1)(c - 1)$.

of some chi-square distributions for various **degrees of freedom.** Notice that the degrees of freedom value for each distribution is the same as the mean for that distribution. The chi-square table tells us how far above this mean we have to go before only 5% of the area remains under the curve. This location is the critical value against which we compare the computed value.

Since the curves are so different for different degrees of freedom, in testing a hypothesis you must take care to use only the tabled value that corresponds to the degrees of freedom for your data. There are four cells in the taco shell data, so there are three degrees of freedom. In the abbreviated version of the chi-square table that comprises table 14.3, you can see that the critical value using the 5% level of significance is 7.815. The +7.815 is the only value we need. (As pointed out earlier, unlike other statistical tests you have studied, the chi-square test is nondirectional and cannot be negative as can the t and z statistics.) The correct table location is indicated by the arrows.

The decision rule that applies to the taco shell data is therefore:

Decision Rule: Reject H_0 if the computed value for chi-square exceeds 7.815.

The computed value of 12.33 is greater than the critical value of 7.815, and so Julius rejected the null hypothesis. From this result Julius knew that the probability that the differences among the frequencies occurred solely due to chance is less than 5%. Therefore, the consumers were not equally attracted to the four types of taco shell packages.

Table 14.3

Degrees of Freedom (*df*)	Level of Significance .05	.01
1	3.841	6.635
2	5.991	9.210
→ 3	7.815	11.341 ←
4	9.488	13.277
—	—	—
—	—	—
—	—	—

Notice that Julius is not yet prepared to say which package(s) is/are the most preferred. All he knows is that they were not equally regarded. Inspection of the observed frequencies points to Design 3 as the most favored design, but if it were necessary to document this more convincingly, it is quite legitimate to compare any cell to any other cell or cells with subsequent chi-square analyses.

MORE ABOUT DETERMINING EXPECTED FREQUENCIES

Because the null hypothesis was that the four package designs were equally attractive, the expected frequencies for the taco shell data were all equal and were found by dividing the total frequency by the number of cells. This is by no means always the case in the application of the one-variable chi-square statistic. For example, a quality control officer representing the U.S. government was testing a sample lot of 100 mortar shells. The manufacturer said that 70% of the mortar shells would hit within 50 feet of the designated impact area, 20% would hit outside of 50 feet but within 100 feet, and only 10% would hit beyond 100 feet from the designated impact area. The job of the quality control officer was to evaluate the manufacturer's claim of the accuracy of the mortar shells, and so 100 shells were fired under carefully controlled testing conditions. The observed frequencies appear in table 14.4 along with the appropriate expected frequencies.

Notice how the expected frequencies relate to the statement of the problem. With no other information to go on, the officer must assume that the manufacturer's claim is correct. The null hypothesis is that any differences between the observed frequencies and expected frequencies are due to chance and are insignificant. Using the .01 level of significance complete

Table 14.4

	Impact Zone of Mortar Shell		
	Within 50′	Between 50′ and 100′	Beyond 100′
Obtained freq.:	62	17	21
Expected freq.:	70	20	10

the chi-square analysis of these data. What is your conclusion? You may check your work in the "Answers to selected exercises" section for this chapter in Appendix D.

The Chi-Square Two-Variable Case

Independence. The entries in a contingency table are said to reflect independence if the effect of the column variable on the pattern of cell frequencies is independent of (i.e., not contingent upon) the effect of the row variable upon the pattern of cell frequencies.

Contingency Table. A table with r rows and c columns in which each row and column represents a mutually exclusive category.

A common name for the two-variable chi-square test is the chi-square test of independence. You have seen the term **independence** in a variety of different contexts by this point in the text, but the meaning has remained essentially the same. This term was mentioned in the context of correlation. When the value of one variable depends upon the value of another variable, the two variables are functionally (although not necessarily causally) *related*. Thus, independent means the opposite of correlated and correlated means the same as dependent. In the context of probability, to describe events as independent means that the occurrence or lack of occurrence of one event does not affect the probability of occurrence of another event.

The concept of independence is at the center of the chi-square statistic. To understand this, let us consider the data upon which the two-variable chi-square test is performed. They are frequencies in a two-dimensional **contingency table.** The rows represent r categories of the row variable and the columns represent c categories of the column variable. Thus, the contingency table has $r \times c$ cells. In this context, independence means that the effect of the column variable upon the cell frequencies is independent of (or not contingent upon) the effect of the row variable on the cell frequencies. This is a rather abstract concept, so let us make it more concrete with a simple example.

For one month a librarian kept a tally of books that were checked out from the Leisure Reading Room according to four categories (romance, historical novel, biography, and mystery) and according to whether or not the books were returned late or on time. As was true for our earlier one-variable chi-square example, no person was allowed to contribute more than one tally to the data. Because the books in the Leisure Reading Room are the most current and popular ones, only one at a time may be checked out. This avoided the problem of multiple entries from a reader who returned one book on time and another late. Also, once a person's "book-returning behavior" was registered one time in the tally, no further entries were made concerning that person.

The librarian's tally was kept by using the method in table 14.5.

Table 14.5

	Punctuality	
Type of Book	On Time	Late
Romance	~~////~~ // . . . etc.	~~////~~ ~~////~~
History	~~////~~ // . . . etc.	~~////~~ ~~////~~ ///
Biography	~~////~~ // . . . etc.	~~////~~
Mystery	~~////~~ // . . . etc	~~////~~ ~~////~~ ~~////~~

She was interested in finding a relationship between the type of a book and the tendency of borrowers to be on time versus late in returning the book to the library. If the ratio of punctual returns to late returns is the same for all the types of books, then there is no dependent relationship between the timeliness of a book's return and the type of book borrowed. This is the case in table 14.6. Across all four book categories roughly the same percentage of borrowers (10%) returned their books late. So, if the librarian were asked, "What percentage of people tend to return their library book late?" her response would be a straightforward "Ten percent."

Table 14.6

	On Time	**Late**
Romance	90	10
History	88	13
Biography	45	5
Mystery	150	15

If, on the other hand, the table looked like this:

Table 14.7

	On Time	Late
Romance	90	10
History	48	53
Biography	45	5
Mystery	150	15

the returns in the History category stand out as having a different pattern. If these were actual data and the librarian were asked, "What percentage of people tend to return their borrowed library books late?" her response would be, "Well, it *depends* upon the subject matter of the book," and she may go on to explain in greater detail that books in the history category are more likely than others to be returned late.

The word "depends" was emphasized above because what the librarian is really saying about the table 14.7 data is that the punctuality variable appears to have a dependent relationship with the book category variable. In table 14.6 the ratio of late to on-time books is not *contingent upon* the category to which the borrowed book belongs. That is, there is no dependent relationship between the type of book and the tendency for it to be returned late, so one may describe the behavior of returning books late (10% of borrowers do it) without reference to the type of book.

In table 14.7, however, there *is* a dependent relationship between the variables. The returns of history books deviate from the ratio in the other three categories, so the description of book-borrowing behavior must take the type of book into consideration. The flat statement that 10% of borrowers return books late no longer applies across all categories.

In table 14.7 we noted what appears to be a dependent relationship between row and column categories after a simple inspection of the data. In practice, however, impressions must be backed up with a sound and appropriate statistical analysis. The chi-square two-variable analysis (the chi-square test of independence) allows us to compare the expected frequencies in a contingency table with the observed frequencies to determine whether there is a significant degree of dependence between the row and column variables. As was true for the single variable case, the first step in the analysis is to derive the expected frequencies.

Table 14.8

The leisure reading room book-returning data.

	Punctuality		
Type of Book	On Time	Late	Row Totals
Romance	90	10	100
History	48	53	101
Biography	45	5	50
Mystery	150	15	165
Column Totals:	333	83	416

Table 14.9

The expected cell frequencies for the data shown in table 14.8.

	Punctuality		
Type of Book	On Time	Late	Row Totals
Romance	80.05	19.95	100
History	80.85	20.15	101
Biography	40.02	9.98	50
Mystery	132.08	32.92	165
Column Totals:	333	83	416

Here is the procedure for computing the expected frequencies just as it is done in the CHISQUAR.BAS data analysis program in *Stat/Tutor.*

Step 1. Add the frequencies across each row of the table and down each column of the table. Then add the row or column sums to arrive at a total frequency count for the whole table. As a check, the row totals and the column totals should sum to the same overall total.

Step 2. To get the expected frequency for each cell, the row total of the row that the cell is in is multiplied by the column total of the column that the cell is in. This product is then divided by the overall total and the answer is the expected frequency of that cell. For example, to get the expected frequency of the cell in the first row and first column (Romance—On-Time) we must multiply 100, the total of the first row, by 333, the total of the first column, and divide the resulting product of 33,300 by 416, the overall total. The answer is 80.05. Thus, the observed frequency for that cell is 90, but the expected frequency is 80.05. When this algorithm is applied to the data for all the cells, we get expected frequencies that are proportional to the marginal totals. Table 14.9 shows the results of expected frequencies for the library data.

Notice that the row and column totals in the table of expected frequencies remain the same as in the table of observed frequencies.

THE COMPUTATION OF CHI-SQUARE

The procedure for computing the chi-square statistic is essentially the same as we used for the single variable case. For each cell the squared difference between the observed and expected frequencies is divided by the expected frequency. The resulting values are then added across all cells. The formula that embodies these operations appears below.

$$\chi^2 = \Sigma \frac{(f_o - f_e)^2}{f_e}$$

Here are the actual computations for the library data from tables 14.8 and 14.9:

$$\chi^2 = \frac{(90 - 80.05)^2}{80.05} + \frac{(48 - 80.85)^2}{80.85} + \frac{(45 - 40.02)^2}{40.02} + \ldots$$

$$+ \frac{(150 - 132.08)^2}{132.08} + \frac{(10 - 19.95)^2}{19.95} + \frac{(53 - 20.15)^2}{20.15} + \ldots$$

$$+ \frac{(5 - 9.98)^2}{9.98} + \frac{(15 - 32.92)^2}{32.92}$$

$$\chi^2 = 1.24 + 13.35 + 0.62 + 2.43 + 4.96 + 53.55 + 2.49 + 9.75$$

$$\chi^2 = 88.39$$

If you do the same analysis using CHISQUAR.BAS you will get a slightly different result of 88.38. This is because there is less rounding error in the way the computer carries out the computations.

The degrees of freedom value for the two-variable chi-square test is found by multiplying the number of columns minus one times the number of rows minus one. Thus, $df = (r - 1)(c - 1)$, where r is the number of rows and c is the number of columns. There are $(4 - 1)(2 - 1) = 3$ degrees of freedom for the 4×2 matrix in the present example, and so the tabled value against which we should compare the computed value of chi-square appears on the row of the table where $df = 3$. The value, as you can see from the segment of the table that is shown at the beginning of the chapter or from the complete table in Appendix A, equals 7.815.

Since the computed value of 88.39 is greater than the tabled value of 7.815 we reject the null hypothesis that the row and column variables are independent. In the context of the present problem, this means that the tendency to return a book on time versus late is, at least in part, a function of the subject matter of the book. Perhaps the romantic novels, the biographies, and the mysteries were shorter and the readers tended to finish them on time, whereas the longer historical books took more time and effort to read.

ASSUMPTIONS OF THE CHI-SQUARE STATISTIC

Just because the chi-square statistic may be used when the data are nominal, the lowest level of measurement, does not mean that it may be applied without any cautions. Even chi-square has underlying assumptions that must be met for its legitimate use. The most fundamental is that each cell entry must be independent from any other cell entry. To be sure that this assumption is met, precautions must be taken to guarantee that a single subject contributes only a single data point. If you reread the descriptions of both the one-variable and two-variable sample problems (taco shell data and library data), you will see that all data collection was guided by the "one subject, one data point" precaution. If one subject were allowed to contribute more than a single tally to the data, the total frequency across all cells would be greater than the real number of independent observations. Naturally, this is not a potential problem for the mortar shell experiment because a shell can only be fired once.

The second assumption relates to the expected frequency for each cell. If there are two or more degrees of freedom associated with the analysis, the expected frequency should be at least five for all the cells. If there is only a single degree of freedom, the expected frequency for all cells must be at least ten. The sampling distribution that results when these assumptions are violated does not match the real chi-square distribution, so the tabled chi-square values that we use for hypothesis testing will not exactly match the true critical values if applied to such data.

Yates Correction for Discontinuity. An adjustment to the chi-square formula that enables the computed statistic more nearly to approximate the distribution of the chi-square statistic when there is only one degree of freedom.

If there is only a single degree of freedom in the chi-square analysis, as would be the case for a 2 × 2 contingency table, even if all four cells have expected values of ten or more, there is still some distortion in the chi-square sampling distribution. To correct for this problem you may apply the **Yates correction for discontinuity.** This involves a simple modification to the usual chi-square computation as illustrated in the formula below. (If you use the Yates correction for discontinuity you should be aware that it tends to overcorrect, resulting in a conservative test. Thus, if you use the Yates correction for discontinuity to compute χ^2 when $df = 1$, the true probability of Type I error is likely to be less than the .05 or .01 listed for the critical values (3.84 and 6.64) in the χ^2 table.)

$$\chi^2 = \Sigma \frac{(|f_o - f_e| - .5)^2}{f_e}$$

Before squaring the difference between each cell's observed and expected frequencies, .5 is subtracted from the absolute value of the difference between the observed cell frequency and the expected cell frequency. This slightly reduces the computed value for each cell and results in a better

Table 14.10

	Punctuality		
Type of Book	On Time	Late	Row Totals
Romance	90	10	100
History	48	53	101
Column Totals	138	63	201

Table 14.11

	Punctuality		
Type of Book	On Time	Late	Row Totals
Romance	68.66	31.34	100
History	69.34	31.66	101
Column Totals	138	63	201

fit of the computed statistic to the theoretical chi-square distribution. In CHISQUAR.BAS the Yates correction for discontinuity is applied automatically whenever there is only one degree of freedom.

Let us work through an example for which the Yates correction for discontinuity is necessary. The library data for only the Romance and History categories are reproduced in table 14.10.

Table 14.11, which is above, shows expected frequencies that were computed by using the algorithm described earlier for determining the expected frequencies in an $r \times c$ contingency table.

Here are the data as they should be applied to the chi-square formula with the Yates correction included:

$$\chi^2 = \frac{(|90 - 68.66| - .5)^2}{68.66} + \frac{(|10 - 31.34| - .5)^2}{31.34} + \ldots + \frac{(|48 - 69.34| - .5)^2}{69.34} + \frac{(|53 - 31.66| - .5)^2}{31.66}$$

$$\chi^2 = 6.33 + 13.86 + 6.26 + 13.71$$

$\chi^2 = 40.16$ (Because of less rounding error, the more accurate result from CHISQUAR.BAS is 40.177.)

With the level of significance set at .01, the critical value of chi-square when $(r - 1)(c - 1) = (2 - 1)(2 - 1) = 1$ degree of freedom is 6.635. The computed value of chi-square exceeds this critical value, so there is a significant relationship between type of book (Romance vs. History) and whether or not a book will tend to be returned on time or late.

Summary

We learned how to use the chi-square statistic to make comparisons between categories when the data are nominal for both single variable and two variable experimental designs. We emphasized correctly identifying nominal data and the interpretation of a significant chi-square test.

Key Terms

Categorical Data
Contingency Table
Degrees of Freedom
Expected Frequencies
Frequency Data
Independence
Observed Frequencies
Tallies
Yates Correction for Discontinuity

Exercises

The following problems are appropriately analyzed using the chi-square statistic. State H_0, H_1, a decision rule, and a statement of conclusion following the analysis. (CHISQUAR.BAS may be used for the data analysis.)

1. A psychologist participated in a project to assess the attitudes of cancer patients who were receiving chemotherapy to control their disease. Chemotherapy often controls and sometimes cures cancer, but the side effects can be very uncomfortable and can have significant impact on the quality of life. Each patient was asked, "In general, do you feel you are better off, worse off or unchanged when you compare your situation before chemotherapy to after chemotherapy?"

This procedure was followed for six groups of patients. Each group of patients received a different course of chemotherapy (different medicine or combination of medicines). Does patient attitude depend upon the type of therapy used? Choose your own α level.

	Patient Responses		
	Better Off	Worse Off	Unchanged
Chemo 1	12	8	5
Chemo 2	14	8	4
Chemo 3	3	14	10
Chemo 4	11	13	9
Chemo 5	7	4	14
Chemo 6	15	6	18
	62	53	60

2. Compare Chemo 2 with 3 using only the "better off" and "worse off" categories. Don't forget that the Yates correction for discontinuity is desirable when $df = 1$.
3. Is there a difference in the response rate for the three categories across all types of chemotherapy?

Patient Responses		
Better Off	Worse Off	Unchanged
62	53	60

4. When young persons embrace the philosophies of so-called religious cults, parents sometimes hire "deprogrammers" to convince their child to break his/her ties to the cult. Below are the records of eight professional deprogrammers. Is there any difference in their effectiveness, or is the success rate about the same for all of them? Use the .05 level of significance.

Deprogrammer	Successes	Failures
MRS. S	12	21
DR. B.	7	11
MS. L.	21	7
REV. T.	6	8
MR. J.	10	6
REV. C.	13	6

5. Twenty cows from each of five breeds were artificially inseminated at the Veterinary Science Center. Not all the inseminated cows became pregnant. Did the fertility rate among the cows vary as a function of the breed, or did all breeds experience roughly the same pregnancy rate? Here are the data.

	Pregnant	
Breed	Yes	No
Holstein	16	4
Jersey	12	8
Charolais	10	10
Limousin	17	3
Beefalo	15	5

6. Why is it desirable to use a correction for discontinuity when $df = 1$?
7. Explain what is meant by the underlying assumption of chi-square that each cell entry be independent from another cell entry? Describe a violation of this assumption in the data collection stage of an experiment. (Hint: Why did the consumers in the Taco Shell Study "vote" only once?)
8. How can you avoid incorrectly labeling data presented in a contingency table as ratio data when it is really nominal data?
9. Four kinds of gift-wrapping paper were available at the customer service counter at a local department store. An employee kept a record of how many customers chose each kind of wrapping paper for their gifts. Were the four kinds of paper equally regarded, or was one (or more) preferred over one (or more) of the others? Use $\alpha = .05$.

Paper A	*Paper B*	*Paper C*	*Paper D*
78	92	68	102

10. In an effort to target their advertising dollars effectively, the Alcohol Producers of America wish to investigate a speculation that drinking preferences are different for different socioeconomic levels in American society. They did a survey to study consumption of beer, wine, and distilled spirits among consumers belonging to three socioeconomic classes roughly defined as low, average, and high. Tallies were made in response to annual income and the question, "What is your preferred alcoholic beverage?" Is there evidence for different drinking preferences as a function of socioeconomic class? Use $\alpha = .05$.

	Socioeconomic Level		
	Low	*Average*	*High*
Beer	34	27	24
Wine	26	30	37
Spirits	12	12	22

11. A school official did a survey of all the high school graduates over the past ten years and gathered information about level of job satisfaction and level of post-high school formal education. Is there a dependent relationship between job satisfaction and post-high school formal education? Use $\alpha = .05$.

	Level of College Education			
Job Satisfaction	*None*	*2 Years*	*4-yr Degree*	*Postgraduate Degree*
Low	22	31	42	14
Medium	33	37	85	12
High	14	22	79	21

12. A toxic substance that is known to be present in industrial waste is suspected of producing congenital defects in infants born of parents who live near a particular factory. In a study with pregnant laboratory rats, some females were exposed to the substance and others were not. Following the birth of their litters their pups were inspected and rated as normal or abnormal in their physical development. The data appear below. Is there evidence that the presence of the substance in the environment can contribute to congenital defects? Use $\alpha = .05$.

	Exposed to Toxic Substance	
Development	*Yes*	*No*
Normal	55	65
Abnormal	23	7

13. In a study of the highly charged abortion issue, a survey was conducted to examine the distribution of pro-choice and pro-life advocates across different religious affiliations.
   a. Does one's position on this issue tend to depend on one's religious affiliation?
   b. After computing the chi-square statistic for all the data, do an analysis on only affiliations C, D, and E.
   c. Do an analysis on only affiliations A, B, and E.

	Religious Affiliation				
	A	*B*	*C*	*D*	*E*
Pro-Choice	43	62	12	5	40
Pro-Life	13	10	81	35	37

14. Pilot trainees were assigned five, ten, or fifteen hours of aircraft simulator time doing instrument approaches before attempting the maneuver in a real aircraft. Following simulator training, a score was recorded for each pilot designating whether or not an acceptable instrument landing approach was ("Success") or was not ("Failure") executed in the aircraft on at least one of the first three attempts. Did the competence of the pilots vary as a function of time spent in the simulator? Use $\alpha = .05$.

	Simulator Time		
	5 Hours	*10 Hours*	*15 Hours*
Success	8	14	20
Failure	15	12	7

15. A researcher designed an experiment to determine whether aggressive behavior among males of a particular inbred strain of laboratory mouse is dependent upon the presence of male sex hormone. Eighty male mice were neutered before puberty. Once they reached adulthood they were divided into four groups of 20 mice each and placed on a program of placebo injections, low dose testosterone replacement, medium dose testosterone replacement, or high dose testosterone replacement. After two weeks of replacement therapy they were tested for aggression. The dependent measure was simply whether they did or did not fight.

a. According to the data below, did fighting behavior depend upon the degree of testosterone (male sex hormone) replacement therapy? Use $\alpha = .01$.

Treatment	Fighting Behavior *Yes*	*No*
Placebo	2	18
Low Dose	3	17
Medium Dose	8	12
High Dose	12	8

b. Collapse across the low dose and placebo groups and do the chi-square analysis on the resulting 3×3 contingency table.

Treatment	Fighting Behavior *Yes*	*No*
Placebo/Low	5	35
Medium Dose	8	12
High Dose	12	8

CHAPTER 15

Inside the Analysis of Variance (ANOVA)

ANOVA. An abbreviation for the ANalysis Of VAriance.

The analysis of variance (commonly abbreviated as **ANOVA**) is a very powerful, very versatile, and very widely used statistical tool for experimental design and data analysis in the behavioral sciences. It is applied to the type of data for which the *t*-test is appropriate, but, whereas the *t*-test is limited to making a comparison between two groups, the ANOVA has the added advantage of being able to evaluate differences among several groups.

In its application to the design and analysis of sophisticated research projects, the ANOVA can appear very complicated. It need not, however, be intimidating. In this chapter the most fundamental ANOVA design, the single factor independent groups design, will be dissected and explained within the context of a sampling experiment. Eventually, in the next chapter, the focus will be on the computational procedures of the ANOVA, the practical application of the ANOVA to experimental data for testing hypotheses, and the interpretation of the results. While some information in the present chapter does touch upon those topics, the objective here is to develop an understanding of the underlying rationale of the ANOVA so you will know why it works. This will be done without relying on complex mathematical derivations. We shall, as we have done before with other sampling experiment presentations, develop an understanding of the theory behind a statistic through empirical verification of theoretically predicted results.

The sampling experiment and analysis in this chapter are patterned after the ANOVATUT.BAS computer tutorial and represents only one of a great many possible configurations for this program. After reading this chapter you are encouraged to run some sampling experiments on your own with group sizes (n) and numbers of groups (k) that differ from the examples used here. This will strengthen your understanding of the points raised in this chapter. (For detailed information on the ANOVATUT.BAS program consult the *Manual for Stat/Tutor*.)

A RANDOM SAMPLING EXPERIMENT

In this experiment four samples ($k = 4$) of seven scores each ($n = 7$) were drawn from a population with a mean of 50 and a standard deviation of 10. The data are presented in table 15.1 and are intended to simulate an experiment with four treatments and seven scores per treatment.

Expected Value. The theoretically expected value of a computed result as in $E(F) = 1.00$. ("The expected value of the F ratio equals 1.00.")

Because each of the 28 scores represents a random sample from a population with a mean of 50, the **expected value** of each sample score is 50. If this is so, it may strike you as somewhat unusual that only two scores out of the 28 in the data set have the exact value of 50. As you learned in chapter 10 (and in SAMPLING.BAS), even though we expect each sample value to equal 50 if the mean of the population is 50, we also know that the laws of chance that govern the selection process will result in a distribution of values of which some, just by chance, will be greater than 50 and some less than 50.

Chance alone is assumed to be the only reason for a score departing from the expected value of 50, so each score may be represented as μ, the mean of the population, plus some deviation from μ that is attributable to random (i.e., chance) factors.

$$X_{ij} = \mu + E_{ij}$$

Table 15.1

Four samples of 7 scores each drawn randomly from a population with a mean of 50 and a standard deviation of 10.

Sample 1	*Sample 2*	*Sample 3*	*Sample 4*
41	58	56	58
53	54	29	64
39	41	50	61
50	44	44	34
35	38	51	56
64	45	44	39
31	53	55	67

Table 15.2

The structural model for the 4 × 7 data matrix when the null hypothesis is true. Each score equals the mean plus a contribution of random error unique to the selection of that score.

$X_{11} = \mu + E_{11}$	$X_{12} = \mu + E_{12}$	$X_{13} = \mu + E_{13}$	$X_{14} = \mu + E_{14}$
$X_{21} = \mu + E_{21}$	$X_{22} = \mu + E_{22}$	$X_{23} = \mu + E_{23}$	$X_{24} = \mu + E_{24}$
⋮	⋮	⋮	⋮
$X_{i1} = \mu + E_{i1}$	$X_{i2} = \mu + E_{i2}$	$X_{i3} = \mu + E_{i3}$	$X_{i4} = \mu + E_{i4}$
⋮	⋮	⋮	⋮
$X_{71} = \mu + E_{71}$	$X_{72} = \mu + E_{72}$	$X_{73} = \mu + E_{73}$	$X_{74} = \mu + E_{74}$

Table 15.3

The data of Table 15.1 presented in the form of the ANOVA structural model: the population mean plus random error.

Sample 1	*Sample 2*	*Sample 3*	*Sample 4*
50 − 9	50 + 8	50 + 6	50 + 8
50 + 3	50 + 4	50 − 21	50 + 14
50 − 11	50 − 9	50 + 0	50 + 11
50 + 0	50 − 6	50 − 6	50 − 16
50 − 15	50 − 12	50 + 1	50 + 6
50 + 14	50 − 5	50 − 6	50 − 11
50 − 19	50 + 3	50 + 5	50 + 17

This expression says that the value of each sample score may be regarded as a composite of μ, the mean of the population from which the sample was drawn, plus some random deviation from μ (represented by the symbol E) that is unique to the selection in the ith row and the jth column. The subscript i goes from 1 to n, the number of scores in each sample, and the subscript j goes from 1 to k, the number of samples. For our set of data $n = 7$ and $k = 4$, so each score in the 7 × 4 data matrix in table 15.1 can be expressed as the value of the population mean ($\mu = 50$) plus random error (E_{ij}). This is represented symbolically in table 15.2 and numerically in table 15.3. Notice in table 15.3 that the random error component can be either positive or negative, producing random deviations both above and below the population mean of 50.

WHAT IF THE RANDOMLY SELECTED SCORES WERE REAL DATA?

Let us regard our 28 randomly selected scores in a different light—as data from an actual experiment. In this experiment there is an untreated control group, a placebo control group, a group treated with Drug X, and a group

Table 15.4

Four sets of randomly selected scores as they might appear if they were real experimental data.

Untreated	*Placebo*	*Drug X*	*Drug Y*
41	58	56	58
53	54	29	64
39	41	50	61
50	44	44	34
35	38	51	56
64	45	44	39
31	53	55	67

Table 15.5

The structural model for the data when the null hypothesis is not true. Each score equals the mean plus a contribution from the treatment effect plus a contribution of random error.

$X_{11} = \mu + T_1 + E_{11}$	$X_{12} = \mu + T_2 + E_{12}$	$X_{13} = \mu + T_3 + E_{13}$	$X_{14} = \mu + T_4 + E_{14}$
$X_{21} = \mu + T_1 + E_{21}$	$X_{22} = \mu + T_2 + E_{22}$	$X_{23} = \mu + T_3 + E_{23}$	$X_{24} = \mu + T_4 + E_{24}$
⋮	⋮	⋮	⋮
$X_{i1} = \mu + T_1 + E_{i1}$	$X_{i2} = \mu + T_2 + E_{i2}$	$X_{i3} = \mu + T_3 + E_{i3}$	$X_{i4} = \mu + T_4 + E_{i4}$
⋮	⋮	⋮	⋮
$X_{71} = \mu + T_1 + E_{71}$	$X_{72} = \mu + T_2 + E_{72}$	$X_{73} = \mu + T_3 + E_{73}$	$X_{74} = \mu + T_4 + E_{74}$

Treatment Effect. Variation among the treatment totals (or means) that is attributable to an effect of the independent variable.

Structural Model. The mathematical model that equates the value of a datum to the mean of the null hypothesis population, plus some departure from that mean resulting from a treatment effect, plus further departure due to random factors.

treated with Drug Y. The scores are assumed to reflect some measurable response to drug therapy, and they are presented as experimental data in table 15.4.

The null hypothesis for this experiment simply states the reality of our sampling experiment, namely, that all the scores are members of the same population (or from populations with equal means). In other words, the null hypothesis assumes the absence of any **treatment effect.** If, however, a treatment effect did exist, it would also contribute to the value of each score. This is represented in the ANOVA model in the following way:

$$X_{ij} = \mu + T_j + E_{ij}$$

To summarize, the ANOVA **structural model,** as embodied in the equation above, says that the value of any score in an experiment is a composite of the population mean, plus some deviation from the mean due to a treatment effect (T), plus more deviation due to random error (E). Individual scores are represented in this fashion in table 15.5.

The T_j term refers to the impact of treatment effect j on the value of the scores in that treatment. Within any given treatment the treatment effect is assumed to be a constant and is assumed to operate by adding a constant value to or subtracting a constant value from each $\mu + E_{ij}$ composite score. The assumption that the treatment effect exerts a constant influence upon all scores within a treatment means that the only factor that can account for the fluctuation among score values within a treatment is random error. This is because, as covered in chapter 3 and as demonstrated at the end of the VARSD.BAS tutorial, adding a constant to or subtracting a constant from each score in a set does not affect the dispersion of the scores in the set.

Before proceeding with a discussion of the underlying logic of the ANOVA, it is important that you realize that when working with real data as opposed to random samples from a population with known parameters, there is no way to break down the value of a score as a composite of the population mean plus a treatment effect plus a random error component as shown in the following equation.

$$X_{ij} = \mu + T_j + E_{ij}$$

Nevertheless, by assuming that this structural model is an accurate representation of the value of each piece of data, an avenue of hypothesis testing for multigroup experiments is opened to us.

THE EXPECTED VALUE OF THE *F* STATISTIC

If there is no treatment effect (i.e., if the null hypothesis is true) the fluctuations in value among scores that are in *different* treatments are also due only to random error. In the absence of a treatment effect, both the variability among scores within treatments and the variability among scores that are in different treatments are both caused by the same random factors. Therefore, if we compute the variance within treatment and the variance between treatment, these variances may be used as two independent estimates of the same population variance, σ^2. When these variances are used to form a ratio, the expected value is 1.00 as seen in the following equation.

$$\frac{\text{variance between treatments}}{\text{variance within treatments}} = \frac{\text{error variance}}{\text{error variance}} = 1.00 = F$$

This is the fundamental objective of the analysis of variance—to compute two independent estimates of the same population variance to see how close the ratio of the two estimates, the *F* statistic, comes to the expected value of 1.00. In the next section we shall do this analysis on the data in tables 15.1 and 15.4.

Partitioning Variation

SS. Notation for the variation ("sum of squares") in a set. The SS of any set of raw or composite scores may be computed using the General Rule.

Before variances are computed, we must first work with the variation (sum of squares or **SS**) of the scores. As a first step in computing the two estimates of variance, we shall compute the total variation among the 28 scores in our data (SS_{total}). Then this total variation will be partitioned into a part that is attributable to the fluctuations in score values across different treatments ($SS_{\text{between treatment}}$) and a part that is attributable to the fluctuations in score values within the same treatments ($SS_{\text{within treatment}}$).

$$SS_{\text{total}} = SS_{\text{between treatment}} + SS_{\text{within treatment}}$$

or, in more compact form:

$$SS_{\text{total}} = SS_{\text{b.t.}} + SS_{\text{w.t.}}$$

Total Variation

If the 28 scores are lumped together as one set and the total variation among the 28 scores is computed using the usual computational formula for variation,

$$\Sigma X^2 - \frac{(\Sigma X)^2}{n}$$

$$\text{Thus, } SS_{\text{total}} = 68426 - \frac{1354^2}{28} = 2950.43$$

Within Treatment Variation

$SS_{\text{within treatment}}$. The $SS_{\text{w.t.}}$ is that portion of the total variation that is variation that is attributable to random error.

Now let us once again regard the 28 scores as four separate samples of 7 scores each and compute the variation separately for each sample. When the individual variation scores for each sample are computed and added ("pooled") together, this will give us the portion of the total variation called the $\mathbf{SS}_{\text{within treatment}}$.

$$\text{SS(sample 1)} = 14793 - \frac{313^2}{7} = 797.43$$

$$\text{SS(sample 2)} = 16175 - \frac{333^2}{7} = 333.72$$

$$\text{SS(sample 3)} = 15975 - \frac{329^2}{7} = 512.00$$

$$\text{SS(sample 4)} = 21483 - \frac{379^2}{7} = 962.86$$

$$+$$

$$SS_{\text{within treatment}} = 2606.01$$

Between Treatment Variation

$SS_{\text{between treatment}}$. The $SS_{\text{b.t.}}$ is that portion of the total variation that is in part attributable to systematic (nonrandom) differences between the treatments.

The next step is to compute the $\mathbf{SS}_{\text{between treatment}}$, which may be done by finding the variation among the treatment totals.

313 333 329 379

Unlike a real experiment, here we know that the null hypothesis is true. We know that the four "treatments" are really four independent random samples from the same population, and we know that the only reason for differences among the treatment totals is random error. To find the variation among the four totals we must apply a more detailed version of the familiar computational formula. This is because each total is not just one score. Each treatment total is a composite score made up of 7 individual pieces of data. Here is the familiar computational formula from chapter 3:

$$\text{Variation} = \text{SS} = \Sigma X^2 - \frac{(\Sigma X)^2}{n}$$

Here it is written in a slightly different way:

$$\frac{\Sigma X^2}{i} - \frac{(\Sigma X)^2}{n}$$

The left term says to square each number in the set, add the squares, and divide by the number of scores represented in each number of the set. Up to now we have applied this formula only when a number in a set represented one data point. Since the division by one has no impact, it is omitted. Similarly, the right term says to square the sum of the set and divide by the number of scores represented in the sum. Up to now this has always been n, the number of individual elements in the set.

Now, however, we must find the variation among a set of treatment *totals* as opposed to individual raw scores. Each total is a composite of 7 scores, and this must be taken into account in computing variation. Similarly, the sum of the treatment totals represents $4 \times 7 = 28$ scores, not simply 4.

THE GENERAL RULE

The computation of sum of squares for any set of data (either raw scores or totals) may be expressed as follows:

Two separate quantities must be computed from the data. To get Quantity 1, square each individual number in the set and sum the squares. Then divide the resulting sum by the quantity of individual data points represented in each number in the set.

The General Rule. The general computational procedure for determining the variation (SS) in any set of raw or composite scores. See text for details.

If the **General Rule** is being applied to a set of raw scores then each number in the set represents a single data point. The division step may be omitted because division by 1.00 will not change the value of the sum of the squared scores.

$$\frac{\Sigma X^2}{1} = \Sigma X^2$$

But if each score in the set is a total of, say, n individual raw scores, to get Quantity 1 we must divide the sum of the squared scores by n. This is because each number in the set is a total (or *composite*) of n raw scores, and this must be taken into account in computing Quantity 1.

$$\frac{(\text{total } 1)^2 + (\text{total } 2)^2 + \cdots + (\text{total } k)^2}{n}$$

To get Quantity 2 add all the numbers in the set, square this sum and divide by the number of individual raw scores represented in the sum of the set. The sum of squares (variation) of the set is Quantity 1 minus Quantity 2.

For example, to find the sum of squares among the four treatment totals in our data, the computation according to the general rule takes the following form:

$$SS_{\text{between treatment}} = \frac{313^2 + 333^2 + 329^2 + 379^2}{7} - \frac{1354^2}{28}$$

$$SS_{\text{between treatment}} = \frac{460{,}740}{7} - \frac{1{,}833{,}316}{28}$$

$$SS_{\text{between treatment}} = 344.43$$

Notice that on the left (Quantity 1) each treatment total is squared before being added and that the resulting sum of 460,740 is divided by 7, the number of individual raw scores (n) that are represented in each treatment total. Similarly, on the right (Quantity 2) the grand total of all 28 scores in the data matrix (1354) is squared and divided by the number of individual raw scores ($nk = 28$) represented in the grand total.

Partitioning SS. The process of dividing the total variation (SS_{total}) into that portion attributable only to random factors ($SS_{\text{w.t.}}$) and that portion attributable to both random factors and, possibly, treatment effects ($SS_{\text{b.t.}}$).

Variation is now partitioned:

$$SS_{\text{total}} = SS_{\text{between treatment}} + SS_{\text{within treatment}}$$

$$2950.43 = 344.42 + 2606.01$$

The **partitioning of SS_{total}** for the 28 scores into $SS_{\text{b.t.}}$ and $SS_{\text{w.t.}}$ is also shown in figure 15.1.

Degrees of Freedom. In the context of the single factor ANOVA, $df_{\text{total}} = nk - 1$, $df_{\text{between treatment}} = k - 1$, and $df_{\text{within treatment}} = k(n - 1)$.

From SS to MS

Let us now convert both the $SS_{\text{b.t.}}$ and $SS_{\text{w.t.}}$ terms from variation (SS) to variance (s^2) by dividing by **degrees of freedom.** As explained in chapters 3 and 11, this "average variation per degree of freedom" provides an unbiased estimate of population variance from sample data. The degrees of freedom for

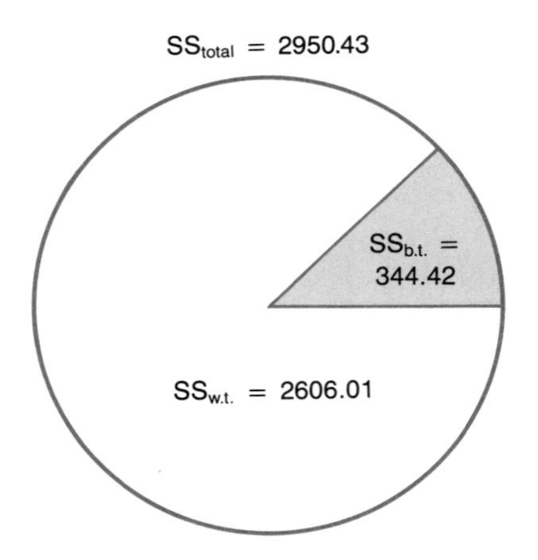

Figure 15.1

The partition of 2950.43 total units of variation into $SS_{\text{b.t.}}$ and $SS_{\text{w.t.}}$ using the data of table 15.1.

each SS term equals the number of elements in the set that was used in the computation of SS minus one. SS_{total} was computed for 28 scores and has 27 degrees of freedom. $SS_{between\ treatment}$ was computed for 4 treatment totals and has 3 degrees of freedom. $SS_{within\ treatment}$ is really the sum of the variation within each of the 4 treatments. Each of the 4 treatments has 7 scores and 6 degrees of freedom, and so there are $4 \times 6 = 24$ degrees of freedom for the $SS_{within\ treatment}$. Notice how total degrees of freedom (27) equals between treatment degrees of freedom (3) plus within treatment degrees of freedom (24). The variance between treatments, called $\mathbf{MS_{b.t.}}$, equals

MS. Mean square ("MS") is really just a variance. It is the average variation per degree of freedom or, said another way, SS divided by the appropriate *df* as in:

$$MS_{b.t.} = \frac{SS_{b.t.}}{k - 1}$$

$$MS_{b.t.} = \frac{SS_{b.t.}}{3} = \frac{344.42}{3} = 114.8$$

MS stands for "mean square" and is really just another name for variance. Since MS is SS/df, each MS is really the average (or *mean*) variation per degree of freedom, hence the name "mean square." The variance within treatment, called $\mathbf{MS_{w.t.}}$, equals

$MS_{within\ treatment}$. A mean square ("MS") is a variance. The $MS_{w.t.}$ is the $SS_{w.t.}$ divided by $k(n - 1)$ degrees of freedom and is used as the denominator of the F ratio.

$$MS_{w.t.} = \frac{SS_{w.t.}}{24} = \frac{2606.01}{24} = 108.58$$

The last step is to compute the ***F* ratio** by dividing the $\mathbf{MS_{b.t.}}$ by the $MS_{w.t.}$.

***F* ratio.** The ratio of the $MS_{b.t.}$ to the $MS_{w.t.}$. According to the structural model of the ANOVA, if the null hypothesis is true and there are no treatment effects, the expected value of the F ratio is 1.00.

$$F = \frac{114.80}{108.58} = 1.05$$

Notice how close this F value is to the expected value of 1.00.

$$F = \frac{\text{random variance} + \text{contribution of the treatment effect}}{\text{random variance}}$$

If the null hypothesis is true, as it is for our data, only random factors are causing the treatment totals to differ from each other. Because there is no contribution from a treatment effect, the variance between treatment and the variance within treatment are really independent estimates of the same population variance. Theoretically, the ratio of the two variances should equal 1.00, and we came very close with $F = 1.05$.

$MS_{between\ treatment}$. A Mean Square ("MS") is a variance. The $MS_{b.t.}$ is the $SS_{b.t.}$ divided by $(k - 1)$ degrees of freedom and is used as the numerator of the F ratio.

Creating a Treatment Effect

To illustrate the effect upon the F ratio when there is a treatment effect, let us superimpose a treatment effect on our data. The treatment effect that is unique to each treatment is assumed to be a constant, and so all we have to do is add a constant to (or subtract a constant from) all scores within a treatment. Here we shall assume that the untreated control group (sample 1) and

Table 15.6

The four sets of randomly selected scores from table 15.4 with a constant "treatment effect" added to each score within each of four "treatments."

Untreated	*Placebo*	*Drug X*	*Drug Y*
41	58	60	65
53	54	33	71
39	41	54	68
50	44	48	41
35	38	55	63
64	45	48	46
31	53	59	74

Table 15.7

The data from table 15.6 broken down according to the ANOVA structural model: population mean plus treatment effect plus random error.

Untreated	*Placebo*	*Drug X*	*Drug Y*
50 + 0 − 9	50 + 0 + 8	50 + 4 + 6	50 + 7 + 8
50 + 0 + 3	50 + 0 + 4	50 + 4 − 21	50 + 7 + 14
50 + 0 − 11	50 + 0 − 9	50 + 4 + 0	50 + 7 + 11
50 + 0 + 0	50 + 0 − 6	50 + 4 − 6	50 + 7 − 16
50 + 0 − 15	50 + 0 − 12	50 + 4 + 1	50 + 7 + 6
50 + 0 + 14	50 + 0 − 5	50 + 4 − 6	50 + 7 − 11
50 + 0 − 19	50 + 0 + 3	50 + 4 + 5	50 + 7 + 17

the placebo control group (sample 2) are providing the baseline data, and they will be left as is. We will assume that Drug *X* had a moderate effect reflected in an increase in the scores in that group and that Drug *Y* had an even stronger effect. We can simulate this by adding 4 to every score in the Drug *X* group and 7 to every score in the Drug *Y* group. The transformed data with the treatment effect added in are presented in table 15.6. These same data are shown in table 15.7 broken down into their population mean, treatment effect, and random error components. (Remember, this partitioning of data values according to the ANOVA structural model can only be done within the present artificial environment. This cannot be done with real experimental data.)

If we repeat the computations for SS_{total} for the data in table 15.6 and partition SS_{total} using the same procedures presented above, we can see the impact of adding a "treatment" component to the data. The partitioning of SS_{total} for these data is shown in figure 15.2. If you compare figure 15.2 to figure 15.1 you should notice that the addition of the treatment effects caused the SS_{total} to increase and the $SS_{b.t.}$ to increase, but the $SS_{w.t.}$ did not change.

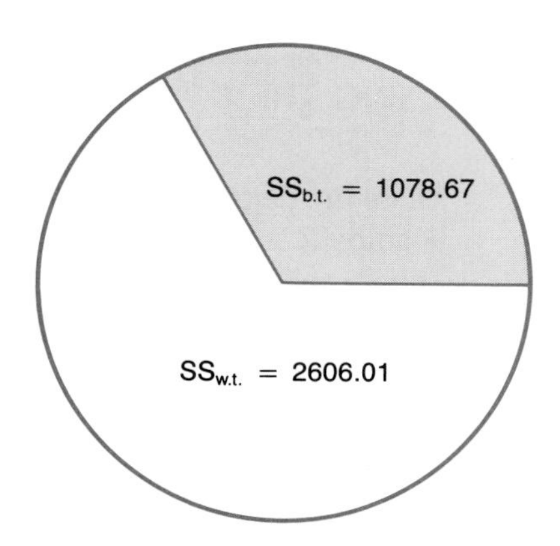

Figure 15.2

The partition of the 4374.68 units of total variation into the Sum of Squares between treatment and the Sum of Squares within treatment. The data are in table 15.5.

Similarly, when the variance within treatment ($MS_{w.t.}$) is recomputed for these modified data the result is the same (108.58) as in the original analysis. This is because adding a constant to or subtracting a constant from every element in a set does not affect the dispersion of the scores in that set. By comparison, when the variance between treatment ($MS_{b.t.}$) is recomputed, the MS now equals 359.55 instead of the former 114.8. This three-fold increase in variance is apparent from inspection and comparison of the two sets of treatment totals. Notice how much more dispersed the totals from the data that contain the treatment effect are compared to the original.

	Treatments			
	1	*2*	*3*	*4*
original totals:	313	333	329	379
totals with treatment effects:	313	333	357	428

Forming the F ratio:

$$F = \frac{MS_{b.t.}}{MS_{w.t.}} = \frac{359.55}{108.58} = 3.31$$

With the addition of the treatment effects, the $MS_{b.t.}$ is now more than three times as large as the $MS_{w.t.}$. This is because the treatment effects are causing the treatment totals to vary from each other more than can be accounted for by random variation alone. Just how far away F must be from its expected value of 1.00 before the treatment effect is regarded as significant is given in the F table.

USING THE *F* TABLE

Once the degrees of freedom for both the numerator and denominator of the *F* statistic have been determined, we may look up the critical value for *F* in the *F* table (Appendix A). The critical value for *F* is the *F* ratio that will be equalled or exceeded only 5% of the time *if the null hypothesis is true* (i.e., there is no treatment effect). Let us first review the determination of degrees of freedom for the current example, then, by entering the table with these values, we will find the critical value for *F*.

The degrees of freedom associated with the *SS* of a set is *k*, the number of scores in the set, minus one and is written: df $= k - 1$. As explained in chapter 11, this is because the sum of the deviations of each score from the mean of all the scores must equal zero, and the one deviation score that is not free to vary results in a loss of one degree of freedom. For the current example, the $SS_{\text{between treatment}}$ was computed using the four treatment totals, and so $k = 4$ and $k - 1 = 4 - 1 = 3$.

The degrees of freedom associated with the $SS_{\text{within treatment}}$ is the degrees of freedom within treatment 1 $(n_1 - 1)$ plus the degrees of freedom within treatment 2 $(n_2 - 1)$, plus . . . plus the degrees of freedom within treatment *k* $(n_k - 1)$. The value of degrees of freedom associated with the $SS_{\text{within treatment}}$ in the current example is

$$6 + 6 + 6 + 6 = 24.$$

To compute the degrees of freedom within treatment in one step simply solve $k(n - 1)$. For the current example $k(n - 1) = 4 \cdot 6 = 24$.

Once we have divided the $SS_{\text{between treatment}}$ and the $SS_{\text{within treatment}}$ by the appropriate degrees of freedom, and once we have computed the *F* ratio with these mean squares ($F = MS_{\text{b.t.}}/MS_{\text{w.t.}}$), we are ready to look up the critical value of the *F* statistic in the *F* table. In our example we have 3 and 24 degrees of freedom. The *F* table is entered by finding the column that corresponds to the degrees of freedom for the numerator (3). Then we move down that column and stop at the row that corresponds to the degrees of freedom for the denominator (24). Two values are printed in the intersecting cell of the *F* table. The larger value (in boldface) is the critical ratio for an *F* test at the .01 level of significance, and the smaller value printed in lighter type is the critical ratio for an *F* test at the .05 level of significance. Looking in column 3 and row 24 we find the value 3.01 as the critical ratio for *F* at the .05 level of significance. This is often written as:

$$F(3{,}24) = 3.01$$

and is read, "The critical value of *F* with 3 and 24 degrees of freedom equals 3.01." A facsimile of the *F* table is reproduced on the next page with the entry for the cell with $df = 3{,}24$.

Degrees of Freedom	**Degrees of Freedom** (*numerator*)				
(*denominator*)	1	2	3	4	5 . . . . . .
1			.		
2			.		
.			.		
.			.		
.			.		
			.		
24 .... →			3.01 ←		
			4.72		

The critical value at the .05 level of significance equals 3.01, and since 3.31, the computed value for F, exceeds 3.01 we have a significant treatment effect.

F and Type I Error

When there are 3 and 24 degrees of freedom, an F ratio as large or larger than 3.01 will occur by chance 5% or less of the time. Thus, if you repeated this random sampling experiment using ANOVATUT.BAS with $n = 7$ and $k = 4$ one hundred times, in five out of those one hundred experiments you would theoretically expect to get a significant F ratio (i.e., > 3.01) *just by chance*. You know there is no treatment effect in such a random sampling experiment, and yet the analysis says otherwise. This is what we have been calling Type I error, and it is a fact of life in statistical analysis of data that we must learn to take into account.

All the various values of F that would result from the one hundred ANOVATUT.BAS sampling experiments should approximate the F distribution with 3 and 24 degrees of freedom. In fact, for every combination of degrees of freedom there is a different F distribution, so, like the t statistic, if we look up the wrong value in the table we are, in effect, locating our computed statistic on the wrong distribution.

What Does a Significant *F* Mean?

A significant F means that some treatment or combination of treatments is different from some other treatment or combination of treatments. The overall ANOVA does not provide information to make specific group-to-group comparisons. In practice, inspection of the treatment totals or means usually reveals the main contributor(s) to the treatment effect. At this point in our data analysis we do not really know whether there is a difference between the placebo group and the untreated control group or between the placebo group and the Drug X group. It is fairly apparent, however, that the Drug Y group is a principal contributor to the between treatment variance because its treatment total is so much greater than the others.

To get specific information about the significant or nonsignificant relationships between groups, the overall ANOVA must be followed with an analysis called Individual Comparisons. This will be covered in chapter 17. For reasons that will be explained in the presentation of the individual comparisons analysis, multiple t-tests between various pairs of groups is *not* a legitimate course of action to determine the specific relationships between groups.

A COMPARISON BETWEEN t AND F

The t statistic and the F statistic have a very direct functional relationship: $t^2 = F$. Assuming the underlying assumptions have been met, data from a two-group experiment may be analyzed with either t or an ANOVA. The same result, rejection or no rejection of the null hypothesis, will be obtained. Another way of demonstrating the relationship between t and F is to square the critical values in the t table and compare them to the first column of the F table. We use the first column in the F table because, in a two-group experiment, the numerator of the F statistic, $MS_{b.t.}$ has only one degree of freedom. The t^2 and F values are the same. The principal difference between the two statistics is that F allows comparisons among several groups, whereas the t statistic is limited to the comparison of only two groups.

In the next chapter the focus will be on the more applied side of ANOVA: analyzing and interpreting data from single factor independent groups and repeated measures (correlated groups) designs. Before you go on to this material, if you have a microcomputer available try running ANOVATUT.BAS under a variety of configurations. This will strengthen your grasp of the concepts that have been covered in this chapter.

Summary

We examined the underlying rationale of the analysis of variance (ANOVA) by using the sampling experiment approach that is employed in the ANOVATUT.BAS computer tutorial. We computed and partitioned the variation in a set of randomly selected scores, then constructed an F ratio. We repeated this with the addition of treatment effects to demonstrate the change in the value of the F statistic that results from the introduction of a systematic source of variance. Finally, we discussed the use of the F table along with a comparison of the t and F statistics.

Key Terms

ANOVA
Between Treatment SS and MS
Degrees of Freedom
Expected Value
***F* Ratio**
MS
Partitioning SS
SS
Structural Model
The General Rule
Treatment Effect
Within Treatment SS and MS

Exercises

1. Why does the expected value of the F statistic equal 1.00 when the null hypothesis is true?
2. Why does the value of the F ratio exceed 1.00 when there is a treatment effect?
3. Explain the following statement. "When the null hypothesis is true, the $MS_{between\ treatment}$ and the $MS_{within\ treatment}$ are both estimates of error variance."
4. Why doesn't superimposing "treatment effects" on the randomly selected scores affect the $SS_{within\ treatment}$?
5. If the results of a two-group experiment are analyzed using an independent groups t-test and $t = 2.00$ ($df = 22$), the F statistic for these same data would equal _____, the degrees of freedom between treatment would equal _____, and the degrees of freedom within treatment would equal _____.
6. What is the structural model of the ANOVA when the null hypothesis is true? X_{ij} = ____________________
7. What is the structural model of the ANOVA when the null hypothesis is not true? X_{ij} = ____________________
8. State the General Rule for computing the SS of a set of raw scores or treatment totals.
9. Explain the "pooling" procedure for the computation of the within treatment SS.
10. Explain the computation of the degrees of freedom for the within treatment and between treatment terms.
11. Why is SS/df called a "mean square?"
12. How do we use the $MS_{between\ treatment}$ and the $MS_{within\ treatment}$ to compute the F ratio?
13. If you have an I.B.M. PC (or compatible) handy, run ANOVATUT.BAS with various numbers of treatments (k) and sample sizes (n) to strengthen your understanding of the material presented in chapter 15.
14. Following are 24 *randomly* selected scores that were generated from the ANOVATUT.BAS computer tutorial (parameters of the population from which the samples were drawn: $\mu = 50$, $\sigma = 10$). These randomly selected scores are

being used to represent 8 scores in each of 3 treatments. The totals for each treatment, the Grand Total (G), the sum of the squared scores for each treatment, and the overall sum of the squared scores are presented along with the raw data.

	Treatments			
	1	*2*	*3*	
	59	51	59	
	44	59	41	
	43	61	49	
	42	54	53	
	51	56	46	
	54	49	44	
	50	48	41	
	61	54	59	
Totals:	404	432	392	Grand Total = 1228
$\Sigma X^2 =$	20,768	23,476	19,586	$\Sigma\Sigma X^2 = 63{,}830$

a. Using the General Rule, regard the scores as one big set of 24 scores and use the quantities provided above to compute the SS for that set.

b. Using the General Rule, regard each "treatment" as a separate set and use the quantities provided above to compute the SS for each of the 3 sets.

c. Using the General Rule, regard the 3 treatment totals as a set and find the SS among the 3 treatment totals. (Be sure to take into account that each total is a composite of 8 raw scores.)

d. Check to see that the sum of the SS values for the 3 individual sets of 8 (the $SS_{\text{within treatment}}$) and the SS for the 3 treatment totals (the $SS_{\text{between treatment}}$) sum to the answer to question 14*a* (the SS_{total}).

e. Convert the $SS_{\text{within treatment}}$ and the $SS_{\text{between treatment}}$ to mean squares by dividing each term by the appropriate degrees of freedom.

f. Form a ratio of the $MS_{\text{between treatment}}$ divided by the $MS_{\text{within treatment}}$. Why do we expect the solution of this ratio to equal 1.00?

15. The scores below represent the same experiment as in question 14 above except that simulated "treatment effects" have been introduced. Three units were added to each of the scores in the first treatment, 6 units were added to each of the scores in the second treatment, and 0 was added to the scores in the third treatment. As in question 14, the data are presented in partially analyzed form.

	Treatments			
	1	*2*	*3*	
	62	57	59	
	47	65	41	
	46	67	49	
	45	60	53	
	54	62	46	
	57	55	44	
	53	54	41	
	64	60	59	
Totals:	428	480	392	Grand Total = 1300
$\Sigma X^2 =$	23,264	28,948	19,586	$\Sigma\Sigma X^2 = 71{,}798$

a. Using the General Rule, regard the scores as one complete set of 24 scores and use the quantities provided above to compute the SS for that set.

b. Using the General Rule, regard *each* "treatment" as a separate set and use the quantities provided above to compute the SS for each of the 3 sets.

c. Using the General Rule, regard the 3 treatment totals as a set and find the SS among the 3 treatment totals. (Be sure to take into account that each total is a composite of 8 raw scores.)

d. Check to see that the sum of the SS values for the 3 individual sets of 8 (the $SS_{\text{within treatment}}$) and the SS for the 3 treatment totals (the $SS_{\text{between treatment}}$) sum to the answer to question 14*a* (the SS_{total}).

e. Why did the $SS_{\text{within treatment}}$ for these modified data exactly equal the $SS_{\text{within treatment}}$ for the data presented in question 14?

f. Convert the $SS_{\text{within treatment}}$ and the $SS_{\text{between treatment}}$ to mean squares by dividing each term by the appropriate degrees of freedom.

g. Form a ratio of the $MS_{\text{between treatment}}$ divided by the $MS_{\text{within treatment}}$. Why do we expect the solution of this ratio to be greater than 1.00?

CHAPTER 16

Using the Single Factor Analysis of Variance

If you have studied the previous chapter and have followed up with a few runs of ANOVATUT.BAS in various configurations, you should understand how the analysis of the variance in data can be used to evaluate the significance of treatment effects in an independent groups experimental design. The focus in this chapter is in a more practical vein: the application of the ANOVA to experimental data and the interpretation of the results of the analysis. First the necessary notation will be presented, then the procedure will be applied to a set of experimental data.

SOME NEW NOTATION

The independent groups experimental design may be regarded as an extension of the *t*-test. Instead of the two basic groups of the control group versus experimental group design, the experimental design for which the ANOVA is appropriate may contain any number of groups. Each group in such a multigroup experiment will have its own set of scores and its own total, and there must be a way of labeling such values because they are needed for various computations. In table 16.1 there is a symbolic representation of a data set from a multigroup experiment. (The notation system is that of B. J. Winer, 1962.)

Table 16.1
A symbolic representation of a set of experimental data for the independent groups ANOVA.

Treatment							
1	2	3	...	j	...	k	
X_{11}	X_{12}	X_{13}	...	X_{1j}	...	X_{1k}	
X_{21}	X_{22}	X_{23}	...	X_{2j}	...	X_{2k}	
⋮	⋮	⋮		⋮		⋮	
X_{i1}	X_{i2}	X_{i3}	...	X_{ij}	...	X_{ik}	
⋮	⋮	⋮		⋮		⋮	
X_{n1}	X_{n2}	X_{n3}	...	X_{nj}	...	X_{nk}	
T_1	T_2	T_3	...	T_j	...	T_k	$G = \Sigma T_j$

The symbolic representation of the data set as presented in table 16.1 shows that the treatments are labeled from 1 to k, and j is used as the general designation of a treatment. The rows of the table are labeled from 1 to n, and i is used as the general designation of a row. In labeling each score in the data set the subscripts i and j are used. Thus, X_{23} is the second score in the third treatment ($i = 2$ and $j = 3$), and X_{ij} is used as the general designation of a single score.

Two important totals are used to compute the analysis of variance. The letter T is used to indicate the total of the scores within each of the k treatments, and G is the grand total of all the scores in the experiment.

THE COMPUTATIONAL COMPONENTS

Computational Components. The special values computed from the data that are used to compute total variation and partition it into its component parts.

To do an ANOVA we must first compute three special numbers called **computational components.** By manipulating these components in specified ways, we can partition the variation in the data set into the part that can be attributed to a treatment effect and the part that can be attributed to random error. The three components are

1. G^2/nk (Sum all the scores in the data set, square that sum, and divide by the total number of scores in the data set.)

Table 16.2

A computational guide to the ANOVA Summary Table for the independent groups experimental design.

ANOVA Summary Table

Source of Variation	*df*	SS	MS	*F*
Between treatment	$k - 1$	(3) − (1)	$\frac{(3) - (1)}{k - 1}$	$\frac{MS_{b.t.}}{MS_{w.t.}}$
Within treatment	$k(n - 1)$	(2) − (3)	$\frac{(2) - (3)}{k(n - 1)}$	
Totals	$nk - 1$	(2) − (1)		

2. $\Sigma\Sigma X_{ij}^2$ (Square each score in the data set and add to get the total of the squared scores. The double Σ is a reminder to carry out the squaring operation across all rows (i) and columns (j).)

3. $\Sigma T_j^2/n$ (Square each treatment total, add the squared totals, and divide by n, the number of scores within each treatment.)

THE ANALYSIS OF VARIANCE SUMMARY TABLE

ANOVA Summary Table. The tabular display of the results of an Analysis of Variance showing the Source of Variation, *df*, SS, MS, and the *F* ratio.

Once the values of the computational components are known, the **ANOVA Summary Table** may be prepared. In table 16.2 there are directions for filling in the cells of the ANOVA Summary Table for any independent groups design. The numbers within parentheses, (1), (2), and (3), refer to the computational components.

The variation attributable to the treatment effect, $SS_{between\ treatment}$, is computed by subtracting (1) from (3). If you flip back to the discussion of the General Rule in the last chapter, you will recognize (3) − (1) as an application of this rule. The variance for the between treatment source ($MS_{between\ treatment}$) is computed by dividing the $SS_{between\ treatment}$ by $k - 1$. The $k - 1$ quantity, the number of treatments in the experiment less one, is the *degrees of freedom* for the between treatment source of variation.

The error variation ($SS_{within\ treatment}$) is computed by subtracting (3) from (2). The error variance ($MS_{within\ treatment}$) is computed by dividing the $SS_{within\ treatment}$ by $k(n - 1)$, which is the degrees of freedom within treatment. As a check on your computations, the $SS_{between\ treatment}$ and the $SS_{within\ treatment}$ must sum to (2) − (1), the SS_{total}, and the between treatment ($k - 1$) and within treatment ($k(n - 1)$) degrees of freedom must sum to the total degrees of freedom, $nk - 1$.

Table 16.3

The number of correct responses on a discrimination reversal task: the data for Problem 1.

	Level of Contamination				
	None	Low	Moderate	High	
	12	10	15	11	
	11	13	12	8	
	13	14	12	6	
	15	9	7	7	
	10	11	11	10	
	8	16	13	8	
Totals =	69	73	70	50	G = 262

The final computation in the table, the F statistic, is computed by dividing the $MS_{\text{between treatment}}$ by the $MS_{\text{within treatment}}$. This is the F value, with $(k - 1)$ and $k(n - 1)$ degrees of freedom, which must be compared to the tabled F value to test for the presence of a significant treatment effect. The use of the F table will be covered within the context of the example that follows.

Analyzing the Data of a Multigroup Single Factor Experiment

Problem 1. In a behavioral assay for the possible toxic effects of eating fish contaminated with PCBs (polychlorinated biphenyls) a researcher fed one group of laboratory rats uncontaminated fish. Three other groups were fed contaminated fish that, for the sake of simplicity, will be described here as the conditions of low contamination, moderate contamination, and high contamination. The data presented in table 16.3 represent the number of correct responses in a discrimination reversal task. Was there any difference in the performance of the laboratory animals as a function of the level of PCB contamination in their diet?

The null hypothesis for this experiment is that food contaminated with PCBs will not affect the behavior of laboratory rats in a problem-solving situation. The alternative hypothesis is that the PCB toxicity will affect problem-solving behavior. These hypotheses may be represented symbolically as follows:

$H_0: \mu_1 = \mu_2 = \mu_3 = \mu_4$
H_1: not H_0

Table 16.4

A section of the F table that contains the critical value for the experiment described in Problem 1.

	Degrees of Freedom (*df*) for the Treatment Effect				
***df* for the Error Term**	1	2	3	4	...
1					
⋮	⋮	⋮	⋮	⋮	
18	4.41 **8.28**	3.55 **6.01**	3.16 **5.09**	2.93 **5.58**	... ...
19	4.38 **8.18**	3.52 **5.93**	3.13 **5.01**	2.90 **4.50**	... ...
20	4.35 **8.10**	3.49 **5.85**	3.10 **4.94**	2.87 **4.43**	... ...
21	4.32 **8.02**	3.47 **5.78**	3.07 **4.87**	2.84 **4.37**	... ...
⋮	⋮	⋮	⋮	⋮	

The decision rule is to reject the null hypothesis if the computed value for the F statistic exceeds the tabled value for F with $k - 1$ and $k(n - 1)$ degrees of freedom. In the present problem, because there are 4 treatments and 6 scores within each treatment, the degrees of freedom between treatment equals 3 ($k - 1 = 4 - 1 = 3$) and the degrees of freedom within treatment equals 20 ($k(n - 1) = 4\ (6 - 1) = 20$). The $df_{\text{between treatment}}$ plus the $df_{\text{within treatment}}$ add up to the df_{total} ($df_{\text{total}} = nk - 1 = 6 \cdot 4 - 1 = 23$ and $df_{\text{between treatment}}$ plus $df_{\text{within treatment}} = 3 + 20 = 23$).

To find the critical value of F from the F table, the column in the table that corresponds to the $df_{\text{between treatment}}$ must be located. Then the row of the table that corresponds to the $df_{\text{within treatment}}$ is located. At the intersection of the row and column there are two values. The larger boldfaced value on the bottom is the critical value to use when the alpha level is set at .01, and the smaller value is used when alpha is set at .05. The section of the F table that contains the critical value for these data is reproduced in table 16.4.

As you can see from table 16.4 (or from the entire F table in Appendix A), the critical value for F with 3 and 20 degrees of freedom ($\alpha = .05$) is 3.10. The decision rule may, therefore, be stated as follows:

Decision Rule: Reject the null hypothesis if the computed value of the *F* statistic is greater than or equal to 3.10.

Table 16.5

The analysis of variance summary for the data in Problem 1.

ANOVA Summary Table

Source of Variation	*df*	SS	MS	*F*
Between treatment	3	54.83	18.27	3.12
Within treatment	20	117.00	5.84	
Totals	23	171.83		

Crunching the Numbers

The data analysis that follows is presented in the same format as used in the ONEWAY.BAS data analysis program in *Stat/Tutor*. For the data in Problem 1 the computational components are

1. $G^2/nk = 262^2/24 = 2860.17$

2. $\Sigma\Sigma X^2 = 12^2 + 11^2 + \cdots + 8^2 = 3032$

3. $\Sigma T_j^2/n = \dfrac{69^2 + 73^2 + 70^2 + 50^2}{6} = 2915$

Following the directions in table 16.2 for manipulating the computational components, we get the ANOVA Summary displayed in table 16.5.

Since the computed F value of 3.12 is greater than the critical value of 3.10 that is stated in the decision rule, we must reject the null hypothesis. Thus, the performance of the animals is not uniform across all the treatment conditions.

Interpretation. Inspection of the treatment means will usually reveal what treatment (or treatments) are contributing the most to the between treatment source of variation. In the present example the treatment means are

Treatment Condition	Means
Control	11.50
Low	12.17
Medium	11.67
High	8.33

When the means from the low and medium dose conditions are compared to the control group mean, there is very little apparent difference. When, however, the same comparison is made with the high dose mean, the difference is relatively large. We can, therefore, attribute the presence of a significant effect in the analysis of variance to a suppression in the number of correct responses experienced by the animals in the high dose group. (More formal methods for making comparisons between the means of specific experimental groups will be presented in chapter 17.)

The Repeated Measures (Correlated Groups) Single Factor Analysis of Variance

At the beginning of this chapter the statement was made that the independent groups ANOVA may be regarded as an extension of the independent groups t-test. Whereas the independent groups t-test is used to compare two experimental conditions, the ANOVA may be used to compare any number of experimental conditions. Since you know that there are two kinds of t-tests, one for independent groups and one for correlated groups, it should not surprise you to find out that there is also a logical extension of the correlated groups t-test that permits comparisons among several treatment groups in the case where the data are correlated. Most often the correlated analysis is used when all treatments are experienced by the same set of subjects, but a correlated analysis is also appropriate if there is intentional matching of the groups along some dimension (e.g., I.Q., body weight, manual dexterity, age, ethnic background, etc.) before the experiment is carried out. Thus, the considerations that dictate the use of the independent groups versus correlated groups t-test are also relevant for choosing the appropriate single factor ANOVA for experiments with several treatment conditions.

In table 16.6 a symbolic representation of the data set of a repeated measures experimental design is given. This table is very similar in appearance to table 16.1 except that labels for the rows (Subjects) and row totals (P values) have been added.

The Computational Components

The three computational components that are used to partition the SS_{total} in the independent groups ANOVA are also used in the correlated groups ANOVA, and they will be repeated below for ready reference. In addition to these three, there is one more that we need, and it is labeled "**4**".

1. G^2/nk (Sum all the scores in the data set, square that sum and divide by the total number of scores in the data set.)

2. $\Sigma\Sigma X_{ij}^2$ (Square each individual score in the data set and add to get the total of the squared scores. The double Σ is a reminder to carry out the squaring operation across all rows (i) and columns (j).)

Table 16.6

A symbolic representation of a set of experimental data for a correlated groups ANOVA.

	Treatment								
Subjects	1	2	3	. . .	j	. . .	k		
S_1	X_{11}	X_{12}	X_{13}	. . .	X_{1j}	. . .	X_{1k}	P_1
S_2	X_{21}	X_{22}	X_{23}	. . .	X_{2j}	. . .	X_{2k}	P_2
⋮	⋮	⋮	⋮		⋮		⋮	⋮
S_i	X_{i1}	X_{i2}	X_{i3}	. . .	x_{ij}	. . .	X_{ik}	P_i
⋮	⋮	⋮	⋮		⋮		⋮	⋮
S_n	X_{n1}	X_{n2}	X_{n3}	. . .	X_{nj}	. . .	X_{nk}	P_n
	T_1	T_2	T_3	. . .	T_j	. . .	T_k	$G = \Sigma T_j$

Table 16.7

A computational guide to the ANOVA Summary Table for the single factor correlated groups ANOVA.

ANOVA Summary Table

Source of Variation	df	SS	MS	F
Between subjects	$n - 1$	(4) − (1)		
Within subjects	$n(k - 1)$	(2) − (4)		
Between treatment	$k - 1$	(3) − (1)	$\frac{(3) - (1)}{k - 1}$	$\frac{MS_{b.t.}}{MS_{res.}}$
Residual	$(n - 1)(k - 1)$	(2) − (3) − (4) + (1)	$\frac{(2) - (3) - (4) + (1)}{(n - 1)(k - 1)}$	
Totals	$nk - 1$	(2) − (1)		

3. $\Sigma T_j^2/n$ (Square each treatment total, add the squared totals, and divide by n, the number of scores within each treatment.)

4. $\Sigma P_i^2/k$ (Square each row total, (P_i), add the squared row totals, and divide by k, the number of treatments.)

The directions for applying the computational components to the partitioning of the SS_{total} in the single factor correlated groups ANOVA are given in table 16.7. As before, the computational components are enclosed in parentheses, n is the number of subjects (i.e., the number of rows in the data set), and k is the number of treatments in the experiment.

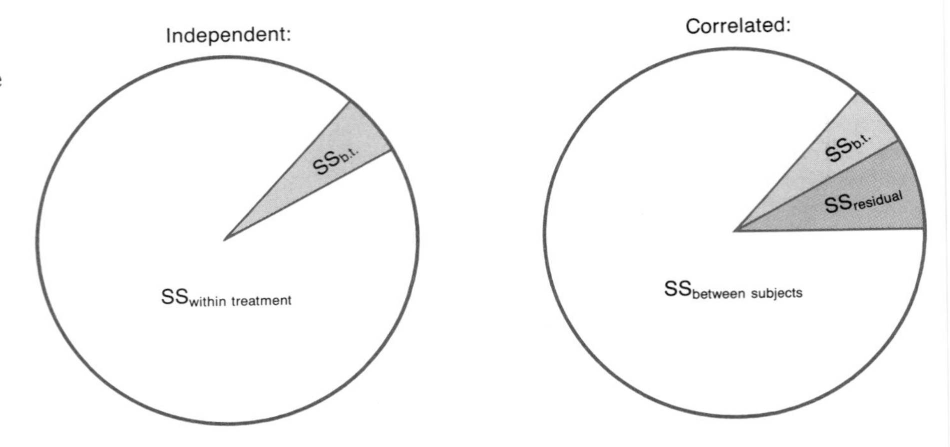

Figure 16.1

A comparison between the independent and correlated groups ANOVA for the data of Problem 2.

The partitioning of the total variation is handled differently in the correlated groups analysis as compared to the independent groups analysis, as in figure 16.1. Notice that in the correlated groups design it is possible to remove the variation attributable to individual differences between subjects ($SS_{between\ subjects}$) from the estimate of error that was computed in the independent groups analysis ($SS_{within\ treatment}$). This provides us with a term called **Residual,** which is an estimate of error with the effect of systematic individual differences removed. If the variable being measured is one that subjects tend to possess with large individual differences, the smaller error estimate provided by the correlated groups design makes it more powerful than the independent groups design. In the independent groups design it is impossible to discriminate systematic individual differences between subjects from random error.

Residual. The portion of total variation in the repeated measures ANOVA that is unexplained and is attributable to random (error) factors.

The relationship between the within treatment estimate of error from the independent groups analysis and the residual estimate of error from the correlated analysis can easily be demonstrated by doing both the independent and correlated analyses on the exact same data matrix. The $SS_{between\ subjects}$ and the $SS_{residual}$ of the correlated groups analysis will add up to the $SS_{within\ treatment}$ of the independent groups analysis. The $SS_{between\ treatment}$ will be exactly the same for both types of analyses. There is an option in the ONEWAY.BAS data analysis program that may be used for viewing both independent and correlated analyses on the same data matrix. (Naturally, with actual experimental data only one type of analysis would be correct.)

The manipulations of computational components (as shown in table 16.7) to yield the desired partitioning of SS_{total} are really just applications of the general computational rule for computing the variation in any set of numbers. (This rule is discussed in the previous chapter and in ANOVATUT.BAS.) Computational components are used just to make it easier to keep track of the process. The $SS_{residual}$ term, however, is an exception. When you see that

$SS_{residual}$ is computed by (2) − (3) − (4) + (1), this does not appear to be an application of the General Rule, and it isn't. This computation really represents SS_{total} minus $SS_{between\ treatment}$ minus $SS_{between\ subjects}$ = $SS_{residual}$ or:

$$SS_{total} - SS_{between\ treatment} - SS_{between\ subjects} = SS_{residual}$$
$$((2) - (1)) - ((3) - (1)) - ((4) - (1)) = SS_{residual}$$

By removing parentheses we have

$$(2) - (1) - (3) + (1) - (4) + (1) = SS_{residual}$$

Cancel −(1) and +(1) and the result is

$$(2) - (3) - (4) + (1) = SS_{residual}$$

As you can see, the Residual term is aptly named; it is what is left over when all other identifiable sources of variation are accounted for and are subtracted from the SS_{total} and is, therefore, assumed to result from chance alone.

Crunching the Numbers

Problem 2. A group of eight laboratory rats was used in an experiment to evaluate a group of two newly synthesized drugs for potential tranquilizer potency. After establishing a baseline activity score, each rat received a therapeutic dose of a drug and, after sufficient time had elapsed for the drug to take effect, an activity score was recorded by housing individual animals in an activity wheel apparatus. (Activity in animal populations is sometimes used in pharmaceutical research to reflect the potency of a tranquilizer.) Three days later, after all traces of the first drug were gone from an individual animal's system, a second drug was administered and activity data were again collected. The activity scores corresponding to the baseline control condition and the two different drug conditions are presented in table 16.8. Was there any difference among the three treatment conditions in spontaneous activity?

The first step is to compute the four computational components that are used to complete the entries in table 16.7.

1. $G^2/nk = 519^2/24 = 11{,}223.4$
2. $\Sigma\Sigma X_{ij}^2 = 22^2 + 32^2 + 26^2 + \cdots + 25^2 + 19^2 = 11{,}829$
3. $\Sigma T_j^2/n = (186^2 + 168^2 + 165^2)/8 = 11{,}255.6$
4. $\Sigma P^2/k = (60^2 + 85^2 + 71^2 + 56^2 + 67^2 + 44^2 + 85^2 + 51^2)/3 = 11{,}751$

Table 16.8.

Activity wheel scores for a group of rats tested under the influence of three drugs: the data of Problem 2.

Rat #	Baseline	Drug 1	Drug 2	P_i
1	22	20	18	60
2	32	26	27	85
3	26	24	21	71
4	20	19	17	56
5	23	22	22	67
6	15	13	16	44
7	31	29	25	85
8	17	15	19	51
Totals	186	168	165	G = 519

Table 16.9

The analysis of variance summary for the data of Problem 2.

ANOVA Summary Table

Source of Variation	*df*	SS	MS	F
Between subjects	7	527.60		
Within subjects	16	78.00		
Between treatment	2	32.20	16.10	4.92
Residual (error)	14	45.80	3.27	
Totals	23	605.60		

Once the appropriate substitutions are made in table 16.7 we get the ANOVA Summary Table as presented in table 16.9.

The critical value for the *F* statistic with 2 and 14 degrees of freedom is 3.74 ($\alpha = .05$). The computed *F*, ($MS_{between\ treatment}$ divided by $MS_{residual}$) is 4.92, and so there is a significant difference among the three treatment conditions. Further information is available from inspection of the means:

	Baseline	Drug 1	Drug 2
Means	23.25	21.00	20.63

These values suggest that both drug groups experienced roughly the same suppression of activity, and both are lower than the baseline level. It does not appear that the two drugs differed from each other in their effect on activity.

POTENTIAL PROBLEMS IN THE INTERPRETATION OF THE PROBLEM 2 DATA

Let us examine the possible reasons for the decline of running wheel activity across the three data collection periods.

1. The effects were caused by the tranquilizing action of the drugs.
2. The effects were caused by factors that had nothing to do with the drugs. For example, perhaps during the final test period (Drug 2) the laboratory was unusually warm and the animals were relatively inactive.
3. The effects were a fluke and occurred by chance (Type I error).
4. The effects were caused by the stress of drug administration rather than by the drug itself.
5. The effects were caused by the animals' adaptation to the apparatus. Perhaps at first the rats "enjoyed" the novelty of the running wheel, but with repeated exposure they became less interested in running.
6. Perhaps there was a learned association between the Drug 1 administration (e.g., injection) and the consequent drug effect that carried over to the evaluation of Drug 2. ("Here we go again! This stuff really relaxed me last time!")
7. Perhaps the exposure to Drug 1 affected the animals' response to Drug 2. For example, Drug 2 may have had an appetite stimulating side effect in addition to a tranquilizing effect. The additional eating and increase in body weight may have resulted in some short-term sluggishness even after the drug was undetectable in the animals' blood.

Maybe you can come up with some alternative explanations of your own. The important thing to realize is that a statistical analysis that indicates a significant experimental effect is blind to potential experimental design shortcomings. The analysis of the data will produce results that are only as meaningful as the data itself.

These alternative explanations are testable, but some of the experimental designs would require changes that would place the analysis beyond the scope of this text. The experiment described in Problem 2 would be a useful pilot study, a preliminary assessment of the tranquilizing properties of two new drugs. But the precision that is demanded of serious research and the ability to answer some complex questions is often beyond the scope of the single factor ANOVA. This point will be pursued in the chapter on the two factor ANOVA that follows.

Counterbalancing

Sequence Effect. A sequence effect exists in a repeated measures design when the response to a treatment condition is partly determined by a residual effect from a preceding treatment.

Order Effect. An effect that results from the order in which a subject experiences a treatment.

Counterbalancing. An approach to the design of an experiment that allows one to spread out possible sequence and order effects evenly across all treatments.

Some of the effects alluded to in the above explanations have names. For example, explanations 5, 6, and 7 are called **sequence** and **order effects.** If explanation 5 is true, the level of activity in the Drug 2 treatment is the lowest because it is last in the *testing order*. That is, by the time the animals are evaluated for their response to Drug 2 the novelty of the running wheel has worn off and they are less likely to work for the stimulation it gives them. On the other hand, assuming only Drug 1 has the appetite stimulating side effect referred to in explanation 7, it is its *sequence*, coming before the Drug 2 treatment, that allows it to affect the treatment 3 results. Explanation 6 could be a sequence or an order effect depending upon whether it made a difference which drug was administered first.

When we specifically do not want to evaluate competing explanations from consideration by adding the appropriate control groups, the next best approach is to spread out their possible influence across all the treatments. This is called **counterbalancing.** To counterbalance for sequence and order effects we could use the approach in table 16.10. This describes an experiment that would be run in replications of 6 animals each.

Every possible sequence and order is represented in table 16.10. For example, Treatment 1 (Baseline) is positioned first, second, and third in testing order (first: 1–2–3, 1–3–2; second: 2–1–3, 3–1–2; and third: 2–3–1, 3–2–1), and is sequenced after both of the other treatments (after Treatment 2: 2–1–3, 3–2–1; and after Treatment 3: 2–3–1, 3–1–2). Because every treatment follows every other treatment and every treatment is administered in every order, whatever sequence and order effects there may be would presumably cancel or "counterbalance" each other.

Individual Differences in the Independent Versus Correlated Designs

Before ending this chapter, let us purposely analyze this set of correlated data using the wrong ANOVA analysis. Specifically, the correlated data of Problem 2 will be analyzed by using the independent groups method. This will provide a demonstration of the effect of removing the systematic individual differences from the estimate of error variance. Look at table 16.11 to see the incorrect independent groups analysis of the Problem 2 data.

Notice how the $SS_{\text{within treatment}}$ in table 16.10 equals (with minimal rounding error of 0.01) the sum of the SS_{residual} plus the $SS_{\text{between subject}}$ from table 16.9 ($573.38 = 527.63 + 45.74$). Also, notice the effect of the inflated error term upon the value of the F statistic. Even though both analyses were done on the same data, in table 16.9 $F = 4.93$, whereas in table 16.11 $F = 0.59$. The independent groups analysis has more degrees of freedom (2 and 21 instead of 2 and 14), but, in this instance, the loss of degrees of

Table 16.10

A single factor ANOVA design that counterbalances sequence and order effects.

Subject	Treatment Sequence
1	1, 2, 3
2	1, 3, 2
3	2, 1, 3
4	2, 3, 1
5	3, 1, 2
6	3, 2, 1

Table 16.11

The incorrect independent groups analysis on the correlated groups data of Problem 2.

Analysis of Variance Summary Table

Source of Variation	*df*	SS	MS	*F*
Between treatment	2	32.20	16.10	0.59
Within treatment	21	573.40	27.30	
Totals	23	605.60		

freedom in setting up the experiment as a correlated groups design has been more than compensated for by being able to remove individual differences from the estimate of random error.

The correlated groups design has its advantages, but it is not possible, or even advisable, to always try to use the correlated groups experimental design in research. For example, there is always the risk that a prior treatment (or treatments) will affect the reaction of the subjects to subsequent treatments, and this effect will be "confounded" (inextricably intertwined) with the effect of the treatments themselves. To summarize, in deciding whether or not to use a correlated groups experimental design in research, one must weigh the loss of degrees of freedom against the potential gain in the precision of estimating error variance. If the variable under study is known to be present in the population with relatively large individual differences, and if a correlated design can be implemented without confounding, it is often the design of choice for a research project.

In doing the exercises that follow, it would be wise to do at least one independent groups analysis and one correlated groups analysis with a hand calculator just to guarantee your understanding of the computational method. You can check all your work by doing the analysis with ONEWAY.BAS.

Summary

We studied a computational method for both the single factor independent groups ANOVA and the single factor repeated measures ANOVA. The information provided by the analyses, and the lack thereof, was a topic of discussion within the context of research examples. We looked for the relative strengths and weaknesses of these designs, and made some specific comparisons regarding the computation of error variation.

Key Terms

ANOVA Summary Table
Computational Components
Counterbalancing
Order Effect
Residual
Sequence Effect

Exercises

1. Below are 32 *randomly* selected scores that were generated from the ANOVATUT.BAS computer tutorial (parameters of the population from which the samples were drawn: $\mu = 50$, $\sigma = 10$). These randomly selected scores are being used to represent 8 scores in each of 4 treatments, and these data are presented in partially analyzed form.

	Treatments			
	1	2	3	4
	61	51	64	42
	46	51	43	45
	45	65	77	36
	44	54	68	43
	53	56	46	30
	56	45	49	35
	52	48	46	40
	63	62	42	44
Totals:	420	432	435	315

ANOVA Summary Table

Source	*df*	SS	MS	*F*
Between treatment	______	______	______	______
Within treatment	______	2123.75	75.85	
Total:	______			

1. $G^2/nk = 80{,}200.2$
2. $\Sigma\Sigma X^2 = 83{,}558$
3. $\Sigma T^2/n = 81{,}434.3$

2. **a.** The expected value for the F ratio in this sampling experiment is ______.
b. Which of the four treatment totals is the most deviant from its theoretically expected value? ______
c. What is the critical value from the table against which we compare our computed F (let $\alpha = .05$)? ______
d. Is the computed value for F significant? ______
e. If this random sampling experiment were repeated 100 times, how many times would you expect to get a significant F ratio? ______
f. With another set of scores the F ratio equaled 1.54. Which F ratio is a more typical result, the 5.42 from the above data or the 1.54 from the second set of data (not shown)? ______

Answer questions 3–7 true or false. If false, change the statement so that it is correct.

3. The expected value of any score selected at random from a population is μ, the mean of the population.

4. If the null hypothesis is true, any score in an experiment may be represented by the model:

$$X_{ij} = \mu + E_{ij}$$

5. Mean Squares in the ANOVA Summary Table are computed by multiplying each sum of squares by the appropriate degrees of freedom (*df*).

6. Unlike the z and t statistics, the critical value of the F statistic is always positive.

7. To be significant the computed F must be less than the critical value from the F table.

8. The expected value of the F statistic, if we assume the null hypothesis is true, is always equal to ______.

9. Six rats were tested on a learning task daily for four days. In order to determine if significant progress had been made over the course of the four days of testing, the data (number of correct responses) were analyzed using a repeated measures ANOVA design. Here is the design:

	Day 1	Day 2	Day 3	Day 4
S1				
S2				
S3				
S4				
S5				
S6				

Below is the ANOVA Summary Table for this experiment. Fill in the missing entries.

Analysis of Variance Summary Table

	df	SS	MS	*F*
Between subjects	—	60.8		
Within subjects	—	80.2		
Between treatment	—	42.0	—	—
Residual	—	—	—	—
Total				

10. A group of 15 subjects was randomly divided into 3 groups of 5 subjects each. A complex tracking task was performed under three different conditions of stimulus illumination. Each group of subjects was tested under a different condition. The scores represent the number of errors each subject made in the tracking task. Did the stimulus illumination affect the error rate? Use $\alpha = .05$. Here are the data:

Level of Stimulus Illumination (groups)		
1 *Low*	2 *Medium*	3 *High*
10	8	6
11	4	8
12	6	6
14	4	4
14	7	4

11. Three weight training programs were evaluated by the United States Weight Lifting Association for their effectiveness in building strength in the three Olympic lifts. The subjects in the experiment were drawn from the pool of applicants to the Olympic team. Three subjects within each of six weight classes were matched for strength, then the subjects were randomly assigned to one of the three weight training programs. Thus, 18 subjects in total participated in the experiment.

The variable under study was the change in total pounds lifted before the training programs were initiated compared to the total pounds lifted after the program had been in effect for three months. The experimental design, the row and column totals, and the value of one computational component ($\Sigma\Sigma X^2$) are presented below. (Each subject is numbered from 1 to 18.) Use this information to generate a complete ANOVA Summary Table and offer an interpretation of the results within the context of the problem.

Weight Class	Program 1	Program 2	Program 3	Row Totals
1	S_1	S_7	S_{13}	107
2	S_2	S_8	S_{14}	117
3	S_3	S_9	S_{15}	124
4	S_4	S_{10}	S_{16}	130
5	S_5	S_{11}	S_{17}	137
6	S_6	S_{12}	S_{18}	147
Totals:	252	210	300	G = 762
Means:	42	35	50	
$\Sigma\Sigma X^2 = 34210$				

12. To demonstrate the influence of hunger on the performance of a learned response, five groups of laboratory rats, which had been taught a lever-pressing skill in an earlier experiment, were deprived of food until they reached 95%, 90%, or 85% of their original body weight. A control group was maintained at 100% of original body weight. The animals were tested and the number of lever presses was recorded. Did the degree of food deprivation affect the animal's motivation to engage in the lever pressing task? Use $\alpha = .05$.

Control	95%	90%	85%
12	17	20	28
11	13	23	19
8	9	17	16
9	16	22	21
6	7	15	11

13. Professor Jervis teaches three sections of History 100. Is there a difference, among the sections, in the students' performance on the first examination? Use $\alpha = .05$.

Section 1	Section 2	Section 3
83	81	76
84	52	69
81	80	78
96	97	76
89	76	85
82	88	82
92	91	65
93	95	90
81	92	81
61	79	76

14. A group of monkeys was tested on a series of problems. Although the specific solution to each problem was different, the correct strategy for approaching the solution was the same for all the problems. The data below represent the number of trials it took the animals to solve five separate problems. Did the animals gain in problem-solving skill as a function of prior problem-solving experience?

	Problems				
Subjects	1	2	3	4	5
Jojo	15	14	15	11	8
Mickey	22	23	19	8	12
Bobo	12	6	7	9	5
Pepe	10	14	14	6	5
Mumu	8	4	3	3	2

15. A group of laboratory rats was taught to make a discrimination. Pressing a lever while the correct stimulus was on a visual display resulted in a food reward, whereas pressing the lever while no stimulus or an incorrect stimulus was on the display did not result in food reward. After the response was learned to a criterion of success, food reward for lever pressing was stopped, but correct and incorrect stimuli continued to appear on the display. Lever presses were recorded for 15 seconds following the presentation of each correct stimulus. Was there any change in the lever-pressing response to the correct stimulus over the first four nonrewarded (extinction) trials? Use $\alpha = .05$.

Subjects	Trial 1	Trial 2	Trial 3	Trial 4
1	11	13	8	8
2	18	12	11	12
3	14	18	5	6
4	22	24	18	13
5	9	9	8	11
6	17	14	11	4
7	21	18	15	7

16. Near the end of the season a gambler selected what he believed were the top four teams in a basketball league. He wanted to do a comparison of the average point production of the starting five players on each team. He believed that this would help him to predict the winner of the end of the season intraleague tournament. Was there a difference in the point production of the four teams the gambler compared? Use $\alpha = .01$.

Team 1	Team 2	Team 3	Team 4
18	26	16	22
16	21	11	19
19	22	17	18
23	19	14	25
21	32	17	12

CHAPTER 17

Post ANOVA Tests

In our study of the analysis of variance (ANOVA) in the last chapter, you learned that a significant F ratio reveals that somewhere, among the set of k treatment means, there is a lack of uniformity, and this is reflected in the size of the mean square between treatment relative to the mean square within treatment: the F ratio.

$$F = \frac{MS_{\text{between treatment}}}{MS_{\text{within treatment}}}$$

When the F ratio is far enough above its expected value of 1.00 to occur by chance only 5% of the time, a chance explanation of the variance among the treatment means is rejected, and an experimental or "treatment" effect is said to exist.

Usually, insight into the pattern of differences among treatments that resulted in a significant F can be gained by careful inspection of the relative magnitudes of the treatment means. For example, let's suppose that you ran a four-group experiment that yielded the following treatment means,

I	II	III	IV
54.57	59.21	52.39	72.21

and you found a significant F ratio. It is rather obvious then that the differences between the first three treatment means and the Treatment IV mean were the major contributors to the size of the $MS_{\text{between treatment}}$.

Often, however, we need a more precise evaluation of the relationships among the k treatments. Because the mean of Treatment III is the lowest, the mean of Treatment IV is the highest, and F is significant, we may, for example, feel safe in saying that the effect of Treatment IV was significantly different from the effect of Treatment III without making the specific statistical comparison between these two treatments. But what about Treatment IV versus Treatment II or Treatment III versus Treatment II? Are these differences also statistically significant? Until the ANOVA is carried further, we cannot evaluate the significance of specific comparisons. Remember, a significant F ratio does not tell us what the specific pattern of differences is among the set of treatment means. Instead, the information is rather *non-specific*. A significant F only tells us that the variance among the set of k treatment means is unlikely to have arisen from chance factors alone.

A PRIORI TESTS

Before we run the data collection phase of an experiment, we are sometimes able to predict that a specific pattern of differences will exist among the treatments. Predictions are not guesses. They should be a natural outgrowth of our knowledge of related research findings and their logical relationship to the design and interpretation of the intended experiment. If these conditions are met, namely, that (1) the differences among the set of treatment means were predicted *before* the experimental data were collected and (2) the specific comparisons targeted for statistical evaluation make sense within the overall context of the experiment, then we are entitled to use a so-called **a priori test** to make the comparisons.

A Priori Tests. Computational procedures that permit comparisons among treatment means when the comparisons were planned prior to running the experiment.

A POSTERIORI TESTS

On the other hand, if a researcher has completed the data collection phase of an experiment without making specific predictions, an a priori test is not appropriate for comparing specific treatments. For example, let us say an industrial psychologist must evaluate five different control panel designs for their effectiveness in displaying critical information. Independent groups of operators are tested on all five panels for their ability to read, interpret, and act upon the information displayed on the control panels. Since the control panel designs are new and untested, the researcher is unable to predict ahead of time which panel, if any, will eventually prove to be superior to the other four.

After the performance data are collected and an ANOVA reveals a significant F, the researcher may wish to make specific comparisons between some of the relatively low scoring and high scoring groups. Because this is a case in which the specific pattern of obtained differences was not predicted to exist prior to data collection, the statistical significance of these differences must be evaluated using an **a posteriori test.**

A Posteriori Tests (also called post hoc tests). Computational procedures that permit comparisons among treatment means when the comparisons were thought of after examining the data rather than being planned prior to running the experiment.

Why Must We Draw a Distinction between A Priori and A Posteriori Statistical Tests?

To understand why we must draw a distinction between a priori and a posteriori tests, let us do another sampling experiment. Assume we have a very large number of baskets and they all contain identical population distributions. We go from basket to basket, selecting one sample of n scores from each of the k population distributions. When all the samples have been collected a mean is computed for each of the samples.

According to the principles of hypothesis testing, if any two samples are selected *at random* from the set of k samples, and we compare the two sample means by using a t-test, 95% of the time the t-test will correctly indicate that the two samples were drawn from identical populations. That is, the null hypothesis stating that both samples were drawn from identical populations will not be rejected. The other 5% of the time the means will, *by chance*, be different enough from each other for the t-test to indicate falsely that the two samples were drawn from different populations—a Type I error.

Another Sampling Experiment

But what if the two means are *not* selected at random? To take the extreme situation, what if we selected the sample with the largest mean in the set of k means and compared it to the sample with the smallest mean in the set of k means. The t-test would be significant far more than 5% of the time, or, said another way, the probability of Type I error would be higher than the assumed .05.

This experiment may be done by taking the output of SAMPLING.BAS (say, 15 samples of 10 scores each) and running a t-test (TEETWO.BAS) between the samples with smallest and largest means. Even though we know the null hypothesis is true because every sample was selected from an identical population, a significant t (Type I error) is very likely.

Here is an actual run of this experiment. The set of 15 means is given below along with the sample data that yielded the two most different means: 46.9 and 54.7. Here are the 15 sample means (arranged in ascending order):

46.9, 47.0, 47.1, 47.9, 48.2, 49.0, 49.4, 49.6, 50.4, 50.9, 51.0, 51.1, 51.7, 52.6, 54.7

Here are the data from the two most extreme samples:

Lowest: 46, 42, 36, 35, 51, 57, 56, 52, 35, 59.
Mean 1 = 46.9
Highest: 56, 60, 66, 45, 53, 48, 49, 58, 58, 54.
Mean 2 = 54.7

An independent groups t-test run on these data yields a computed t value of -2.18. The critical value of t with $df = 18$ is 2.101, so the difference between the two sample means is significant. This, of course, is a Type I error, because all 15 samples were selected from identical populations. By selecting two samples from the set of k samples in a nonrandom fashion, we increase the chance of a Type I error. By taking the two most extreme samples, we practically guarantee a Type I error.

In the control panel experiment described on page 348, if the researcher decided to make a number of specific comparisons between relatively high scoring groups and relatively low scoring groups with no a priori reason for doing so, this would be analogous to the nonrandom selection of samples in the sampling experiment described above.

A PRIORI VERSUS A POSTERIORI COMPARISONS

The statistical inference tests that you have been using up to this point in one- and two-group tests have all been a priori tests. The alternative hypothesis (also called the experimental hypothesis), H_1, is a formal statement of our expectations—it is the difference that we anticipate finding if the experimental effect exists and it is the difference we pronounce as significant after H_0 is rejected. Unlike the rather specific alternative hypotheses of one group (H_1: $\mu_0 \neq 50$) and two group tests (H_1: $\mu_1 \neq \mu_2$), the alternative hypothesis for the analysis of variance is usually a vague "not H_0." One reason the alternative hypothesis in the analysis of variance is often stated in this way is because of the numerous possible patterns of results among k treatment means that could lead to the rejection of H_0 and the impracticality of listing all of them.

$$H_0: \mu_1 = \mu_2 = \ldots = \mu_j = \ldots = \mu_k$$
$$H_1: \text{not } H_0$$

Another reason for expressing H_1 as "not H_0" could be that not enough knowledge exists about the effects of the treatments on the dependent variable to be able to anticipate a specific pattern of differences among the treatments. Once the experiment is over and the analysis of variance reveals a

Table 17.1

The ten possible paired comparisons in a single factor experiment with five treatment conditions.

	Treatments				
Treatments	I	II	III	IV	V
I	—	1	2	3	4
II	—	—	5	6	7
III	—	—	—	8	9
IV	—	—	—	—	10
V	—	—	—	—	—

Post Hoc Tests. (See a posteriori tests defined above.)

Multiple Comparisons. Evaluating the differences between all possible pairs of treatment means in a multigroup experiment. If done using the *t*-test, this results in alpha inflation and the near certainty of committing a Type I error.

significant *F* ratio, the experimenter often wishes to evaluate unanticipated differences between specific pairs of means for significance. An a posteriori (or **post hoc**) test must be used for such an evaluation.

The primary feature of the a posteriori tests is the control of alpha, the probability of making a Type I error. This must be done because when we use the "shotgun" approach of **multiple comparisons** comparing every treatment mean to every other treatment mean, the real probability of making a Type I error tends to climb to an unacceptable level. Specifically, in a posteriori multiple comparisons,

$$\alpha_r = 1 - (1 - \alpha)^r$$

where r is the number of comparisons made and α is the significance level (usually .05) that is used for a single test. For example, in a single factor experiment with five treatment conditions it is possible to make 10 different paired comparisons. See table 17.1.

Let us assume that H_1 is a simple "not H_0" and that you decided to make the 10 comparisons using 10 separate *t*-tests. If we solve the equation

$$\alpha_r = 1\ (1 - \alpha)^r$$

where $r = 10$ and $\alpha = .05$

$$\alpha_{10} = 1 - (1 - .05)^{10}$$
$$\alpha_{10} = 1 - (.95)^{10}$$
$$\alpha_{10} = 1 - .6$$
$$\alpha_{10} = .4$$

Thus, if every one of the 10 possible comparisons is made among the five treatment means, the probability of making at least one Type I error is .4 rather than .05. This means that of the 10 possible comparisons, 4 are likely

Alpha Level Inflation. The increase in the probability of Type I error when multiple *t*-tests are used to make all possible paired comparisons among a set of treatment means.

Tukey HSD Test. The Honestly Significant Difference post hoc test that permits making all possible paired comparisons while controlling alpha inflation.

to involve the commission of a Type I error. The a posteriori tests control for this **alpha level inflation** by making it more difficult to reject H_0 than would be the case if all possible pairs of treatments were compared using 10 separate *t*-tests. There are several statistics that are used specifically for making unplanned comparisons after the computation of a significant *F* ratio, and they vary in the degree of control exerted upon alpha level inflation.

Some post hoc tests are regarded as conservative because they are very effective in holding down alpha level inflation. The differences between treatment means must be relatively large to achieve statistical significance when using a conservative test. For example, the Scheffé test, which is presented later in this chapter, is considered to be rather conservative. Other tests are not quite so rigorous in their control of Type I error, namely the Duncan test. (See Winer (1971) for a comparison of a posteriori tests.)

A balance must be struck between avoiding Type I error and losing the power to detect a difference that really exists (Type II error). A good compromise in the level of control for alpha inflation, and the test that shall be presented below, is the **Tukey HSD (honestly significant difference) test.**

THE TUKEY HSD TEST

The Tukey HSD test maintains the alpha level at .05 for the set of comparisons taken as a whole. This means that specific comparisons in the set of all possible comparisons will have an actual level of significance that can reach a maximum of alpha, but some comparisons will have a level of significance less than alpha. Thus, if we decided to make the 10 possible comparisons among a set of five treatment means (see table 17.1), instead of an alpha level of .40 that would exist if 10 separate *t*-tests were done, the Tukey HSD test will hold the probability of Type I error for the set of 10 comparisons to a maximum of .05.

The Tukey HSD uses the *Q* statistic, which is defined in the following formula.

$$Q = \frac{\overline{X}_i - \overline{X}_j}{\sqrt{\frac{MS_{error}}{n}}}$$

where:
$\overline{X}_i$ is the larger of the two treatment means being compared.
$\overline{X}_j$ is the smaller of the two treatment means being compared, MS_{error} is the $MS_{within\ treatment}$ (or $MS_{residual}$ if the groups are correlated) from the ANOVA summary table, and n is the number of scores within each treatment.

You will probably notice that the equation for the Q statistic resembles the equation for the t statistic. In both tests the difference between two treatment means is divided by an estimate of the standard error of the difference. However, unlike the computation of the t statistic, which estimates the standard error of the difference (i.e., the denominator of the t formula) using data only from the treatments being compared (treatment i and treatment j), in computing Q the data of all k treatments are used to estimate the standard error of the difference. The $MS_{\text{within treatment}}$ entry in the ANOVA summary table (or the MS_{residual} in the case of a single factor correlated groups design) is a variance that reflects the amount of dispersion in the data that is attributable to random unsystematic causes. When this variance is divided by n, the sample size for each treatment, and then the square root of the result is computed, we have an estimate of the standard error of the theoretical distribution of the $\overline{X}_i - \overline{X}_j$ difference scores.

To compute Q, the difference between the two means that appear in the numerator is divided by the estimate of random error from the denominator. The difference between the two means in the numerator is considered to be significant if the computed value for Q is greater than or equal to the tabled value of Q. To look up the critical value of Q in the Q table you must know k, the number of treatments in the experiment, and the degrees of freedom (df) for the error term ($MS_{\text{within treatment}}$ for the single factor independent groups design or MS_{residual} for the single factor correlated groups design). The ANOVA error term is the MS value that is entered in the denominator of the Q formula. To clarify the application and computational procedure of the Tukey HSD test we shall work through an example.

Problem 1. This is the same Problem 1 that was posed in the previous chapter regarding the effects of eating fish contaminated with PCBs upon performance of rats in a discrimination reversal task. The original data of this four-group experiment are reproduced in table 17.2 and the ANOVA is reproduced in table 17.3.

Setting up the Table of Differences

The first step in computing the Q statistic is to set up a table to display the difference scores between all possible pairs of means. To accomplish this, arrange the means in numerical sequence and use the set of ordered means to label the rows and columns as shown in table 17.4. Then enter the difference between each row and column label in the appropriate cell of the table. Thus, the first row of table 17.4 represents the differences between the mean of treatment 4 and treatments 1, 3, and 2, respectively. As you can see from inspecting the entries in table 17.4, the largest difference is the entry on the far right of the first row (treatment 4 vs. treatment 2). As you move to the left and, eventually, to the lower rows of the table, the differences get smaller and smaller.

Table 17.2

The number of correct responses on a discrimination reversal task: the data for Problem 1.

	Level of Contamination			
None	Low	Moderate	High	
12	10	15	11	
11	13	12	8	
13	14	12	6	
15	9	7	7	
10	11	11	10	
8	16	13	8	
Totals = 69	73	70	50	G = 262

Table 17.3

The analysis of variance summary for the data in Problem 1.

ANOVA Summary Table

Source of Variation	*df*	SS	MS	*F*
Between treatment	3	54.83	18.27	3.12
Within treatment	20	117.00	5.84	
Totals	23	171.83		

Table 17.4

The table of differences between the treatment means in Problem 1.

	Trt. 4	**Trt. 1**	**Trt. 3**	**Trt. 2**
Ordered Means:	8.33	11.50	11.67	12.17
Trt. 4 (8.33)	—	3.17	3.34	3.84
Trt. 1 (11.50)		—	0.17	0.67
Trt. 3 (11.67)			—	0.50
Trt. 2 (12.17)				—

The difference scores in table 17.4 represent five possible numerators for the Q statistic $(\overline{X}_i - \overline{X}_j)$. To get the denominator we must use the $MS_{\text{within treatment}}$ from the ANOVA Summary Table (table 17.3), divide it by n, and take the square root as shown below.

$$\sqrt{\frac{MS_{\text{within treatment}}}{n}} = \sqrt{\frac{5.84}{6}} = .9866$$

The critical value of the Q statistic is found in the Q table with $k = 4$ (there were four treatments in the experiment) and $df = 20$ (the $MS_{\text{within treatment}}$ has 20 degrees of freedom associated with it). The critical value for Q with the alpha level set to .05 is 3.96.

We start computing Q by using the largest difference score (3.84) and continue with the smaller difference scores until the computed value for Q is lower than the critical value of 3.96. At this point, at the first failure to reject H_0, you are supposed to stop. This is just common sense because after one failure to find a significant difference, there is no chance of finding another with the even smaller difference scores that remain.

A post hoc analysis of the data in Problem 1 using the Tukey HSD test shows that none of the differences between specific pairs of means are significant. The critical value for the Q statistic for these data is 3.96, and the largest computed Q value is 3.89. Normally, we would not proceed with further computations of Q because none of the remaining difference scores can possibly be significant. Nevertheless, for illustration purposes, here is the Q formula along with the Q values for the difference scores on the first row of table 17.4.

$$Q = \frac{\overline{X}_i - \overline{X}_j}{\sqrt{\frac{MS_{\text{error}}}{n}}}$$

Treatment 4 versus 2:

$$Q = \frac{3.84}{0.9866} = 3.89$$

Treatment 4 versus 3:

$$Q = \frac{3.34}{0.9866} = 3.39$$

Treatment 4 versus 1:

$$Q = \frac{3.17}{0.9866} = 3.21$$

The pattern of differences that was noted by simple inspection of the means has not been confirmed with this post hoc analysis. The failure to find a significant difference between even one pair of treatment means following an overall significant F ratio is rather atypical, but this example was chosen specifically to alert you to the fact that it is indeed possible. This finding does not invalidate the significant F ratio that was found in the overall ANOVA of these same data, but, with the additional protection the Tukey HSD provides against making a Type I error, the differences among the groups are simply not large enough to register as significant. By comparison, if we fail to follow the proper procedures for making a posteriori comparisons and use the "illegal" tactic of doing multiple t-tests to compare all possible pairs of means, the results are quite different.

In table 17.5 the computed t values are shown for all possible group comparisons for the Problem 1 data. Since the critical value at the .05 level of significance for t with 10 degrees of freedom ($n1 + n2 - 2 = 6 + 6 - 2 = 10$) is 2.228, all tests between treatment 4 and the other three treatments register as significant. Are the differences really significant at the .05 level? It is most unlikely for the reasons explained above regarding alpha level inflation.

Table 17.5

The t values for all possible comparisons among the four treatment groups in Problem 1.

Groups:	I	II	III	IV
I	—	−0.46	−0.11	2.53
II		—	0.33	2.91
III			—	2.52
IV				—

THE SCHEFFÉ TEST

Scheffé Test. A relatively conservative post hoc test for evaluating differences between all possible pairs of treatments. The probability of Type I error is held to a maximum of alpha.

The **Scheffé test** is an alternative a posteriori test for evaluating differences between all possible pairs of treatments while holding the probability of Type I error to a maximum of alpha (.05 or .01). The distinguishing feature of the Scheffé test is that it is even more conservative about the control over Type I errors than the Tukey HSD test. The extra degree of conservatism stems from two features of the computational method that is used in doing the Scheffé test.

First, the $SS_{\text{between treatment}}$ that is computed for the Scheffé test uses only the data from the two treatments being compared. Of course, in the original ANOVA the data from all the treatments is used to compute the $SS_{\text{b.t.}}$.

The Computation of $SS_{\text{between treatment}}$ for the Scheffé Test

$$SS_{\text{b.t.}} = \frac{(T_1^2 + T_2^2)}{n} - \frac{(T_1 + T_2)^2}{2 \cdot n}$$

To solve for the expression on the left we must square the totals of the two treatments we are comparing, add the squared totals, and divide by n, the number of scores within a treatment. (The assumption is made that $n1 = n2$.) To solve for the expression on the right we must first add the two treatment totals, square the resulting sum, and divide by $2 \cdot n$ (or $n1 + n2$), the number of scores in both treatments combined.

The computation of $SS_{\text{b.t.}}$ using this method eliminates from the analysis any treatment effects from other than the two specific treatments being compared. The result of omitting the data from the other treatments when calculating $SS_{\text{b.t.}}$ is to reduce the size of the $SS_{\text{b.t.}}$ relative to the $SS_{\text{b.t.}}$ of the original ANOVA.

Second, the degrees of freedom value that is divided into the $SS_{\text{b.t.}}$ value to get the $MS_{\text{b.t.}}$ uses the full complement of $k - 1$ degrees of freedom from the original ANOVA. If we did an ordinary ANOVA with two treatments, the $MS_{\text{b.t.}}$ would have only one degree of freedom ($df = 1$), but in the Scheffé test we use $df = k - 1$. Dividing the variation (sum of squares) between only two treatments ($df = 1$) by the degrees of freedom for all $k - 1$ treatments results in an $MS_{\text{b.t.}}$ that is relatively small. Thus, assuming k, the number of treatments, is greater than 2,

$$MS_{\text{b.t.}} = \frac{SS_{\text{b.t.}}}{k - 1}$$

will always be less than

$$\frac{SS_{b.t.}}{1}$$

No additional computations are necessary to determine the value of the $MS_{w.t.}$ (or $MS_{residual}$ if a repeated measures design is used). The same $MS_{w.t.}$ value that appears in the original ANOVA summary table is used as the denominator of the F ratio in doing the Scheffé test.

In summary, to do a Scheffé test compute

$$F = \frac{\frac{SS_{b.t.}}{k-1}}{\frac{SS_{w.t.}}{k(n-1)}} = \frac{MS_{b.t.}}{MS_{w.t.}}$$

where the $SS_{b.t.}$ is computed using only the data of the two treatments being compared. The between and within treatment degrees of freedom and the $SS_{w.t.}$ and $MS_{w.t.}$ are the same values computed for the original ANOVA.

An Example Using the Scheffé Test

We shall use the data in Problem 1 from the exercises section of chapter 16 to demonstrate the use of the Scheffé test. If you completed the ANOVA summary table as requested for this problem, your table should be the same as table 17.6 on the next page.

The treatment totals for this four-group experiment were, respectively, 420, 432, 435, and 315. Let us compare treatment 3 and treatment 4, the two most extreme outcomes: $T_3 = 435$ and $T_4 = 315$. The computation of the $SS_{b.t.}$ for the Scheffé test takes the following form:

$$SS_{b.t.} = \frac{435^2 + 315^2}{8} - \frac{(435 + 315)^2}{16}$$

$$SS_{b.t.} = \frac{288{,}450}{8} - \frac{562{,}500}{16}$$

$$SS_{b.t.} = 36{,}056.25 - 35{,}156.25$$

$$SS_{b.t.} = 900$$

To get the $MS_{b.t.}$ we must divide $SS_{b.t.}$ by $k - 1$.

$$MS_{b.t.} = \frac{SS_{b.t.}}{k-1} = \frac{900}{3} = 300$$

Table 17.6

The analysis of variance summary table for Problem 1 in the exercises section of chapter 16.

ANOVA Summary Table

Source of Variation	*df*	SS	MS	*F*
Between treatment	3	1234.1	411.36	5.42
Within treatment	28	2123.75	75.84	
Totals	31	3357.85		

The *F* ratio for the Scheffé test is formed by dividing the specially computed $MS_{b.t.}$ by the $MS_{w.t.}$ from the original ANOVA Summary Table.

$$F = \frac{MS_{b.t.}}{MS_{w.t.}} = \frac{300}{75.84} = 3.96$$

The *F* value of 3.96 is tested against the same critical value that was used in the original ANOVA: *F* with $(k - 1)$ and $k(n - 1)$ degrees of freedom. For the present analysis, using the .05 level of significance,

$$F_{\text{critical}} = F(3,28) = 2.95$$

Since the computed *F* value of 3.96 is greater than the critical value, the difference between treatment 3 and treatment 4 is significant. Similarly, treatment 3 is significantly different from both treatment 4 ($F = 3.76$) and treatment 1 ($F = 3.028$). No other pairings (e.g., treatment 1 vs. treatment 2, treatment 1 vs. treatment 3, or treatment 2 vs. treatment 3) will result in an *F* value that will exceed the critical *F* value of 2.95.

The Scheffé test is very conservative, so we can have an extra measure of confidence that these differences are truly significant and that we have avoided a Type I error.

PLANNED COMPARISONS

When an experiment is a logical extension of a documented series of experiments or when the theoretical underpinnings of a research area are rather well understood, the experimental hypotheses regarding the relationships among treatment means are likely to be quite specific. For example, assume a medical researcher has data from a pilot study indicating that two newly

Table 17.7

The experimental design of Problem 2: a study to evaluate the synergistic action of two drugs.

I	II	III	IV	V
No Treatment ($n_1 = 8$)	Placebo ($n_2 = 8$)	Drug A ($n_3 = 8$)	Drug B ($n_4 = 8$)	Drugs A + B ($n_5 = 8$)

synthesized experimental anti-cancer drugs have a synergistic effect on inducing shrinkage of a specific kind of tumor. When Drug A or Drug B were administered alone to the animal test subjects in a pilot study, the therapeutic effect was minimal or absent, but when both drugs were administered at the same time both qualitative and quantitative changes in tumor structure were noted. With this promising start, the research was implemented on a larger scale, and the experimental design depicted in table 17.7 was used to evaluate the Drug A/Drug B combination for cancer therapy.

As shown in table 17.1, in a single factor experiment with 5 treatment groups, 10 comparisons are possible. In this experiment, however, the researcher is *not* employing a "shotgun" approach to evaluate the therapeutic effects of various drug therapies. He is looking for a certain pattern. Specifically, if the pattern observed in the pilot study repeats itself, there should be a relatively uniform cluster among treatments I, II, III, and IV with treatment V standing apart from the other four treatments due to the synergism of the Drug A/Drug B combination. The **planned comparisons** would likely be

Planned Comparisons. Comparisons between treatments that were planned before execution of the experiment. These comparisons usually flow logically from the experimental rationale.

1. Compare Group I to II to rule out a placebo effect.
2. Assuming no placebo effect is found between Groups I and II, the average of these two groups could then be compared to Group III for one comparison, and then to Group IV for another comparison. If the pattern observed in the pilot data repeats itself, we would not expect to find a significant difference in either comparison owing to the weak effect of either drug when used alone.
3. The last comparison would be between the average of Groups I and II and Group V. If the expected significant difference were found in this comparison and none of the above comparisons were significant, this would document the existence of a synergistic effect from the combination therapy.

The planned comparisons discussed above are meaningful, anticipated, and logical within the context of the experiment, and, since they were predicted prior to running the experiment, we may make the planned comparisons using the t statistic without worrying about alpha inflation. Also, it is not necessary to have a significant F in the overall ANOVA to proceed with planned comparisons. (A significant F *is* a requirement before proceeding with a posteriori tests.)

Orthogonal Comparisons

One approach to planned comparisons (and some say the preferred approach) is to divide the $SS_{between\ treatment}$ into $k - 1$ independent (orthogonal) parts. The degrees of freedom for the $SS_{between\ treatment}$ is $k - 1$, and each comparison uses one degree of freedom. Therefore, we are limited to conducting $k - 1$ **orthogonal comparisons** among a set of k treatment means. When comparisons are orthogonal we have the advantage of knowing how much of the $SS_{between\ treatment}$ is accounted for by each specific comparison in the set of all orthogonal comparisons. When all $k - 1$ comparisons have been done, then all of the $SS_{between\ treatment}$ is accounted for.

Orthogonal Comparisons. An approach to planned comparisons that involves dividing the $SS_{b.t.}$ into $k - 1$ nonoverlapping ("orthogonal") parts. This allows the exact contribution of each individual comparison to the $SS_{b.t.}$ to be determined.

Despite the latter advantage of orthogonal comparisons, there is a disadvantage: the set of tests among the treatment means that satisfy the requirements of orthogonality may not be the most meaningful comparisons for the experiment. (This, for example, happens to be the case for the present drug study example depicted in table 17.7.) For this reason, in this text we shall follow the less rigorous approach to planned comparisons that permits a nonorthogonal set of comparisons as long as they are meaningful, anticipated, and logical within the context of the experiment.*

Problem 2. The data for the drug therapy study discussed above and the ANOVA of the data are presented in tables 17.8 and 17.9, respectively. The numbers represent a measure of cancer cell mortality from microscopic examination of tumor tissue following a course of therapy. The larger the score value is, the more the cancer cells show the effects of the therapy.

Table 17.8

The data of the drug therapy experiment presented as Problem 2.

	Control	Placebo	Drug A	Drug B	Drugs A + B
	45	44	33	34	59
	53	52	47	50	68
	52	57	64	59	72
	39	42	59	54	63
	40	36	52	51	47
	51	59	55	60	58
	50	48	51	58	54
	52	38	46	38	49
$T_j =$	382	376	407	404	470
$\bar{T}_j =$	47.75	47.00	50.88	50.50	58.75

*The interested reader may consult Winer (1971) pp. 170–77 for a thorough discussion of orthogonal comparisons and the steps for their computation.

Table 17.9

The analysis of variance summary for the data in Problem 1.

ANOVA Summary Table

Source of Variation	*df*	SS	MS	F
Between treatment	4	695.00	173.75	2.39
Within treatment	35	2539.86	72.56	
Totals	39	3234.86		

The critical value for F with 4 and 35 degrees of freedom ($\alpha = .05$) is 2.65, and so the computed F ratio of 2.39 is not significant. We may, nevertheless, proceed with the set of planned comparisons by using the following formula.

$$t = \frac{\overline{T}_i - \overline{T}_j}{\sqrt{\frac{2\ \text{MS}_{\text{error}}}{n}}}$$

Where $\overline{T}_i$ and $\overline{T}_j$ are the two treatment means being compared and MS_{error} is the $\text{MS}_{\text{within treatment}}$ from the ANOVA Summary Table (table 17.9). The degrees of freedom for this t-test between two independent groups appears in the ANOVA summary table as the df for the $\text{MS}_{\text{within treatment}}$; $df = k(n - 1)$. (Following a repeated measures (correlated groups) ANOVA, we would, instead, use the $\text{MS}_{\text{residual}}$ for MS_{error} and the df for the $\text{MS}_{\text{residual}}$; $df = (k - 1)(n - 1)$.

Notice how all the data in the experiment are used to get the estimate of error variance. In a usual t-test only the data from the two treatments being compared are used to compute the standard error of the difference in the denominator of the t formula. Using the MS_{error} gives us a better (and usually smaller) estimate of error, and this gives us more statistical power.

The first comparison, the test for the existence of a placebo effect, is the untreated control group (1) versus the placebo group (2). The critical value for t ($df = 35$) is 2.031.

$$t = \frac{47.75 - 47.00}{\sqrt{\frac{2(72.56)}{8}}} = \frac{0.75}{4.26} = 0.04$$

Next, the plan calls for comparing the average of Groups 1 and 2 to Group 3 and the average of Groups 1 and 2 to Group 4. Group 3 versus the average of Groups 1 and 2:

$$t = \frac{50.875 - 47.375}{\sqrt{\frac{2(72.56)}{8}}} = \frac{3.50}{4.26} = 0.821$$

Group 4 versus the average of Groups 1 and 2:

$$t = \frac{50.50 - 47.375}{\sqrt{\frac{2(72.56)}{8}}} = \frac{3.125}{4.26} = 0.73$$

Not one of these comparisons shows even the slightest trend toward significance. This outcome is consistent with the data from the pilot study, which showed basically no effect on cancer cell mortality when the drugs were used alone.

The last planned comparison is between Group 5 and the average of the two control Groups (1 and 2).

$$t = \frac{58.75 - 47.375}{\sqrt{\frac{2(72.56)}{8}}} = \frac{11.375}{4.26} = 2.67$$

The last step is to compare the computed value for t (2.67) to the critical value for t. The $MS_{\text{within treatment}}$ that was entered into the denominator of the planned comparisons version of the t formula has $df = 35$, and this is the df value that is used to determine the critical value for t. The critical value of t with alpha set to .05 and $df = 35$ is 2.031. The computed t value is greater than 2.031, so the null hypothesis of no experimental effect may be rejected. The combination drug therapy produced significant histological evidence of cancer cell mortality.

Summary

We examined three methods (the Tukey HSD test, the Scheffé test, and Planned Comparisons) for further evaluation of experimental data after the overall analysis of variance had been completed. In most instances when you are faced with choosing a statistical analysis to use on data you must consider carefully the scaling of the data, the type of question that the experiment is designed to answer, etc. Here, however, when considering the choice of an a priori versus an a posteriori post-ANOVA test, the characteristics of the data do not determine the choice of test. Instead, the choice of test is a function of whether or not the pattern of differences was predicted before the experiment was done, whether or not the predictions were based upon sound logic and/or the results of prior research, and the cost of making a Type I versus Type II error.

Key Terms

Alpha Level Inflation
A Posteriori Tests
A Priori Tests
Multiple Comparisons
Orthogonal Comparisons
Planned Comparisons
Post Hoc Tests
Scheffé Test
Tukey HSD Test

Exercises

1. Explain the considerations that dictate the application of an a priori versus an a posteriori test. Why must we draw a distinction between these two types of tests?
2. Why does the application of an a priori test to an a posteriori statistical comparison result in an unacceptably high probability of committing a Type I error?
3. A professor randomly divided forty completed essay examinations into four stacks of ten each and asked each of his four graduate teaching assistants to read a stack and assign grades on a scale of 0 to 100. The forty grades assigned by the teaching assistants appear below.

Teaching Assistants			
Venezia	Itsuko	Wilson	Bracy
80	76	80	69
72	97	68	69
89	93	66	90
85	90	68	81
67	88	85	79
53	81	71	84
93	82	74	95
74	75	78	82
81	94	64	91
97	88	80	79

a. Do an ANOVA on these data to evaluate whether or not the teaching assistants tend to have uniform grading practices. Did one or two assistants tend to grade more leniently than the others?

b. Follow the ANOVA with the Tukey HSD test to examine specifically the pattern of lenient versus strict grading practices among the four assistants.

c. Apply the Scheffé test to the same data. Do the two post hoc analyses, the Tukey HSD test, and the Scheffé test support different conclusions about the uniformity of grading practices among the teaching assistants? If so, why?

4. Each of five building inspectors in a medium-sized American city was sent out to examine the same eight run-down buildings and to report the number of code violations discovered. This was done in response to complaints from within the agency that one of the inspectors (Mr. Smith) was either not doing his job conscientiously or, perhaps, was being bribed by landlords not to report all the violations he discovered. The data on the reported violations appear below. Do they support the contention that Smith is reporting significantly fewer code violations than the other inspectors?

	Inspectors				
Buildings	Smith	Leotta	Castiglia	Mintz	Benway
A	8	9	9	7	8
B	4	7	10	9	5
C	5	9	8	11	11
D	4	6	8	6	5
E	5	8	9	11	6
F	4	6	5	7	7
G	8	13	11	14	10
H	5	8	10	7	5

5. The data below are from Problem 10 in chapter 16. A complex tracking task was performed under three different conditions of stimulus illumination. Each group of subjects was tested under a different condition. The scores represent the number of errors each subject made in the tracking task. Consult the ANOVA you did for these data and conduct two planned comparisons: Low versus Medium and Low versus High. Use $\alpha = .05$.

Level of Stimulus Illumination (groups)		
1	2	3
Low	*Medium*	*High*
10	8	6
11	4	8
12	6	6
14	4	4
14	7	4

6. The data below are from Problem 12 in chapter 16. To demonstrate the influence of hunger on the performance of a learned response, five groups of laboratory rats that had been taught a lever pressing skill in an earlier experiment were partially deprived of food until they reached 95%, 90%, or 85% of their original body weight. A control group was maintained at 100% of original body weight. The animals were tested and the number of lever presses was recorded. Follow up the overall ANOVA you did on these data and do a Tukey HSD test to compare all possible pairs of treatments.

Control	95%	90%	85%
12	17	20	28
11	13	23	19
8	9	17	16
9	16	22	21
6	7	15	11

7. The data below are from Problem 14 in chapter 16. A group of monkeys was tested on a series of problems. Although the specific solution to each problem was different, the correct strategy for approaching the solution was the same for all the problems. The data below represent the number of trials it took the animals to solve five separate problems. Follow up the overall ANOVA you did on these data to determine how much prior problem-solving experience was necessary to result in a significant reduction in the number of trials needed to solve a problem.

   For example, did the monkeys solve the second problem faster than the first problem, or did it take experience with, say, three problems before the number of trials decreased? Did performance level off after a few problems (e.g., is there a difference in the performance for problems 4 and 5)? Such questions may be answered by running a Tukey HSD test to compare all the means to each other.

	Problems				
Subjects	1	2	3	4	5
Jojo	15	14	15	11	8
Mickey	22	23	19	8	12
Bobo	12	6	7	9	5
Pepe	10	14	14	6	5
Mumu	8	4	3	3	2

8. The following data are from Problem 15 in chapter 16. A group of laboratory rats was taught to make a discrimination. Pressing a lever while the correct stimulus was on a visual display resulted in a food reward, whereas pressing the lever while no stimulus or an incorrect stimulus was on the display did not result in a food reward. After the response was learned to a criterion of success, food reward for lever pressing was stopped, but correct and incorrect stimuli continued to appear on the display. Lever presses were recorded for fifteen seconds following the presentation of each correct stimulus.

Do both a planned comparison and a Scheffé test to compare the performance on Trial 1 and Trial 4. Do the tests yield consistent results? Is a preplanned comparison justified to compare Trial 1 to Trial 4?

	Trials			
Subjects	1	2	3	4
1	11	13	8	8
2	18	12	11	12
3	14	18	5	6
4	22	24	18	13
5	9	9	8	11
6	17	14	11	4
7	21	18	15	7

9. The data following are from Problem 16 in chapter 16. Near the end of the season a gambler selected what he believed were the top four teams in a basketball league. He wanted to do a comparison of the average point production of the starting five players on each team. He believed that this would help him to predict the winner of the end of the season intraleague tournament. The overall ANOVA showed that the teams were not all equal in their point production. Follow up this ANOVA with a Tukey HSD test to reveal the exact pattern of differences in scoring ability among these four teams.

Position	Team 1	Team 2	Team 3	Team 4
Guard 1	18	26	16	22
Guard 2	16	21	11	19
Forward 1	19	22	17	18
Forward 2	23	19	14	25
Center	21	32	17	12

10. A consumer group was preparing to write an article comparing four brands of luxury automobiles. One of the variables was frequency of repair. Purchasers of new luxury cars were surveyed. The data below represent the number of times it was necessary for the owner to return the car to the dealer for other than scheduled maintenance during the first year of ownership. Is there a difference in the reliability of the various brands? Do the overall ANOVA, then compare each brand to every other brand using the Tukey HSD test.

Brand of Automobile			
A	B	C	D
6	7	2	4
5	3	2	4
2	4	1	3
3	6	0	6
0	6	3	2
3	5	0	5

CHAPTER 18

An Introduction to the Multifactor Analysis of Variance: The Two Factor Experiment

If the curriculum followed by the behavioral or biological science majors at your school is typical of most colleges and universities, students start out with an introductory survey course in their chosen field of study (e.g., Psychology 100) followed by more advanced and specialized courses in later semesters (e.g., Learning, Physiological Psychology, etc.). In preparation for the advanced courses, most students will be required to take a course in statistics, such as the one you are now taking.

One reason for the statistics requirement is that as you progress from the introductory level survey course to the more advanced courses, you will be reading some of the original journal articles that make up the scientific literature of your course of study. Because these articles are usually written by highly trained researchers for reading by other highly trained researchers, understanding the reports can pose a formidable challenge to students. In this regard your knowledge of statistics will serve you well, because in your reading you are likely to encounter some of the same statistical tests, experimental designs, and elements of statistical reasoning we have covered in this text.

The analysis of variance (ANOVA) is particularly well represented in the research literature. Using the single factor ANOVA (chapter 16) you learned how to make comparisons among several groups at once and follow up with specific individual comparisons (chapter 17). Nevertheless, as powerful and as useful as the single factor ANOVA is, many research issues are simply too complex to be addressed within the context of a single factor experiment. If your experience is typical, in your advanced courses you will come across an imposing variety of multifactor ANOVA designs in which several layers of complexity are added to the relatively simple single factor design.

The Next Level of Complexity in the Analysis of Variance

Perhaps you will give complex ANOVA designs serious study at some future time at the advanced undergraduate or graduate level. Although this will not be attempted here, for those students who want (or are required to have) a preview of the next level of complexity in research design, the rationale and computational procedures that relate to one version of the two-factor experiment will be presented.

In this chapter you shall learn some new concepts, such as main effects and interactions, and you shall view several different hypothetical patterns of results within the context of a simple example. This will help you to appreciate the alternative patterns and subsequent interpretations of data that are possible in a two-factor experiment.

Next, we shall work through two examples within a specific research scenario. The computational method we shall apply to the experimental data is an extension of the one we used for the single factor ANOVA and is available for your use in the TWOWAY.BAS computer program.

Keep in mind that although the specific type of two-factor ANOVA design covered in this chapter is very basic, *all factorial designs have certain elements in common*. Specifically, the practice you get interpreting different patterns of main effects and interactions in the very basic designs presented here may make it possible for you to understand the interpretations given to a wide variety of relatively complex ANOVA analyses you come across in the scientific literature.

The Factorial Experiment

Factorial Design. An experimental design in which two or more variables (called "factors") are manipulated simultaneously. The two-factor design defines $p \cdot q$ different experimental conditions called "cells."

As applied to the data of a single factor multigroup experiment, the ANOVA (chapter 16) enables us to assess the effects of two or more levels of a single independent variable upon some dependent measure. By comparison, when using a **factorial design** it is possible to assess the effects of two or more independent variables within the framework of a single analysis. The two variable factorial design is illustrated in general schematic form in table 18.1.[1] Factor A, the row variable, has p levels, factor B, the column variable,

[1]As with the single factor ANOVA, the notation is that of B. J. Winer from his classic graduate level text, *Statistical Principles in Experimental Design*, New York, McGraw-Hill, 1962, 1971.

Table 18.1
A general schematic representation of the two-factor factorial design showing the levels of factors A and B and the $p \times q$ possible treatment combinations ("cells").

Levels of Factor A	Levels of Factor B						
	b_1	b_2	$\cdots$	b_j	$\cdots$	b_q
a_1	AB_{11}	AB_{12}	$\cdots$	AB_{1j}	$\cdots$	AB_{1q}
a_2	AB_{21}	AB_{22}	$\cdots$	AB_{2j}	$\cdots$	AB_{2q}
$\vdots$	$\vdots$	$\vdots$		$\vdots$		$\vdots$
a_i	AB_{i1}	AB_{i2}	$\cdots$	AB_{ij}	$\cdots$	AB_{iq}
$\vdots$	$\vdots$	$\vdots$		$\vdots$		$\vdots$
a_p	AB_{p1}	AB_{p2}	$\cdots$	AB_{pj}	$\cdots$	AB_{pq}

has q levels, and together the design defines $p \times q$ treatment combinations or *cells*. Each cell has a general designation of ab_{ij}. The $_i$ can take values from 1 to p and the $_j$ can take values from 1 to q.

A Research Scenario: Example 1. A psychologist designed an experiment to evaluate the relative effectiveness of two strategies in the teaching of two skills to U.S. Air Force Cadets enrolled in an experimental instrument flight training program. Each teaching strategy was a programmed lesson plan built around real time computer-based simulations of flight instrument readouts. The dependent measure was the number of trials it took a Cadet to learn a specific skill that conformed to an established criterion of success. It is worth stressing that, unlike some measures of learning with which you may be more familiar (e.g., examination scores), when the number of trials it takes to learn a skill is the dependent measure, high scores do not represent excellence in performance. Rather, subjects who learn the skill in relatively *few* trials are considered to be the better performers. This fact must be understood in order to give an accurate interpretation of the experimental results.

The two levels of the Skill variable (1 and 2) and the two levels of the Teaching Strategy variable (1 and 2) form four possible treatment combinations:

1. Skill 1 taught using Teaching Strategy 1
2. Skill 1 taught using Teaching Strategy 2
3. Skill 2 taught using Teaching Strategy 1
4. Skill 2 taught using Teaching Strategy 2

Table 18.2

The 2 × 2 factorial design of Example 1 showing schematically the cell means, ($\overline{AB}_{ij}$), the row means ($\overline{A}_i$), the column means ($\overline{B}_j$), and the grand mean ($\overline{G}$).

	Type of Skill Being Taught (B)		
Teaching Method (A)	Skill 1	Skill 2	Row Means
Strategy 1	$\overline{AB}_{11}$	$\overline{AB}_{12}$	$\overline{A}_1$
Strategy 2	$\overline{AB}_{21}$	$\overline{AB}_{22}$	$\overline{A}_2$
Column Means:	$\overline{B}_1$	$\overline{B}_2$	$\overline{G}$

The twenty randomly picked Cadets who participated in the experiment were randomly divided into four groups of five subjects each for assignment to the four treatment combinations (cells) formed by the 2 × 2 (read as "two by two") experimental design. This so-called randomized groups design gets its name from this random assignment procedure.

The four cells of the present experimental design are illustrated using notation in table 18.2. The entries in table 18.2 refer to the factor A (row) means ($\overline{A}_i$), the factor B (column) means ($\overline{B}_j$), and the individual cell means ($\overline{AB}_{ij}$).

Main Effects. Before introducing the computational procedures that would be used to analyze the data from such an experiment, let us first deal with some conceptual underpinnings of this type of experimental design. Using this 2 × 2 factorial design the psychologist may compare the performance of the Cadets who learned Skill 1 to the performance of the Cadets who learned Skill 2. This may be done by comparing the column (factor B) means. Similarly, the relative effectiveness of the two teaching strategies may be assessed by comparing the row (factor A) means. Such comparisons, in which the experimental effects attributable to different levels of one variable are assessed after averaging across all levels of another variable, are called **main effects.** In this experiment the potential main effects are differences in performance due to the teaching strategy (factor A) that was used to teach a skill and differences in performance due to the relative difficulty of the specific type of skill being taught (factor B).

Main Effect. An experimental effect that is attributable to different levels of one factor. It is assessed after averaging across all levels of the other factor.

If the simultaneous evaluation of two classes of main effects were the only advantage of the factorial experiment it would have little advantage over the single factor ANOVA. One could simply do two separate experiments: one to compare the effectiveness of the two teaching strategies and one to compare the relative difficulty in learning the two skills. (For this we would not even need the ANOVA. An independent groups *t* test could be used to analyze each set of experimental data.)

Interaction. In the context of the two-factor design, an interaction is an experimental effect that results from certain factor A–factor B combinations that cannot be accounted for by the individual contributions of factor A and factor B.

Synergism. The action of two experimental variables upon a dependent measure that produces an effect greater than the individual contribution of each variable taken independently. A synergistic effect is an interaction.

Interactions. The unique contribution of the factorial experiment is that it permits the evaluation of **interaction** effects. Interactions, within the context of a two-factor design, are experimental effects that result from certain row variable—column variable combinations that cannot be explained simply by adding the individual contributions of the two variables. One pattern of interaction is closely related to the concept of **synergism** from physiology. According to Webster's Collegiate Dictionary, synergism refers to "cooperative actions of discrete agencies such that the total effect is greater than the sum of the two effects taken independently, as in the action of mixtures of certain drugs." For example, let us assume that

1. following a certain diet program has been shown to add five years to human life expectancy;
2. following a certain exercise regimen has been shown to add four years to human life expectancy;
3. following both the diet program *and* the exercise regimen has been shown to add fourteen years to human life expectancy.

You can see that the combination of diet (5 years) and exercise (4 years) results in an effect that is not predictable from the two variables considered singly ($5 + 4 = 9$, not 14). The extra five years in life expectancy that results from following both a healthy diet and a beneficial exercise program is a synergistic effect. Again, the unique combination results in a greater gain in life expectancy than would be predicted by simply adding the individual beneficial effects of diet and exercise.

Similarly, to follow along with the drug analogy from the dictionary definition, it is possible for two medicines to have beneficial therapeutic effects when used alone and to have a diminished effect when used together. Thus, an interaction can express itself in a negative way as well as in a positive way.

Data Patterns for Main Effects and Interactions

Even in the relatively simple 2×2 experiment there are several different potential patterns of experimental results with respect to main effects and interactions. We shall first examine the evidence for main effects and interactions that is reflected in various patterns of cell, row, and column means. Then, in the next section, we shall examine these same patterns of cell means as they appear in graphic form.

Table 18.3

The pattern of cell means (average number of trials needed to reach criterion) for hypothetical Result 1: main effect for factor A with no A × B interaction.

	Type of Skill Being Taught (B)		
Teaching Method (A)	Skill 1	Skill 2	Row Means
Strategy 1	62	66	64
Strategy 2	36	34	35
Column Mean:	49	50	Grand Mean = 49.5

Table 18.4

The pattern of cell means (average number of trials needed to reach criterion) for hypothetical Result 2: main effect for factor B with no A × B interaction.

	Type of Skill Being Taught (B)		
Teaching Method (A)	Skill 1	Skill 2	Row Means
Strategy 1	62	34	48
Strategy 2	66	36	51
Column Mean:	64	35	Grand Mean = 49.5

Result 1: Main Effect—Factor A Only (No A × B Interaction)[2]

The pattern of row means shown in table 18.3 indicates that, on the average, the Cadets taught with Teaching Strategy 2 learned the skills in fewer trials than did the Cadets taught with Teaching Strategy 1. The data also reveal that this relationship was basically of the same magnitude within both Skill 1 (62 vs. 36) and Skill 2 (66 vs. 34). The column means are almost identical, so there is no indication that Skill 1 was any more or less difficult to learn than Skill 2.

Result 2: Main Effect—Factor B Only (No A × B Interaction)

Inspect the means of table 18.4. In this pattern the column means are now quite different from each other (64 vs. 35) and the row means are relatively close (48 vs. 51).

[2]This is read "A by B."

Table 18.5

The pattern of cell means (average number of trials needed to reach criterion) for hypothetical Result 3: main effects for both factor A and factor B with no A × B interaction.

	Type of Skill Being Taught (B)		
Teaching Method (A)	Skill 1	Skill 2	Row Means
Strategy 1	22	52	37
Strategy 2	42	72	57
Column Mean:	32	62	Grand Mean = 47

The pattern of column means shown in table 18.4 indicates that, on the average, Skill 2 was learned in fewer trials than Skill 1, and this relationship was basically of the same magnitude within both Teaching Strategy 1 (62 vs. 34) and Teaching Strategy 2 (66 vs. 36). As mentioned above, the row means are relatively close in value (48 vs. 51), and so from appearances alone there is no indication that Teaching Strategy 1 was any more or less effective in teaching the skills than Teaching Strategy 2.

Result 3: Main Effects for Both A and B (No A × B Interaction)

In table 18.5 we see the pattern of means that would result when both factor A *and* factor B are exerting an experimental effect on the Cadets' performance.

The pattern of the column means shown in table 18.5 (32 vs. 62) indicates that, on the average, Skill 1 was learned in fewer trials than Skill 2, and this relationship was basically of the same magnitude within both Teaching Strategy 1 (22 vs. 52) and Teaching Strategy 2 (42 vs. 72). The row means also reveal a difference (37 vs. 57), so there is an indication that, on the average, Teaching Strategy 1 was more effective in teaching the skills than Teaching Strategy 2. As in the other interaction-free patterns discussed above, the magnitudes separating the row entries (22 vs. 52 and 42 vs. 72) and the column entries (22 vs. 42 and 52 vs. 72) are equivalent. In this case, in fact, the magnitudes are identical: 30 units separate both sets of row entries and 20 units separate both sets of column entries.

Result 4: A × B Interaction with No Main Effects

The pattern of means shown in table 18.6 reveals virtually no evidence of any main effect for either factor A or factor B. The row means (48 and 51) and the column means (49 and 50) are quite close in value.

In the absence of main effects do we conclude that skill acquisition in this experiment was unaffected by the Teaching Strategy that was used and that Skill 1 and Skill 2 were equally difficult to learn? The answer is no.

Table 18.6

The pattern of cell means (average number of trials needed to reach criterion) for hypothetical Result 4: A × B interaction with no main effects.

	Type of Skill Being Taught (B)		
Teaching Method (A)	Skill 1	Skill 2	Row Means
Strategy 1	62	34	48
Strategy 2	36	66	51
Column Mean:	49	50	Grand Mean = 49.5

Table 18.7

The pattern of cell means (average number of trials needed to reach criterion) for hypothetical Result 5: A × B interaction with main effects.

	Type of Skill Being Taught (B)		
Teaching Method (A)	Skill 1	Skill 2	Row Means
Strategy 1	67	69	68
Strategy 2	21	71	46
Column Mean:	44	70	Grand Mean = 57

These variables *did* register effects, but the effects of a given variable did not register in a consistent manner across all levels of the second variable.

The principal feature of these data identifying the pattern as interactive is that Teaching Strategy 2 was rather effective in teaching Skill 1 (only 36 trials to criterion), but this same strategy was relatively ineffective for teaching Skill 2 (66 trials to criterion). Similarly, Teaching Strategy 1 was rather effective in teaching Skill 2 (34 trials to criterion), but not for teaching Skill 1 (62 trials to criterion). Based upon the presence of such an interactive pattern, if the question were asked, "Which teaching strategy is the most effective for teaching complex skills to Cadet trainees?" the response would have to be, "It depends upon the skill you wish to teach." And if the question were asked, "Which skill, 1 or 2, is easier for the Cadets to learn?" the response would have to be, "It depends upon which teaching strategy you use."

Result 5: A × B Interaction with Main Effects

The pattern of means in table 18.7 is a good representation of the synergism referred to earlier. Notice that three of the cells are rather uniform, but when a particular teaching strategy (Strategy 2) is used to teach a particular skill (Skill 1), the learning takes place relatively fast. Only an average of 21 trials were needed to reach criterion in contrast to over 67 for all the other Strategy/Skill combinations.

It is particularly important to notice how the presence of an interaction in table 18.7 affects the interpretation of the main effects in the data. Even though main effects for both factor A and factor B are assumed to be present in this hypothetical pattern, are we really justified in saying that Skill 1 is easier to learn than Skill 2 (44 trials vs. 70 trials)? This was true only when Teaching Strategy 2 was used. Also, are we really justified in saying that Teaching Strategy 2 was more effective in teaching the skills than Teaching Strategy 1 (46 trials vs. 68 trials)? This was only true for Skill 1. In general, in the presence of an A × B interaction we must interpret main effects with great caution.

MAIN EFFECTS AND INTERACTIONS: A VISUAL REPRESENTATION

The graphic plots of the cell means for all five hypothetical patterns of results discussed above are shown in figures 18.1 to 18.5, respectively. Each line in these figures represents the results of one teaching strategy in teaching the two skills. In figure 18.1 you can see that the number of trials needed to reach criterion was roughly the same for Skill 1 and Skill 2, and this is consistent with the absence of a main effect for Skill (factor B). The main effect for Strategy (factor A) shows up as a uniform superiority of Strategy 2 over Strategy 1. That is, fewer trials were needed to learn the skills when Strategy 2 was employed, and this was true for both Skill 1 and Skill 2.

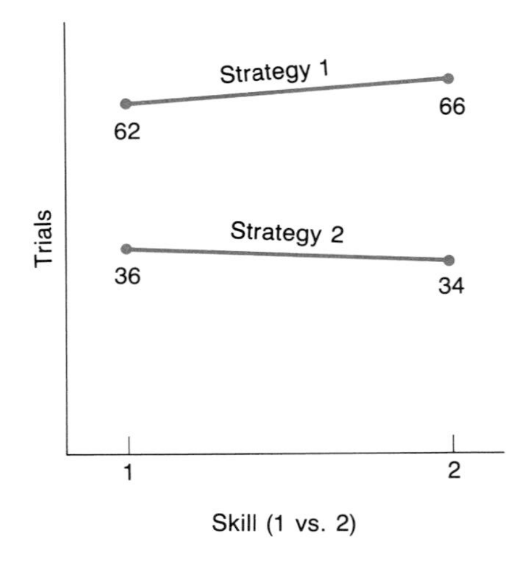

Figure 18.1

A visual representation of hypothetical result #1: main effect for factor A, no main effect for factor B, and no A × B interaction.

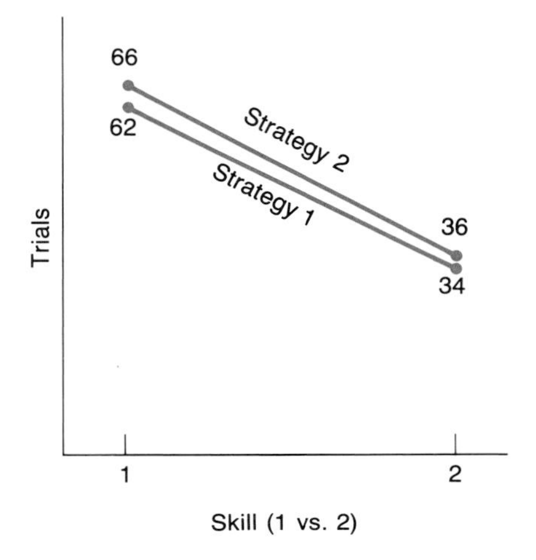

Figure 18.2

A visual representation of hypothetical result #2: main effect for factor B, no main effect for factor A, and no A × B interaction.

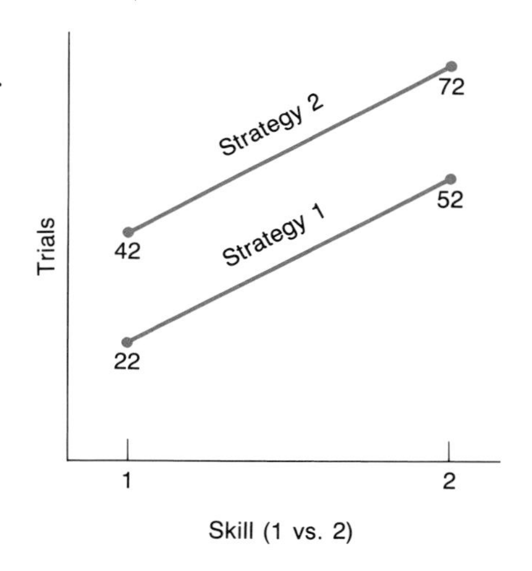

Figure 18.3

A visual representation for hypothetical result #3: main effects for factors A and B, but no A × B interaction.

In figure 18.2 we can see from the closeness of the Strategy 1 and Strategy 2 plots that neither was more or less effective than the other in teaching the skills. The drop in trials to criterion from Skill 1 to Skill 2 (main effect: factor B) shows that Skill 2 was learned with relative ease compared to Skill 1 no matter which teaching strategy was employed.

In figure 18.3 both A and B main effects are evident. Strategy 1 is uniformly superior to Strategy 2 in teaching the skills and Skill 1 is learned more easily than Skill 2.

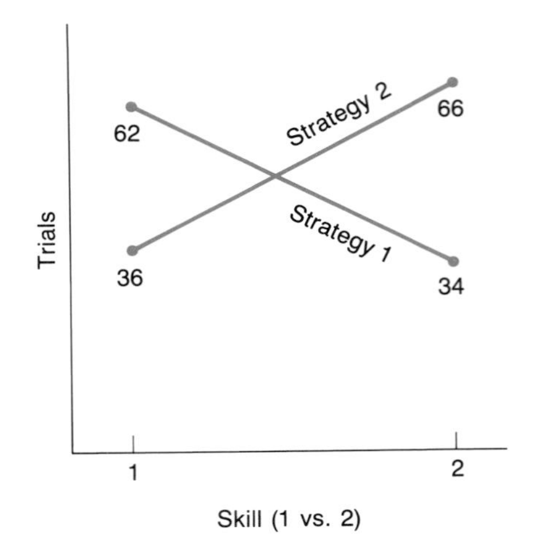

Figure 18.4

A visual representation of hypothetical result #4: an A × B interaction with no main effect for factor A and no main effect for factor B.

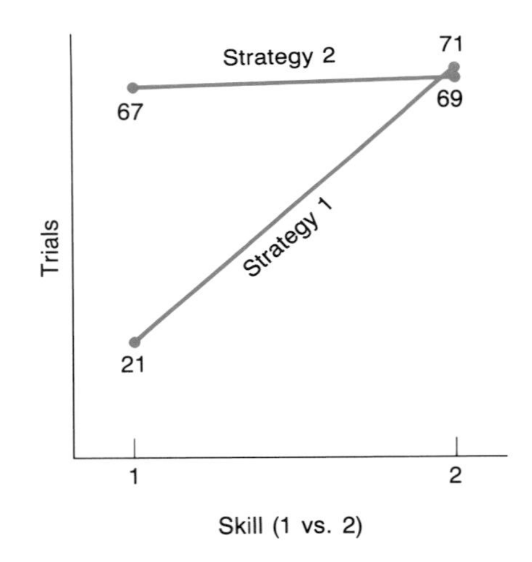

Figure 18.5

A visual representation of hypothetical result #5: main effects for factors A and B as well as an A × B interaction.

In the next two illustrations, figures 18.4 and 18.5, we see a pattern that is quite different from the preceding three. Now, instead of the parallel or roughly parallel functions that characterized the plots of the first three results, the lines cross (figure 18.4) or converge (figure 18.5). This lack of parallelism in the plot of the cell means, whether it be an actual cross or a convergence, is the visual clue that an interactive effect is likely to emerge from the ANOVA.

The Null and Alternative Hypotheses

As you can see from the set of hypothetical experimental outcomes discussed previously, there are several different patterns of results that can characterize the presence of some experimental effect due to factor A and/or factor B and/or the A $\times$ B interaction. There is, however, only one hypothetical experimental result within which absolutely no experimental effects are present. This is the case in which only chance is operating to produce variation in the dependent measure. This null hypothesis, that chance alone is responsible for any apparent differences in performance among the Cadets, is retained unless and until the weight of evidence in the experimental data persuades us to reject it. The null hypotheses for Example 1 are as follows:

1. Factor A: When the number of learning trials used by each Teaching Strategy is averaged across both levels of factor B, Teaching Strategy 1 is as effective as Teaching Strategy 2 in teaching complex skills to Cadet trainees.

2. Factor B: When the number of learning trials necessary to learn each of the three skills is averaged across both levels of factor A, it takes the same number of learning trials for Cadet trainees to learn Skill 1 as it takes for them to learn Skill 2.

3. A $\times$ B Interaction: There is no factor contributing to the relative ease or difficulty in learning other than from the independent contributions of factor A and/or factor B (main effects).

These three null hypotheses may be expressed symbolically as well as verbally:

1. Factor A

$$H_0: \mu_{A_1} = \mu_{A_2}$$

In words, the data used to compute both row means are from the same population, so any difference between the row means is attributable to random variation.

2. Factor B

$$H_0: \mu_{B_1} = \mu_{B_2}$$

In words, the data used to compute both column means are from the same population, so any difference between the column means is attributable to random variation.

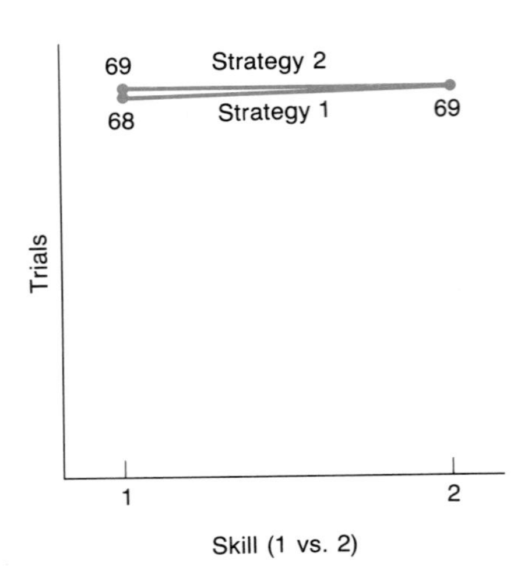

Figure 18.6

An illustration of a plot of cell means when the null hypothesis is true.

3. A × B Interaction

$$H_0: \mu_{AB_{11}} = \mu_{AB_{12}} = \mu_{AB_{21}} = \mu_{AB_{22}}$$

In words, with the influence of any main effects removed, the data within each cell are assumed to represent random samples from the same population, so any variation among the cell means may be attributed to chance. The alternative hypotheses to any of the above null hypotheses may be simply stated as:

$$H_1: \text{not } H_0$$

just as we did for the single factor ANOVA.

Some hypothetical patterns of results that would cause a rejection of one or more of the null hypotheses have been presented in tables 18.3, 18.4, 18.5, 18.6, and 18.7 and graphically in figures 18.1, 18.2, 18.3, 18.4, and 18.5. By comparison, inspect figure 18.6, which shows the plot of the cell means when the null hypothesis is true. In this situation the cell means are identical to each other, or nearly so, and there is no indication of either a factor A or factor B main effect or an A × B interaction.

Table 18.8

The raw data, cell totals (AB_{ij}), row totals (A_i), column totals (B_j), and the grand total (G) for Example 1.

Data for Example 1

	Skill 1	Skill 2	
Teaching Strategy 1	68	50	
	62	44	
	83	85	
	77	89	
	45	77	
	$AB_{11} = 335$	$AB_{12} = 345$	$A_1 = 680$
	Skill 1	Skill 2	
Teaching Strategy 2	45	79	
	38	76	
	29	87	
	52	51	
	41	62	
	$AB_{21} = 205$	$AB_{22} = 355$	$A_2 = 560$
	$B_1 = 540$	$B_2 = 700$	$G = 1,240$

THE COMPUTATIONAL METHOD FOR THE TWO-FACTOR ANOVA[3]

In the preceding section we examined various hypothetical outcomes of a specific research scenario (Example 1) using tables of cell means to represent five possible combinations of A, B, and A × B treatment effects, and

[3]The technical name for this design is the fixed factor randomized groups design. Equal numbers of observations per cell are assumed. See Winer (1971) for technical details that relate to this most basic factorial design.

one outcome to represent the absence of any treatment effects. Now, within the context of the same 2×2 scenario and with the same null and alternative hypotheses, we shall analyze a set of experimental data (table 18.8). Then, with the aid of points that were raised in the preceding section and with the decision rules that we shall write, we shall interpret the results of the ANOVA. As we proceed, each entry in the ANOVA summary table will be discussed both in general terms as it may apply to any two-factor ANOVA and in terms specific to the data of the present 2×2 example.

Partitioning Variation (SS) in the Two-Factor Experiment

In any two variable factorial design there are npq scores, where n is the number of scores within each cell, p is the number of levels of factor A, and q is the number of levels of factor B. For the present example $npq = 5 \cdot 2 \cdot 2 = 20$. The two-factor ANOVA allows us to partition the total variation among the entire set of npq scores into that portion that is attributable to the effect of factor A, that portion that is attributable to the effect of factor B, that portion that is attributable to the interaction between factor A and factor B, and that portion that is unexplained error variation. The **partitioning of total variation** into its component parts may be illustrated using a pie chart. Such a chart is in figure 18.7.

Partitioning Total Variation (SS). In the context of the two-factor design, it is the division of the SS_{total} to identify the contribution of factor A, factor B, and the $A \times B$ interaction.

The portion of total variation attributable to random error is referred to as the variation within cell. The reason for this is that the contribution of factor A, factor B, and the $A \times B$ interaction to the value of all scores within a particular cell is assumed to be a constant. If you recall, adding a constant to all elements of a set does not affect the dispersion of the set. Since we assume that the independent variables do not affect the variability among scores within a specific cell, the $\mathbf{SS_{within\ cell}}$ may be used to estimate the extent of error variation. This is basically the same justification given for using the $SS_{within\ treatment}$ as the estimate of error variation in the single factor ANOVA.

$SS_{within\ cell}$. The variation among the cells. An estimate of error variation.

The experimental sources of variation (factor A, factor B, and the $A \times B$ interaction) are collectively referred to as the between cell portion of the total variation (figure 18.8). This is because each cell of a factorial design defines a unique combination of treatments—subjects assigned to a specific cell experience a specific level of factor A combined with a specific level of factor B. In this sense the $\mathbf{SS_{between\ cell}}$ of the factorial experiment is analogous to the $SS_{between\ treatment}$ of the single factor ANOVA. The main difference between the single factor ANOVA and the two-factor ANOVA is that in the single factor ANOVA there is presumably only one independent variable (or "factor") that is the source of variation between treatment. By comparison, in the factorial design there are two different independent variables

$SS_{between\ cell}$. The variation among the $p \cdot q$ cells in a factorial design. Factor A, factor B, and the $A \times B$ interaction all contribute to the $SS_{between\ cell}$.

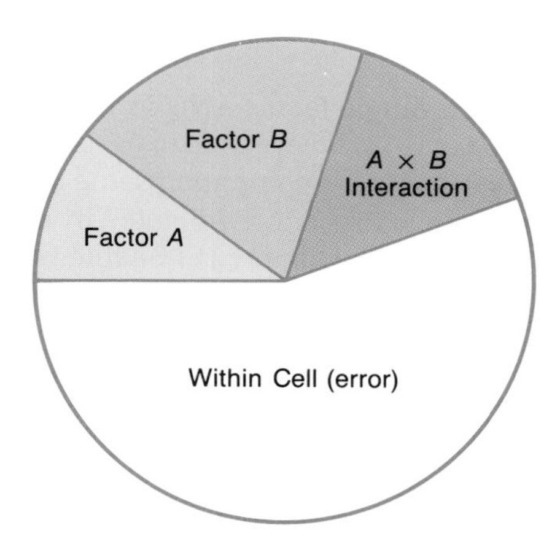

Figure 18.7
The partitioning of total variation into its component parts. The data used are from table 18.8. The shaded area is the between cell variation.

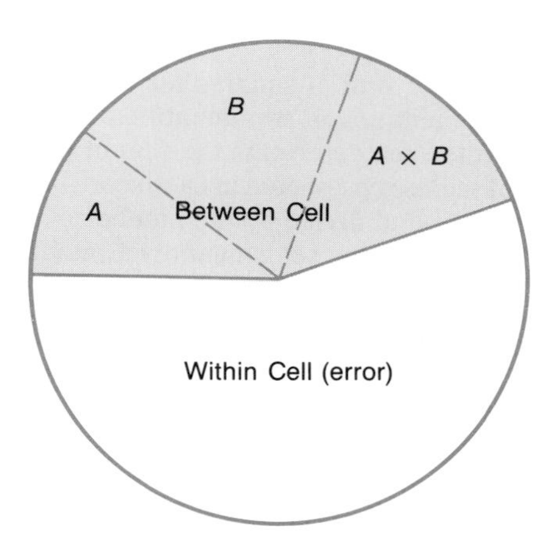

Figure 18.8
The partitioning of total variation into between cell and within cell components, and the partitioning of between cell variation according to the contributions of factor A, factor B, and the A × B interaction.

that contribute to the treatment variation (factor A and factor B) and a third source of variation owing to a possible interaction between the two factors (the A × B interaction). By using the factorial ANOVA to partition the $SS_{\text{between cell}}$ we may identify the relative contributions of factor A, factor B, and the A × B interaction.

The computational method that follows will detail the procedures that permit the partitioning of total variation into its component parts. After that, variances (mean squares) will be computed as well as the *F* ratios that are needed for the final step of hypothesis testing: comparing the computed statistic to the value stated in the decision rules.

Crunching the Numbers

Computational Components. The special values computed from the data that are used to partition total variation.

When we applied the single factor ANOVA to k independent treatments of n scores each (chapter 16) we were able to partition the total variation (SS_{total}) among the nk scores by first computing some special numbers called **computational components.** Procedures dictated by a general computational rule (called the general rule in chapter 15) enabled us to use the computational components to partition the sum of squares into its component parts. When the general rule was applied to the total data set of nk scores the result was the SS_{total}, when the general rule was applied to the set of treatment totals the result was the $SS_{between\ treatment}$, and when the general rule was applied separately to the scores within each of the k treatments the result, after pooling the SS within each of the k treatments, was the $SS_{within\ treatment}$.

We shall use this same **general rule** to partition the SS_{total} for the data of the factorial experiment summarized in table 18.8. To review, the general rule states:

The General Rule. The general computational procedure for determining the variation (SS) in any set of raw or composite scores. See text in chapter 15 for details.

> The computation of sum of squares for any set of either raw scores or totals requires the computation of two quantities. To get quantity 1 square each individual score in the set, determine the sum of the squared scores, and divide by the number of scores represented in each score of the set. To get quantity 2 square the sum of the set and divide by the number of scores represented in the sum. The sum of squares of the set is quantity 1 minus quantity 2.

When we applied this rule to partition the sum of squares of a single factor experiment we needed only three computational components. For the two-factor experiment we shall need five components. In preparation for solving for the values of the computational components we must first organize an AB summary table from the raw data. This AB summary is shown using notation in table 18.9 and with the experimental data in table 18.10. The entries in the AB summary table are the cell totals, the row totals, the column totals, and the grand total from table 18.8. This is very much like table 18.2 except that the cell, row, and column *totals* are provided instead of the means.

With the AB summary table and the raw data available, we have all we need to compute the five computational components.

The Computational Components

1. G^2/npq (Sum the npq scores in the data set, square that sum, and divide the squared sum by npq.)

2. $\Sigma\Sigma X_{ij}^2$ (Square each one of the npq scores in the data, then add all the squared scores.)

Table 18.9

The AB summary table for a 2 × 2 factorial experiment showing the notation for the cell (AB_{ij}), row (A_i), column (B_j), and grand (G) totals.

	Type of Skill Being Taught (B)		
Teaching Method (A)	Skill 1	Skill 2	Row Totals
Strategy 1	AB_{11}	AB_{12}	A_1
Strategy 2	AB_{21}	AB_{22}	A_2
Column Totals:	B_1	B_2	G

Table 18.10

The same cell, row, column, and grand totals that were shown with the raw data in table 18.8 are displayed here as an AB summary table.

	Type of Skill Being Taught (B)		
Teaching Method (A)	Skill 1	Skill 2	Row Totals
Strategy 1	335	345	680
Strategy 2	205	355	560
Column Totals:	540	700	1,240

3. $\Sigma A_i^2/nq$ (Square each of the p row totals, add up the squared values and divide by nq, the number of scores represented in each row total.)

4. $\Sigma B_j^2/np$ (Square each of the q column totals, add up the squared values and divide by np, the number of scores represented in each column total.)

5. $\Sigma AB_{ij}^2/n$ (Square each of the pq cell totals, add up the squared totals and divide by n, the number of scores represented in each cell total.)

For the present data set (table 18.8):

1. $G^2/npq = \dfrac{1{,}240^2}{20} = \dfrac{1{,}537{,}600}{20} = 76{,}880$

2. $\Sigma\Sigma X_{ij}^2 = 68^2 + 62^2 + \cdots + 51^2 + 62^2 = 83{,}578$

3. $\Sigma A_i^2/nq = \dfrac{680^2 + 560^2}{10} = \dfrac{776{,}000}{10} = 77{,}600$

4. $\Sigma B_j^2/np = \dfrac{540^2 + 700^2}{10} = \dfrac{781{,}600}{10} = 78{,}160$

5. $\Sigma AB_{ij}^2/n = \dfrac{335^2 + 345^2 + 205^2 + 355^2}{5} = \dfrac{399{,}300}{5} = 79{,}860$

Applying the General Rule Using the Computational Components

To get the SS for factor A we operate the general rule using the set of row totals. In terms of the computational components:

$$\text{SS for factor A} = (3) - (1) = 77{,}600 - 76{,}880 = 720$$

To get the SS for factor B we operate the general rule using the set of column totals:

$$\text{SS for factor B} = (4) - (1) = 78{,}160 - 76{,}880 = 1{,}280$$

To get the entire $SS_{\text{between cell}}$, the combined variation due to factor A, factor B, and the A × B interaction, we operate the general rule using the set of *pq* cell totals:

$$SS_{\text{between cell}} = (5) - (1) = 79{,}860 - 76{,}880 = 2{,}980$$

The A × B interaction is a residual. It is the variation in the $SS_{\text{between cell}}$ that is left over when the contributions of factors A and B have been removed. We may compute the SS for the A × B interaction as follows:

$$\begin{aligned} SS_{A \times B} &= SS_{\text{between cell}} - SS_A - SS_B \\ &= ((5) - (1)) - ((3) - (1)) - ((4) - (1)) \\ &= (5) - (1) - (3) + (1) - (4) + (1) \\ &= (5) - (3) - (4) + (1) \end{aligned}$$

For the current data:

$$SS_{\text{between cell}} = 79{,}860 - 77{,}600 - 78{,}160 + 76{,}880 = 980$$

The sum of squares within cell is used as the estimate of error variation and is computed by applying the general rule to the raw data within each cell. We could do this separately for each cell and then add ("pool") the SS computed for each cell to get the $SS_{\text{within cell}}$, but the manipulation (2) − (5) allows us to get the sum of squares within cell value in one step. For the current data:

$$SS_{\text{within cell}} = (2) - (5) = 83{,}548 - 79{,}860 = 3{,}688$$

Degrees of Freedom (*df*) for the Factorial Design

In chapter 15 you learned that the *df* that is associated with the sum of squares of a set is the number of scores in the set minus one. We may use this same principle to derive the *df* values needed for the present analysis. Specifically, we use the set of pq cell totals to compute the $SS_{\text{between cell}}$, and so according to this principle, the $SS_{\text{between cell}}$ has $df = pq - 1$. For the data we are currently analyzing:

$$df_{\text{between cell}} = pq - 1 = 2 \cdot 2 - 1 = 3.$$

We use the p row totals to compute the SS for factor A, so the SS for factor A has $df = p - 1$. We use the q column totals to compute the SS for factor B, so the SS for factor B has $df = q - 1$. Since both factor A and factor B have only two levels each in the present data set, the *df* in both cases is 1:

$$df_{\text{factor A}} = p - 1 = 2 - 1 = 1$$
$$df_{\text{factor B}} = q - 1 = 2 - 1 = 1$$

When the *df* for factors A and B are subtracted from the $pq - 1$ between cell *df*, $(p - 1)(q - 1)$ degrees of freedom remain for the A × B interaction. Since A and B have only two levels apiece:

$$df_{A \times B} = (p - 1)(q - 1) = (2 - 1)(2 - 1) = 1 \cdot 1 = 1.$$

The n scores within each cell are used to compute the pooled $SS_{\text{within cell}}$, so the SS within any one cell is associated with $n - 1$ degrees of freedom. Since there are pq cells in the factorial design, the pooled $SS_{\text{within cell}}$ has $df = pq(n - 1)$. For the present data set:

$$df_{\text{within cell}} = pq(n - 1) = 2 \cdot 2(5 - 1) = 4 \cdot 4 = 16$$

Lastly, the SS_{total} has $df = npq - 1$, the total number of scores in the data set less one. For the current data:

$$df_{\text{total}} = npq - 1 = 5 \cdot 2 \cdot 2 - 1 = 20 - 1 = 19$$

As a check on computing degrees of freedom, the *df* associated with the A, B, and A × B sum of squares must sum to the $df_{\text{between cell}}$, which equals $pq - 1$. Also, the $df_{\text{between cell}}$ and $df_{\text{within cell}}$ must sum to $npq - 1$, the total *df* for the data set.

Table 18.11

The ANOVA summary for the Example 1 data displayed in Table 18.8.

Analysis of Variance Summary Table

Source	*df*	SS	MS	F
Between Cell	3	2,980		
Strategy (A)	1	720	720	3.12
Skill (B)	1	1,280	1,280	5.55
A × B	1	980	980	4.25
Within cell (Error)	16	3,688	230.5	
Total	19	6,668		

The Mean Squares and the *F* Ratio

The mean square (MS) must be computed for each of the following sources of variation: factor A, factor B, the A × B interaction, and the within cell. This is done by dividing each ANOVA summary table SS entry by its degrees of freedom, just as we did in the single factor ANOVA. The 2 × 2 factorial design is a special case because factor A, factor B, and the A × B interaction all have only one degree of freedom. To get the MS value for each between cell source of variation we divide SS by 1. Because division by 1 does not change the SS value, the mean square and the sum of squares values for the between cell sources of variation are the same in the 2 × 2 design. The $MS_{\text{within cell}}$ is $3688/16 = 230.5$.

$MS_{\text{within cell}}$. The variance within cells. An estimate of the error variance that is sometimes written MS_{error}. In the two-factor design, the $MS_{\text{within cell}} = SS_{\text{within cell}}/pq(n-1)$.

The last step in the factorial ANOVA is to compute the *F* ratios. There are three *F* ratios to compute: the *F* ratio for factor A, factor B, and the A × B interaction. The three *F* ratios are formed by dividing the respective treatment mean squares (A, B, and A × B) by the $MS_{\text{within cell}}$ (the estimate of error). The *F* ratios for the current analysis are

$$F \text{ ratio for factor A} = 720/230.5 = 3.12$$
$$F \text{ ratio for factor B} = 1{,}280/230.5 = 5.55$$
$$F \text{ ratio for A} \times \text{B interaction} = 980/230.5 = 4.25$$

We have now completed the necessary computations for the analysis of variance and may summarize the results as shown in table 18.11. All the computational methods we applied to the data in table 18.8 are summarized in table 18.12.

Table 18.12

General directions for inserting values in the ANOVA summary table of the independent groups two-factor experiment.

Analysis of Variance Summary Table

Source	*df*	SS	MS	*F*
Between Cell	$pq - 1$	(5) − (1)		
Factor A	$p - 1$	(3) − (1)	$SS_A/(p-1)$	MS_A/MS_{error}
Factor B	$q - 1$	(4) − (1)	$SS_B/(q-1)$	MS_B/MS_{error}
A × B	$(p-1)(q-1)$	(5) − (3) − (4) + (1)	$SS_{A \times B}/(p-1)(q-1)$	$MS_{A \times B}/MS_{error}$
Within Cell (Error)	$pq(n-1)$	(1) − (5)	$SS_{error}/pq(n-1)$	
Total	$npq - 1$	(2) − (1)		

The Decision Rules

Because we have three separate *F* ratios to evaluate for significance, we must have three decision rules. The general form of the decision rule is

> **Reject H_0 if the computed value for *F* equals or exceeds the critical value for *F*.**

The critical values for *F* that are listed in the *F* Table are

F with $df = (p - 1) / pq(n - 1)$ when factor A is being evaluated,

F with $df = (q - 1) / pq(n - 1)$ when factor B is being evaluated,

and

F with $df = (p - 1)(q - 1) / pq(n - 1)$ when the A × B interaction is being evaluated.

In the present example, since the computed *F* values all have $df = 1,16$ (read "Degrees of freedom equal one and sixteen") the critical value for *F* is the tabled value with 1 and 16 degrees of freedom. As with the single factor ANOVA, the *df* for a treatment effect (A, B, or A × B) determines the column

Table 18.13

The cell means for the Example 1 data presented in Table 18.8.

	Type of Skill Being Taught (B)		
Teaching Method (A)	Skill 1	Skill 2	Row Means
Strategy 1	67	69	68
Strategy 2	41	71	56
Column Mean:	54	70	Grand Mean = 62

of the F table that is used, and the *df* for error determines the row of the F table that is used. If you look in the column of the F table headed with $df = 1$ and the row with $df = 16$, you shall see the two values 4.49 and 8.53.

$$F\,(1{,}16) = 4.49\ (\alpha = .05)$$
$$F\,(1{,}16) = 8.53\ (\alpha = .01)$$

The value for $\alpha = .01$ is in boldface in the table and the value for $\alpha = .05$ is printed in lighter type.

In comparing the critical value for F to the computed values in the ANOVA summary table, we see that only factor B was statistically significant: the computed F value of 5.55 is greater than the critical value of 4.25 ($df = 1{,}16$).

Interpreting the ANOVA Results

We just determined that the ANOVA on the Example 1 data permitted rejection of the null hypothesis only for the comparison between the two levels of factor B (Skill 1 vs. Skill 2). Inspection of the means (table 18.13) for the two levels of factor B (54 trials to criterion vs. 70 trials to criterion) reveals the direction of this difference: Skill 1 was learned in significantly fewer trials than Skill 2. This result supports the interpretation, "Skill 1 was easier for the Cadets to learn than Skill 2."

Unfortunately, as so often happens in research, the results of this experiment are somewhat equivocal. There is a feature of the data that would tend to erode one's confidence in the latter interpretation. If you inspect the plot of the cell means (figure 18.9) for the Example 1 data you should notice that the appearance is very much like hypothetical Result 5 as shown in figure 18.5. If you recall, Result 5 was presented as an outcome that is indicative of an A × B interaction, but even though figure 18.9 seems to mirror that pattern, the ANOVA did not reveal a significant A × B interaction. True, the ANOVA did result in an F ratio of 4.25 for the A × B interaction—close to

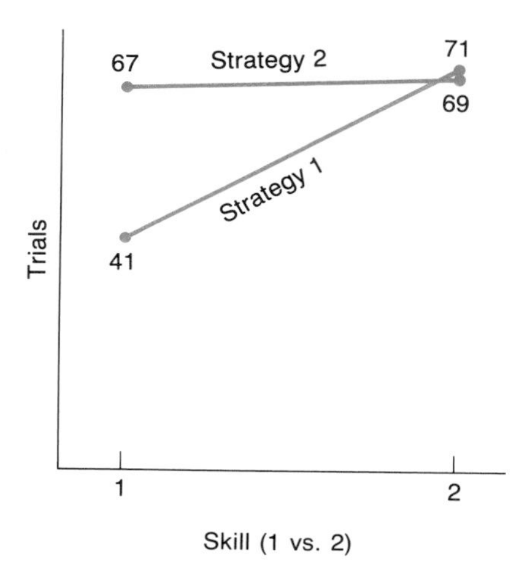

Figure 18.9

The plot of cell means for the data in table 18.8 (example #1).

the 4.49 needed for significance at the .05 level of significance. But, as you surely know by now, in hypothesis testing, close is not enough. The decision criteria is fixed, and if you miss, you miss. We can, however, do another experiment (a "replication") any time we are worried about having committed a Type I error or a Type II error.

EXAMPLE 2: THE NEXT EXPERIMENT

The experiment described below as Example 2 was not a literal replication of the earlier experiment. The same two teaching strategies were used, but this time they were applied to the teaching of three rather than only two skills. The experimental design is shown in table 18.14 along with the raw data, cell totals (AB_{ij}), row totals (A_i), column totals (B_j), and a grand total (G) all of which we shall need in order to do the factorial ANOVA with the computational components method depicted in table 18.12. Notice that in table 18.14 teaching strategy has been arbitrarily labeled as factor A, just as it was in the original experiment, and it has two levels: Strategy 1 and Strategy 2. Factor B is skill and this factor has three levels corresponding to the three different skills that the various groups of Cadets were taught.

Besides the extension of the skill factor to three from two levels, one other departure from the first experiment is that more subjects were randomly assigned to each of the cells defined by the experimental design. This was done in an effort to increase power because, as you know, the larger the sample size, the smaller the estimate of error variance tends to be, and the more power the statistical test has to detect relatively subtle effects caused

Table 18.14

The raw data, the cell totals (AB_{ij}), the row totals (A_i), the column totals (B_j), and the grand total (G) for Example 2.

	Skill 1	Skill 2	Skill 3	
Strategy 1	83	50	60	
	42	89	87	
	58	60	83	
	72	83	73	
	71	78	75	
	59	70	82	
	68	60	87	
	67	70	77	
	$AB_{11} = 520$	$AB_{12} = 560$	$AB_{13} = 624$	$A_1 = 1{,}704$
Strategy 2	41	87	85	
	40	55	79	
	49	79	73	
	35	66	89	
	29	71	65	
	44	72	76	
	35	67	69	
	39	71	64	
	$AB_{21} = 312$	$AB_{22} = 568$	$AB_{23} = 600$	$A_2 = 1{,}480$
	$B_1 = 832$	$B_2 = 1{,}128$	$B_3 = 1{,}224$	$G = 3{,}184$

by the experimental variables. Since the second experiment was run to try to evaluate more intensively the possibility of an interactive effect between factor A and factor B, and since it is possible that what looked like the tendency toward an interaction effect in the original experiment may have fallen short because of a lack of power, additional power within the second experiment was especially desirable. In this 2 × 3 factorial experiment there were eight rather than five subjects randomly assigned to each of the six cells for a total of forty-eight subjects.

The Null Hypotheses, Alternative Hypothesis, and Decision Rules for Example 2

The null hypotheses are basically the same as in Example 1. The only difference is that the statements reflect the inclusion of three rather than two skills in the experiment.

1. Factor A: When the learning scores are averaged across all levels of factor B, Teaching Strategy 1 is as effective as Teaching Strategy 2 in teaching three complex skills to Cadet trainees. Symbolically,

$$H_0: \mu_{A_1} = \mu_{A_2}$$

2. Factor B: When the learning scores are averaged across all levels of factor A, there is no difference in the number of trials that it takes the Cadet trainees to learn the three different skills. Symbolically,

$$H_0: \mu_{B_1} = \mu_{B_2} = \mu_{B_3}$$

3. A $\times$ B Interaction: There is no effect on learning within any of the $p \times q$ treatment combinations (cells) that cannot be explained by the effects from factor A and/or factor B acting independently of each other. In other words, with any existing factor A or factor B effects removed, the cell means should be equal. Symbolically,

$$H_0: \mu_{AB_{11}} = \mu_{AB_{12}} = \cdots = \mu_{AB_{23}}$$

As before, the alternative hypothesis may be simply stated as:

$$H_1: \text{not } H_0$$

The decision rules for Example 2 follow the same format outlined for Example 1. The critical values for F that are listed in the F table are

F with $df = (p - 1) / pq(n - 1)$ when factor A is being evaluated,

F with $df = (q - 1) / pq(n - 1)$ when factor B is being evaluated,

F with $df = (p - 1)(q - 1) / pq(n - 1)$ when the A $\times$ B interaction is being evaluated.

For Example 2 the critical values with the level of significance set to .05 are

Factor A (Teaching Strategy): $F(1,42) = 4.07$

(Read "F with one and forty-two degrees of freedom equals 4.07.")

Factor B (Skill): $F(2,42) = 3.22$

A × B Interaction: $F(2,42) = 3.22$

Crunching the Numbers

Here are the solutions to the five computational components for the data of the 2 × 3 factorial experiment shown in table 18.14.

1. $G^2/npq = \dfrac{3{,}184^2}{8 \cdot 2 \cdot 3} = \dfrac{10{,}137{,}856}{48} = 211{,}205.33$

2. $\Sigma\Sigma X_{ij}^2 = 83^2 + 42^2 + \cdots + 69^2 + 64^2 = 223{,}414$

3. $\Sigma A_i^2/nq = \dfrac{1{,}704^2 + 1{,}480^2}{8 \cdot 3} = \dfrac{5{,}094{,}016}{24} = 212{,}250.67$

4. $\Sigma B_j^2/np = \dfrac{832^2 + 1{,}128^2 + 1{,}224^2}{8 \cdot 2} = \dfrac{3{,}462{,}784}{16} = 216{,}424$

5. $\Sigma AB_{ij}^2/n = \dfrac{520^2 + 560^2 + 624^2 + 312^2 + 568^2 + 600^2}{n}$

$$= \frac{1{,}753{,}344}{8} = 219{,}168$$

Substituting as indicated in table 18.12 yields the ANOVA summary table presented in table 18.15. When the computed F ratios are compared to the values listed in the decision rules we see that all the statistical comparisons are significant. Factor A is significant because the computed F value of 11.57 is greater than 4.07. Factor B and the A × B interaction are significant because the computed F ratios of 28.88 and 9.40 are greater than the critical value of 3.22.

Interpreting the ANOVA Results

The table of row, column, and individual cell means from a factorial experiment provides more explicit information regarding the nature of the statistically significant differences revealed in the ANOVA. In Example 2 significant differences were found for factor A, factor B, and the A × B interaction. Using the means shown in table 18.16, an interpretation will be offered for each of these significant results.

Table 18.15

The ANOVA summary for the Example 2 data displayed in table 18.14.

Analysis of Variance Summary Table

Source	*df*	SS	MS	*F*
Between Cell	5	7,962.67		
Strategy (A)	1	1,045.67	1,045.67	11.57
Skill (B)	2	5,218.67	2,609.34	28.88
A × B	2	1,699.33	849.67	9.40
Within cell (Error)	42	4,246.00	90.34	
Total	47	12,208.67		

Table 18.16

The cell means for the Example 2 data presented in table 18.14.

	Type of Skill Being Taught (B)			
Teaching Method (A)	Skill 1	Skill 2	Skill 3	Row Means
Strategy 1	65	70	78	71.00
Strategy 2	39	71	75	61.67
Column Mean:	52.00	70.5	76.50	Grand Mean = 66.33

Factor A. The mean of all the data collected under level one of factor A ($\overline{A}_1 = 71.00$) is higher than the mean for level two of factor A ($\overline{A}_2 = 61.67$). This indicates that Strategy 2 was, on the average, more effective (i.e., required fewer trials) for teaching the skills to the Cadets. This is consistent with the direction of the difference that was obtained in the original 2 × 2 experiment ($\overline{A}_1 = 68$ and $\overline{A}_2 = 56$), but that difference was not significant (see table 18.11).

Factor B. The means for the three levels of factor B are, respectively, 52.0, 70.5, and 76.5. Apparently, Skill 1 is the easiest to learn (i.e., was learned in the fewest trials), followed by Skill 2 and Skill 3. The finding that Skill 1 is relatively easy to learn replicates the sole significant finding in Example 1: Skill 1 was learned more rapidly than Skill 2 ($\overline{B}_1 = 54$ and $\overline{B}_2 = 70$).

A × B Interaction. The interaction that approached significance in Example 1 was significant in the second experiment and inspection of the cell means (table 18.16) reveals the source of this interaction. There were only slight differences in the effectiveness of the strategy variable within level 2 (70 vs. 71) and within level 3 (78 vs. 75) of the skill variable. By comparison, within level 1 of the skill variable, we see that Skill 1 is learned with relative ease if it is taught using Strategy 2 ($\overline{AB}_{21} = 39$) rather than Strategy 1 ($\overline{AB}_{11} = 65$). Apparently, there is something about the combination of Strategy 2 and Skill 1 that results in relatively rapid learning. Moreover, the rapid learning cannot be explained solely by the relative ease with which Skill 1 can be learned, nor the relative superiority of Teaching Strategy 2.

Summary

The rationale of the two-factor ANOVA factorial design was explained in terms of its power to assess the effects of two different independent variables ("factors") within the context of a single analysis. Differences attributable to factors acting alone are called main effects. In addition, the unique effect arising from factors acting together may be assessed in a factorial design. This is called an interaction effect. Various hypothetical patterns of main effects and interactions were presented for the relatively basic 2 × 2 factorial design, followed by an ANOVA of a set of experimental results. The same experimental scenario was extended to a 2 × 3 design, an ANOVA for a data set was computed, and the results were interpreted within the context of the experimental scenario using the table of row, column, and cell means.

Key Terms

Computational Components
Factorial Design
General Rule
Interaction
Main Effects
$\mathbf{MS}_{\text{within cell}}$
Partitioning Total Variation
$\mathbf{SS}_{\text{between cell}}$
$\mathbf{SS}_{\text{within cell}}$
Synergism

Exercises

1. This problem is an exercise in the application of the General Rule for computing the variation (SS) in any set of scores. Nine numbers appear on the next page. In configuration 1 the numbers are a simple set of raw scores. In configuration 2 the numbers represent the raw data for a three treatment single factor ANOVA. In configuration 3 the numbers represent the 9 cell totals of a 3 × 3 factorial design ($n = 4$ subjects per cell).

1: 28, 34, 32, 19, 21, 23, 17, 22, 16

2:

Treat. 1	Treat. 2	Treat. 3
28	19	17
34	21	22
32	23	16

3:

	a_1	a_2	a_3
b_1	$AB_{11} = 28$	$AB_{12} = 19$	$AB_{13} = 17$
b_2	$AB_{21} = 34$	$AB_{22} = 21$	$AB_{23} = 22$
b_3	$AB_{31} = 32$	$AB_{23} = 23$	$AB_{33} = 16$

a. Using configuration 1, find the SS for the set.
b. Using configuration 2, find the SS within each of the three treatments.
c. Using configuration 3, find the $SS_{\text{between cell}}$.

Instructions for Two-Factor ANOVA Exercises

The following experimental scenarios are all randomized groups factorial designs and the data are suitable for analysis using the methods presented in the present chapter. If you choose to do an analysis using a hand calculator to test your understanding of the computational method, you may check the accuracy of your work with TWOWAY.BAS, the two-factor ANOVA program in *Stat/Tutor*. For each problem, state the null hypothesis, alternative hypothesis, and a decision rule (use $\alpha = .05$). Then, after you complete the computations and your ANOVA summary table, offer an interpretation of the results within the context of the problem.

2. A study was done to compare the level of protection afforded by seat belts versus air bags at two different impact speeds (30 mph and 45 mph). A fleet of 28 standard test vehicles was randomly divided into two groups of 14 each. The 14 vehicles in one group were fitted with seat belts and the other 14 were fitted with air bags. Special test mannequins were constructed from materials designed to simulate human skeletal and tissue characteristics, and one mannequin was installed in each vehicle. Half of the vehicles equipped with seat belts and half of the vehicles equipped with air bags were run into a solid wall at 30 miles per hour and the remaining vehicles were run into the wall at 45 miles per hour.

Following each crash test, trauma points (fractures, lacerations, etc.) were identified and counted for each mannequin. The data are summarized in the following table.

Impact Speed	Number of Trauma Points Seat Belt	 Air Bag
30 mph	3	3
	4	0
	3	1
	3	1
	1	4
	3	0
	4	5
45 mph	7	4
	6	7
	9	4
	9	3
	5	3
	8	5
	5	2

3. A metallurgist believed that the addition of Bivanium, a new man-made compound, would increase the tensile strength of a light steel alloy. The metallurgist knew that Bivanium is very slow to dissolve. He anticipated that the alloy would probably require extensive heat treatment before any change in tensile strength would be realized, but the exact treatment temperature and duration of treatment necessary to produce the anticipated effect was unknown. The following experiment was designed in an effort to discover this important information. Forty-five standard bars of Bivanium alloy were randomly selected from the stockroom and were randomly divided into 9 groups of 5 bars each. The bars were subjected to heat treatment according to the experimental design that is presented next. The tensile strength data in the table represent 10,000 lb. equivalents. For example, a score of 14.2 equals 142,000 lbs. of tensile strength.

Length of Heat Treatment	Treatment Temperature (Fahrenheit)		
	1,500	1,550	1,600
60 min	14.3	14.7	14.5
	15.1	14.9	14.5
	14.5	14.3	14.8
	15.2	15.1	14.9
	14.1	14.0	14.3
90 min	14.2	14.5	14.4
	15.1	14.7	14.6
	14.6	14.9	15.4
	14.6	15.2	15.1
	14.4	14.3	14.4
120 min	14.4	15.6	15.1
	14.6	16.2	16.0
	15.4	15.5	15.7
	15.3	15.8	16.4
	14.3	14.9	15.8

4. Laboratory rats were given one of two different preliminary tasks that they had to learn to a predetermined criterion (either 3, 6, or 9 correct responses in a row). Following completion of the preliminary task, all the animals were tested on the same standard task. The data below are the number of correct responses the animals made on the first 30 trials of the standard task.

	Training Trials to Criterion		
	3 Trials	6 Trials	9 Trials
Preliminary Task 1	19	20	17
	9	15	24
	13	17	20
	15	18	22
	9	15	18
Preliminary Task 2	9	10	10
	15	9	6
	10	5	9
	11	10	6
	10	11	9

5. Students at State U. can choose whether or not to live in a coed versus unisex dormitory. Also, half of the coed and half of the unisex dormitories have strictly enforced quiet hours, while the other half of the residence halls are less restrictive. A study was done to examine the students' freshman year academic performance as a function of the living arrangements they chose. According to the grade data below from a random sample of students from each type of living environment, did students living in a certain type of campus housing get better or worse grades than students living in some other type of housing?

	Coed Dormitory	
	Yes	**No**
Quiet Dormitory	3.22	2.64
	2.89	3.19
	3.36	3.20
	2.93	3.60
	3.40	2.22
	2.44	2.75
Normal Dormitory	2.24	2.12
	3.10	2.00
	1.97	1.90
	3.34	2.26
	3.00	2.50
	3.10	2.85

a. Do a two-way ANOVA on the data above and present your conclusions. Use $\alpha = .05$ for all tests.
b. Can we attribute the results to the different environments? What nonenvironmental bias could be affecting the results?

6. Assume the four values 20, 20, 50, and 50 represent four cell means. Form a 2×2 table of cell means using these values that would be indicative of

a. a main effect for factor A,
b. a main effect for factor B,
c. an $A \times B$ interaction

7. Explain the kinship between the concept of synergism and the concept of interaction.

8. Why must one be very cautious in interpreting the absence of main effects in the presence of a significant interaction effect?

9. In a 3 × 4 factorial design, the $SS_{\text{between cell}}$ will have df = ______, the SS_A will have df = ______, the SS_B will have df = ______, and the $SS_{A \times B}$ will have df = ______. If there are 5 scores in each of the 12 cells of the experiment, the SS_{error} will have df = ______ and the SS_{total} will have df = ______.

10. A college instructor taught one very large section and two small sections of the same course. Only students with freshman or sophomore standing were allowed to enroll in the course. The students in both the large and small classes were given the same midterm examination. Ten freshmen and ten sophomores were randomly selected from the roster of the large class, and ten freshmen and ten sophomores were randomly selected from the roster of the smaller class. Their midterm examination scores are presented in the following table.

	Small Class		**Large Class**	
Freshmen	90	84	65	71
	93	85	72	64
	64	75	86	73
	91	83	75	68
	85	81	74	70
Sophomores	84	82	91	72
	76	92	83	78
	91	83	85	81
	85	86	76	90
	80	90	78	82

a. Was there any difference in the performance of the freshmen versus the sophomores?

b. Did the students who attended the large lecture class do any differently on the midterm examination than the students who attended the smaller classes?

c. Was there any interaction between the two variables (factor A = class standing; factor B = class size)?

CHAPTER 19

Using Statistics: What's Next?

This is the last chapter of your introduction to statistics and data analysis, but for you it may be more of a beginning than an end. This is because many students who pursue academic careers in the empirical sciences take introductory level statistics to prepare for the next level of academic training: understanding and doing formal research. In advanced content courses you shall no doubt study many of the original journal articles that make up the research literature of your chosen course of study and your understanding of these original reports will depend in part upon your mastery of statistics. In advanced methods courses your statistical background will also prove valuable as you receive further training in the design, analysis, and interpretation of your very own original research.

This chapter highlights some of the statistical issues you will likely encounter in your research methods courses by means of some practical problem-solving exercises. Instead of focusing on your ability to arrive at a correct numerical answer for a problem, the emphasis will instead be on the considerations that dictate the appropriate statistical approach to the problem. In the first section of the chapter the problems will be presented, then each will be discussed in detail. Before we get to the practice problems, however, I want to tell you about a trip I took many years ago when I lived in Indiana.

"Hoosier Hysteria" . . . and I Don't Mean Basketball!

Most of us enjoy traveling, but sometimes unpleasant scenarios unfold on the road that make us wish we had never left home. One such white-knuckle encounter is the experience of being lost in an unfamiliar maze of on/off ramps, cloverleafs, detours, and intersecting highways. On one ill-fated trip through the Midwest I was headed from Lexington, Kentucky, to Lafayette, Indiana, by way of Indianapolis. Because of confusion arising from highway construction and traffic detours, I missed the exit from I-74 to I-65 and wound up circling Indianapolis on 465. Eventually, I pulled off on a secondary road to find a 'Naptown native who could point me toward Lafayette. My nerves were frazzled by this time and, as I sought help, the last thing I needed or wanted was a comedian, but that is what I got.

"I'm sorry, pal. You can't get there from here."

Perhaps the remark was intended to be humorous, a friendly gesture to lighten the mood, but my reaction showed no sign of amusement. There had to be a way to get back to the I-65 interchange from my present location without going all the way around Indianapolis, construction or no construction. Probably reacting to my stony silence, my Hoosier guide hastily explained that I had passed the designated detour exit for "through traffic" to I-65 and that I could not get back to this exit because the on ramp on the other side of the highway was under construction. I realized that I would either have to circle Indianapolis on the route 465 beltway to get back to the Lafayette exit or figure out a detour around the Highway Department's detour. Too stubborn to do the former, I tried the latter, setting into motion a comedy of errors that, at the height of confusion, seemed amply to justify the pessimistic sentiment behind the "You can't get there from here" remark.

AN INSOLUBLE DILEMMA

In research there is a dilemma similar to the "You can't get there from here" problem that is guaranteed to cause at least as much discomfort and confusion. The dilemma may be stated,

> "You can't test that hypothesis with these data."
> or,
> "The information you seek is not recoverable from these data."

In research, however, instead of being a sarcastic remark or an overstatement of the difficulty one may encounter in solving a research riddle, such a pronouncement may mark a real dead end to an expensive, difficult, and time-consuming experimental effort. Just about every statistically skilled researcher who is routinely asked to help analyze data for statistically unskilled researchers has a collection of horror stories concerning this type of insoluble dilemma.

Usually the reason data turn out to be inadequate or inappropriate for testing experimental hypotheses is a methodological flaw (or flaws) in the design of the experiment. For example, assume you have data showing that animal subjects injected with an experimental drug tend to register behavioral and physiological symptoms of stress following treatment. The absence of a placebo control group (i.e., a group that receives an injection with no active ingredient) would make it impossible to determine how much of the stress response was a reaction to the drug itself and how much was a consequence of the pain and discomfort from the method used to administer the drug. Because of this design flaw, in order to evaluate properly possible side effects of the experimental drug the only recourse is to repeat the study with the appropriate control groups (an untreated control group and a placebo control group)

Learning how to design experiments that permit collecting important information while avoiding methodological flaws that can confuse efforts to interpret data is the subject matter of a research methods course that, in many college curricula, follows a basic statistics course. Although a discussion of the logical principles that govern experimental design is beyond the scope of this text, we can address a somewhat different problem that comes up in research using the statistical skills you already have.

A SOLUBLE DILEMMA

We all know that traveling over well-marked and well-maintained roads in good weather is no guarantee that we will complete a trip without losing our way. This is especially so if the route of the trip is complex. Similarly, just because the methodology that was used for an experiment was well-planned and logically sound, it may be difficult to get the information from the data that is necessary to evaluate the experimental hypothesis. Because of this, the data analysis phase of a research project deserves just as much advanced planning as the experiment itself.

The end of a research project can be a very exciting time. The planning and execution of the experiment are over and you look forward with eager anticipation to viewing the results of your labors. The only task that remains is the analysis and interpretation of the data. If you have planned ahead for your data analysis, this phase of a project is a joy, but if you have not planned ahead you must postpone analysis and interpretation until you can reach a decision on how to process the data. Uncertainty concerning the choice of statistical analysis for experimental data creates unnecessary delays in the research effort. The uncertainty may even suggest that you have failed to develop an adequate understanding of the research problem you are investigating. If you do not plan ahead for this phase of the experiment, perhaps while you are floundering around with your data, a rival researcher will publish the results of a similar experiment and get the recognition for a discovery that could have been yours.

Researchers who do not plan ahead must search for an answer to the following important question:

> "I have my data. Now which test do I use?"

Those who seek an answer to this question may be fortunate enough to find the solution somewhere in the pages of a statistics text, or perhaps a colleague with extensive experience in data analysis will be able to determine the appropriate test for the experimental data. Even though the problems surrounding the choice of statistics for data analysis may have solutions, why live with the uncertainty when planning ahead can prevent it? Remember, researchers who plan ahead for data analysis will never hear a consultant say, "You can't get there from here."

MATCHING STATISTICS TO YOUR DATA

Up to now, as explained earlier in chapter 14, you have been doing statistical analyses on data within a somewhat artificial environment. The chapter exercises at the end of the chi-square chapter are obviously intended to give you practice with the chi-square statistic, the exercises at the end of the analysis of variance chapter are intended to give you practice with the analysis of variance, and so forth. In this chapter you will practice matching statistical analyses to data without the constraints of this artificial environment. No fundamentally new material is presented in this chapter. You simply apply what you have already learned about data analysis and interpretation to the various problems and compare your assessment of the problem to the discussion that follows at the end of the chapter.

In the sets of experimental data that will be presented, we shall assume that the procedures that governed the data collection process were methodologically sound. (We make this assumption because no analysis can lead to meaningful and interpretable experimental results if the experimental design is flawed.) The choice of analysis will be determined by examining the properties of the data and considering the type of information that is to be retrieved from the data. You will, in effect, be working as a statistical consultant and, in this role, will gain experience exercising the same skills that are used for advanced planning of statistical analyses in an actual research setting. Hopefully, by focusing on the considerations that govern the choice of statistical analysis for certain types of data, you will become more sensitive to the issue of advanced planning for the analysis of research results.

Problem 1. A graduate student in Agricultural Science visited farms in six counties across New York State to gather information on the problems that farmers were experiencing. She asked the question, "Of the problems you routinely face producing your crops, which has been the most troublesome for you this growing season: insects, fungus infections, or soil conditions?"

Do the kinds of problems farmers are experiencing depend upon the region of the state in which they are located or do farmers experience these problems in the same proportions in all regions? Here are the data from the survey.

Farmer Survey Responses

County	Insects	Fungi	Soil
Erie	14	8	5
Wayne	18	11	8
Lewis	11	9	11
Chemung	7	4	18
Greene	15	6	12
Saratoga	8	5	21

Problem 1a. In general, was there a tendency for the farmers to experience one problem more than another (insect problems vs. plant fungi vs. soil conditions)?

Problem 2. Ten different varieties of corn seed were for sale at the Farm Supply Store. The farmer could have merely picked the least expensive seed, but he was concerned about the possibility of a poor germination rate. He decided to plant 10 experimental seed beds in the greenhouse containing 50 seeds each to see if there was a significant difference in the germination rate among the 10 brands. Was there a difference?

Brand	Germinated Yes	No
A	41	9
B	45	5
C	39	11
D	46	4
E	32	18
F	39	11
G	40	10
H	48	2
I	38	12
J	43	7

Problem 3. In another experiment with corn seed the purpose was to evaluate the effect of presoaking the seed prior to planting to see if this treatment would give the germination process a head start. One hundred seeds were randomly selected from each of ten different sacks containing the same ten seed varieties that were tested in Problem 2. Fifty of each brand were presoaked prior to planting and the other fifty were planted without presoaking. Each cell in the table is a record of how many of the fifty seeds that were planted produced seedlings within seven days of planting. Did the soaking affect the speed of germination?

Brand	Soaked Yes	No
A	41	9
B	45	5
C	39	11
D	46	4
E	32	18
F	39	11
G	40	10
H	48	2
I	38	12
J	43	7

Problem 4. Prior to being trained as a leader dog for the blind, a puppy is raised to maturity by a family in a typical household. Once an animal is old enough, it is returned to the leader dog program, evaluated for its leader dog potential and, if it passes, formal training begins. In an effort to improve upon the number of dogs that are found to be acceptable, a researcher decided to impose more structure on how the dogs were being raised so she could determine, as a long range goal, the optimum rearing environment for a leader dog.

Three pups from a newly weaned litter were assigned to three families for rearing and each of the three littermates was raised using a different rearing program. One pup was raised using Rearing Program A, one was raised using Rearing Program B, and one was raised using Rearing Program C. This arrangement was replicated with six separate litters, and so eighteen dogs in all (six litters, three dogs per litter) participated in the experiment. At the appropriate age the animals were evaluated for their leader dog potential by means of a screening test. The numbers in the following table represent the number of correct responses the dogs obtained on the 60 trial screening test. Was there any difference in the rearing programs for preparing the dogs to begin leader dog training?

Program A	Program B	Program C
30	26	38
32	31	40
38	33	47
42	35	50
46	36	56
47	39	31

Problem 5. A teaching assistant for the introductory survey course in psychology was teaching discussion sections for two professors. The professors were using different textbooks and each text was supplied with its own test bank. On an experimental basis, the teaching assistant decided to give both sections a quiz using questions from only one test bank. He reasoned that if there was a high correlation between the grade distributions of the two classes, the questions of one test bank could be considered fair for both texts. He would then routinely use the same test questions for both classes and avoid the task of making up separate tests.

The two grade distributions are presented on the next page. Can the teaching assistant correlate the Section 1 and Section 2 data sets to help him decide on the fairness of using the single test bank?

Rank	Section 1	Section 2
1	98	84
2	91	82
3	88	79
4	85	77
5	83	73
6	80	71
7	75	68
8	73	67
9	70	63
10	68	54

Problem 6. Twelve American college students volunteered to take part in what was represented as a taste experiment. Each subject was told that they would be given two small sample cups of vanilla flavored ice cream and that their task would be to rate the quality of each sample on a scale from 1 to 100. In reality, the two cups each subject received contained identical ice cream. On one cup, however, foreign writing (Japanese) was clearly visible, while on the other cup the words "Ice Cream" and "Made in the U.S.A." could be seen. Was the evaluation of the ice cream quality influenced by the domestic versus foreign labeling of the containers? The data appear below.

	Labeling	
Subject	Domestic	Foreign
1	81	70
2	82	80
3	68	75
4	81	75
5	83	70
6	80	65
7	98	90
8	89	85
9	71	76
10	97	80
11	87	75
12	80	90

Discussion of the Practice Problems

Problem 1. The correct analysis to use on these data is the two variable chi-square statistic. If you arrived at this conclusion you no doubt noticed that the scaling of the data are nominal. This is because a farmer's assessment of his most troublesome problem is being measured as a simple tally recorded in one of three categories (insects vs. fungi vs. soil conditions). The frequencies in the 18 cells that make up the 3 × 6 contingency table represent the responses of all 192 farmers who were interviewed.

The other reason for choosing chi-square is because of the question we seek to answer: Does the column variable depend upon the row variable or, specifically, does a farmer's most troublesome problem depend upon where in New York State his farm happens to be located?

In the second part of Problem 1 (Problem 1a) rather than evaluating the dependence/independence of the row and column variables, we are instead concerned with finding whether or not the farmers' responses are uniformly distributed across the three categories. To see if one of the three possible responses is given more frequently than another we must collapse across the six counties and arrive at the following table of frequencies:

Survey Responses

insects	fungi	soil condition
74	43	75

The null hypothesis states that farmers are not experiencing one type of problem more than another. To find if the observed differences in the frequencies among these three categories is significant the chi-square one variable test is appropriate. If there is no preference for one type of response over another the 192 responses should be evenly distributed over the three categories. Thus, the expected value for each cell is $192/3 = 64$. From inspection there does not seem to be as much of a problem with fungi as with the other problem categories and this is in fact what the chi-square analysis shows.

Problem 2. Sometimes students make impulsive decisions regarding the choice of statistical test to use on data. There is a tendency to rely on visual impressions of the data summary table rather than making the extra effort to really understand the data, the experimental procedure that gave rise to the data, and the reason for doing the experiment. If you went by first impressions in giving an answer to Problem 2, you may have regarded these data as suitable for a correlated *t*-test or, perhaps a sign test or Wilcoxon T. There are, after all, two columns of data, each with its own column heading, and this resembles the format for presenting the data of a two group experiment. Also, the fact that the rows are labeled gives the appearance that two separate measures are being taken on each row entity (subject, company, city, neighborhood, etc.), and this is what students are used to seeing in examples of correlated two-group tests. If, however, you gave careful consideration to these data, chances are that you arrived at the correct answer: the chi-square statistic.

As with Problem 1, the data are nominal. A seed either germinates or it doesn't, and the event is tallied in the appropriate column. Each row in the table represents the responses for 50 separate germination/no germination events. The 50 events are tallied separately in the "yes" cells and the "no" cells. Also, as in Problem 1, the question we seek to answer is whether the column variable depends upon the row variable. Specifically, does the event of germination depend upon the brand of seed being used? In other words, is germination in part a function of the brand of seed, or is this event independent of brand? We are *not* interested in determining if more seeds germinate than do not germinate, which, if it were appropriate for these data, is the question the t-test would address.

Problem 3. Just to drive home the last point, Problem 3 presents the exact same data as for Problem 2, but within a different context. For these data each cell is a record of how many out of a potential maximum of 50 seeds germinated, and the data satisfy all the criteria for ratio level measurement. Unlike Problem 2, we *are* interested in evaluating the difference between the column means. The column labels used in this problem refer to different experimental conditions (soaked vs. not soaked) rather than response categories.

If the null hypothesis is true, any difference between the average germination scores of soaked versus nonsoaked seeds is due to chance. It is common for different varieties of seed for a given crop to have different germination rates (e.g., hybrids are sometimes very sensitive to cool and/or moist soil conditions) and it makes sense to design the experiment with the capability to account for individual differences between brands. The correlated groups t-test is the appropriate test for these data.

Problem 4. The evaluation test that was used on the dogs can reasonably be assumed to reflect at least interval level measurement and, because this is a multigroup experiment, the analysis of variance is the statistic of choice. The null hypothesis is that the rearing programs resulted in dogs of equal competence on the screening test, while the alternative hypothesis is that the rearing programs affect the performance capabilities of the dogs.

Perhaps you correctly identified the analysis of variance as the statistic of choice, but did you notice that the experimental design involves correlated groups? The data table as presented with the problem did not label the rows according to litter so as not to make the correlated feature too obvious. The data table with the labels for litters appears below.

Litter	Program A	Program B	Program C
1	30	26	38
2	32	31	40
3	38	33	47
4	42	35	50
5	46	36	56
6	47	39	31

This type of experiment is called a split litter design. To the extent that genetic relationships among siblings and being reared in the same environment (prior to weaning) by the same mother influence the later behavior of siblings, a dog's behavior is a function of its litter or its "family of origin." The correlated nature of the data arising from a litter effect can even be seen from superficial inspection of the data. For example, Litter 5 animals tended to excel in the screening test, but Litter 1 animals had uniformly lower scores than the others.

The amount of the total variation among the scores that can be attributed to the litter variable can be determined using the correlated version of the single factor analysis of variance just as we were able to determine the amount of variation due to individual differences among subjects in some earlier examples (e.g., chapter 16, Exercise Problem 9). Analyze these data with ONEWAY.BAS as a correlated groups design. Then select the option at the end of the program to see the independent groups ANOVA. The advantage to removing the variation due to litter from the estimate of error will become clear. The correlated analysis reveals a significant effect of rearing program upon screening test performance, while the independent groups analysis fails to show a significant effect.

Problem 5. If you saw that a correlation statistic could not possibly be used to relate the performance of the two classes, congratulate yourself on having more savvy than the teaching assistant who actually tried to do this. Since there was no rationale for pairing specific scores in one class with specific scores in the other class, the assistant decided to rank the scores within each class and use this as a basis for pairing. This, of course, insured a near perfect positive correlation and was used by the assistant to provide "overwhelming justification" for using only one test bank.

The proper approach to use in comparing the performance of the two discussion sections on the quiz is to regard "section" as a treatment. Two groups of students take the same test, but one group prepared for the test with Text A while the other prepared using Text B. The null hypothesis is that the performance of the two groups on the test is the same, and the alternative hypothesis is that the performance of the two groups is not the same. The independent groups *t*-test may be used to test this hypothesis. The significant difference between the groups that you will find if you analyze these data with TEETWO.BAS leads to the conclusion that the difference in performance between the groups is significant. Assuming the two sections of students have equivalent academic ability, this result does not support the use of one test bank for quiz questions when two different texts are being used.

Problem 6. This is a rather straightforward two treatment experiment in which each subject generates data for both treatments. If you decided to use the correlated groups *t*-test for these data you were on the right track, but you failed to notice that the data are ordinal. As discussed in chapter 1, subjective evaluations or ratings cannot be defended as interval or ratio level measurement. The Wilcoxon signed ranks test is compatible with ordinal data and is the statistic of choice for the experiment described in Problem 6.

If you have made mistakes in this practice chapter, learn from them and resign yourself to the fact that they are unlikely to be the last mistakes that you make in doing statistics. Even seasoned researchers make mistakes and, if you attend a paper session at a scientific meeting, you may even get to see a researcher twisting in the wind before a roomful of colleagues while being chastised for an inappropriate experimental design or an incorrect approach to data analysis. Sometimes the criticisms are unfounded or reflect a matter of opinion, but at other times the mistakes are real. I always remember the response of one fellow to a particularly scathing criticism that followed the presentation of his research findings. "By gosh you're right! I guess I'll have to do the data analysis over again." The group applauded.

APPENDIX A

Tables

Column A lists the values of the z statistic only for the positive (right) side of the z curve. The z values on the left side are exactly the same except that they are negative in sign.

Column B lists the proportion of area under the curve between the mean of the z statistic ($\bar{z}$ = 0) and the value of z.

Column C lists the proportion of area under the curve that is beyond z, in the tail of the distribution.

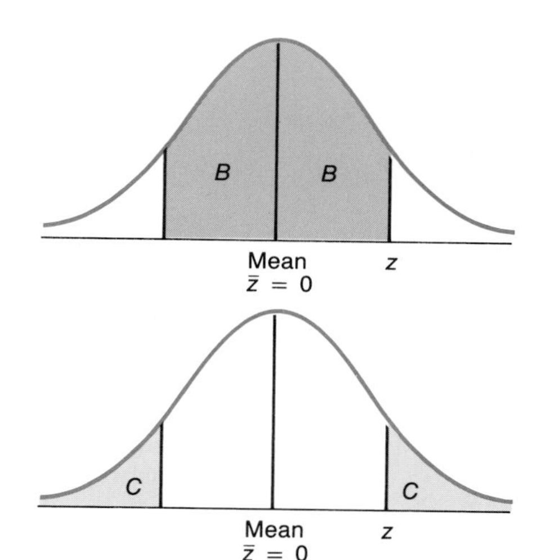

Table A

Normal curve table

z	**Area Between Mean and *z***	**Area Beyond *z***	*z*	**Area Between Mean and *z***	**Area Beyond *z***
A	B	C	A	B	C
0.00	.0000	.5000	0.25	.0987	.4013
0.01	.0040	.4960	0.26	.1026	.3974
0.02	.0080	.4920	0.27	.1064	.3936
0.03	.0120	.4880	0.28	.1103	.3897
0.04	.0160	.4840	0.29	.1141	.3859
0.05	.0199	.4801	0.30	.1179	.3821
0.06	.0239	.4761	0.31	.1217	.3783
0.07	.0279	.4721	0.32	.1255	.3745
0.08	.0319	.4681	0.33	.1293	.3707
0.09	.0359	.4641	0.34	.1331	.3669
0.10	.0398	.4602	0.35	.1368	.3632
0.11	.0438	.4562	0.36	.1406	.3594
0.12	.0478	.4522	0.37	.1443	.3557
0.13	.0517	.4483	0.38	.1480	.3520
0.14	.0557	.4443	0.39	.1517	.3483
0.15	.0596	.4404	0.40	.1554	.3446
0.16	.0636	.4364	0.41	.1591	.3409
0.17	.0675	.4325	0.42	.1628	.3372
0.18	.0714	.4286	0.43	.1664	.3336
0.19	.0753	.4247	0.44	.1700	.3300
0.20	.0793	.4207	0.45	.1736	.3264
0.21	.0832	.4168	0.46	.1772	.3228
0.22	.0871	.4129	0.47	.1808	.3192
0.23	.0910	.4090	0.48	.1844	.3156
0.24	.0948	.4052	0.49	.1879	.3121

Table A
Continued

z	Area Between Mean and z	Area Beyond z	z	Area Between Mean and z	Area Beyond z
A	B	C	A	B	C
0.50	.1915	.3085	0.85	.3023	.1977
0.51	.1950	.3050	0.86	.3051	.1949
0.52	.1985	.3015	0.87	.3078	.1922
0.53	.2019	.2981	0.88	.3106	.1894
0.54	.2054	.2946	0.89	.3133	.1867
0.55	.2088	.2912	0.90	.3159	.1841
0.56	.2123	.2877	0.91	.3186	.1814
0.57	.2157	.2843	0.92	.3212	.1788
0.58	.2190	.2810	0.93	.3238	.1762
0.59	.2224	.2776	0.94	.3264	.1736
0.60	.2257	.2743	0.95	.3289	.1711
0.61	.2291	.2709	0.96	.3315	.1685
0.62	.2324	.2676	0.97	.3340	.1660
0.63	.2357	.2643	0.98	.3365	.1635
0.64	.2389	.2611	0.99	.3389	.1611
0.65	.2422	.2578	1.00	.3413	.1587
0.66	.2454	.2546	1.01	.3438	.1562
0.67	.2486	.2514	1.02	.3461	.1539
0.68	.2517	.2483	1.03	.3485	.1515
0.69	.2549	.2451	1.04	.3508	.1492
0.70	.2580	.2420	1.05	.3531	.1469
0.71	.2611	.2389	1.06	.3554	.1446
0.72	.2642	.2358	1.07	.3577	.1423
0.73	.2673	.2327	1.08	.3599	.1401
0.74	.2704	.2296	1.09	.3621	.1379
0.75	.2734	.2266	1.10	.3643	.1357
0.76	.2764	.2236	1.11	.3665	.1335
0.77	.2794	.2206	1.12	.3686	.1314
0.78	.2823	.2177	1.13	.3708	.1292
0.79	.2852	.2148	1.14	.3729	.1271
0.80	.2881	.2119	1.15	.3749	.1251
0.81	.2910	.2090	1.16	.3770	.1230
0.82	.2939	.2061	1.17	.3790	.1210
0.83	.2967	.2033	1.18	.3810	.1190
0.84	.2995	.2005	1.19	.3830	.1170

Table A
Continued

z	Area Between Mean and z	Area Beyond z	z	Area Between Mean and z	Area Beyond z
A	B	C	A	B	C
1.20	.3849	.1151	1.55	.4394	.0606
1.21	.3869	.1131	1.56	.4406	.0594
1.22	.3888	.1112	1.57	.4418	.0582
1.23	.3907	.1093	1.58	.4429	.0571
1.24	.3925	.1075	1.59	.4441	.0559
1.25	.3944	.1056	1.60	.4452	.0548
1.26	.3962	.1038	1.61	.4463	.0537
1.27	.3980	.1020	1.62	.4474	.0526
1.28	.3997	.1003	1.63	.4484	.0516
1.29	.4015	.0985	1.64	.4495	.0505
1.30	.4032	.0968	1.65	.4505	.0495
1.31	.4049	.0951	1.66	.4515	.0485
1.32	.4066	.0934	1.67	.4525	.0475
1.33	.4082	.0918	1.68	.4535	.0465
1.34	.4099	.0901	1.69	.4545	.0455
1.35	.4115	.0885	1.70	.4554	.0446
1.36	.4131	.0869	1.71	.4564	.0436
1.37	.4147	.0853	1.72	.4573	.0427
1.38	.4162	.0838	1.73	.4582	.0418
1.39	.4177	.0823	1.74	.4591	.0409
1.40	.4192	.0808	1.75	.4599	.0401
1.41	.4207	.0793	1.76	.4608	.0392
1.42	.4222	.0778	1.77	.4616	.0384
1.43	.4236	.0764	1.78	.4625	.0375
1.44	.4251	.0749	1.79	.4633	.0367
1.45	.4265	.0735	1.80	.4641	.0359
1.46	.4279	.0721	1.81	.4649	.0351
1.47	.4292	.0708	1.82	.4656	.0344
1.48	.4306	.0694	1.83	.4664	.0336
1.49	.4319	.0681	1.84	.4671	.0329
1.50	.4332	.0668	1.85	.4678	.0322
1.51	.4345	.0655	1.86	.4686	.0314
1.52	.4357	.0643	1.87	.4693	.0307
1.53	.4370	.0630	1.88	.4699	.0301
1.54	.4382	.0618	1.89	.4706	.0294

Table A
Continued

z	Area Between Mean and z	Area Beyond z	z	Area Between Mean and z	Area Beyond z
A	B	C	A	B	C
1.90	.4713	.0287	2.25	.4878	.0122
1.91	.4719	.0281	2.26	.4881	.0119
1.92	.4726	.0274	2.27	.4884	.0116
1.93	.4732	.0268	2.28	.4887	.0113
1.94	.4738	.0262	2.29	.4890	.0110
1.95	.4744	.0256	2.30	.4893	.0107
1.96	.4750	.0250	2.31	.4896	.0104
1.97	.4756	.0244	2.32	.4898	.0102
1.98	.4761	.0239	2.33	.4901	.0099
1.99	.4767	.0233	2.34	.4904	.0096
2.00	.4772	.0228	2.35	.4906	.0094
2.01	.4778	.0222	2.36	.4909	.0091
2.02	.4783	.0217	2.37	.4911	.0089
2.03	.4788	.0212	2.38	.4913	.0087
2.04	.4793	.0207	2.39	.4916	.0084
2.05	.4798	.0202	2.40	.4918	.0082
2.06	.4803	.0197	2.41	.4920	.0080
2.07	.4808	.0192	2.42	.4922	.0078
2.08	.4812	.0188	2.43	.4925	.0075
2.09	.4817	.0183	2.44	.4927	.0073
2.10	.4821	.0179	2.45	.4929	.0071
2.11	.4826	.0174	2.46	.4931	.0069
2.12	.4830	.0170	2.47	.4932	.0068
2.13	.4834	.0166	2.48	.4934	.0066
2.14	.4838	.0162	2.49	.4936	.0064
2.15	.4842	.0158	2.50	.4938	.0062
2.16	.4846	.0154	2.51	.4940	.0060
2.17	.4850	.0150	2.52	.4941	.0059
2.18	.4854	.0146	2.53	.4943	.0057
2.19	.4857	.0143	2.54	.4945	.0055
2.20	.4861	.0139	2.55	.4946	.0054
2.21	.4864	.0136	2.56	.4948	.0052
2.22	.4868	.0132	2.57	.4949	.0051
2.23	.4871	.0129	2.58	.4951	.0049
2.24	.4875	.0125	2.59	.4952	.0048

Table A
Continued

z	Area Between Mean and z	Area Beyond z	z	Area Between Mean and z	Area Beyond z
A	B	C	A	B	C
2.60	.4953	.0047	2.95	.4984	.0016
2.61	.4955	.0045	2.96	.4985	.0015
2.62	.4956	.0044	2.97	.4985	.0015
2.63	.4957	.0043	2.98	.4986	.0014
2.64	.4959	.0041	2.99	.4986	.0014
2.65	.4960	.0040	3.00	.4987	.0013
2.66	.4961	.0039	3.01	.4987	.0013
2.67	.4962	.0038	3.02	.4987	.0013
2.68	.4963	.0037	3.03	.4988	.0012
2.69	.4964	.0036	3.04	.4988	.0012
2.70	.4965	.0035	3.05	.4989	.0011
2.71	.4966	.0034	3.06	.4989	.0011
2.72	.4967	.0033	3.07	.4989	.0011
2.73	.4968	.0032	3.08	.4990	.0010
2.74	.4969	.0031	3.09	.4990	.0010
2.75	.4970	.0030	3.10	.4990	.0010
2.76	.4971	.0029	3.11	.4991	.0009
2.77	.4972	.0028	3.12	.4991	.0009
2.78	.4973	.0027	3.13	.4991	.0009
2.79	.4974	.0026	3.14	.4992	.0008
2.80	.4974	.0026	3.15	.4992	.0008
2.81	.4975	.0025	3.16	.4992	.0008
2.82	.4976	.0024	3.17	.4992	.0008
2.83	.4977	.0023	3.18	.4993	.0007
2.84	.4977	.0023	3.19	.4993	.0007
2.85	.4978	.0022	3.20	.4993	.0007
2.86	.4979	.0021	3.21	.4993	.0007
2.87	.4979	.0021	3.22	.4994	.0006
2.88	.4980	.0020	3.23	.4994	.0006
2.89	.4981	.0019	3.24	.4994	.0006
2.90	.4981	.0019	3.30	.4995	.0005
2.91	.4982	.0018	3.40	.4997	.0003
2.92	.4982	.0018	3.50	.4998	.0002
2.93	.4983	.0017	3.60	.4998	.0002
2.94	.4984	.0016	3.70	.4999	.0001

Table B
Binomial distribution

N	No. of *P* or *Q* Events	*P* or *Q*									
		.05	.10	.15	.20	.25	.30	.35	.40	.45	.50
1	0	.9500	.9000	.8500	.8000	.7500	.7000	.6500	.6000	.5500	.5000
	1	.0500	.1000	.1500	.2000	.2500	.3000	.3500	.4000	.4500	.5000
2	0	.9025	.8100	.7225	.6400	.5625	.4900	.4225	.3600	.3025	.2500
	1	.0950	.1800	.2550	.3200	.3750	.4200	.4550	.4800	.4950	.5000
	2	.0025	.0100	.0225	.0400	.0625	.0900	.1225	.1600	.2025	.2500
3	0	.8574	.7290	.6141	.5120	.4219	.3430	.2746	.2160	.1664	.1250
	1	.1354	.2430	.3251	.3840	.4219	.4410	.4436	.4320	.4084	.3750
	2	.0071	.0270	.0574	.0960	.1406	.1890	.2389	.2880	.3341	.3750
	3	.0001	.0010	.0034	.0080	.0156	.0270	.0429	.0640	.0911	.1250
4	0	.8145	.6561	.5220	.4096	.3164	.2401	.1785	.1296	.0915	.0625
	1	.1715	.2916	.3685	.4096	.4219	.4116	.3845	.3456	.2995	.2500
	2	.0135	.0486	.0975	.1536	.2109	.2646	.3105	.3456	.3675	.3750
	3	.0005	.0036	.0115	.0256	.0469	.0756	.1115	.1536	.2005	.2500
	4	.0000	.0001	.0005	.0016	.0039	.0081	.0150	.0256	.0410	.0625
5	0	.7738	.5905	.4437	.3277	.2373	.1681	.1160	.0778	.0503	.0312
	1	.2036	.3280	.3915	.4096	.3955	.3602	.3124	.2592	.2059	.1562
	2	.0214	.0729	.1382	.2048	.2637	.3087	.3364	.3456	.3369	.3125
	3	.0011	.0081	.0244	.0512	.0879	.1323	.1811	.2304	.2757	.3125
	4	.0000	.0004	.0022	.0064	.0146	.0284	.0488	.0768	.1128	.1562
	5	.0000	.0000	.0001	.0003	.0010	.0024	.0053	.0102	.0185	.0312
6	0	.7351	.5314	.3771	.2621	.1780	.1176	.0754	.0467	.0277	.0156
	1	.2321	.3543	.3993	.3932	.3560	.3025	.2437	.1866	.1359	.0938
	2	.0305	.0984	.1762	.2458	.2966	.3241	.3280	.3110	.2780	.2344
	3	.0021	.0146	.0415	.0819	.1318	.1852	.2355	.2765	.3032	.3125
	4	.0001	.0012	.0055	.0154	.0330	.0595	.0951	.1382	.1861	.2344
	5	.0000	.0001	.0004	.0015	.0044	.0102	.0205	.0369	.0609	.0938
	6	.0000	.0000	.0000	.0001	.0002	.0007	.0018	.0041	.0083	.0156
7	0	.6983	.4783	.3206	.2097	.1335	.0824	.0490	.0280	.0152	.0078
	1	.2573	.3720	.3960	.3670	.3115	.2471	.1848	.1306	.0872	.0547
	2	.0406	.1240	.2097	.2753	.3115	.3177	.2985	.2613	.2140	.1641
	3	.0036	.0230	.0617	.1147	.1730	.2269	.2679	.2903	.2918	.2734
	4	.0002	.0026	.0109	.0287	.0577	.0972	.1442	.1935	.2388	.2734
	5	.0000	.0002	.0012	.0043	.0115	.0250	.0466	.0774	.1172	.1641
	6	.0000	.0000	.0001	.0004	.0013	.0036	.0084	.0172	.0320	.0547
	7	.0000	.0000	.0000	.0000	.0001	.0002	.0006	.0016	.0037	.0078
8	0	.6634	.4305	.2725	.1678	.1001	.0576	.0319	.0168	.0084	.0039
	1	.2793	.3826	.3847	.3355	.2670	.1977	.1373	.0896	.0548	.0312
	2	.0515	.1488	.2376	.2936	.3115	.2965	.2587	.2090	.1569	.1094
	3	.0054	.0331	.0839	.1468	.2076	.2541	.2786	.2787	.2568	.2188
	4	.0004	.0046	.0185	.0459	.0865	.1361	.1875	.2322	.2627	.2734

Table B

Continued

N	No. of *P* or *Q* Events	.05	.10	.15	.20	.25	.30	.35	.40	.45	.50
		P or *Q*									
	5	.0000	.0004	.0026	.0092	.0231	.0467	.0808	.1239	.1719	.2188
	6	.0000	.0000	.0002	.0011	.0038	.0100	.0217	.0413	.0703	.1094
	7	.0000	.0000	.0000	.0001	.0004	.0012	.0033	.0079	.0164	.0312
	8	.0000	.0000	.0000	.0000	.0000	.0001	.0002	.0007	.0017	.0039
9	0	.6302	.3874	.2316	.1342	.0751	.0404	.0277	.0101	.0046	.0020
	1	.2985	.3874	.3679	.3020	.2253	.1556	.1004	.0605	.0339	.0176
	2	.0629	.1722	.2597	.3020	.3003	.2668	.2162	.1612	.1110	.0703
	3	.0077	.0446	.1069	.1762	.2336	.2668	.2716	.2508	.2119	.1641
	4	.0006	.0074	.0283	.0661	.1168	.1715	.2194	.2508	.2600	.2461
	5	.0000	.0008	.0050	.0165	.0389	.0735	.1181	.1672	.2128	.2461
	6	.0000	.0001	.0006	.0028	.0087	.0210	.0424	.0743	.1160	.1641
	7	.0000	.0000	.0000	.0003	.0012	.0039	.0098	.0212	.0407	.0703
	8	.0000	.0000	.0000	.0000	.0001	.0004	.0013	.0035	.0083	.0176
	9	.0000	.0000	.0000	.0000	.0000	.0000	.0001	.0003	.0008	.0020
10	0	.5987	.3487	.1969	.1074	.0563	.0282	.0135	.0060	.0025	.0010
	1	.3151	.3874	.3474	.2684	.1877	.1211	.0725	.0403	.0207	.0098
	2	.0746	.1937	.2759	.3020	.2816	.2335	.1757	.1209	.0763	.0439
	3	.0105	.0574	.1298	.2013	.2503	.2668	.2522	.2150	.1665	.1172
	4	.0010	.0112	.0401	.0881	.1460	.2001	.2377	.2508	.2384	.2051
	5	.0001	.0015	.0085	.0264	.0584	.1029	.1536	.2007	.2340	.2461
	6	.0000	.0001	.0012	.0055	.0162	.0368	.0689	.1115	.1596	.2051
	7	.0000	.0000	.0001	.0008	.0031	.0090	.0212	.0425	.0746	.1172
	8	.0000	.0000	.0000	.0001	.0004	.0014	.0043	.0106	.0229	.0439
	9	.0000	.0000	.0000	.0000	.0000	.0001	.0005	.0016	.0042	.0098
	10	.0000	.0000	.0000	.0000	.0000	.0000	.0000	.0001	.0003	.0010
11	0	.5688	.3138	.1673	.0859	.0422	.0198	.0088	.0036	.0014	.0005
	1	.3293	.3835	.3248	.2362	.1549	.0932	.0518	.0266	.0125	.0054
	2	.0867	.2131	.2866	.2953	.2581	.1998	.1395	.0887	.0513	.0269
	3	.0137	.0710	.1517	.2215	.2581	.2568	.2254	.1774	.1259	.0806
	4	.0014	.0158	.0536	.1107	.1721	.2201	.2428	.2365	.2060	.1611
	5	.0001	.0025	.0132	.0388	.0803	.1231	.1830	.2207	.2360	.2256
	6	.0000	.0003	.0023	.0097	.0268	.0566	.0985	.1471	.1931	.2256
	7	.0000	.0000	.0003	.0017	.0064	.0173	.0379	.0701	.1128	.1611
	8	.0000	.0000	.0000	.0002	.0011	.0037	.0102	.0234	.0462	.0806
	9	.0000	.0000	.0000	.0000	.0001	.0005	.0018	.0052	.0126	.0269
	10	.0000	.0000	.0000	.0000	.0000	.0000	.0002	.0007	.0021	.0054
	11	.0000	.0000	.0000	.0000	.0000	.0000	.0000	.0000	.0002	.0005

Table B
Continued

N	No. of P or Q Events	.05	.10	.15	.20	.25	.30	.35	.40	.45	.50
		P* or *Q									
12	**0**	.5404	.2824	.1422	.0687	.0317	.0138	.0057	.0022	.0008	.0002
	1	.3413	.3766	.3012	.2062	.1267	.0712	.0368	.0174	.0075	.0029
	2	.0988	.2301	.2924	.2835	.2323	.1678	.1088	.0639	.0339	.0161
	3	.0173	.0852	.1720	.2362	.2581	.2397	.1954	.1419	.0923	.0537
	4	.0021	.0213	.0683	.1329	.1936	.2311	.2367	.2128	.1700	.1208
	5	.0002	.0038	.0193	.0532	.1032	.1585	.2039	.2270	.2225	.1934
	6	.0000	.0005	.0040	.0155	.0401	.0792	.1281	.1766	.2124	.2256
	7	.0000	.0000	.0006	.0033	.0115	.0291	.0591	.1009	.1489	.1934
	8	.0000	.0000	.0001	.0005	.0024	.0078	.0199	.0420	.0762	.1208
	9	.0000	.0000	.0000	.0001	.0004	.0015	.0048	.0125	.0277	.0537
	10	.0000	.0000	.0000	.0000	.0000	.0002	.0008	.0025	.0068	.0161
	11	.0000	.0000	.0000	.0000	.0000	.0000	.0001	.0003	.0010	.0029
	12	.0000	.0000	.0000	.0000	.0000	.0000	.0000	.0000	.0001	.0002
13	**0**	.5133	.2542	.1209	.0550	.0238	.0097	.0037	.0013	.0004	.0001
	1	.3512	.3672	.2774	.1787	.1029	.0540	.0259	.0113	.0045	.0016
	2	.1109	.2448	.2937	.2680	.2059	.1388	.0836	.0453	.0220	.0095
	3	.0214	.0997	.1900	.2457	.2517	.2181	.1651	.1107	.0660	.0349
	4	.0028	.0277	.0838	.1535	.2097	.2337	.2222	.1845	.1350	.0873
	5	.0003	.0055	.0266	.0691	.1258	.1803	.2154	.2214	.1989	.1571
	6	.0000	.0008	.0063	.0230	.0559	.1030	.1546	.1968	.2169	.2095
	7	.0000	.0001	.0011	.0058	.0186	.0442	.0833	.1312	.1775	.2095
	8	.0000	.0000	.0001	.0011	.0047	.0142	.0336	.0656	.1089	.1571
	9	.0000	.0000	.0000	.0001	.0009	.0034	.0101	.0243	.0495	.0873
	10	.0000	.0000	.0000	.0000	.0001	.0006	.0022	.0065	.0162	.0349
	11	.0000	.0000	.0000	.0000	.0000	.0001	.0003	.0012	.0036	.0095
	12	.0000	.0000	.0000	.0000	.0000	.0000	.0000	.0001	.0005	.0016
	13	.0000	.0000	.0000	.0000	.0000	.0000	.0000	.0000	.0000	.0001
14	**0**	.4877	.2288	.1028	.0440	.0178	.0068	.0024	.0008	.0002	.0001
	1	.3593	.3559	.2539	.1539	.0832	.0407	.0181	.0073	.0027	.0009
	2	.1229	.2570	.2912	.2501	.1802	.1134	.0634	.0317	.0141	.0056
	3	.0259	.1142	.2056	.2501	.2402	.1943	.1366	.0845	.0462	.0222
	4	.0037	.0349	.0998	.1720	.2202	.2290	.2022	.1549	.1040	.0611
	5	.0004	.0078	.0352	.0860	.1468	.1963	.2178	.2066	.1701	.1222
	6	.0000	.0013	.0093	.0322	.0734	.1262	.1759	.2066	.2088	.1833
	7	.0000	.0002	.0019	.0092	.0280	.0618	.1082	.1574	.1952	.2095
	8	.0000	.0000	.0003	.0020	.0082	.0232	.0510	.0918	.1398	.1833
	9	.0000	.0000	.0000	.0003	.0018	.0066	.0183	.0408	.0762	.1222

Table B
Continued

N	No. of P or Q Events	.05	.10	.15	.20	.25	.30	.35	.40	.45	.50
						P or Q					
	10	.0000	.0000	.0000	.0000	.0003	.0014	.0049	.0136	.0312	.0611
	11	.0000	.0000	.0000	.0000	.0000	.0002	.0010	.0033	.0093	.0222
	12	.0000	.0000	.0000	.0000	.0000	.0000	.0001	.0005	.0019	.0056
	13	.0000	.0000	.0000	.0000	.0000	.0000	.0000	.0001	.0002	.0009
	14	.0000	.0000	.000	.0000	.0000	.0000	.0000	.0000	.0000	.0001
15	0	.4633	.2059	.0874	.0352	.0134	.0047	.0016	.0005	.0001	.0000
	1	.3658	.3432	.2312	.1319	.0668	.0305	.0126	.0047	.0016	.0005
	2	.1348	.2669	.2856	.2309	.1559	.0916	.0476	.0219	.0090	.0032
	3	.0307	.1285	.2184	.2501	.2252	.1700	.1110	.0634	.0318	.0139
	4	.0049	.0428	.1156	.1876	.2252	.2186	.1792	.1268	.0780	.0417
	5	.0006	.0105	.0449	.1032	.1651	.2061	.2123	.1859	.1404	.0916
	6	.0000	.0019	.0132	.0430	.0917	.1472	.1906	.2066	.1914	.1527
	7	.0000	.0003	.0030	.0138	.0393	.0811	.1319	.1771	.2013	.1964
	8	.0000	.0000	.0005	.0035	.0131	.0348	.0710	.1181	.1647	.1964
	9	.0000	.0000	.0001	.0007	.0034	.0116	.0298	.0612	.1048	.1527
	10	.0000	.0000	.0000	.0001	.0007	.0030	.0096	.0245	.0515	.0916
	11	.0000	.0000	.0000	.0000	.0001	.0006	.0024	.0074	.0191	.0417
	12	.0000	.0000	.0000	.0000	.0000	.0001	.0004	.0016	.0052	.0139
	13	.0000	.0000	.0000	.0000	.0000	.0000	.0001	.0003	.0010	.0032
	14	.0000	.0000	.0000	.0000	.0000	.0000	.0000	.0000	.0001	.0005
	15	.0000	.0000	.0000	.0000	.0000	.0000	.0000	.0000	.0000	.0000
16	0	.4401	.1853	.0743	.0281	.0100	.0033	.0010	.0003	.0001	.0000
	1	.3706	.3294	.2097	.1126	.0535	.0228	.0087	.0030	.0009	.0002
	2	.1463	.2745	.2775	.2111	.1336	.0732	.0353	.0150	.0056	.0018
	3	.0359	.1423	.2285	.2463	.2079	.1465	.0888	.0468	.0215	.0085
	4	.0061	.0514	.1311	.2001	.2252	.2040	.1553	.1014	.0572	.0278
	5	.0008	.0137	.0555	.1201	.1802	.2099	.2008	.1623	.1123	.0667
	6	.0001	.0028	.0180	.0550	.1101	.1649	.1982	.1983	.1684	.1222
	7	.0000	.0004	.0045	.0197	.0524	.1010	.1524	.1889	.1969	.1746
	8	.0000	.0001	.0009	.0055	.0197	.0487	.0923	.1417	.1812	.1964
	9	.0000	.0000	.0001	.0012	.0058	.0185	.0442	.0840	.1318	.1746
	10	.0000	.0000	.0000	.0002	.0014	.0056	.0167	.0392	.0755	.1222
	11	.0000	.0000	.0000	.0000	.0002	.0013	.0049	.0142	.0337	.0667
	12	.0000	.0000	.0000	.0000	.0000	.0002	.0011	.0040	.0115	.0278
	13	.0000	.0000	.0000	.0000	.0000	.0000	.0002	.0008	.0029	.0085
	14	.0000	.0000	.0000	.0000	.0000	.0000	.0000	.0001	.0005	.0018
	15	.0000	.0000	.0000	.0000	.0000	.0000	.0000	.0000	.0001	.0002
	16	.0000	.0000	.0000	.0000	.0000	.0000	.0000	.0000	.0000	.0000

Table B
Continued

N	No. of P or Q Events	.05	.10	.15	.20	.25	.30	.35	.40	.45	.50
						P or Q					
17	0	.4181	.1668	.0631	.0225	.0075	.0023	.0007	.0002	.0000	.0000
	1	.3741	.3150	.1893	.0957	.0426	.0169	.0060	.0019	.0005	.0001
	2	.1575	.2800	.2673	.1914	.1136	.0581	.0260	.0102	.0035	.0010
	3	.0415	.1556	.2359	.2393	.1893	.1245	.0701	.0341	.0144	.0052
	4	.0076	.0605	.1457	.2093	.2209	.1868	.1320	.0796	.0411	.0182
	5	.0010	.0175	.0668	.1361	.1914	.2081	.1849	.1379	.0875	.0472
	6	.0001	.0039	.0236	.0680	.1276	.1784	.1991	.1839	.1432	.0944
	7	.0000	.0007	.0065	.0267	.0668	.1201	.1685	.1927	.1841	.1484
	8	.0000	.0001	.0014	.0084	.0279	.0644	.1143	.1606	.1883	.1855
	9	.0000	.0000	.0003	.0021	.0093	.0276	.0611	.1070	.1540	.1855
	10	.0000	.0000	.0000	.0004	.0025	.0095	.0263	.0571	.1008	.1484
	11	.0000	.0000	.0000	.0001	.0005	.0026	.0090	.0242	.0525	.0944
	12	.0000	.0000	.0000	.0000	.0001	.0006	.0024	.0081	.0215	.0472
	13	.0000	.0000	.0000	.0000	.0000	.0001	.0005	.0021	.0068	.0182
	14	.0000	.0000	.0000	.0000	.0000	.0000	.0001	.0004	.0016	.0052
	15	.0000	.0000	.0000	.0000	.0000	.0000	.0000	.0001	.0003	.0010
	16	.0000	.0000	.0000	.0000	.0000	.0000	.0000	.0000	.0000	.0001
	17	.0000	.0000	.0000	.0000	.0000	.0000	.0000	.0000	.0000	.0000
18	0	.3972	.1501	.0536	.0180	.0056	.0016	.0004	.0001	.0000	.0000
	1	.3763	.3002	.1704	.0811	.0338	.0126	.0042	.0012	.0003	.0001
	2	.1683	.2835	.2556	.1723	.0958	.0458	.0190	.0069	.0022	.0006
	3	.0473	.1680	.2406	.2297	.1704	.1046	.0547	.0246	.0095	.0031
	4	.0093	.0700	.1592	.2153	.2130	.1681	.1104	.0614	.0291	.0117
	5	.0014	.0218	.0787	.1507	.1988	.2017	.1664	.1146	.0666	.0327
	6	.0002	.0052	.0310	.0816	.1436	.1873	.1941	.1655	.1181	.0708
	7	.0000	.0010	.0091	.0350	.0820	.1376	.1792	.1892	.1657	.1214
	8	.0000	.0002	.0022	.0120	.0376	.0811	.1327	.1734	.1864	.1669
	9	.0000	.0000	.0004	.0033	.0139	.0386	.0794	.1284	.1694	.1855
	10	.0000	.0000	.0001	.0008	.0042	.0149	.0385	.0771	.1248	.1669
	11	.0000	.0000	.0000	.0001	.0010	.0046	.0151	.0374	.0742	.1214
	12	.0000	.0000	.0000	.0000	.0002	.0012	.0047	.0145	.0354	.0708
	13	.0000	.0000	.0000	.0000	.0000	.0002	.0012	.0045	.0134	.0327
	14	.0000	.0000	.0000	.0000	.0000	.0000	.0002	.0011	.0039	.0117
	15	.0000	.0000	.0000	.0000	.0000	.0000	.0000	.0002	.0009	.0031
	16	.0000	.0000	.0000	.0000	.0000	.0000	.0000	.0000	.0001	.0006
	17	.0000	.0000	.0000	.0000	.0000	.0000	.0000	.0000	.0000	.0001
	18	.0000	.0000	.0000	.0000	.0000	.0000	.0000	.0000	.0000	.0000

Table B

Continued

N	No. of P or Q Events	.05	.10	.15	.20	.25	.30	.35	.40	.45	.50
						P or Q					
19	0	.3774	.1351	.0456	.0144	.0042	.0011	.0003	.0001	.0000	.0000
	1	.3774	.2852	.1529	.0685	.0268	.0093	.0029	.0008	.0002	.0000
	2	.1787	.2852	.2428	.1540	.0803	.0358	.0138	.0046	.0013	.0003
	3	.0533	.1796	.2428	.2182	.1517	.0869	.0422	.0175	.0062	.0018
	4	.0112	.0798	.1714	.2182	.2023	.1491	.0909	.0467	.0203	.0074
	5	.0018	.0266	.0907	.1636	.2023	.1916	.1468	.0933	.0497	.0222
	6	.0002	.0069	.0374	.0955	.1574	.1916	.1844	.1451	.0949	.0518
	7	.0000	.0014	.0122	.0443	.0974	.1525	.1844	.1797	.1443	.0961
	8	.0000	.0002	.0032	.0166	.0487	.0981	.1489	.1797	.1771	.1442
	9	.0000	.0000	.0007	.0051	.0198	.0514	.0980	.1464	.1771	.1762
	10	.0000	.0000	.0001	.0013	.0066	.0220	.0528	.0976	.1449	.1762
	11	.0000	.0000	.0000	.0003	.0018	.0077	.0233	.0532	.0970	.1442
	12	.0000	.0000	.0000	.0000	.0004	.0022	.0083	.0237	.0529	.0961
	13	.0000	.0000	.0000	.0000	.0001	.0005	.0024	.0085	.0233	.0518
	14	.0000	.0000	.0000	.0000	.0000	.0001	.0006	.0024	.0082	.0222
	15	.0000	.0000	.0000	.0000	.0000	.0000	.0001	.0005	.0022	.0074
	16	.0000	.0000	.0000	.0000	.0000	.0000	.0000	.0001	.0005	.0018
	17	.0000	.0000	.0000	.0000	.0000	.0000	.0000	.0000	.0001	.0003
	18	.0000	.0000	.0000	.0000	.0000	.0000	.0000	.0000	.0000	.0000
	19	.0000	.0000	.0000	.0000	.0000	.0000	.0000	.0000	.0000	.0000
20	0	.3585	.1216	.0388	.0115	.0032	.0008	.0002	.0000	.0000	.0000
	1	.3774	.2702	.1368	.0576	.0211	.0068	.0020	.0005	.0001	.0000
	2	.1887	.2852	.2293	.1369	.0669	.0278	.0100	.0031	.0008	.0002
	3	.0596	.1901	.2428	.2054	.1339	.0716	.0323	.0123	.0040	.0011
	4	.0133	.0898	.1821	.2182	.1897	.1304	.0738	.0350	.0139	.0046
	5	.0022	.0319	.1028	.1746	.2023	.1789	.1272	.0746	.0365	.0148
	6	.0003	.0089	.0454	.1091	.1686	.1916	.1712	.1244	.0746	.0370
	7	.0000	.0020	.0160	.0545	.1124	.1643	.1844	.1659	.1221	.0739
	8	.0000	.0004	.0046	.0222	.0609	.1144	.1614	.1797	.1623	.1201
	9	.0000	.0001	.0011	.0074	.0271	.0654	.1158	.1597	.1771	.1602
	10	.0000	.0000	.0002	.0020	.0099	.0308	.0686	.1171	.1593	.1762
	11	.0000	.0000	.0000	.0005	.0030	.0120	.0336	.0710	.1185	.1602
	12	.0000	.0000	.0000	.0001	.0008	.0039	.0136	.0355	.0727	.1201
	13	.0000	.0000	.0000	.0000	.0002	.0010	.0045	.0146	.0366	.0739
	14	.0000	.0000	.0000	.0000	.0000	.0002	.0012	.0049	.0150	.0370
	15	.0000	.0000	.0000	.0000	.0000	.0000	.0003	.0013	.0049	.0148
	16	.0000	.0000	.0000	.0000	.0000	.0000	.0000	.0003	.0013	.0046
	17	.0000	.0000	.0000	.0000	.0000	.0000	.0000	.0000	.0002	.0011
	18	.0000	.0000	.0000	.0000	.0000	.0000	.0000	.0000	.0000	.0002
	19	.0000	.0000	.0000	.0000	.0000	.0000	.0000	.0000	.0000	.0000
	20	.0000	.0000	.0000	.0000	.0000	.0000	.0000	.0000	.0000	.0000

Table C

Critical values of Student's t distribution

'Table C is taken from Table III of Fisher & Yates': *Statistical Tables for Biological, Agricultural and Medical Research,* published by Longman Group UK Ltd. London (previously published by Oliver and Boyd Ltd, Edinburgh), and by permission of the authors and publishers.

The values listed in the table are the critical values of t for the specified degrees of freedom (left column) and the alpha level (column heading). For two-tailed alpha levels, t_{crit} is both + and −. To be significant, $|t_{obt}| \geq |t_{crit}|$.

df	Level of Significance for One-Tailed Test					
	.10	.05	.025	.01	.005	.0005
	Level of Significance for Two-Tailed Test					
	.20	.10	.05	.02	.01	.001
1	3.078	6.314	12.706	31.821	63.657	636.619
2	1.886	2.920	4.303	6.965	9.925	31.598
3	1.638	2.353	3.182	4.541	5.841	12.941
4	1.533	2.132	2.776	3.747	4.604	8.610
5	1.476	2.015	2.571	3.365	4.032	6.859
6	1.440	1.943	2.447	3.143	3.707	5.959
7	1.415	1.895	2.365	2.998	3.499	5.405
8	1.397	1.860	2.306	2.896	3.355	5.041
9	1.383	1.833	2.262	2.821	3.250	4.781
10	1.372	1.812	2.228	2.764	3.169	4.587
11	1.363	1.796	2.201	2.718	3.106	4.437
12	1.356	1.782	2.179	2.681	3.055	4.318
13	1.350	1.771	2.160	2.650	3.012	4.221
14	1.345	1.761	2.145	2.624	2.977	4.140
15	1.341	1.753	2.131	2.602	2.947	4.073
16	1.337	1.746	2.120	2.583	2.921	4.015
17	1.333	1.740	2.110	2.567	2.898	3.965
18	1.330	1.734	2.101	2.552	2.878	3.922
19	1.328	1.729	2.093	2.539	2.861	3.883
20	1.325	1.725	2.086	2.528	2.845	3.850
21	1.323	1.721	2.080	2.518	2.831	3.819
22	1.321	1.717	2.074	2.508	2.819	3.792
23	1.319	1.714	2.069	2.500	2.807	3.767
24	1.318	1.711	2.064	2.492	2.797	3.745
25	1.316	1.708	2.060	2.485	2.787	3.725
26	1.315	1.706	2.056	2.479	2.779	3.707
27	1.314	1.703	2.052	2.473	2.771	3.690
28	1.313	1.701	2.048	2.467	2.763	3.674
29	1.311	1.699	2.045	2.462	2.756	3.659
30	1.310	1.697	2.042	2.457	2.750	3.646
40	1.303	1.684	2.021	2.423	2.704	3.551
60	1.296	1.671	2.000	2.390	2.660	3.460
120	1.289	1.658	1.980	2.358	2.617	3.373
∞	1.282	1.645	1.960	2.326	2.576	3.291

'I am grateful to the Literary Executor of the late Sir Ronald A. Fisher, F.R.S. to Dr. Frank Yates, F.R.S. and the Longman Group Ltd, London for permission to reprint Tables III and VI from their book *Statistical Tables for Biological, Agricultural and Medical Research* (6th Edition 1974).'

Table D

Critical values of the Pearson r

	Level of Significance for One-Tailed Test			
	.05	.025	.01	.005
	Level of Significance for Two-Tailed Test			
$df = n - 2$*	.10	.05	.02	.01
1	.9877	.9969	.9995	.9999
2	.9000	.9500	.9800	.9900
3	.8054	.8783	.9343	.9587
4	.7293	.8114	.8822	.9172
5	.6694	.7545	.8329	.8745
6	.6215	.7067	.7887	.8343
7	.5822	.6664	.7498	.7977
8	.5494	.6319	.7155	.7646
9	.5214	.6021	.6851	.7348
10	.4973	.5760	.6581	.7079
11	.4762	.5529	.6339	.6835
12	.4575	.5324	.6120	.6614
13	.4409	.5139	.5923	.6411
14	.4259	.4973	.5742	.6226
15	.4124	.4821	.5577	.6055
16	.4000	.4683	.5425	.5897
17	.3887	.4555	.5285	.5751
18	.3783	.4438	.5155	.5614
19	.3687	.4329	.5034	.5487
20	.3598	.4227	.4921	.5368
25	.3233	.3809	.4451	.4869
30	.2960	.3494	.4093	.4487
35	.2746	.3246	.3810	.4182
40	.2573	.3044	.3578	.3932
45	.2428	.2875	.3384	.3721
50	.2306	.2732	.3218	.3541
60	.2108	.2500	.2948	.3248
70	.1954	.2319	.2737	.3017
80	.1829	.2172	.2565	.2830
90	.1726	.2050	.2422	.2673
100	.1638	.1946	.2301	.2540

*n = number of pairs

'Table D is taken from Table VI of Fisher & Yates': *Statistical Tables for Biological, Agricultural and Medical Research*, published by Longman Group UK Ltd. London (previously published by Oliver and Boyd Ltd, Edinburgh), and by permission of the authors and publishers.'

'I am grateful to the Literary Executor of the late Sir Ronald A. Fisher, F.R.S. to Dr. Frank Yates, F.R.S. and the Longman Group Ltd, London for permission to reprint Tables III and VI from their book *Statistical Tables for Biological, Agricultural and Medical Research* (6th Edition 1974).'

Table E

Critical values of the Spearman rho

	Level of Significance for One-Tailed Test			
	.05	.025	.01	.005
	Level of Significance for Two-Tailed Test			
n*	.10	.05	.02	.01
5	.900	1.000	1.000	—
6	.829	.886	.943	1.000
7	.714	.786	.893	.929
8	.643	.738	.833	.881
9	.600	.683	.783	.833
10	.564	.648	.746	.794
12	.506	.591	.712	.777
14	.456	.544	.645	.715
16	.425	.506	.601	.665
18	.399	.475	.564	.625
20	.377	.450	.534	.591
22	.359	.428	.508	.562
24	.343	.409	.485	.537
26	.329	.392	.465	.515
28	.317	.377	.448	.496
30	.306	.364	.432	.478

*n = number of pairs

Table F

Critical values of T for Wilcoxon signed ranks test

The values listed in the table are the critical values of T for the specified N (left column) and alpha level (column heading). To be significant, $T_{obt} \leq T_{crit}$.

	Level of Significance for One-Tailed Test					Level of Significance for One-Tailed Test			
	.05	.025	.01	.005		.05	.025	.01	.005
	Level of Significance for Two-Tailed Test					Level of Significance for Two-Tailed Test			
N	.10	.05	.02	.01	N	.10	.05	.02	.01
5	0	—	—	—	28	130	116	101	91
6	2	0	—	—	29	140	126	110	100
7	3	2	0	—	30	151	137	120	109
8	5	3	1	0	31	163	147	130	118
9	8	5	3	1	32	175	159	140	128
10	10	8	5	3	33	187	170	151	138
11	13	10	7	5	34	200	182	162	148
12	17	13	9	7	35	213	195	173	159
13	21	17	12	9	36	227	208	185	171
14	25	21	15	12	37	241	221	198	182
15	30	25	19	15	38	256	235	211	194
16	35	29	23	19	39	271	249	224	207
17	41	34	27	23	40	286	264	238	220
18	47	40	32	27	41	302	279	252	233
19	53	46	37	32	42	319	294	266	247
20	60	52	43	37	43	336	310	281	261
21	67	58	49	42	44	353	327	296	276
22	75	65	55	48	45	371	343	312	291
23	83	73	62	54	46	389	361	328	307
24	91	81	69	61	47	407	378	345	322
25	100	89	76	68	48	426	396	362	339
26	110	98	84	75	49	446	415	379	355
27	119	107	92	83	50	466	434	397	373

Table G-1

Critical values of U and U' for a one-tailed test at $\alpha = 0.005$ or a two-tailed test at $\alpha = 0.01$

To be significant for any given n_1 and n_2: U_{obt} must be equal to or less than the value shown in the table and U'_{obt} must be equal to or greater than the value shown in the table.

n_2 \ n_1	1	2	3	4	5	6	7	8	9	10	11	12	13	14	15	16	17	18	19	20
1	—	—	—	—	—	—	—	—	—	—	—	—	—	—	—	—	—	—	—	—
2	—	—	—	—	—	—	—	—	—	—	—	—	—	—	—	—	—	—	0 38	0 40
3	—	—	—	—	—	—	—	—	0 27	0 30	0 33	1 35	1 38	1 41	2 43	2 46	2 49	2 52	3 54	3 57
4	—	—	—	—	—	0 24	0 28	1 31	1 35	2 38	2 42	3 45	3 49	4 52	5 55	5 59	6 62	6 66	7 69	8 72
5	—	—	—	—	0 25	1 29	1 34	2 38	3 42	4 46	5 50	6 54	7 58	7 63	8 67	9 71	10 75	11 79	12 83	13 87
6	—	—	—	0 24	1 29	2 34	3 39	4 44	5 49	6 54	7 59	9 63	10 68	11 73	12 78	13 83	15 87	16 92	17 97	18 102
7	—	—	—	0 28	1 34	3 39	4 45	6 50	7 56	9 61	10 67	12 72	13 78	15 83	16 89	18 94	19 100	21 105	22 111	24 116
8	—	—	—	1 31	2 38	4 44	6 50	7 57	9 63	11 69	13 75	15 81	17 87	18 94	20 100	22 106	24 112	26 118	28 124	30 130
9	—	—	0 27	1 35	3 42	5 49	7 56	9 63	11 70	13 77	16 83	18 90	20 97	22 104	24 111	27 117	29 124	31 131	33 138	36 144
10	—	—	0 30	2 38	4 46	6 54	9 61	11 69	13 77	16 84	18 92	21 99	24 106	26 114	29 121	31 129	34 136	37 143	39 151	42 158
11	—	—	0 33	2 42	5 50	7 59	10 67	13 75	16 83	18 92	21 100	24 108	27 116	30 124	33 132	36 140	39 148	42 156	45 164	48 172
12	—	—	1 35	3 45	6 54	9 63	12 72	15 81	18 90	21 99	24 108	27 117	31 125	34 134	37 143	41 151	44 160	47 169	51 177	54 186
13	—	—	1 38	3 49	7 58	10 68	13 78	17 87	20 97	24 106	27 116	31 125	34 125	38 144	42 153	45 163	49 172	53 181	56 191	60 200
14	—	—	1 41	4 52	7 63	11 73	15 83	18 94	22 104	26 114	30 124	34 134	38 144	42 154	46 164	50 174	54 184	58 194	63 203	67 213
15	—	—	2 43	5 55	8 67	12 78	16 89	20 100	24 111	29 121	33 132	37 143	42 153	46 164	51 174	55 185	60 195	64 206	69 216	73 227
16	—	—	2 46	5 59	9 71	13 83	18 94	22 106	27 117	31 129	36 140	41 151	45 163	50 174	55 185	60 196	65 207	70 218	74 230	79 241
17	—	—	2 49	6 62	10 75	15 87	19 100	24 112	29 124	34 148	39 148	44 160	49 172	54 184	60 195	65 207	70 219	75 231	81 242	86 254
18	—	—	2 52	6 66	11 79	16 92	21 105	26 118	31 131	37 143	42 156	47 169	53 181	58 194	64 206	70 218	75 231	81 243	87 255	92 268
19	—	0 38	3 54	7 69	12 83	17 97	22 111	28 124	33 138	39 151	45 164	51 177	56 191	63 203	69 216	74 230	81 242	87 255	93 268	99 281
20	—	0 40	3 57	8 72	13 87	18 102	24 116	30 130	36 144	42 158	48 172	54 186	60 200	67 213	73 227	79 241	86 254	92 268	99 281	105 295

(Dashes in the body of the table indicate that no decision is possible at the stated level of significance.)

From R. P. Runyon and A. Haber, *Fundamentals of Behavioral Statistics*, 3d ed.

Table G–2

Critical values of U and U' for a one-tailed test at $\alpha = 0.01$ or a two-tailed test at $\alpha = 0.02$

To be significant for any given n_1 and n_2: U_{obt} must be equal to or less than the value shown in the table and U'_{obt} must be equal to or greater than the value shown in the table.

n_2 \ n_1	1	2	3	4	5	6	7	8	9	10	11	12	13	14	15	16	17	18	19	20
1	—	—	—	—	—	—	—	—	—	—	—	—	—	—	—	—	—	—	—	—
2	—	—	—	—	—	—	—	—	—	—	—	—	0 26	0 28	0 30	0 32	0 34	0 36	1 37	1 39
3	—	—	—	—	—	—	0 21	0 24	1 26	1 29	1 32	2 34	2 37	2 40	3 42	3 45	4 47	4 50	4 52	5 55
4	—	—	—	—	0 20	1 23	1 27	2 30	3 33	3 37	4 40	5 43	5 47	6 50	7 53	7 57	8 60	9 63	9 67	10 70
5	—	—	—	0 20	1 24	2 28	3 32	4 36	5 40	6 44	7 48	8 52	9 56	10 60	11 64	12 68	13 72	14 76	15 80	16 84
6	—	—	—	1 23	2 28	3 33	4 38	6 42	7 47	8 52	9 57	11 61	12 66	13 71	15 75	16 80	18 84	19 89	20 94	22 93
7	—	—	0 21	1 27	3 32	4 38	6 43	7 49	9 54	11 59	12 65	14 70	16 75	17 81	19 86	21 91	23 96	24 102	26 107	28 112
8	—	—	0 24	2 30	4 36	6 42	7 49	9 55	11 61	13 67	15 73	17 79	20 84	22 90	24 96	26 102	28 108	30 114	32 120	34 126
9	—	—	1 26	3 33	5 40	7 47	9 54	11 61	14 67	16 74	18 81	21 87	23 94	26 100	28 107	31 113	33 120	36 126	38 133	40 140
10	—	—	1 29	3 37	6 44	8 52	11 59	13 67	16 74	19 81	22 88	24 96	27 103	30 110	33 117	36 124	38 132	41 139	44 146	47 153
11	—	—	1 32	4 40	7 48	9 57	12 65	15 73	18 81	22 88	25 96	28 104	31 112	34 120	37 128	41 135	44 143	47 151	50 159	53 167
12	—	—	2 34	5 43	8 52	11 61	14 70	17 79	21 87	24 96	28 104	31 113	35 121	38 130	42 138	46 146	49 155	53 163	56 172	60 180
13	—	0 26	2 37	5 47	9 56	12 66	16 75	20 84	23 94	27 103	31 112	35 121	39 130	43 139	47 148	51 157	55 166	59 175	63 184	67 193
14	—	0 28	2 40	6 50	10 60	13 71	17 81	22 90	26 100	30 110	34 120	38 130	43 139	47 149	51 159	56 168	60 178	65 187	69 197	73 207
15	—	0 30	3 42	7 53	11 64	15 75	19 86	24 96	28 107	33 117	37 128	42 138	47 148	51 159	56 169	61 179	66 189	70 200	75 210	80 220
16	—	0 32	3 45	7 57	12 68	16 80	21 91	26 102	31 113	36 124	41 135	46 146	51 157	56 168	61 179	66 190	71 201	76 212	82 222	87 233
17	—	0 34	4 47	8 60	13 72	18 84	23 96	28 108	33 120	38 132	44 143	49 155	55 166	60 178	66 189	71 201	77 212	82 224	88 234	93 247
18	—	0 36	4 50	9 63	14 76	19 89	24 102	30 114	36 126	41 139	47 151	53 163	59 175	65 187	70 200	76 212	82 224	88 236	94 248	100 260
19	—	1 37	4 53	9 67	15 80	20 94	26 107	32 120	38 133	44 146	50 159	56 172	63 184	69 197	75 210	82 222	88 235	94 248	101 260	107 273
20	—	1 39	5 55	10 70	16 84	22 98	28 112	34 126	40 140	47 153	53 167	60 180	67 193	73 207	80 220	87 233	93 247	100 260	107 273	114 286

(Dashes in the body of the table indicate that no decision is possible at the stated level of significance.)

Table G–3

Critical values of U and U' for a one-tailed test at $\alpha = 0.025$ or a two-tailed test at $\alpha = 0.05$

To be significant for any given n_1 and n_2: U_{obt} must be equal to or less than the value shown in the table and U'_{obt} must be equal to or greater than the value shown in the table.

n_2 \ n_1	1	2	3	4	5	6	7	8	9	10	11	12	13	14	15	16	17	18	19	20
1	—	—	—	—	—	—	—	—	—	—	—	—	—	—	—	—	—	—	—	—
2	—	—	—	—	—	—	—	0 16	0 18	0 20	0 22	1 23	1 25	1 27	1 29	1 31	2 32	2 34	2 36	2 38
3	—	—	—	—	0 15	1 17	1 20	2 22	2 25	3 27	3 30	4 32	4 35	5 37	5 40	6 42	6 45	7 47	7 50	8 52
4	—	—	—	0 16	1 19	2 22	3 25	4 28	4 32	5 35	6 38	7 41	8 44	9 47	10 50	11 53	11 57	12 60	13 63	13 67
5	—	—	0 15	1 19	2 23	3 27	5 30	6 34	7 38	8 42	9 46	11 49	12 53	13 57	14 61	15 65	17 68	18 72	19 76	20 80
6	—	—	1 17	2 22	3 27	5 31	6 36	8 40	10 44	11 49	13 53	14 58	16 62	17 67	19 71	21 75	22 80	24 84	25 89	27 93
7	—	—	1 20	3 25	5 30	6 36	8 41	10 46	12 51	14 56	16 61	18 66	20 71	22 76	24 81	26 86	28 91	30 96	32 101	34 106
8	—	0 16	2 22	4 28	6 34	8 40	10 46	13 51	15 57	17 63	19 69	22 74	24 80	26 86	29 91	31 97	34 102	36 108	38 111	41 119
9	—	0 18	2 25	4 32	7 38	10 44	12 51	15 57	17 64	20 70	23 76	26 82	28 89	31 95	34 101	37 107	39 114	42 120	45 126	48 132
10	—	0 20	3 27	5 35	8 42	11 49	14 56	17 63	20 70	23 77	26 84	29 91	33 97	36 104	39 111	42 118	45 125	48 132	52 138	55 145
11	—	0 22	3 30	6 38	9 46	13 53	16 61	19 69	23 76	26 84	30 91	33 99	37 106	40 114	44 121	47 129	51 136	55 143	58 151	62 158
12	—	1 23	4 32	7 41	11 49	14 58	18 66	22 74	26 82	29 91	33 99	37 107	41 115	45 123	49 131	53 139	57 147	61 155	65 163	69 171
13	—	1 25	4 35	8 44	12 53	16 62	20 71	24 80	28 89	33 97	37 106	41 115	45 124	50 132	54 141	59 149	63 158	67 167	72 175	76 184
14	—	1 27	5 37	9 47	13 51	17 67	22 76	26 86	31 95	36 104	40 114	45 123	50 132	55 141	59 151	64 160	67 171	74 178	78 188	83 197
15	—	1 29	5 40	10 50	14 61	19 71	24 81	29 91	34 101	39 111	44 121	49 131	54 141	59 151	64 161	70 170	75 180	80 190	85 200	90 210
16	—	1 31	6 42	11 53	15 65	21 75	26 86	31 97	37 107	42 118	47 129	53 139	59 149	64 160	70 170	75 181	81 191	86 202	92 212	98 222
17	—	2 32	6 45	11 57	17 68	22 80	28 91	34 102	39 114	45 125	51 136	57 147	63 158	67 171	75 180	81 191	87 202	93 213	99 224	105 235
18	—	2 34	7 47	12 60	18 72	24 84	30 96	36 108	42 120	48 132	55 143	61 155	67 167	74 178	80 190	86 202	93 213	99 225	106 236	112 248
19	—	2 36	7 50	13 63	19 76	25 89	32 101	38 114	45 126	52 138	58 151	65 163	72 175	78 188	85 200	92 212	99 224	106 236	113 248	119 261
20	—	2 38	8 52	13 67	20 80	27 93	34 106	41 119	48 132	55 145	62 158	69 171	76 184	83 197	90 210	98 222	105 235	112 248	119 261	127 273

(Dashes in the body of the table indicate that no decision is possible at the stated level of significance.)

Table G–4

Critical values of U and U' for a one-tailed test at $\alpha = 0.05$ or a two-tailed test at $\alpha = 0.10$

To be significant for any given n_1 and n_2: U_{obt} must be equal to or less than the value shown in the table and U'_{obt} must be equal to or greater than the value shown in the table.

n_2 \ n_1	1	2	3	4	5	6	7	8	9	10	11	12	13	14	15	16	17	18	19	20
1	—	—	—	—	—	—	—	—	—	—	—	—	—	—	—	—	—	—	0 19	0 20
2	—	—	—	—	0 10	0 12	0 14	1 15	1 17	1 19	1 21	2 22	2 24	2 26	3 27	3 29	3 31	4 32	4 34	4 36
3	—	—	0 9	0 12	1 14	2 16	2 19	3 21	3 24	4 26	5 28	5 31	6 33	7 35	7 38	8 40	9 42	9 45	10 47	11 49
4	—	—	0 12	1 15	2 18	3 21	4 24	5 27	6 30	7 33	8 36	9 39	10 42	11 45	12 48	14 50	15 53	16 56	17 59	18 62
5	—	0 10	1 14	2 18	4 21	5 25	6 29	8 32	9 36	11 39	12 43	13 47	15 50	16 54	18 57	19 61	20 65	22 68	23 72	25 75
6	—	0 12	2 16	3 21	5 25	7 29	8 34	10 38	12 42	14 46	16 50	17 55	19 59	21 63	23 67	25 71	26 76	28 80	30 84	32 88
7	—	0 14	2 19	4 24	6 29	8 34	11 38	13 43	15 48	17 53	19 58	21 63	24 67	26 72	28 77	30 82	33 86	35 91	37 96	39 101
8	—	1 15	3 21	5 27	8 32	10 38	13 43	15 49	18 54	20 60	23 65	26 70	28 76	31 81	33 87	36 92	39 97	41 103	44 108	47 113
9	—	1 17	3 24	6 30	9 36	12 42	15 48	18 54	21 60	24 66	27 72	30 78	33 84	36 90	39 96	42 102	45 108	48 114	51 120	54 126
10	—	1 19	4 26	7 33	11 39	14 46	17 53	20 60	24 66	27 73	31 79	34 86	37 93	41 99	44 106	48 112	51 119	55 125	58 132	62 138
11	—	1 21	5 28	8 36	12 43	16 50	19 58	23 65	27 72	31 79	34 87	38 94	42 101	46 108	50 115	54 122	57 130	61 137	65 144	69 151
12	—	2 22	5 31	9 39	13 47	17 55	21 63	26 70	30 78	34 86	38 94	42 102	47 109	51 117	55 125	60 132	64 140	68 148	72 156	77 163
13	—	2 24	6 33	10 42	15 50	19 59	24 67	28 76	33 84	37 93	42 101	47 109	51 118	56 126	61 134	65 143	70 151	75 159	80 167	84 176
14	—	2 26	7 35	11 45	16 54	21 63	26 72	31 81	36 90	41 99	46 108	51 117	56 126	61 135	66 144	71 153	77 161	82 170	87 179	92 188
15	—	3 27	7 38	12 48	18 57	23 67	28 77	33 87	39 96	44 106	50 115	55 125	61 134	66 144	72 153	77 163	83 172	88 182	94 191	100 200
16	—	3 29	8 40	14 50	19 61	25 71	30 82	36 92	42 102	48 112	54 122	60 132	65 143	71 153	77 163	83 173	89 183	95 193	101 203	107 213
17	—	3 31	9 42	15 53	20 65	26 76	33 86	39 97	45 108	51 119	57 130	64 140	70 151	77 161	83 172	89 183	96 193	102 204	109 214	115 225
18	—	4 32	9 45	16 56	 68	28 80	35 91	41 103	48 114	55 123	61 137	68 148	75 159	82 170	88 182	95 193	102 204	109 215	116 226	123 237
19	0 19	4 34	10 47	17 59	23 72	30 84	37 96	44 108	51 120	58 132	65 144	72 156	80 167	87 179	94 191	101 203	109 214	116 226	123 238	130 250
20	0 20	4 36	11 49	18 62	25 75	32 88	39 101	47 113	54 126	62 138	69 151	77 163	84 176	92 188	100 200	107 213	115 225	123 237	130 250	138 262

(Dashes in the body of the table indicate that no decision is possible at the stated level of significance.)

Table H

Critical values of chi-square

	Level of Significance for One-Tailed Test					
	.10	.05	.025	.01	.005	.0005
	Level of Significance for Two-Tailed Test					
df	.20	.10	.05	.02	.01	.001
1	1.64	2.71	3.84	5.41	6.64	10.83
2	3.22	4.60	5.99	7.82	9.21	13.82
3	4.64	6.25	7.82	9.84	11.34	16.27
4	5.99	7.78	9.49	11.67	13.28	18.46
5	7.29	9.24	11.07	13.39	15.09	20.52
6	8.56	10.64	12.59	15.03	16.81	22.46
7	9.80	12.02	14.07	16.62	18.48	24.32
8	11.03	13.36	15.51	18.17	20.09	26.12
9	12.24	14.68	16.92	19.68	21.67	27.88
10	13.44	15.99	18.31	21.16	23.21	29.59
11	14.63	17.28	19.68	22.62	24.72	31.26
12	15.81	18.55	21.03	24.05	26.22	32.91
13	16.98	19.81	22.36	25.47	27.69	34.53
14	18.15	21.06	23.68	26.87	29.14	36.12
15	19.31	22.31	25.00	28.26	30.58	37.70
16	20.46	23.54	26.30	29.63	32.00	39.29
17	21.62	24.77	27.59	31.00	33.41	40.75
18	22.76	25.99	28.87	32.35	34.80	42.31
19	23.90	27.20	30.14	33.69	36.19	43.82
20	25.04	28.41	31.41	35.02	37.57	45.32
21	26.17	29.62	32.67	36.34	38.93	46.80
22	27.30	30.81	33.92	37.66	40.29	48.27
23	28.43	32.01	35.17	38.97	41.64	49.73
24	29.55	33.20	36.42	40.27	42.98	51.18
25	30.68	34.38	37.65	41.57	44.31	52.62
26	31.80	35.56	38.88	42.86	45.64	54.05
27	32.91	36.74	40.11	44.14	46.96	55.48
28	34.03	37.92	41.34	45.42	48.28	56.89
29	35.14	39.09	42.69	46.69	49.59	58.30
30	36.25	40.26	43.77	47.96	50.89	59.70

For *df* greater than 30, the value obtained from the expression $\sqrt{2\chi^2} - \sqrt{2df - 1}$ may be used as a *t*-ratio.

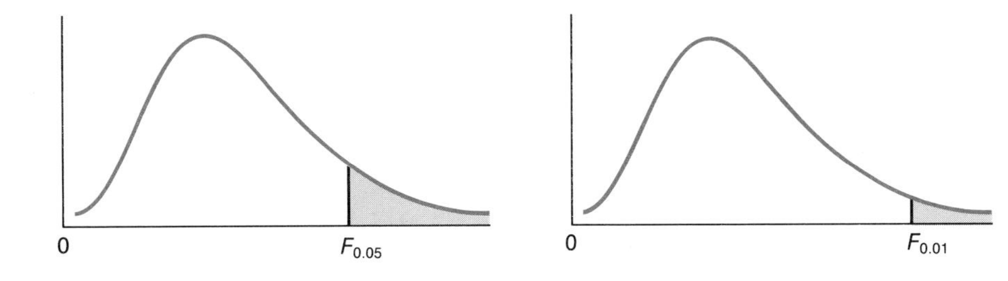

Table I

Critical values of the F distribution for $\alpha = 0.05$ (roman type) and $\alpha =$ **0.01 (boldface type)**

Degrees of Freedom: Denominator (Error)	Degrees of Freedom: Numerator (Treatment) 1	2	3	4	5	6	7	8	9	10	11	12	14	16	20	24	30	40	50	75	100	200	500	∞
1	161	200	216	225	230	234	237	239	241	242	243	244	245	246	248	249	250	251	252	253	253	254	254	254
	4,052	**4,999**	**5,403**	**5,625**	**5,764**	**5,859**	**5,928**	**5,981**	**6,022**	**6,056**	**6,082**	**6,106**	**6,142**	**6,169**	**6,208**	**6,234**	**6,258**	**6,286**	**6,302**	**6,323**	**6,334**	**6,352**	**6,361**	**6,366**
2	18.51	19.00	19.16	19.25	19.30	19.33	19.36	19.37	19.38	19.39	19.40	19.41	19.42	19.43	19.44	19.45	19.46	19.47	19.47	19.48	19.49	19.49	19.50	19.50
	98.49	**99.00**	**99.17**	**99.25**	**99.30**	**99.33**	**99.34**	**99.36**	**99.38**	**99.40**	**99.41**	**99.42**	**99.43**	**99.44**	**99.45**	**99.46**	**99.47**	**99.48**	**99.48**	**99.49**	**99.49**	**99.49**	**99.50**	**99.50**
3	10.13	9.55	9.28	9.12	9.01	8.94	8.88	8.84	8.81	8.78	8.76	8.74	8.71	8.69	8.66	8.64	8.62	8.60	8.58	8.57	8.56	8.54	8.54	8.53
	34.12	**30.82**	**29.46**	**28.71**	**28.24**	**27.91**	**27.67**	**27.49**	**27.34**	**27.23**	**27.13**	**27.05**	**26.92**	**26.83**	**26.69**	**26.60**	**26.50**	**26.41**	**26.35**	**26.27**	**26.23**	**26.18**	**26.14**	**26.12**
4	7.71	6.94	6.59	6.39	6.26	6.16	6.09	6.04	6.00	5.96	5.93	5.91	5.87	5.84	5.80	5.77	5.74	5.71	5.70	5.68	5.66	5.65	5.64	5.63
	21.20	**18.00**	**16.69**	**15.98**	**15.52**	**15.21**	**14.98**	**14.80**	**14.66**	**14.54**	**14.45**	**14.37**	**14.24**	**14.15**	**14.02**	**13.93**	**13.83**	**13.74**	**13.69**	**13.61**	**13.57**	**13.52**	**13.48**	**13.46**
5	6.61	5.79	5.41	5.19	5.05	4.95	4.88	4.82	4.78	4.74	4.70	4.68	4.64	4.60	4.56	4.53	4.50	4.46	4.44	4.42	4.40	4.38	4.37	4.36
	16.26	**13.27**	**12.06**	**11.39**	**10.97**	**10.67**	**10.45**	**10.27**	**10.15**	**10.05**	**9.96**	**9.89**	**9.77**	**9.68**	**9.55**	**9.47**	**9.38**	**9.29**	**9.24**	**9.17**	**9.13**	**9.07**	**9.04**	**9.02**
6	5.99	5.14	4.76	4.53	4.39	4.28	4.21	4.15	4.10	4.06	4.03	4.00	3.96	3.92	3.87	3.84	3.81	3.77	3.75	3.72	3.71	3.69	3.68	3.67
	13.74	**10.92**	**9.78**	**9.15**	**8.75**	**8.47**	**8.26**	**8.10**	**7.98**	**7.87**	**7.78**	**7.72**	**7.60**	**7.52**	**7.39**	**7.31**	**7.23**	**7.14**	**7.09**	**7.02**	**6.99**	**6.94**	**6.90**	**6.88**
7	5.59	4.47	4.35	4.12	3.97	3.87	3.79	3.73	3.68	3.63	3.60	3.57	3.52	3.49	3.44	3.41	3.38	3.34	3.32	3.29	3.28	3.25	3.24	3.23
	12.25	**9.55**	**8.45**	**7.85**	**7.46**	**7.19**	**7.00**	**6.84**	**6.71**	**6.62**	**6.54**	**6.47**	**6.35**	**6.27**	**6.15**	**6.07**	**5.98**	**5.90**	**5.85**	**5.78**	**5.75**	**5.70**	**5.67**	**5.65**
8	5.32	4.46	4.07	3.84	3.69	3.58	3.50	3.44	3.39	3.34	3.31	3.28	3.23	3.20	3.15	3.12	3.08	3.05	3.03	3.00	2.98	2.96	2.94	2.93
	11.26	**8.65**	**7.59**	**7.01**	**6.63**	**6.37**	**6.19**	**6.03**	**5.91**	**5.82**	**5.74**	**5.67**	**5.56**	**5.48**	**5.36**	**5.28**	**5.20**	**5.11**	**5.06**	**5.00**	**4.96**	**4.91**	**4.88**	**4.86**
9	5.12	4.26	3.86	3.63	3.48	3.37	3.29	3.23	3.18	3.13	3.10	3.07	3.02	2.98	2.93	2.90	2.86	2.82	2.80	2.77	2.76	2.73	2.72	2.71
	10.56	**8.02**	**6.99**	**6.42**	**6.06**	**5.80**	**5.62**	**5.47**	**5.35**	**5.26**	**5.18**	**5.11**	**5.00**	**4.92**	**4.80**	**4.73**	**4.64**	**4.56**	**4.51**	**4.45**	**4.41**	**4.36**	**4.33**	**4.31**
10	4.96	4.10	3.71	3.48	3.33	3.22	3.14	3.07	3.02	2.97	2.94	2.91	2.86	2.82	2.77	2.74	2.70	2.67	2.64	2.61	2.59	2.56	2.55	2.54
	10.04	**7.56**	**6.55**	**5.99**	**5.64**	**5.39**	**5.21**	**5.06**	**4.95**	**4.85**	**4.78**	**4.71**	**4.60**	**4.52**	**4.41**	**4.33**	**4.25**	**4.17**	**4.12**	**4.05**	**4.01**	**3.96**	**3.93**	**3.91**
11	4.84	3.98	3.59	3.36	3.20	3.09	3.01	2.95	2.90	2.86	2.82	2.79	2.74	2.70	2.65	2.61	2.57	2.53	2.50	2.47	2.45	2.42	2.41	2.40
	9.65	**7.20**	**6.22**	**5.67**	**5.32**	**5.07**	**4.88**	**4.74**	**4.63**	**4.54**	**4.46**	**4.40**	**4.29**	**4.21**	**4.10**	**4.02**	**3.94**	**3.86**	**3.80**	**3.74**	**3.70**	**3.66**	**3.62**	**3.60**
12	4.75	3.88	3.49	3.26	3.11	3.00	2.92	2.85	2.80	2.76	2.72	2.69	2.64	2.60	2.54	2.50	2.46	2.42	2.40	2.36	2.35	2.32	2.31	2.30
	9.33	**6.93**	**5.95**	**5.41**	**5.06**	**4.82**	**4.65**	**4.50**	**4.39**	**4.30**	**4.22**	**4.16**	**4.05**	**3.98**	**3.86**	**3.78**	**3.70**	**3.61**	**3.56**	**3.49**	**3.46**	**3.41**	**3.38**	**3.36**
13	4.67	3.80	3.41	3.18	3.02	2.92	2.84	2.77	2.72	2.67	2.63	2.60	2.55	2.51	2.46	2.42	2.38	2.34	2.32	2.28	2.26	2.24	2.22	2.21
	9.07	**6.70**	**5.74**	**5.20**	**4.86**	**4.62**	**4.44**	**4.30**	**4.19**	**4.10**	**4.02**	**3.96**	**3.85**	**3.78**	**3.67**	**3.59**	**3.51**	**3.42**	**3.37**	**3.30**	**3.27**	**3.21**	**3.18**	**3.16**
14	4.60	3.74	3.34	3.11	2.96	2.85	2.77	2.70	2.65	2.60	2.56	2.53	2.48	2.44	2.39	2.35	2.31	2.27	2.24	2.21	2.19	2.16	2.14	2.13
	8.86	**6.51**	**5.56**	**5.03**	**4.69**	**4.46**	**4.28**	**4.14**	**4.03**	**3.94**	**3.86**	**3.80**	**3.70**	**3.62**	**3.51**	**3.43**	**3.34**	**3.26**	**3.21**	**3.14**	**3.11**	**3.06**	**3.02**	**3.00**
15	4.54	3.68	3.29	3.06	2.90	2.79	2.70	2.64	2.59	2.55	2.51	2.48	2.43	2.39	2.33	2.29	2.25	2.21	2.18	2.15	2.12	2.10	2.08	2.07
	8.68	**6.36**	**5.42**	**4.89**	**4.56**	**4.32**	**4.14**	**4.00**	**3.89**	**3.80**	**3.73**	**3.67**	**3.56**	**3.48**	**3.36**	**3.29**	**3.20**	**3.12**	**3.07**	**3.00**	**2.97**	**2.92**	**2.89**	**2.87**
16	4.49	3.63	3.24	3.01	2.85	2.74	2.66	2.59	2.54	2.49	2.45	2.42	2.37	2.33	2.28	2.24	2.20	2.16	2.13	2.09	2.07	2.04	2.02	2.01
	8.53	**6.23**	**5.29**	**4.77**	**4.44**	**4.20**	**4.03**	**3.89**	**3.78**	**3.69**	**3.61**	**3.55**	**3.45**	**3.37**	**3.25**	**3.18**	**3.10**	**3.01**	**2.96**	**2.89**	**2.86**	**2.80**	**2.77**	**2.75**

Table I

Continued

Degrees of Freedom: Denominator (Error)	Degrees of Freedom: Numerator (Treatment) 1	2	3	4	5	6	7	8	9	10	11	12	14	16	20	24	30	40	50	75	100	200	500	∞
17	4.45	3.59	3.20	2.96	2.81	2.70	2.62	2.55	2.50	2.45	2.41	2.38	2.33	2.29	2.23	2.19	2.15	2.11	2.08	2.04	2.02	1.99	1.97	1.96
	8.40	**6.11**	**5.18**	**4.67**	**4.34**	**4.10**	**3.93**	**3.79**	**3.68**	**3.59**	**3.52**	**3.45**	**3.35**	**3.27**	**3.16**	**3.08**	**3.00**	**2.92**	**2.86**	**2.79**	**2.76**	**2.70**	**2.67**	**2.65**
18	4.41	3.55	3.16	2.93	2.77	2.66	2.58	2.51	2.46	2.41	2.37	2.34	2.29	2.25	2.19	2.15	2.11	2.07	2.04	2.00	1.98	1.95	1.93	1.92
	8.28	**6.01**	**5.09**	**4.58**	**4.25**	**4.01**	**3.85**	**3.71**	**3.60**	**3.51**	**3.44**	**3.37**	**3.27**	**3.19**	**3.07**	**3.00**	**2.91**	**2.83**	**2.78**	**2.71**	**2.68**	**2.62**	**2.59**	**2.57**
19	4.38	3.52	3.13	2.90	2.74	2.63	2.55	2.48	2.43	2.38	2.34	2.31	2.26	2.21	2.15	2.11	2.07	2.02	2.00	1.96	1.94	1.91	1.90	1.88
	8.18	**5.93**	**5.01**	**4.50**	**4.17**	**3.94**	**3.77**	**3.63**	**3.52**	**3.43**	**3.36**	**3.30**	**3.19**	**3.12**	**3.00**	**2.92**	**2.84**	**2.76**	**2.70**	**2.63**	**2.60**	**2.54**	**2.51**	**2.49**
20	4.35	3.49	3.10	2.87	2.71	2.60	2.52	2.45	2.40	2.35	2.31	2.28	2.23	2.18	2.12	2.08	2.04	1.99	1.96	1.92	1.90	1.87	1.85	1.84
	8.10	**5.85**	**4.94**	**4.43**	**4.10**	**3.87**	**3.71**	**3.56**	**3.45**	**3.37**	**3.30**	**3.23**	**3.13**	**3.05**	**2.94**	**2.86**	**2.77**	**2.69**	**2.63**	**2.56**	**2.53**	**2.47**	**2.44**	**2.42**
21	4.32	3.47	3.07	2.84	2.68	2.57	2.49	2.42	2.37	2.32	2.28	2.25	2.20	2.15	2.09	2.05	2.00	1.96	1.93	1.89	1.87	1.84	1.82	1.81
	8.02	**5.78**	**4.87**	**4.37**	**4.04**	**3.81**	**3.65**	**3.51**	**3.40**	**3.31**	**3.24**	**3.17**	**3.07**	**2.99**	**2.88**	**2.80**	**2.72**	**2.63**	**2.58**	**2.51**	**2.47**	**2.42**	**2.38**	**2.36**
22	4.30	3.44	3.05	2.82	2.66	2.55	2.47	2.40	2.35	2.30	2.26	2.23	2.18	2.13	2.07	2.03	1.98	1.93	1.91	1.87	1.84	1.81	1.80	1.78
	7.94	**5.72**	**4.82**	**4.31**	**3.99**	**3.76**	**3.59**	**3.45**	**3.35**	**3.26**	**3.18**	**3.12**	**3.02**	**2.94**	**2.83**	**2.75**	**2.67**	**2.58**	**2.53**	**2.46**	**2.42**	**2.37**	**2.33**	**2.31**
23	4.28	3.42	3.03	2.80	2.64	2.53	2.45	2.38	2.32	2.28	2.24	2.20	2.14	2.10	2.04	2.00	1.96	1.91	1.88	1.84	1.82	1.79	1.77	1.76
	7.88	**5.66**	**4.76**	**4.26**	**3.94**	**3.71**	**3.54**	**3.41**	**3.30**	**3.21**	**3.14**	**3.07**	**2.97**	**2.89**	**2.78**	**2.70**	**2.62**	**2.53**	**2.48**	**2.41**	**2.37**	**2.32**	**2.28**	**2.26**
24	4.26	3.40	3.01	2.78	2.62	2.51	2.43	2.36	2.30	2.26	2.22	2.18	2.13	2.09	2.02	1.98	1.94	1.89	1.86	1.82	1.80	1.76	1.74	1.73
	7.82	**5.61**	**4.72**	**4.22**	**3.90**	**3.67**	**3.50**	**3.36**	**3.25**	**3.17**	**3.09**	**3.03**	**2.93**	**2.85**	**2.74**	**2.66**	**2.58**	**2.49**	**2.44**	**2.36**	**2.33**	**2.27**	**2.23**	**2.21**
25	4.24	3.38	2.99	2.76	2.60	2.49	2.41	2.34	2.28	2.24	2.20	2.16	2.11	2.06	2.00	1.96	1.92	1.87	1.84	1.80	1.77	1.74	1.72	1.71
	7.77	**5.57**	**4.68**	**4.18**	**3.86**	**3.63**	**3.46**	**3.32**	**3.21**	**3.13**	**3.05**	**2.99**	**2.89**	**2.81**	**2.70**	**2.62**	**2.54**	**2.45**	**2.40**	**2.32**	**2.29**	**2.23**	**2.19**	**2.17**
26	4.22	3.37	2.98	2.74	2.59	2.47	2.39	2.32	2.27	2.22	2.18	2.15	2.10	2.05	1.99	1.95	1.90	1.85	1.82	1.78	1.76	1.72	1.70	1.69
	7.72	**5.53**	**4.64**	**4.14**	**3.82**	**3.59**	**3.42**	**3.29**	**3.17**	**3.09**	**3.02**	**2.96**	**2.86**	**2.77**	**2.66**	**2.58**	**2.50**	**2.41**	**2.36**	**2.28**	**2.25**	**2.19**	**2.15**	**2.13**
27	4.21	3.35	2.96	2.73	2.57	2.46	2.37	2.30	2.25	2.20	2.16	2.13	2.08	2.03	1.97	1.93	1.88	1.84	1.80	1.76	1.74	1.71	1.68	1.67
	7.68	**5.49**	**4.60**	**4.11**	**3.79**	**3.56**	**3.39**	**3.26**	**3.14**	**3.06**	**2.98**	**2.93**	**2.83**	**2.74**	**2.63**	**2.55**	**2.47**	**2.38**	**2.33**	**2.25**	**2.21**	**2.16**	**2.12**	**2.10**
28	4.20	3.34	2.95	2.71	2.56	2.44	2.36	2.29	2.24	2.19	2.15	2.12	2.06	2.02	1.96	1.91	1.87	1.81	1.78	1.75	1.72	1.69	1.67	1.65
	7.64	**5.45**	**4.57**	**4.07**	**3.76**	**3.53**	**3.36**	**3.23**	**3.11**	**3.03**	**2.95**	**2.90**	**2.80**	**2.71**	**2.60**	**2.52**	**2.44**	**2.35**	**2.30**	**2.22**	**2.18**	**2.13**	**2.09**	**2.06**
29	4.18	3.33	2.93	2.70	2.54	2.43	2.35	2.28	2.22	2.18	2.14	2.10	2.05	2.00	1.94	1.90	1.85	1.80	1.77	1.73	1.71	1.68	1.65	1.64
	7.60	**5.42**	**4.54**	**4.04**	**3.73**	**3.50**	**3.33**	**3.20**	**3.08**	**3.00**	**2.92**	**2.87**	**2.77**	**2.68**	**2.57**	**2.49**	**2.41**	**2.32**	**2.27**	**2.19**	**2.15**	**2.10**	**2.06**	**2.03**
30	4.17	3.32	2.92	2.69	2.53	2.42	2.34	2.27	2.21	2.16	2.12	2.09	2.04	1.99	1.93	1.89	1.84	1.79	1.76	1.72	1.69	1.66	1.64	1.62
	7.56	**5.39**	**4.51**	**4.02**	**3.70**	**3.47**	**3.30**	**3.17**	**3.06**	**2.98**	**2.90**	**2.84**	**2.74**	**2.66**	**2.55**	**2.47**	**2.38**	**2.29**	**2.24**	**2.16**	**2.13**	**2.07**	**2.03**	**2.01**
32	4.15	3.30	2.90	2.67	2.51	2.40	2.32	2.25	2.19	2.14	2.10	2.07	2.02	1.97	1.91	1.86	1.82	1.76	1.74	1.69	1.67	1.64	1.61	1.59
	7.50	**5.34**	**4.46**	**3.97**	**3.66**	**3.42**	**3.25**	**3.12**	**3.01**	**2.94**	**2.86**	**2.80**	**2.70**	**2.62**	**2.51**	**2.42**	**2.34**	**2.25**	**2.20**	**2.12**	**2.08**	**2.02**	**1.98**	**1.96**
34	4.13	3.28	2.88	2.65	2.49	2.38	2.30	2.23	2.17	2.12	2.08	2.05	2.00	1.95	1.89	1.84	1.80	1.74	1.71	1.67	1.64	1.61	1.59	1.57
	7.44	**5.29**	**4.42**	**3.93**	**3.61**	**3.38**	**3.21**	**3.08**	**2.97**	**2.89**	**2.82**	**2.76**	**2.66**	**2.58**	**2.47**	**2.38**	**2.30**	**2.21**	**2.15**	**2.08**	**2.04**	**1.98**	**1.94**	**1.91**
36	4.11	3.26	2.86	2.63	2.48	2.36	2.28	2.21	2.15	2.10	2.06	2.03	1.98	1.93	1.87	1.82	1.78	1.72	1.69	1.65	1.62	1.59	1.56	1.55
	7.39	**5.25**	**4.38**	**3.89**	**3.58**	**3.35**	**3.18**	**3.04**	**2.94**	**2.86**	**2.78**	**2.72**	**2.62**	**2.54**	**2.43**	**2.35**	**2.26**	**2.17**	**2.12**	**2.04**	**2.00**	**1.94**	**1.90**	**1.87**
38	4.10	3.25	2.85	2.62	2.46	2.35	2.26	2.19	2.14	2.09	2.05	2.02	1.96	1.92	1.85	1.80	1.76	1.71	1.67	1.63	1.60	1.57	1.54	1.53
	7.35	**5.21**	**4.34**	**3.86**	**3.54**	**3.32**	**3.15**	**3.02**	**2.91**	**2.82**	**2.75**	**2.69**	**2.59**	**2.51**	**2.40**	**2.32**	**2.22**	**2.14**	**2.08**	**2.00**	**1.97**	**1.90**	**1.86**	**1.84**
40	4.08	3.23	2.84	2.61	2.45	2.34	2.25	2.18	2.12	2.07	2.04	2.00	1.95	1.90	1.84	1.79	1.74	1.69	1.66	1.61	1.59	1.55	1.53	1.51
	7.31	**5.18**	**4.31**	**3.83**	**3.51**	**3.29**	**3.12**	**2.99**	**2.88**	**2.80**	**2.73**	**2.66**	**2.56**	**2.49**	**2.37**	**2.29**	**2.20**	**2.11**	**2.05**	**1.97**	**1.94**	**1.88**	**1.84**	**1.81**
42	4.07	3.22	2.83	2.59	2.44	2.32	2.24	2.17	2.11	2.06	2.02	1.99	1.94	1.89	1.82	1.78	1.73	1.68	1.64	1.60	1.57	1.54	1.51	1.49
	7.27	**5.15**	**4.29**	**3.80**	**3.49**	**3.26**	**3.10**	**2.96**	**2.86**	**2.77**	**2.70**	**2.64**	**2.54**	**2.46**	**2.35**	**2.26**	**2.17**	**2.08**	**2.02**	**1.94**	**1.91**	**1.85**	**1.80**	**1.78**
44	4.06	3.21	2.82	2.58	2.43	2.31	2.23	2.16	2.10	2.05	2.01	1.98	1.92	1.88	1.81	1.76	1.72	1.66	1.63	1.58	1.56	1.52	1.50	1.48
	7.24	**5.12**	**4.26**	**3.78**	**3.46**	**3.24**	**3.07**	**2.94**	**2.84**	**2.75**	**2.68**	**2.62**	**2.52**	**2.44**	**2.32**	**2.24**	**2.15**	**2.06**	**2.00**	**1.92**	**1.88**	**1.82**	**1.78**	**1.75**
46	4.05	3.20	2.81	2.57	2.42	2.30	2.22	2.14	2.09	2.04	2.00	1.97	1.91	1.87	1.80	1.75	1.71	1.65	1.62	1.57	1.54	1.51	1.48	1.46
	7.21	**5.10**	**4.24**	**3.76**	**3.44**	**3.22**	**3.05**	**2.92**	**2.82**	**2.73**	**2.66**	**2.60**	**2.50**	**2.42**	**2.30**	**2.22**	**2.13**	**2.04**	**1.98**	**1.90**	**1.86**	**1.80**	**1.76**	**1.72**
48	4.04	3.19	2.80	2.56	2.41	2.30	2.21	2.14	2.08	2.03	1.99	1.96	1.90	1.86	1.79	1.74	1.70	1.64	1.61	1.56	1.53	1.50	1.47	1.45

Table I

Continued

Degrees of Freedom: Denominator (Error)	Degrees of Freedom: Numerator (Treatment) 1	2	3	4	5	6	7	8	9	10	11	12	14	16	20	24	30	40	50	75	100	200	500	∞
	7.19	**5.08**	**4.22**	**3.74**	**3.42**	**3.20**	**3.04**	**2.90**	**2.80**	**2.71**	**2.64**	**2.58**	**2.48**	**2.40**	**2.28**	**2.20**	**2.11**	**2.02**	**1.96**	**1.88**	**1.84**	**1.78**	**1.73**	**1.70**
50	4.03	3.18	2.79	2.56	2.40	2.29	2.20	2.13	2.07	2.02	1.98	1.95	1.90	1.85	1.78	1.74	1.69	1.63	1.60	1.55	1.52	1.48	1.46	1.44
	7.17	**5.06**	**4.20**	**3.72**	**3.41**	**3.18**	**3.02**	**2.88**	**2.78**	**2.70**	**2.62**	**2.56**	**2.46**	**2.39**	**2.26**	**2.18**	**2.10**	**2.00**	**1.94**	**1.86**	**1.82**	**1.76**	**1.71**	**1.68**
55	4.02	3.17	2.78	2.54	2.38	2.27	2.18	2.11	2.05	2.00	1.97	1.93	1.88	1.83	1.76	1.72	1.67	1.61	1.58	1.52	1.50	1.46	1.43	1.41
	7.12	**5.01**	**4.16**	**3.68**	**3.37**	**3.15**	**2.98**	**2.85**	**2.75**	**2.66**	**2.59**	**2.53**	**2.43**	**2.35**	**2.23**	**2.15**	**2.06**	**1.96**	**1.90**	**1.82**	**1.78**	**1.71**	**1.66**	**1.64**
60	4.00	3.15	2.76	2.52	2.37	2.25	2.17	2.10	2.04	1.99	1.95	1.92	1.86	1.81	1.75	1.70	1.65	1.59	1.56	1.50	1.48	1.44	1.41	1.39
	7.08	**4.98**	**4.13**	**3.65**	**3.34**	**3.12**	**2.95**	**2.82**	**2.72**	**2.63**	**2.56**	**2.50**	**2.40**	**2.32**	**2.20**	**2.12**	**2.03**	**1.93**	**1.87**	**1.79**	**1.74**	**1.68**	**1.63**	**1.60**
65	3.99	3.14	2.75	2.51	2.36	2.24	2.15	2.08	2.02	1.98	1.94	1.90	1.85	1.80	1.73	1.68	1.63	1.57	1.54	1.49	1.46	1.42	1.39	1.37
	7.04	**4.95**	**4.10**	**3.62**	**3.31**	**3.09**	**2.93**	**2.79**	**2.70**	**2.61**	**2.54**	**2.47**	**2.37**	**2.30**	**2.18**	**2.09**	**2.00**	**1.90**	**1.84**	**1.76**	**1.71**	**1.64**	**1.60**	**1.56**
70	3.98	3.13	2.74	2.50	2.35	2.23	2.14	2.07	2.01	1.97	1.93	1.89	1.84	1.79	1.72	1.67	1.62	1.56	1.53	1.47	1.45	1.40	1.37	1.35
	7.01	**4.92**	**4.08**	**3.60**	**3.29**	**3.07**	**2.91**	**2.77**	**2.67**	**2.59**	**2.51**	**2.45**	**2.35**	**2.28**	**2.15**	**2.07**	**1.98**	**1.88**	**1.82**	**1.74**	**1.69**	**1.62**	**1.56**	**1.53**
80	3.96	3.11	2.72	2.48	2.33	2.21	2.12	2.05	1.99	1.95	1.91	1.88	1.82	1.77	1.70	1.65	1.60	1.54	1.51	1.45	1.42	1.38	1.35	1.32
	6.96	**4.88**	**4.04**	**3.56**	**3.25**	**3.04**	**2.87**	**2.74**	**2.64**	**2.55**	**2.48**	**2.41**	**2.32**	**2.24**	**2.11**	**2.03**	**1.94**	**1.84**	**1.78**	**1.70**	**1.65**	**1.57**	**1.52**	**1.49**
100	3.94	3.09	2.70	2.46	2.30	2.19	2.10	2.03	1.97	1.92	1.88	1.85	1.79	1.75	1.68	1.63	1.57	1.51	1.48	1.42	1.39	1.34	1.30	1.28
	6.90	**4.82**	**3.98**	**3.51**	**3.20**	**2.99**	**2.82**	**2.69**	**2.59**	**2.51**	**2.43**	**2.36**	**2.26**	**2.19**	**2.06**	**1.98**	**1.89**	**1.79**	**1.73**	**1.64**	**1.59**	**1.51**	**1.46**	**1.43**
125	3.92	3.07	2.68	2.44	2.29	2.17	2.08	2.01	1.95	1.90	1.86	1.83	1.77	1.72	1.65	1.60	1.55	1.49	1.45	1.39	1.36	1.31	1.27	1.25
	6.84	**4.78**	**3.94**	**3.47**	**3.17**	**2.95**	**2.79**	**2.65**	**2.56**	**2.47**	**2.40**	**2.33**	**2.23**	**2.15**	**2.03**	**1.94**	**1.85**	**1.75**	**1.68**	**1.59**	**1.54**	**1.46**	**1.40**	**1.37**
150	3.91	3.06	2.67	2.43	2.27	2.16	2.07	2.00	1.94	1.89	1.85	1.82	1.76	1.71	1.64	1.59	1.54	1.47	1.44	1.37	1.34	1.29	1.25	1.22
	6.81	**4.75**	**3.91**	**3.44**	**3.14**	**2.92**	**2.76**	**2.62**	**2.53**	**2.44**	**2.37**	**2.30**	**2.20**	**2.12**	**2.00**	**1.91**	**1.83**	**1.72**	**1.66**	**1.56**	**1.51**	**1.43**	**1.37**	**1.33**
200	3.89	3.04	2.65	2.41	2.26	2.14	2.05	1.98	1.92	1.87	1.83	1.80	1.74	1.69	1.62	1.57	1.52	1.45	1.42	1.35	1.32	1.26	1.22	1.19
	6.76	**4.71**	**3.88**	**3.41**	**3.11**	**2.90**	**2.73**	**2.60**	**2.50**	**2.41**	**2.34**	**2.28**	**2.17**	**2.09**	**1.97**	**1.88**	**1.79**	**1.69**	**1.62**	**1.53**	**1.48**	**1.39**	**1.33**	**1.28**
400	3.86	3.02	2.62	2.39	2.23	2.12	2.03	1.96	1.90	1.85	1.81	1.78	1.72	1.67	1.60	1.54	1.49	1.42	1.38	1.32	1.28	1.22	1.16	1.13
	6.70	**4.66**	**3.83**	**3.36**	**3.06**	**2.85**	**2.69**	**2.55**	**2.46**	**2.37**	**2.29**	**2.23**	**2.12**	**2.04**	**1.92**	**1.84**	**1.74**	**1.64**	**1.57**	**1.47**	**1.42**	**1.32**	**1.24**	**1.19**
1000	3.85	3.00	2.61	2.38	2.22	2.10	2.02	1.95	1.89	1.84	1.80	1.76	1.70	1.65	1.58	1.53	1.47	1.41	1.36	1.30	1.26	1.19	1.13	1.08
	6.66	**4.62**	**3.80**	**3.34**	**3.04**	**2.82**	**2.66**	**2.53**	**2.43**	**2.34**	**2.26**	**2.20**	**2.09**	**2.01**	**1.89**	**1.81**	**1.71**	**1.61**	**1.54**	**1.44**	**1.38**	**1.28**	**1.19**	**1.11**
∞	3.84	2.99	2.60	2.37	2.21	2.09	2.01	1.94	1.88	1.83	1.79	1.75	1.69	1.64	1.57	1.52	1.46	1.40	1.35	1.28	1.24	1.17	1.11	1.00
	6.64	**4.60**	**3.78**	**3.32**	**3.02**	**2.80**	**2.64**	**2.51**	**2.41**	**2.32**	**2.24**	**2.18**	**2.07**	**1.99**	**1.87**	**1.79**	**1.69**	**1.59**	**1.52**	**1.41**	**1.36**	**1.25**	**1.15**	**1.00**

Reprinted by permission from *Statistical Methods*, Eighth Edition by G. W. Snedecor and W. G. Cochran

Table J

Critical values of the studentized range (Q) distribution

The values listed in the table are the critical values of Q for the .05 and .01 levels of significance as determined by the degrees of freedom of the MS_{error} from the ANOVA and k, the number of means being compared. To be significant the computed value of Q must equal or exceed the tabled value.

df MS_{error}		k (Number of Means)									
	α	2	3	4	5	6	7	8	9	10	11
5	.05	3.64	4.60	5.22	5.67	6.03	6.33	6.58	6.80	6.99	7.17
	.01	5.70	6.98	7.80	8.42	8.91	9.32	9.67	9.97	10.24	10.48
6	.05	3.46	4.34	4.90	5.30	5.63	5.90	6.12	6.32	6.49	6.65
	.01	5.24	6.33	7.03	7.56	7.97	8.32	8.61	8.87	9.10	9.30
7	.05	3.34	4.16	4.68	5.06	5.36	5.61	5.82	6.00	6.16	6.30
	.01	4.95	5.92	6.54	7.01	7.37	7.68	7.94	8.17	8.37	8.55
8	.05	3.26	4.04	4.53	4.89	5.17	5.40	5.60	5.77	5.92	6.05
	.01	4.75	5.64	6.20	6.62	6.96	7.24	7.47	7.68	7.86	8.03
9	.05	3.20	3.95	4.41	4.76	5.02	5.24	5.43	5.59	5.74	5.87
	.01	4.60	5.43	5.96	6.35	6.66	6.91	7.13	7.33	7.49	7.65
10	.05	3.15	3.88	4.33	4.65	4.91	5.12	5.30	5.46	5.60	5.72
	.01	4.48	5.27	5.77	6.14	6.43	6.67	6.87	7.05	7.21	7.36
11	.05	3.11	3.82	4.26	4.57	4.82	5.03	5.20	5.35	5.49	5.61
	.01	4.39	5.15	5.62	5.97	6.25	6.48	6.67	6.84	6.99	7.13
12	.05	3.08	3.77	4.20	4.51	4.75	4.95	5.12	5.27	5.39	5.51
	.01	4.32	5.05	5.50	5.84	6.10	6.32	6.51	6.67	6.81	6.94
13	.05	3.06	3.73	4.15	4.45	4.69	4.88	5.05	5.19	5.32	5.43
	.01	4.26	4.96	5.40	5.73	5.98	6.19	6.37	6.53	6.67	6.79
14	.05	3.03	3.70	4.11	4.41	4.64	4.83	4.99	5.13	5.25	5.36
	.01	4.21	4.89	5.32	5.63	5.88	6.08	6.26	6.41	6.54	6.66
15	.05	3.01	3.67	4.08	4.37	4.59	4.78	4.94	5.08	5.20	5.31
	.01	4.17	4.84	5.25	5.56	5.80	5.99	6.16	6.31	6.44	6.55
16	.05	3.00	3.65	4.05	4.33	4.56	4.74	4.90	5.03	5.15	5.26
	.01	4.13	4.79	5.19	5.49	5.72	5.92	6.08	6.22	6.35	6.46
17	.05	2.98	3.63	4.02	4.30	4.52	4.70	4.86	4.99	5.11	5.21
	.01	4.10	4.74	5.14	5.43	5.66	5.85	6.01	6.15	6.27	6.38
18	.05	2.97	3.61	4.00	4.28	4.49	4.67	4.82	4.96	5.07	5.17
	.01	4.07	4.70	5.09	5.38	5.60	5.79	5.94	6.08	6.20	6.31
19	.05	2.96	3.59	3.98	4.25	4.47	4.65	4.79	4.92	5.04	5.14
	.01	4.05	4.67	5.05	5.33	5.55	5.73	5.89	6.02	6.14	6.25
20	.05	2.95	3.58	3.96	4.23	4.45	4.62	4.77	4.90	5.01	5.11
	.01	4.02	4.64	5.02	5.29	5.51	5.69	5.84	5.97	6.09	6.19
24	.05	2.92	3.53	3.90	4.17	4.37	4.54	4.68	4.81	4.92	5.01
	.01	3.96	4.55	4.91	5.17	5.37	5.54	5.69	5.81	5.92	6.02
30	.05	2.89	3.49	3.85	4.10	4.30	4.46	4.60	4.72	4.82	4.92
	.01	3.89	4.45	4.80	5.05	5.24	5.40	5.54	5.65	5.76	5.85
40	.05	2.86	3.44	3.79	4.04	4.23	4.39	4.52	4.63	4.73	4.82
	.01	3.82	4.37	4.70	4.93	5.11	5.26	5.39	5.50	5.60	5.69
60	.05	2.83	3.40	3.74	3.98	4.16	4.31	4.44	4.55	4.65	4.73
	.01	3.76	4.28	4.59	4.82	4.99	5.13	5.25	5.36	5.45	5.53
120	.05	2.80	3.36	3.68	3.92	4.10	4.24	4.36	4.47	4.56	4.64
	.01	3.70	4.20	4.50	4.71	4.87	5.01	5.12	5.21	5.30	5.37
∞	.05	2.77	3.31	3.63	3.86	4.03	4.17	4.29	4.39	4.47	4.55
	.01	3.64	4.12	4.40	4.60	4.76	4.88	4.99	5.08	5.16	5.23

From E. S. Pearson and H. O. Harley, editors, *Biometrika Tables for Statisticians*, Vol. 1.

APPENDIX B

Glossary of Symbols

The statistical symbols used in this text consist of both upper case and lower case Greek and English letters. This glossary lists all the symbols in alphabetical order with a pronunciation guide (where needed) and a brief definition.

PART I: GREEK LETTERS

α	**("alpha")** (a) The level of significance used when testing a hypothesis. (b) The probability of a Type I Error.
Δ	**("delta")** The change in [**variable name**].
μ	**("myoo")** The mean of a population of raw scores.
$\mu_{\overline{X}}$	**("myoo sub *X* bar")** The mean of a distribution of sample means.
$\mu_{\overline{X}_1 - \overline{X}_2}$	**("myoo sub *X* bar one minus *X* bar 2")** The mean of a distribution of difference scores. Each score in the distribution of difference scores is the difference between two sample means.
ρ	**("row" as in row your boat)** The population parameter representing the true value of the correlation coefficient between two variables.
Σ	**("sigma")** The sum of. . . . (This sigma is upper case.)
σ	**("sigma")** The population parameter representing the standard deviation of a variable. (This sigma is lower case.)
σ^2	**("sigma squared")** The population parameter representing the variance of a variable.
$\sigma_{\overline{X}}$	**("sigma sub *X* bar")** (a) The standard error. (b) The standard deviation of a distribution of sample means.
$\sigma^2_{\overline{X}}$	**("sigma squared sub *X* bar")** (a) The variance error. (b) The variance of a distribution of sample means.

$\sigma_{\overline{X}_1-\overline{X}_2}$	**("sigma sub *X* bar one minus *X* bar two")** (a) The standard error of the difference. (b) The standard deviation of a distribution of difference scores. Each score in the distribution of difference scores is the difference between two sample means.
χ^2	**("ki square" with "ki" pronounced as in "kite")** The chi-square statistic.

PART II: ENGLISH LETTERS

A_i	The sum of all the score values from level i of factor A in the two-way ANOVA.
$A \times B$	**("A by B")** The interaction between factor A and factor B in the two-way ANOVA.
AB_{ij}	**("A B sub *i j*")** The total of the scores from level i of factor A and level j of factor B in the context of the two-way analysis of variance. There are $i \times j$ such cell totals in a two-way factorial design.
$\overline{AB}_{ij}$	**("A B bar sub *i j*")** The mean of the scores from level i of factor A and level j of factor B in the context of the two-way analysis of variance. There are $i \times j$ such cell means in a two-way factorial design.
a_X	**("*a* sub *X*")** The X-intercept of the regression line that is used to predict the value of variable X with the knowledge of Y.
a_Y	**("*a* sub *Y*")** The Y-intercept of the regression line that is used to predict the value of variable Y with the knowledge of X.
ANOVA	The *AN*alysis *O*f *VA*riance.
B_j	The sum of all the score values from level j of factor B in the two-way ANOVA.
b_X	**("*b* sub *X*")** The slope of the regression line used to predict X with the knowledge of Y.
b_Y	**("*b* sub *Y*")** The slope of the regression line that is used to predict Y with the knowledge of X.
c	The number of columns in a contingency table.
crit	The critical value of a statistic for purposes of hypothesis testing. The computed (obtained) value is compared to the critical value found in a statistical table (e.g., $z_{crit} = 1.96$).
Cum f	**("cyoom *f*")** Cumulative frequency, commonly presented in the table of a grouped frequency distribution table.
D	The difference between paired scores, as seen in the correlated t-test and the Spearman rho analyses.
$\overline{D}$	**("*D* bar")** The mean of a set of difference scores.
d	The deviation of a particular difference score from the mean of all the difference scores (D minus D bar).
df	Degrees of freedom.
E	The symbol for expected value as in $E(\overline{X}) = \mu$ ("The expected value of a sample mean equals μ, the mean of the population from which the sample was drawn.")
F	(a) The F statistic. (b) The ratio of two independent estimates of the same population variance.
f	The frequency of a score value (i.e., the number of times a score value occurs in a distribution).

f_e	**("*f* sub *e*")** An expected cell frequency in the context of the chi-square statistic.
f_o	**("*f* sub *o*")** An observed cell frequency in the context of the chi-square statistic.
G	The grand total of all the score values in an experiment. The G notation appears in the computational method that is used to do an analysis of variance.
H_0	**("*H* naught")** The null hypothesis.
H_1	**("*H* one")** The alternative or experimental hypothesis.
i	The width of a class interval. Also, a "wildcard" subscript for a score in a set, as in the set: $X_1, X_2, \ldots X_i \ldots X_N$.
k	The number of treatments in an experiment or, in the context of the Tukey HSD test, the number of treatment means being compared.
MS	The mean square in the analysis of variance: SS divided by *df*.
$MS_{b.t.}$	The mean square between treatment in the analysis of variance.
$MS_{residual}$	The mean square residual from the repeated measures analysis of variance.
$MS_{w.t.}$	The mean square within treatment in the analysis of variance.
MS_A	The mean square for factor A in the analysis of variance. (Similarly for MS_B or $MS_{A \times B}$.)
N	The number of scores in a population or, in the context of a correlation analysis, the number of *pairs* of scores contained in the data.
n	The number of scores in a sample or treatment condition.
obt	The obtained value of a statistic resulting from the solution of a formula as in $t_{obt} = 3.29$.
P	The probability of an event as in $P(A) = .4$ ("The probability of event A equals .4."). In the context of the binomial expansion, P equals the probability of a success.
P_i	**("*P* sub *i*")** The Person (row) totals that are used in the computation of the repeated measures analysis of variance.
p	(a) The number of levels of factor A in the two-way ANOVA. (b) Lower case p may also be used to express a probability value as in $p \leq .05$ ("The probability is less than or equal to .05.").
$P(B/A)$	The probability of B given A has occurred.
Q	(a) The probability of a failure ($Q = 1 - P$). (b) Also, Q is the symbol for the studentized range statistic that is used in the Tukey HSD test.
q	The number of levels of factor B in the two-way ANOVA.
r	The Pearson product moment correlation coefficient.
r^2	The coefficient of determination.
$1 - r^2$	The coefficient of alienation.
rho	The Spearman rank order correlation coefficient.
SD	An abbreviation for standard deviation.
SS	The sum of squares or Variation of a set.
$SS_{b.t.}$	The $SS_{between\ treatment}$ in the analysis of variance.
$SS_{w.t.}$	The $SS_{within\ treatment}$ in the independent groups analysis of variance.
SS_A	The SS for factor A in the analysis of variance. (Similarly for SS_B or $SS_{A \times B}$.)

s	The standard deviation of a sample. When used only to describe the dispersion in a data set $s = SS/n$, but when used as an estimate of σ, the population standard deviation, $s = SS/(n - 1)$.
s_X	**("*s* sub *X*")** The standard deviation as computed from a sample of the *X* scores.
s_Y	**("*s* sub *Y*")** The standard deviation as computed from a sample of the *Y* scores.
$s_{est\ X}$	The standard error of estimate for predicting *X* with the knowledge of *Y*.
$s_{est\ Y}$	The standard error of estimate for predicting *Y* with the knowledge of *X*.
$s_{\overline{X}}$	The standard error of the mean (i.e., the standard deviation of a distribution of sample means) that is computed from sample data to estimate the population parameter.
$s_{\overline{X}_1-\overline{X}_2}$	The standard error of the difference (i.e., the standard deviation of a set of difference scores) that is computed from sample data to estimate the population parameter $\sigma_{\overline{X}_1 - \overline{X}_2}$.
s^2	The variance of a set of sample data.
SP	The Sum of Products or covariation of a set.
T	The Wilcoxon *T* statistic.
T_j	**("*T* sub *j*")** The total of all the score values from treatment *j*.
$\overline{T}_j$	**("*T* bar sub *j*")** The mean of all the score values in treatment *j*.
t	The Student's *t* statistic.
U and U'	The Mann-Whitney *U* statistic.
X_i	**("*X* sub *i*")** The value of score *i* in a set of *n* raw score values of variable *X*.
X'	**("*X* prime")** The value of *X* that is predicted using the regression equation for predicting *X* with the knowledge of *Y*.
x	The deviation of *X* from the mean of all the *X* scores. $x = (X - \overline{X})$.
$\overline{X}$	**("*X* bar")** The mean of a set of raw scores of variable *X*.
Y_i	**("*Y* sub *i*")** The value of score *i* in a set of *n* raw score values of variable *Y*.
$\overline{Y}$	**("*Y* bar")** The mean of a set of raw scores of variable *Y*.
z	The *z* statistic. The value of *z* is the location of a raw score, mean, or difference score in its distribution and is expressed in, respectively, standard deviation units, standard error units, or standard error of the difference units from the mean.

APPENDIX C

A Quick Reference to Equations and Formulae

The equations and formulae used in this text are listed below in order of their appearance. For further details turn to the chapter in which the equation appears.

Chapter 3

$$\overline{X} = \frac{\Sigma X}{n} = \frac{X_1 + X_2 + \cdots X_i + \cdots + X_n}{n}$$

$$\mu = \frac{\Sigma X}{N} = \frac{X_1 + X_2 + \cdots X_i + \cdots + X_N}{N}$$

$$\Sigma(X - \overline{X}) = 0$$

$$\text{Overall Mean} = \frac{(n_1\overline{X}_1) + (n_2\overline{X}_2) + \cdots + (n_i\overline{X}_i) + \cdots + (n_k\overline{X}_k)}{n_1 + n_2 + \cdots + n_i \cdots + n_k}$$

$$\Sigma(X - \overline{X})^2 = \Sigma X^2 - \frac{(\Sigma X)^2}{n}$$

$$SS_X = \Sigma X^2 - \frac{(\Sigma X)^2}{n}$$

$$\Sigma x^2 = \Sigma(X - \overline{X})^2$$

$$\text{Variation} = SS = \text{sum of squares} = \Sigma x^2 = \Sigma(X - \overline{X})^2 = \Sigma X^2 - \frac{(\Sigma X)^2}{n}$$

For a population:

$$\sigma^2 = \frac{\Sigma X^2 - \dfrac{(\Sigma X)^2}{N}}{N} = \frac{SS_X}{N}$$

and for a sample:

$$s^2 = \frac{\Sigma X^2 - \dfrac{(\Sigma X)^2}{n}}{n} = \frac{SS_X}{n}$$

For a population:

$$\sigma = \sqrt{\frac{\Sigma X^2 - \dfrac{(\Sigma X)^2}{N}}{N}} = \sqrt{\frac{SS_X}{N}} = \sqrt{\sigma^2}$$

and for a sample:

$$s = \sqrt{\frac{\Sigma X^2 - \dfrac{(\Sigma X)^2}{n}}{n}} = \sqrt{\frac{SS_X}{n}} = \sqrt{s^2}$$

Chapter 4

$$z = \frac{\text{raw score} - \text{mean}}{\text{standard deviation}} = \frac{X - \mu}{\sigma}$$

Chapter 5

$$\text{slope} = \frac{\Delta Y}{\Delta X} = \frac{\text{change in } Y}{\text{change in } X}$$

$$Y' = a_Y + b_Y X$$

$$b_Y = \frac{\Sigma XY - \dfrac{(\Sigma X)(\Sigma Y)}{N}}{\Sigma X^2 - \dfrac{(\Sigma X)^2}{N}}$$

$$b_Y = \frac{SP_{XY}}{SS_X}$$

$$a_Y = \overline{Y} - b_Y \overline{X}$$

$$S_{\text{est}\,Y} = \sqrt{\frac{\Sigma(Y - Y')^2}{N - 2}}$$

$$S_{\text{est}\,Y} = \sqrt{\frac{SS_Y - \dfrac{SP^2_{XY}}{SS_X}}{N - 2}}$$

$$X' = a_X + b_X Y$$

where:

$$b_X = \frac{SP_{XY}}{SS_Y} = \frac{\Sigma XY - \frac{(\Sigma X)(\Sigma Y)}{N}}{\Sigma Y^2 - \frac{(\Sigma Y)^2}{N}}$$

and

$$a_X = \overline{X} - b_X\overline{Y}$$

$$S_{est_X} = \sqrt{\frac{SS_X - \frac{SP_{XY}^2}{SS_Y}}{N - 2}}$$

Chapter 6

$$r_{XY} = \frac{\Sigma XY - \frac{(\Sigma X)(\Sigma Y)}{N}}{\sqrt{\left[\Sigma X^2 - \frac{(\Sigma X)^2}{N}\right] \cdot \left[\Sigma Y^2 - \frac{(\Sigma Y)^2}{N}\right]}}$$

$$r_{XY} = \frac{SP_{XY}}{\sqrt{SS_X \cdot SS_Y}}$$

$$r_{XY} = \frac{\Sigma z_X z_Y}{N}$$

$$z_{Y'} = r_{XY} \cdot z_X$$

$$\Sigma(Y - \overline{Y})^2 = \Sigma(Y' - \overline{Y})^2 + \Sigma(Y - Y')^2$$

or

$$SS_{total} = SS_{regression} + SS_{residual}$$

$$r^2 = \frac{SS_{regression}}{SS_{total}} = \text{the coefficient of determination}$$

$$1 - r^2 = \frac{SS_{residual}}{SS_{total}} = \text{the coefficient of alienation}$$

or

$$SS_{total} = r^2(SS_{total}) + (1 - r)^2(SS_{total})$$

$$SS_{total} = SS_{regression} + SS_{residual}$$

$$\text{rho} = 1 - \frac{6\Sigma D_i^2}{N^3 - N}$$

Sometimes this formula is written:

$$\text{rho} = 1 - \frac{6\Sigma D_i^2}{N(N^2 - 1)}$$

Chapter 7

$$\text{Probability} = \frac{\text{the number of favorable outcomes}}{\text{the total number of possible outcomes}}$$

or

$$\text{Probability} = \frac{\text{successes}}{\text{successes} + \text{failures}}$$

Chapter 8

The binomial expansion for $N = 5$

$$(P + Q)^5 = P^5 + \frac{N}{1} P^4Q + \frac{N(N-1)}{1 \cdot 2} P^3Q^2 + \frac{N(N-1)(N-2)}{1 \cdot 2 \cdot 3} P^2Q^3 + \ldots$$

$$\ldots + \frac{N(N-1)(N-2)(N-3)}{1 \cdot 2 \cdot 3 \cdot 4} PQ^4 + Q^5$$

The z approximation to the binomial:

$$z = \frac{X \pm .5 - N \cdot P}{\sqrt{N \cdot P \cdot Q}}$$

Chapter 10

$$\sigma_{\overline{X}} = \frac{\sigma_X}{\sqrt{n}}$$

$$z = \frac{\text{(score from a normal distribution)} - \text{(distribution mean)}}{\text{(deviation measure of the distribution)}}$$

$$z = \frac{\overline{X} - \mu}{\sigma / \sqrt{n}}$$

also written:

$$z = \frac{\overline{X} - \mu}{\sigma_{\overline{X}}}$$

Chapter 11

$$t = \frac{\overline{X} - \mu}{\text{estimate of } \sigma_{\overline{X}}}$$

$$t = \frac{\overline{X} - \mu}{s_{\overline{X}}}$$

$$t = \frac{\overline{X} - \mu}{\sqrt{\dfrac{SS_X}{n(n-1)}}}$$

where $$SS_X = \Sigma X^2 - \frac{(\Sigma X)^2}{n}$$

$$s_{\bar{X}} = \sqrt{\frac{SS_X}{n(n-1)}}$$

lower limit of confidence interval:

$$\bar{X} - t_{.05} \cdot s_{\bar{X}}$$

and upper limit of confidence interval:

$$\bar{X} + t_{.05} \cdot s_{\bar{X}}$$

Chapter 12

$$t = \frac{\text{(score in a distribution)} - \text{(mean of the distribution)}}{\text{estimate of the deviation measure of the distribution}}$$

The formula for the independent groups t-test:

$$t = \frac{(\bar{X}_1 - \bar{X}_2) - (\mu_1 - \mu_2)}{\sqrt{\left[\frac{SS_1 + SS_2}{n_1 + n_2 - 2}\right]\left[\frac{1}{n_1} + \frac{1}{n_2}\right]}}$$

The formula for the correlated groups t-test:

$$t = \frac{\bar{D} - (\mu_1 - \mu_2)}{\sqrt{\frac{\Sigma d^2}{n(n-1)}}}$$

Where $$\Sigma d^2 = \Sigma D^2 - \frac{(\Sigma D)^2}{n}$$

$$s_{\bar{X}_1 - \bar{X}_2} = \sqrt{s^2_{\bar{X}_1} + s^2_{\bar{X}_2} - 2r_{12}s_{\bar{X}_1}s_{\bar{X}_2}}$$

Chapter 13

The formulae for the Mann-Whitney U (or U')

$$U = n_1n_2 + \frac{n_1(n_1+1)}{2} - R_1$$

or

$$U = n_1n_2 + \frac{n_2(n_2+1)}{2} - R_2$$

The smaller of the two U values equals U, and the larger equals U'.

Chapter 14

$$\chi^2 = \Sigma \frac{(f_o - f_e)^2}{f_e}$$

with Yates correction for discontinuity

$$\chi^2 = \Sigma \frac{(|f_o - f_e| - .5)^2}{f_e}$$

Chapter 15

$$X_{ij} = \mu + T_j + E_{ij}$$

When the null hypothesis is true:

$$F = \frac{\text{variance between treatment}}{\text{variance within treatment}} = \frac{\text{error variance}}{\text{error variance}} = 1.00$$

$$SS_{\text{total}} = SS_{\text{between treatment}} + SS_{\text{within treatment}}$$

or, in more compact form:

$$SS_{\text{total}} = SS_{\text{b.t.}} + SS_{\text{w.t.}}$$

$$F = \frac{\text{random variance} + \text{contribution of the treatment effect}}{\text{random variance}}$$

$$F = \frac{MS_{\text{b.t.}}}{MS_{\text{w.t.}}}$$

Chapter 16

The Computational Components for the single factor ANOVA:

(1) G^2/nk (Sum all the scores in the data set, square that sum and divide by the total number of scores in the data set.)

(2) $\Sigma\Sigma X_{ij}^2$ (Square each individual score in the data set and add to get the sum of the squared scores. The double Σ is a reminder to carry out the squaring operation across all rows (i) and columns (j).)

(3) $\Sigma T_j^2/n$ (Square each treatment total, add the squared totals, and divide by n, the number of scores within each treatment.)

The Computational Components for the single factor ANOVA with repeated measures:

(1) G^2/nk (Sum all the scores in the data set, square that sum, and divide by the total number of scores in the data set.)

(2) $\Sigma\Sigma X_{ij}^2$ (Square each individual score in the data set and add to get the sum of the squared scores. The double Σ is a reminder to carry out the squaring operation across all rows (i) and columns (j).)

(3) $\Sigma T_j^2/n$ (Square each treatment total, add the squared totals, and divide by n, the number of scores within each treatment.)

(4) $\Sigma P_i^2/k$ (Square each row total, (P_i), add the squared row totals, and divide by k, the number of treatments.

Chapter 17

$$\alpha_r = 1 - (1 - \alpha)^r$$

$$Q = \frac{\overline{X}_i - \overline{X}_j}{\sqrt{\frac{\text{MS}_{\text{error}}}{n}}}$$

Where:
$\overline{X}_i$ is the larger of the two treatment means being compared.
$\overline{X}_j$ is the smaller of the two treatment means being compared.

To do a Scheffé test compute

$$F = \frac{\frac{\text{SS}_{\text{b.t.}}}{k - 1}}{\frac{\text{SS}_{\text{w.t.}}}{k(n - 1)}} = \frac{\text{MS}_{\text{b.t.}}}{\text{MS}_{\text{w.t.}}}$$

where the $\text{SS}_{\text{b.t.}}$ is computed using only the data of the two treatments being compared. The between and within treatment degrees of freedom and the $\text{SS}_{\text{w.t.}}$ and $\text{MS}_{\text{w.t.}}$ are the same values computed for the original ANOVA.

Planned Comparisons:

$$t = \frac{\overline{T}_i - \overline{T}_j}{\sqrt{\frac{2\ \text{MS}_{\text{error}}}{n}}}$$

Where $\overline{T}_i$ and $\overline{T}_j$ are the two treatment means being compared and MS_{error} is the $\text{MS}_{\text{w.t.}}$ from the ANOVA.

Chapter 18

The Computational Components for the two-way ANOVA:

(1) G^2/npq (Sum the npq scores in the data set, square that sum, and divide the squared sum by npq.)

(2) $\Sigma\Sigma X_{ij}^2$ (Square each one of the npq scores in the data, then add all the squared scores.)

(3) $\Sigma A_i^2/nq$ (Square each of the p row totals, add up the squared values and divide by nq, the number of scores represented in each row total.)

(4) $\Sigma B_j^2/np$ (Square each of the q column totals, add up the squared values and divide by np, the number of scores represented in each column total.)

(5) $\Sigma AB_{ij}^2/n$ (Square each of the pq cell totals, add up the squared totals and divide by n, the number of scores represented in each cell total.)

APPENDIX D

Answers to Selected Chapter Exercises

APPENDIX D: ANSWERS TO SELECTED QUESTIONS FROM THE END-OF-CHAPTER EXERCISES

Chapter 1

3. Set *a:*
I. **(a)** 30 **(b)** 190 **(c)** 900
II. 10
III. 6
IV. 10

Set *b:*
I. **(a)** 138 **(b)** 3,412 **(c)** 19,044
II. 238
III. 23
IV. 238

Set *c:*
I. **(a)** 20 **(b)** 95.2 **(c)** 400
II. 15.2
III. 4.0
IV. 15.2

4. **(a)** 11.43 **(b)** 15.15 **(c)** 22.68
(d) 85.50 **(e)** 10.76 **(f)** 32.37
(g) 47.50

5. Scale 1: 42.5 − 43.5
Scale 2: 76.65 − 76.75
Scale 3: 84.225 − 84.235
Scale 4: 31.1765 − 31.1775

10. **(a)** 411 **(b)** 2,401 **(c)** 68
(d) 7 **(e)** 68 **(f)** 9.71

15. **(a)** 11.5 − 12.5 **(b)** 17.75 − 17.85
(c) 18.645 − 18.655 **(d)** 9.0165 − 9.0175
(e) 99.5 − 100.5

16. **(a)** 6.67 **(b)** 6.833 **(c)** 6.7167

17. **(a)** 50 **(b)** 46 **(c)** 26
(d) 53 **(e)** 68 **(f)** 3,500
(g) −20 **(h)** 120 **(i)** 120
(j) 470 **(k)** 874 **(l)** 572

Chapter 2

1. Either these three class intervals:

75 − 82, 67 − 74, 59 − 66

or these three class intervals:

67 − 74, 59 − 66, 51 − 58

2. 67 − 74

3. 82.5, the true upper limit of the 75 − 82 class interval

4. 50.5, the true lower limit of the 51 − 58 interval

5. 43

6. *D*
7. 58.5. The cumulative percent of the 51 − 58 class interval is 34.4%. Thus, roughly one-third (34.4%) of the scores are below 58.5 and roughly two-thirds are above 58.5.
8. 106.5
14. (a) 15 (b) 87 (c) 5.8

X	*f*	Cum *f*	Cum %
3	1	15	100
4	0	14	93
5	4	14	93
6	7	10	67
7	2	3	20
8	1	1	7

Chapter 3

1. (a) 411 (b) 2,401 (c) 7
   (d) 7 (e) 68 (f) 9.71
   (g) 3.116 (h) 6 (i) 68
   (j) 3.116 (k) 9.71 (l) 68
   (m) 68
2. (a) 17 (b) 68
   (c) 9.71 (d) 3.116
   (e) 13
6. 5
7. Both the mean and the median equal 6.00.
10. zero
11. 25 . . . 3
12. median . . . mean
13. 4 . . . 16
14. 10 . . . 100
15. Mean = 7, Median = 7, Mode = 7

    $SS_X = 64$, $s_X^2 = 7.11$, $s_X = 2.67$
16. 10
17. 72.26
18. variance
20. interval or ratio
22. 80.48
23. You made an error in your computations. SS, s^2, *and* s can never be negative.

Chapter 4

1. (a) 10.56 (b) 33.36
   (c) 294 (d) 69.15%
2. (a) 65.98 − 74.02
   (b) 19.71%
   (c) 25.14
   (d) 34
3. (a) 69.15 (b) 58.4
   (c) 191 (d) 6.68
   (e) 43.3 − 56.7
6. (a) 95.54 (b) 18.7
   (c) 248.35 (d) 2.28
   (e) 13.3 − 26.7
7. Tom's score equalled the class average.
8. 96.25
9. No. Only if the mean and standard deviation for both sets of test data were equal.
10. yes
12. 1.00
13. 50%
15. standard deviation

Chapter 5

1. (b) $Y' = -.85.87 + 1.78\ X$
   (d) $S_{est\ Y} = 5.01$
   (e) 29.83
   (f) 44.07
5. (b) $Y' = 25.13 + 0.685\ X$
   (d) $S_{est\ Y} = 4.35$
   (e) 83
10. (b) a negative linear trend
    (c) $Y' = 114.804 + (1.476)\ X$
    (d) 85.28
    (e) $X' = 55.042 + (-0.359)\ Y$
    (f) $S_{est\ Y} = 10.098$
    (g) $S_{est\ X} = 4.98$

Chapter 6

1. (b)

$$r = \frac{28{,}350 - \frac{(605)(620)}{15}}{\sqrt{\left[30{,}675 - \frac{605^2}{15}\right] \cdot \left[28{,}300 - \frac{620^2}{15}\right]}}$$

$r = +.8164$

(c)

$$b_Y = \frac{SP_{XY}}{SS_X} = \frac{3{,}343.33}{6{,}273.33} = 0.5329$$

$$\begin{aligned} a_Y &= \overline{Y} - b_Y\overline{X} \\ &= 41.33 - 0.5329 \cdot 40.33 \\ &= 19.84 \end{aligned}$$

$$Y' = 19.84 + 0.5329\ X$$

(d) Here are the data in ranked form. (The low ranks have been assigned to the numerically high scores for both variables.)

Mite Density Score	Cleanliness Rating
15	1
8.5	8
8.5	9
10	4
11.5	3
13.5	5
1	13
2	13
11.5	7
6.5	6
13.5	2
5	13
6.5	11
3.5	5
3.5	10

Here is the computation of rho using the simplified formula:

$$\text{rho} = 1 - \frac{6 \cdot 1053.5}{3375 - 15} = -0.881$$

If the Spearman rho is computed using the Pearson r formula on the above ranked data, the value of rho equals -0.896. The difference between the two values of rho is a result of the presence of tied ranks.

(f) $Y' = 19.84 + 0.5329 \cdot 37$
$Y' = 39.56$

(g) If $Y' = 19.84 + 0.5329 \cdot 25$
$Y' = 33.16$
and $S_{\text{est } Y} = 8.28$
then the answer is $Y' \pm 1\ S_{\text{est } Y} = 33.16 \pm 8.28 = 24.88$ to 41.44

(h) 40.33, 41.33. This is $\overline{X}$, $\overline{Y}$.

(i) $r_{XY} = 0.8164$, so $r^2_{XY} = .67$

2. truncated range. Both I.Q. and performance were limited to a high and narrow range.

4. Y would be located one standard deviation below the mean of the Y scores.

5. **(a)** The accuracy of prediction decreases.
(b) The accuracy of prediction increases.

8. **(b)** $r_{XY} = .764$ **(c)** 58%

9. **(a)** $r_{XY} = .916$ **(b)** $Y' = 24.33 + 1.01\ X$
(c) 83.9%

Chapter 7

1. **(a)** .1296 **(b)** .4752 **(c)** .0486
(d) .6561 **(e)** .0256 **(f)** .0486
(g) .8704

2. **(a)** .0526 **(b)** .3948
(c) .6009 **(d)** .3991

3. **(a)** .3495 (Computations carried to 6 decimals before rounding.)
(b) .3403 **(c)** .3039 **(d)** .2459

4. **(a)** .0315 **(b)** .3368 **(c)** .5088

5. **(a)** .0029 or 1/343 **(b)** .0787 or 27/343
(c) .1866 or 64/343 **(d)** .1050 or 36/343
(e) .0262 or 9/343 **(f)** .6064 or 208/343
(g) 1 − .1866 = .8134 **(h)** .4198 or 144/343
(i) 1 − .6297 = .3703 **(j)** .0175 or 6/343
(k) .6297 or 216/343 **(l)** .3644 or 125/343
(m) .0787 or 27/343

6. independent

7. mutually exclusive

8. (a) .2266 (b) .3085
(c) .2426 (d) .8413

9. (a) .0951 (b) .2500
(c) .0504 (d) .1889

Chapter 8

1. (a) .1101 (b) .0016 (c) .6302
(d) .1336 (e) .8104 (f) .0197

2. (a) .0563 (b) .2816
(c) .9437 (d) .1877

3. (a) .1468 (b) .2202
(c) .5214 (d) .1010
(e) .0383

5. (a) .0793 (b) .8023

6. (a) .0016 (b) .2508 (c) .3487
(d) .1937 (e) .9984 (f) .2007

8. (a) .5154 (b) .2186
(c) .1268 (d) .0047
(e) .0153

Chapter 9

1. The null hypothesis is that the probability of a correct sex determination equals .5 (i.e., only chance is operating), and the alternative hypothesis is that the probability of a correct response does not equal .5. One could argue in favor of performing a directional (one-tail) test since it is unlikely that Lazar's technique would result in a worse than chance performance. Nevertheless, to be on the conservative side and lessen the probability of Type I error, we shall do a two-tail test. We must add the probabilities of an event as rare or rarer than a 10/2 split if the null hypothesis is true ($p = .5$). The probabilities for such splits (10/2, 11/1, 12/0, 2/10, 1/11, 0/12) sum to .0384. The decision rule is to reject H_0 if $p < .05$. Since .0384 is less than .05 we reject H_0 and conclude that Lazar is indeed operating at a better than chance level.

2. The null hypothesis is that Lewis did not cheat. We, therefore, assume that his competency for sinking foul shots is consistent with his traditional performance level: $p = .85$ for sinking a shot. Because the binomial table in this text has no column entry of .85, we must change the null hypothesis to read: $p = .15$ for missing a shot. Out of 13 shots, Lewis missed 5. The probability of a player of Lewis' calibre missing 5 shots or an event even rarer than that (missing 6, 7, 8, 9, 10, 11, 12, or all 13 foul shots) equals .0341. We reject H_0 and determine that Lewis' performance for the game in question was significantly below his usual level of performance. A further investigation into the allegation of cheating appears to be warranted.

5. H_0: The probability of catching a bass equals .50.
H_1: The probability of catching a bass does not equal .50.
Since the sample size ($N = 26$) is too large for our binomial table, the hypothesis may be tested using the z approximation to the binomial.

$$z = \frac{8 - 13}{\sqrt{.5 \cdot .5 \cdot 26}} = \frac{-5}{2.55} = -1.96$$

Decision Rule: Reject H_0 if the computed value for z is less than or equal to -1.96 or greater than or equal to $+1.96$. Since $z = -1.96$, we reject H_0 and conclude that the percentage of bass in the stocked pond is not 50%.

7. H_0: The probability of finding a defective widget equals .30.
H_1: The probability of finding a defective widget does not equal .30.
Decision Rule: Reject H_0 if, assuming H_0 is true, the probability of finding three or less defective widgets in a sample of 20 is less than or equal to .05.

$$p = .0008 + .0068 + .0278 + .0716 = .107$$

Since .107 is greater than .05 we fail to reject H_0.

9. H_0: The probability of a plant surviving the cold equals .10.
H_1: The probability of a plant surviving the cold does not equal .10.
Decision Rule: Reject H_0 if, assuming H_0 is true, the probability of 6 or more plants surviving out of 20 is less than or equal to .05.

$$p = .0089 + .0020 + .0004 + .0001 = .0114$$

We reject H_0 and conclude that there has been a significant change in the rate of plant survival.

Chapter 10

1. $\mu_{\overline{X}} = 40$ and $\sigma_{\overline{X}} = 4$

2. The computed value of z equals 2.00 and the critical value of z with $\alpha = .05$ equals 1.96. Therefore, student performance improved significantly.

3. The computed value of z equals -1.00 and the critical value with $\alpha = .05$ is 1.96. Therefore, there was not a significant change in the rejection rate.

4. The computed value of z equals 2.00 and the critical value with $\alpha = .01$ is 2.58. We, therefore, conclude that the rumor is not true. We retain the null hypothesis that the average S.A.T. score of freshmen is 1300.

5. The larger the sample size becomes, the smaller the standard error of the mean will be.

6. μ.

12. H_0: There has been no change in the eating habits of the snakes ($\mu = 50$).
H_1: There has been a change in the eating habits of the snakes ($\mu \neq 50$).
Decision Rule: Reject H_0 if the computed value for z is less than or equal to -1.96 or greater than or equal to $+1.96$. (An alternative form of this decision rule is: Reject H_0 if the computed value for z is more extreme than 1.96.)
$z = -1.80$, so we must fail to reject H_0. This two-tail test failed to find a significant change in the eating habits of the snakes.

13. H_0: The current January temperature does not represent a significant departure from the historical average of 52 degrees ($\mu = 52$).
H_1: The current January temperature does represent a significant departure from the historical average of 52 degrees ($\mu \neq 52$).
Decision Rule: Reject H_0 if the computed value of z is less than or equal to -2.58 or greater than or equal to $+2.58$ (An alternative form of this decision rule is: Reject H_0 if the computed value for z is more extreme than 2.58.)
$z = 2.67$, and so we must reject H_0. The January temperature is significantly above normal and may indeed be a sign of a global warming trend.

Chapter 11

1. The increase in water temperature was predicted to affect growth in a positive direction, and so a one-tail test is justified. The computed value for t is 2.86 and the one-tail critical value from the t table with $\alpha = .05$ and $df = 15$ is 1.753. Since the computed value is more extreme than the critical value, we reject H_0 and conclude that the increase in growth was significant.

2. $P(10.1354 \leq \mu \leq 10.9271) = .95$
$P(9.98387 \leq \mu \leq 11.0786) = .99$

3. The computed value for t equals 2.78 and the critical value of t with $\alpha = .05$ and $df = 15$ is 2.131. Since the computed value is more extreme than the critical value we reject H_0 and conclude that the fertilizer produced a significant change in the crop yield.

4. The computed value for t equals 2.27 and the critical value with $\alpha = .05$ and $df = 9$ is 2.262. Since the computed value is more extreme than the critical value, we reject H_0 and conclude that the students spend an average time on the school bus that is significantly different from 30 minutes. (You could make an argument for a directional test for this problem, but the fact that the difference is still significant even when using the somewhat more conservative two-tail test tends to increase confidence in the conclusion.)

5. $P(30.00 \leq \mu \leq 36.40) = .95$
$P(28.61 \leq \mu \leq 37.79) = .99$

8. a, b, and c are *all* algebraically equivalent formulae for the standard error.

12. (a) The computed value for t equals -2.00 and the critical value of t equals 2.064. The computed value is not as extreme as the critical value. Therefore, we must fail to reject H_0.

(b) The computed value for t equals 2.00 and the critical value of t equals 2.064. The computed value is not as extreme as the critical value. Therefore, we must fail to reject H_0.

(c) The computed value for t equals 2.50 and the critical value of t equals 2.064. The computed value is not as extreme as the critical value. Therefore, we must reject H_0.

(d) The computed value for t equals 3.00 and the critical value of t equals 2.064. The computed value is more extreme than the critical value. Therefore, we must reject H_0.

14. (a) The computed value for t equals -1.60 and the critical value of t equals 2.131. The computed value is not as extreme as the critical value. Therefore, we must fail to reject H_0.

(b) The computed value for t equals $+1.60$ and the critical value of t equals 2.131. The computed value is not as extreme as the critical value. Therefore, we must fail to reject H_0.

(c) The computed value for t equals 2.00 and the critical value of t equals 2.131. The computed value is not as extreme as the critical value. Therefore, we must fail to reject H_0.

(d) The computed value for t equals 2.40 and the critical value of t equals 2.131. The computed value is more extreme than the critical value. Therefore, we must reject H_0.

15. H_0: The graduating seniors continue to average nine or less pounds overweight ($\mu \leq 9$).
H_1: The graduating seniors are more than nine pounds overweight ($\mu > 9$).
Decision Rule: Reject H_0 if the computed value for t is more extreme than 1.796.
$t = 2.98$. Therefore, we reject H_0 and conclude that the seniors are more overweight than the previous average of nine pounds.

16. $P(16.87 \leq \mu \leq 55.13) = .95$

Chapter 12

1. A correlated groups t-test is appropriate for this problem. In the absence of convincing information that the affect of the experimental drug on activity, if any, will necessarily be to depress activity, it is better to use a two-tail test than a one-tail test.

The computed value of t equals 4.71. The critical values for the t statistic are 2.202 ($\alpha = .05$) and 3.106 ($\alpha = .01$). Whether you choose to use $\alpha = .05$ or .01, in either case you should reject H_0 and conclude that the drug did indeed suppress activity to a significant degree.

2. The correlated groups t-test is applied to the shoplifting data because each store is being assessed twice ("before and after"). If some stores are in low crime neighborhoods and others are in high crime neighborhoods a correlation is not only possible, it is quite likely. This is because the stores in the low crime areas (e.g., Store 6) will tend to have a uniformly low shoplifting problem regardless of the security system that is used, whereas those in the high crime areas (e.g., Store 7) will always have a relatively greater problem.

The computed value for t equals 2.994, and this is greater (i.e., more extreme) than the critical value of 2.228 ($df = 10$, $\alpha = .05$). There was a significant change in shoplifter detection following installation of the new security system.

3. The independent groups t-test is appropriate for analyzing the toilet training data. With $\alpha = .05$ and $df = 20$, the critical value of the t statistic equals 2.086. The computed value of t equals 1.203, and so we should retain the null hypothesis that there is no difference in the average age of toilet training between the two groups.

6. Type I error for Problem 1: Determining that the drug affected activity level when it really did not. Perhaps, despite careful adherence to random sampling procedures, several of the inherently more active animals were, by chance, assigned to the drug-treated group.

Type I error for Problem 2: Determining that one security system is better than the other when there really is no difference. Perhaps the new system was evaluated during a period of particularly severe weather when shopper turnout (thieves included) was very low.

Type II error for Problem 3: Determining that the two methods do not differ in the capacity to teach toilet training to children when one method is truly superior. Perhaps the techniques that were supposed to be applied in the superior method struck the mothers as being bizarre, inappropriate, too bothersome, etc., and they did not apply the method as directed.

10. H_0: There is no difference in the number of trials it takes the dogs to learn the skill using Schedule A versus Schedule B. $\mu_1 - \mu_2 = 0$.

H_1: There is a difference in the acquisition of the skill using Schedule A versus Schedule B.
Decision Rule: Reject H_0 if the computed value for t is more extreme than 2.086.

$t = 0.72$. Therefore, we fail to reject H_0. Apparently, there is no significant difference in the ability of the dogs to learn the skill using Schedule A versus Schedule B.

12. H_0: The point production is the same under the new coach as it was under the former coach ($\mu_1 - \mu_2 = 0$).

H_1: The point production under the new coach is different from what it was under the old coach ($\mu_1 - \mu_2 \neq 0$).
Decision Rule: Reject H_0 if the computed value for t is more extreme than 2.202.

$t = -3.44$. Therefore, we reject H_0 and conclude that point production under the new coach is significantly different (i.e., more) than what it was under the former coach.

Chapter 13

1. Because the two groups are independent and the data are ordinally scaled the Mann-Whitney *U*-test was used. The computed value of the *U* statistic equals 45.5 ($U' = 54.5$). The two values in the *U* table for $n_1 = 10$, $n_2 = 10$, and $\alpha = .05$ are 23 and 77. Since *U* and *U'* are within the range of these values we fail to reject the null hypothesis. In the opinion of the fur experts there was no difference in fur quality between the animals that were fed the additive and those that were not.

2. As in Problem 1, this problem also involves two independent groups. To avoid concerns that the data may not be normally distributed the Mann-Whitney *U*-test is used as an alternative to the *t*-test. The computed value of the Mann-Whitney *U* is 23 ($U' = 58$). The critical range with n_1 and n_2 equal to 9 and $\alpha = .05$ is 17 to 64. Since *U* and *U'* fall inside this range we fail to reject the null hypothesis. Apparently, there was no difference in the number of errors made by the two groups.

3. Two measures were taken on the same set of individuals, and so a test for correlated groups is appropriate. Subjective rating scores are assumed to be ordinal and the Wilcoxon analysis of these data results in a T value of 1.5. The critical value for T with 8 pairs equals 5. (Note that two ties, 7.5 − 7.5 and 9.5 − 9.5, were dropped from the analysis, reducing the original 10 pairs to 8.) The null hypothesis is rejected because the computed T value is less than the critical value. Apparently the District A judges are less generous in scoring dives than the District B judges.

4. The matching procedure that was used in setting up the experiment dictates the use of a correlated groups test. The rating scores are assumed to be ordinal, and so the Wilcoxon test is appropriate. The computed T value is 12.5 and, because this is less than the critical T value of 17 ($n = 13$ and $\alpha = .05$), we must reject the null hypothesis. The two therapies resulted in different recovery rates.

7. $U = 9.5 \quad U' = 54.5$ With $n_1 = 8$ and $n_2 = 8$, the critical range from the Mann-Whitney table ($\alpha = .05$) is 13 to 51. Since the computed values for *U* and *U'* are outside the critical range, we reject H_0. Strain 2 was rated more difficult to handle than Strain 1.

8. $U = 36$, $U' = 64$ The critical range for *U* and *U'* with both n_1 and $n_2 = 10$ and $\alpha = .05$ is 23 to 77. Since the computed values fall within the critical range, we fail to reject H_0. The difference in litter size between the two strains of rats was not significant.

9. $U = 8.5$ and $U' = 55.5$. The critical range for *U* and *U'* with n_1 and $n_2 = 8$ and $\alpha = .05$ is 13 to 51. Since the computed values fall outside the critical range, we reject H_0. The training in stress management apparently lowered the perceived level of stress among the trained mothers compared to the untrained mothers.

10. The Wilcoxon T = 4. The critical value of T with $n = 11$ is 10. Since the computed T value is less than the critical value, we reject H_0. The training session raised the performance ratings of the sales personnel.

11. The Wilcoxon T = 0. The critical value of T with $n = 12$ is 13. Since the computed value of zero is less than the critical value of 13, we reject H_0. Humidification did affect perceived comfort level.

Chapter 14

Before listing the solutions to the chapter 14 exercises, here is the analysis of the mortar shell data that you were asked to complete with the chi-square goodness-of-fit test.

$$\chi^2 = \frac{(62 - 70)^2}{70} + \frac{(17 - 20)^2}{20} + \frac{(21 - 10)^2}{10}$$

$$\chi^2 = 13.49$$

The critical value of chi-square with $df = 2$ and $\alpha = 0.01$ equals 9.20. Since the computed value of chi-square exceeds the critical value ($13.49 > 9.20$), the obtained cell frequencies are significantly different from the expected frequencies. In the context of the mortar shell evaluation, the test revealed that the shells were not as accurate as the manufacturer claimed. The principal deviation from the expected frequency can be found in the last cell in which more than twice the expected number of shells (21 actual vs. 10 expected) fell beyond 100′ from the designated impact area.

1. The computed value of the chi-square statistic equals 28.034. With $df = 10$, the critical value with $\alpha = .05$ is 18.31. With $\alpha = .01$ the critical value is 23.21. Regardless of which alpha level is used, the null hypothesis must be rejected. The patients' responses to the question ("better off, worse off, or unchanged") is a function of the type of chemotherapy they received.

2. If you computed a chi-square it would equal 6.484, but these data violate the assumption that, with $df = 1$, all cells must have expected values greater than 10. Two cells do not, and so we may not use the chi-square test here. Another nonparametric test called the

Fisher Exact Probability Test (Siegel, 1956) is a better choice.

3. This comparison may be made using the chi-square single variable ("goodness of fit") test. The computed value of the chi-square statistic equals 0.77 and, with $df = 2$ and $\alpha = .05$, the critical value equals 3.84. There was no difference in the responses when they were added across all types of chemotherapy.

4. The computed value of the chi-square statistic equals 13.509. With $df = 5$ and $\alpha = .05$, the critical value of chi-square is 11.07. We reject the null hypothesis and conclude that the success rate one might expect to achieve in deprogramming cult members depends upon the deprogrammer that is used.

5. The computed value of the chi-square statistic equals 8.095. With $df = 4$ and $\alpha = .05$, the critical value of chi-square is 9.49. We reject the null hypothesis and conclude that there is no difference in the insemination success rate for the breeds of cows that were included in the experiment.

9. Chi-square = 7.952 and $df = 3$. Since the computed value is greater than the critical value of 7.815 ($\alpha = .05$), we reject the null hypothesis. The four kinds of wrapping paper were not equally regarded by the customers.

10. Chi-square = 6.50 and $df = 4$. Since the computed value of chi-square is less than the critical value of 9.488 ($\alpha = .05$), we fail to reject H_0. The differences in drinking preferences across the three socioeconomic levels was not significant.

11. Chi-square = 18.65 and $df = 6$. Since the computed value of chi-square is greater than the critical value of 12.592 ($\alpha = .05$), we reject H_0. These data support the contention that job satisfaction depends, at least in part, upon one's level of education.

12. Chi-square = 9.06 and $df = 1$ (Yates correction applied.) Since the computed value for chi-square is greater than the critical value of 3.84 ($\alpha = .05$), we reject H_0. The data support the contention that the toxic substance can contribute to congenital defects.

15. **(a)** Two cells have expected frequencies that are less than 5.00. This violates an assumption of the statistic. We may, however, collapse across categories. (See part **b.**)

(b) Chi-square = 14.95 and $df = 2$. Since the computed value of chi-square is greater than the critical value of 9.21 ($\alpha = .01$), we reject H_0. The tendency of the mice to fight depends upon the dose of replacement therapy they receive.

Chapter 15

1. When the null hypothesis is true, the treatment means vary from each other only to the extent that random (error) variation is present. This is also the only reason for scores within a treatment to vary from each other. Therefore, both the within treatment variance and the between treatment variance are estimates of the same error variance. When H_0 is true:

$$F = \frac{MS_{between}}{MS_{within}} = \frac{\text{error variance}}{\text{error variance}} = 1.00$$

2. When H_0 is not true, there are two causes for scores in different treatments to differ from each other: error variation and the treatment effect. As you can see from the equation below, the existence of a treatment effect will inflate the numerator and give a result greater than 1.00.

$$F = \frac{\text{error variance} + \text{treatment variance}}{\text{error variance}} > 1.00$$

4. The treatment effect for any one treatment is assumed to be a constant, affecting all subjects within that treatment equally. In the structural model the treatment effect is treated as the addition or subtraction of a constant. Since adding a constant to or subtracting a constant from all elements of a set does not affect the variance of the set, the variance of scores within a treatment is unaffected by the presence of a treatment effect.

5. $F = 4$, $df = 1, 22$

6. $X_{ij} = \mu + E_{ij}$

7. $X_{ij} = \mu + E_{ij} + T_j$

11. SS/df is the average ("mean") variation per degree of freedom, hence the name Mean Square.

12. We divide the $MS_{b.t.}$ by the $MS_{w.t.}$.

14. **(a)** 997.39
(b) $SS_1 = 365.99$, $SS_2 = 148$, $SS_3 = 378$
(c) 105.4
(d) $105.4 + (365.99 + 148 + 378) = 997.39$
(e) $MS_{between\ treatment} = 52.7$ $df = 2$
$MS_{within\ treatment} = 42.47$ $df = 21$
(f) $F = 1.24$

15. **(a)** 1381.35
(b) $SS_1 = 365.99$, SS_2 148, SS_3 378
(c) 489.35
(d) $489.35 + (365.99 + 148 + 378) = 1381.35$
(e) Adding a constant to all numbers in a set does not affect the dispersion of the set.

(f) $MS_{between\ treatment} = 244.67$
$MS_{within\ treatment} = 42.47$
(g) $F = 5.76$

Chapter 16

1. The ANOVA solutions presented below were done by computer. Slight differences between these results and your hand calculations are most likely due to rounding error.

ANOVA Summary Table

Source	*df*	SS	MS	*F*
Between treatment	3	1,234.10	411.36	5.42
Within treatment	28	2,123.75	75.85	
Total	31	3,357.85		

2. (a) 1.00
   (b) treatment 4
   (c) 2.95
   (d) Yes
   (e) 5 times
   (f) The second result of 1.54 is closer to the expected value of 1.00.
3. True
4. True
5. False. Change "multiplying" to "dividing."
6. True
7. False. Change "less" to "more."
8. 1.00
9.

Analysis of Variance Summary Table

Source	*df*	SS	MS	*F*
Between Subjects	5	60.80		
Within Subjects	18	80.20		
Between treatment	3	42.00	14.00	5.49
Residual	15	38.20	2.55	
Total	23	141.00		

10.

ANOVA Summary Table

Source	*df*	SS	MS	*F*
Between treatment	2	140.93	70.46	22.97
Within treatment	12	36.80	3.06	
Total	14	177.73		

The computed value for *F* exceeds the critical value of 3.88, and so we conclude that the stimulus illumination did affect the error rate.

11.

Analysis of Variance Summary Table

Source	*df*	SS	MS	*F*
Between Subjects	5	339.33		
Within Subjects	12	1,612.67		
Between treatment	2	676.00	338.00	3.61
Residual	10	936.67	93.67	
Total	17	1,952.00		

The ANOVA Summary was completed using the following computational components:
(1) $G^2/18 = 32{,}258$
(2) $\Sigma\Sigma X^2 = 34{,}210$ (This value was given in the problem.)
(3) $\Sigma T_k^2/6 = 32{,}934$
(4) $\Sigma P_i^2/3 = 32{,}597.33$
The computed *F* value of 3.61 is less than the critical *F* value of 4.10. We must fail to reject the null hypothesis and conclude that no difference has been demonstrated in the effectiveness of the three training programs.

12.

Source	***df***	**SS**	**MS**	***F***
Between treatment	3	378.8	126.26	6.71
Within treatment	16	301.2	18.82	
Total	19	680		

13.

Source	***df***	**SS**	**MS**	***F***
Between treatment	2	234.17	117.08	1.09
Within treatment	27	2,894.10	107.18	
Total	29	3,128.27		

14.

Analysis of Variance Summary Table

Source	*df*	SS	MS	*F*
Between Subjects	4	468.39		
Within Subjects	20	333.60		
Between treatment	4	192.40	48.10	5.45
Residual	16	141.20	8.82	
Total	24	802		

Chapter 17

3. (a)

ANOVA Summary Table

Source	df	SS	MS	F
Between treatment	3	887.65	295.88	3.33
Within treatment	36	3,198.52	88.84	
Total	39	4,086.17		

The critical value for F with 3 and 36 degrees of freedom is 2.86. Thus, some difference does exist in grading practices among the four teaching assistants.

(b) To follow up the overall ANOVA with the Tukey HSD test we need the table of differences between treatment means:

Treatment: **Ordered Means:**	**3** **73.4**	**1** **79.1**	**4** **81.9**	**2** **86.4**
3 (73.4)	—	5.7	8.5	13.0
1 (79.1)		—	2.8	7.3
4 (81.9)			—	4.5
2 (86.4)				—

According to the Q table, the critical value for the Q statistic with $k = 4$ and $df = 36$ is between 4.10 ($df = 30$) and 4.04 ($df = 40$). Let us be conservative and use 4.10 as the critical value. (We could interpolate between 4.10 and 4.04, but the difference is so slight between these two values it is hardly worthwhile.) Only the difference of 13, between Itsuko and Wilson ($Q = 4.36$) is significant. Apparently, these two teaching assistants differ in the grading criteria they use.

(c) In comparing the extreme cases of Itsuko and Wilson with the Scheffé test, $F = 3.17$. This is larger than the critical value of $F(3,36) = 2.84$, and the difference is, therefore, significant. No other comparison is significant.

4. In this problem a prediction was made prior to data collection that the code violations reported by Mr. Smith will be less than the violations reported by the other inspectors. Thus, we may do a priori planned comparisons to evaluate this prediction, and a significant F value in the overall ANOVA is not required to do the individual comparisons between the various building inspectors.

Analysis of Variance Summary Table

Source	df	SS	MS	F
Between Subjects	7	109.60		
Within Subjects	32	132.80		
Between treatment	4	70.65	17.66	7.95
Residual	28	62.14	2.22	
Total	39	242.40		

The computed F value of 7.95 is greater than the critical value $F(4,28) = 2.71$ and is, therefore, significant.

The individual comparisons between Mr. Smith and the other four inspectors are done using the formula:

$$t = \frac{\bar{T}_i - \bar{T}_j}{\sqrt{\frac{2\ \text{MS}_{\text{error}}}{n}}}$$

Since these data were analyzed using a repeated measures (correlated groups) ANOVA, the MS error for the above formula is the MS residual from the ANOVA Summary Table.

The t values for Smith versus Laird, Castiglia, Mintz, and Benway are, respectively: 3.86, 4.54, 4.87, and 2.36. The critical value for t with $df = 7$ is 2.365.

(Note that since this is a correlated groups comparison, $df = n - 1$ just as if we were doing a normal correlated *t*-test, and *not* $n_1 + n_2 - 2$. The *df* value $n_1 + n_2 - 2$ is used in the independent groups *t*-test and in planned comparisons between independent groups.) Mr. Smith found fewer violations than Laird, Castiglia, and Mintz, but not significantly fewer than Benway.

7. The first step in doing the Tukey HSD test is to organize the table of differences between all possible pairs of treatment means. (Here, "treatment" = Problem #.)

Problem:	**5**	**4**	**3**	**2**	**1**
Ordered Means:	**6.4**	**7.4**	**11.6**	**12.2**	**13.4**
5 (6.4)	—	1.00	5.2	5.8	7.0
4 (7.4)		—	4.2	4.8	6.0
3 (11.6)			—	0.6	1.8
2 (12.2)				—	1.2
1 (13.4)					—

$$Q = \frac{\overline{X}_i - \overline{X}_j}{\sqrt{\frac{MS_{error}}{n}}}$$

Because the repeated measures ANOVA was done on these correlated data, the MS_{error} we must substitute in the Q formula is the $MS_{residual}$. From the ANOVA summary table (chapter 16, Problem 14) we see that the $MS_{residual}$ equals 8.82. To compute the denominator of the Q statistic, we must divide 8.82 by 5, the number of scores within each treatment, and take the square root of the resulting quantity. This equals 1.33. The values in the above table of differences are then divided by 1.33 starting with the largest difference score (7.00) and continuing with successively smaller values (6.00, 5.8, 5.2, etc.) until the computed Q value fails to exceed the critical value of 4.33 ($\alpha = .05$).

Problem 1 vs. 5: $Q = 7/1.33 = 5.26$
Problem 1 vs. 4: $Q = 6/1.33 = 4.51$
Problem 2 vs. 5: $Q = 5.8/1.33 = 4.36$
Problem 3 vs. 5: $Q = 5.2/1.33 = 3.91$

The first three comparisons are significant because they exceed the critical value of 4.33. The fourth, Problem 3 versus Problem 5 is not significant, and so we stop here. We do not bother to compute the Q statistic using the numerically smaller difference scores in the table because they could not possibly be significant (i.e., $Q > 4.33$).

The Tukey HSD test tells us that Problem 5 was solved faster than Problems 1 and 2, and Problem 4 was solved faster than Problem 1. Apparently, solving three prior problems was a minimum level of practice necessary to produce a significant improvement in problem-solving ability in this experiment.

Chapter 18

The ANOVA solutions presented below were done by computer. Slight differences between these results and your hand calculations are most likely due to rounding error.

1. $SS = 330.22$
2. $SS_1 = 18.67$
   $SS_2 = 8.00$
   $SS_3 = 20.67$
3. $SS_{between\ cell} = 82.56$
4.

Analysis of Variance Summary Table

Source	*df*	SS	MS	*F*
Between cell	3	98		
Speed (A)	1	63	63	23.63
Protection (B)	1	28	28	10.50
A × B	1	7	7	2.63
Within cell	24	64	2.67	
Total	27	162		

In the F table $F(1,24) = 4.26$ with $\alpha = .05$ and 7.82 with $\alpha = .01$. The computed values for factors A and B are more extreme than 4.26. Thus, the contribution of factors A and B to the $MS_{\text{between cell}}$ would be regarded as significant for both $\alpha = .05$ and $\alpha = .01$.

Analysis of Variance Summary Table

Source	*df*	SS	MS	*F*
Between cell	8	8.54		
Time (A)	2	5.62	2.81	15.35
Temperature (B)	2	1.24	0.62	3.38
A × B	4	1.67	0.42	2.28
Within cell	36	6.59	0.18	
Total	44	15.13		

Using $\alpha = .05$, the critical value for evaluating both factor A and factor B is $F(2,36) = 3.26$. The critical value for evaluating the A × B interaction is $F(4,36) = 2.63$. Factor A and factor B made a significant contribution to the variance between cell, but the A × B interaction was not significant. Inspection of the cell means reveals that they are relatively uniform with the exception of $AB_{32} = 15.6$ and $AB_{33} = 15.8$. From inspection of the means, it appears that the combination of 120 minutes of heat treatment with temperature set at 1,550 degrees or 1,600 degrees allows the Bivanium to dissolve, and this results in an increased tensile strength. We would expect this interactive effect of time and temperature to register as an A × B interaction in the data analysis. The A × B interaction was, however, not significant, and it is likely that the metallurgist would want to repeat the experiment with a larger sample size to obtain more power. From these data it appears that the trend toward a large jump in tensile strength at two particular time/temperature combinations is worth pursuing with a larger scale experiment.

6.

Analysis of Variance Summary Table

Source	*df*	SS	MS	*F*
Between cell	5	564.17		
Task (A)	1	410.70	410.70	54.52
Trials (B)	2	22.07	11.03	1.46
A × B	2	131.40	65.70	8.72
Within cell	24	180.80	7.53	
Total	29	744.97		

If $\alpha = .05$ the critical value for evaluating factor A is $F(1,24) = 4.26$, and for factor B and the A × B interaction the critical value is $F(2,24) = 3.40$. Factor A and the A × B interaction are significant.

Inspection of the cell means reveals that experience with Preliminary Task 1 served to facilitate performance on the standard task, while experience with Preliminary Task 2 tended to impair performance on the standard task. (The first effect is called positive transfer and the second effect is called negative transfer.) Factor B, the number of training trials to criterion, did not register as significant because the pattern of means within Task 1 was the opposite to the pattern of means within Task 2. That is, the more experience a rat had with Preliminary Task 1, the *more* correct responses the animal gave on the standard task, but the more experience a rat had with Preliminary Task 2, the *fewer* correct responses the animal gave on the standard task. The result of such a pattern is to cancel out a factor B main effect. Instead, this interactive pattern registered as a significant A × B interaction in the ANOVA summary table. Also, if you plot the means you should notice the nonparallelism that is indicative of an interaction effect.

7. (a)

Analysis of Variance Summary Table

Source	*df*	SS	MS	*F*
Between cell	3	2.09		
Quiet/normal (A)	1	1.24	1.24	6.20
Coed/unisex (B)	1	0.59	0.59	2.94
A × B	1	0.26	0.26	1.28
Within cell	20	4.00	0.20	
Total	23	6.09		

$F(1,20) = 4.35$, so factor A is significant ($6.20 > 4.35$). The students who lived in the quiet dormitories got higher grades than the students who lived in regular dormitories.

Glossary

Addition Rule. For mutually exclusive events:

$$P(A \text{ or } B) = P(A) + P(B)$$

For nonmutually exclusive events:

$$P(A \text{ or } B) = P(A) + P(B) - P(A + B)$$

154

Alpha Level. The Greek α represents the level of significance that is used in a statistical test. It is also the probability of falsely rejecting the null hypothesis. *189*

Alpha Level Inflation. The increase in the probability of Type I error when multiple *t*-tests are used to make all possible paired comparisons among a set of treatment means. *352*

Alternative Hypothesis. A logical state contradictory to the equality that is formally stated in the null hypothesis. For example, if the null hypothesis in a coin flipping experiment is that $P(\text{Head}) = .5$ ("The coin is fair."), the alternative hypothesis will be $P \neq .5$. ("The coin is not fair.") The alternative hypothesis states that nonchance factors will influence the results of the sampling experiment. The alternative hypothesis, also called the experimental hypothesis, always contains a statement of inequality. *187, 212*

ANOVA. An abbreviation for the ANalysis Of VAriance. *308*

ANOVA Summary Table. The tabular display of the results of an Analysis of Variance showing the Source of Variation, *df*, SS, MS, and the *F* ratio. *328*

A Posteriori Tests (also called post hoc tests). Computational procedures that permit comparisons among treatment means when the comparisons were thought of after examining the data rather than being planned prior to running the experiment. *349*

A Priori Tests. Computational procedures that permit comparisons among treatment means when the comparisons were planned prior to running the experiment. *348*

"as extreme or even more extreme". (*See* "as rare or rarer than.") *189*

"as rare or rarer than". In Step 4 of hypothesis testing, assuming the null hypothesis is true, we must determine the probability of obtaining a statistic as rare or rarer than (as extreme or even more extreme than) the computed value. This value is then used in Step 5. *189*

Before and After Design. A type of repeated measures experimental design. A single group of subjects is tested before exposure to the experimental treatment in order to get a baseline measure (the control condition). Then the same group is retested after exposure to the experimental treatment. *243*

Bell-shaped Distribution. The characteristic shape of the distribution of a normally distributed variable. *See* Normal Distribution. *71*

Best-Fit Line. The linear function derived from a least squares solution that is used to represent the linear trend of a scatterplot. Each scatterplot has two best-fit lines: one for predicting Y with the knowledge of X and one for predicting X with the knowledge of Y. *97*

Bias. A factor (or factors), other than chance or experimentally controlled variables, capable of influencing the results of an experiment. *152*

Binomial Expansion. The expansion of the expression $(P + Q)^N$. Each of the $N + 1$ terms in the expansion yields a probability, and all the probabilities sum to 1.00. *170*

Categorical Data. A synonym for nominal or frequency data. Data typically take the form of tallies in discrete categories. *292*

Causality. Causality exists between variables X and Y when changes in the value of variable X are the direct cause of changes in the value of variable Y. All causally related variables are also functionally related, but functionally related variables are not necessarily causally related. For example, as temperature goes up, so does the electrical output of solar cells. But the temperature increase doesn't cause the increase in electrical output. Both temperature increase and solar cell output are caused by a third variable: the intensity of the available sunlight. *139*

Central Limit Theorem. A mathematical theorem that allows one to predict the characteristics (mean and deviation measure) of the sampling distribution of the sample mean. According to the central limit theorem, the sample mean has an expected value equal to the mean of the population from which the sample was drawn, and the deviation measure of the distribution of sample means (called the standard error) has an expected value equal to the standard deviation of the raw score population divided by the square root of the sample size. In notation, $E(\overline{X}) = \mu$ and $E(\sigma_{\overline{X}}) = \sigma_X/\sqrt{n}$. *202*

Central Tendency. The statistical description of a distribution in terms of an average or typical value. The mean, median, and mode are measures of central tendency. *29, 44*

Class Interval. The range that is used to group the scores in a distribution into discrete clusters or "classes." According to convention, the ideal size of the class interval is usually fairly close to the range of the data divided by 15. *31*

Coefficient of Alienation. The proportion of variation in the values of a variable (usually Y) that is not predictable (unexplained) from the value of a predictor (usually X). *128*

Coefficient of Determination. The proportion of variation in the values of a variable (usually Y) that is predictable (explained) from the value of a predictor (usually X). *128*

Computational Components. The special values computed from the data that are used to compute total variation and partition it into its component parts. *327, 387*

Confidence Interval. An interval of score values within which the population mean is expected to lie with a specified degree of confidence (usually 95% or 99%). *232*

Contingency Table. A table with r rows and c columns that shows the contingency between two variables. Each row represents a mutually exclusive category of the row variable, and each column represents a mutually exclusive category of the column variable. The table has $r \times c$ cells, and the entries in the cells are frequencies. *296*

Continuous Variable. A variable is continuous if, as it changes from value A to value B, it passes through all the possible values that exist between A and B (e.g., height and weight are continuous variables). *7*

Control Group. A group that is as similar as possible to the experimental group in composition and experience except for exposure to the experimental treatment. The control group provides baseline data against which the performance of the experimental group may be compared. *242*

Correction for Discontinuity. A correction that is applied to improve accuracy when the distribution of the z statistic is used to approximate the distribution of the binomial. *176*

Correlated Experimental Designs. There are two types of correlated experimental designs. In the matched pairs or correlated groups design, before the experiment is begun, each subject that is assigned to the control condition is matched in some way (or ways) to a subject in the experimental condition. Matching may be done with reference to any variable that is thought to be relevant to the experiment, such as I.Q., age, religious affiliation, etc. The second type of correlated design is the repeated measures design. The term *correlated groups design* is sometimes used interchangeably with *repeated measures design*, even though, technically, the designs are different. In the repeated measures design the "matching" is perfect because the same subject is tested under both experimental and control conditions. In the correlated groups (i.e., matched pairs) design the subjects in the control group and the experimental group are, although matched, not the same individuals. *243*

Correlated Groups Design. *See* Correlated Experimental Designs.

Correlation. A statistic that quantifies the extent of positive or negative linear trend that exists in the relationship between two variables. *111*

Counterbalancing. An approach to the design of an experiment that allows one to spread out possible sequence and order effects evenly across all treatments. *338*

Critical Region. (*See* Region of Rejection.) *209*

Cumulative Frequency. The frequency of scores in a distribution that have values equal to or less than the true upper limit of a class interval. *35*

Cumulative Percent. The percent of scores in a distribution that have values equal to or less than the true upper limit of a class interval. *35*

Decision Rule. A statement of the standard that will be applied in deciding whether or not to reject or retain the null hypothesis. For example, in the context of the z test, the decision rule for a two-tail test with the alpha level set at .05 is "Reject the null hypothesis if the computed value for z is greater than or equal to $+1.96$ or less than or equal to -1.96." *188, 211*

Degrees of Freedom. The number of elements of data that are free to vary in calculating a statistic. *222, 294, 316*

Dependent Variable. The variable that is measured in an experiment. It is assumed to vary as a function of the independent variable. *6*

Descriptive Statistic. A number that reflects a specific characteristic of a set of data. *8*

Deviation Score. The difference between a score value and the mean of the distribution to which the score belongs. In notation, the deviation score for X is written $(X - \overline{X})$. *46*

Dichotomous Variable. A variable that can take only one of two possible values (e.g., true/false, on/off, etc.). *7*

Difference Score. The difference score is the difference in value between the control score and the experimental score for each subject in a repeated measures design (or matched pair of subjects in a matched groups design). *244*

Direct Difference Method. The computational method for the correlated groups or repeated measures t-test. *258*

Discontinuous Variable. A variable is discontinuous if, as it changes from value A to value B, it changes abruptly without passing through all the values that exist between A and B (e.g., family size). *7*

Dispersal. The degree to which the score values in a distribution are spread about the central (i.e., average) value. The range is a measure of dispersal. *28*

Dispersion. A statistical representation of the degree to which the scores in a distribution are dispersed about the central value. Variation (SS), variance (σ^2) and standard deviation (σ) are statistical measures of dispersion. *44*

Expected Frequencies. The frequencies that each cell would be expected to have if the null hypothesis were true. *292*

Expected Value. The value that a sample statistic is theoretically expected to equal within the restraints of a given sampling experiment. For example, $E(\overline{X}) = \mu$ says that the expected value of a sample mean equals the mean of the population from which the sample was drawn. *202, 309*

Experimental Group. The group in an experiment that is randomly designated to receive the experimental treatment. *242*

Factorial Design. An experimental design in which two or more variables (called "factors") are manipulated simultaneously. In the two-factor design, factor A has p levels and factor B has q levels. Therefore, the design defines $p \cdot q$ different experimental conditions called "cells." The principal advantage of the factorial design is that it permits the assessment of interactions among variables. *371*

***F* ratio.** The ratio of the $MS_{b.t.}$ to the $MS_{w.t.}$. According to the structural model of the ANOVA, if the null hypothesis is true and there are no treatment effects, the expected value of the F ratio is 1.00. *317*

Frequency. The number of times a particular score value or range of score values appears in a distribution. *28*

Frequency Data. A synonym for nominal or categorical data. *292*

Frequency Polygon. A graph of a distribution with score frequency on the Y-axis and score value on the X-axis. Inspection of the graph will reveal how many times each score occurs in the distribution. *36*

General Rule. The general computational procedure for determining the variation (SS) in any set of raw or composite scores. *See* text in chapter 15 for details. *315, 386*

Grouped Frequency Distribution. The tabular summary of an ungrouped frequency distribution that is accomplished by dividing the entire range of the data into 15 or so equal-sized ranges called class intervals. A tally is taken to determine how many scores fall within the range of each class interval. *26*

Histogram. A graphic representation of interval or ratio data in which the frequencies of score values or class intervals appear as contiguous bars. *36*

Homoscedasticity. One underlying assumption of the Pearson r statistic stating that the scatterplot must have a uniform cross-sectional width along its length. *125*

Independence. In the context of the chi-square statistic, the entries in a contingency table are said to reflect independence if the effect of the column variable on the pattern of cell frequencies is independent of (i.e., not contingent upon) the effect of the row variable upon the pattern of cell frequencies. *296*

Independent. When the occurrence or nonoccurrence of one event in no way influences the occurrence or nonoccurrence of another event, the events are independent. *149*

Independent Groups Design. Subjects are randomly assigned to the treatment conditions of an experiment. *253*

Independent Variable. A variable that is manipulated by the experimenter (e.g., the treatment administered to a subject in an experiment). *6*

Inferential Statistics. Drawing conclusions about the characteristics of populations from the information in sample data. *9*

Interaction. In the context of the two-factor design, an interaction is an experimental effect that results from certain factor A–factor B combinations that cannot be accounted for by the individual contributions of factor A and factor B. *374*

Interval Estimation. Specifying a range of values that has a certain likelihood of containing the value of a parameter (e.g., μ) as opposed to the specific value stated in a point estimate. *230*

Interval Scale. A measurement scale with an arbitrary zero point in which numerically equal intervals at different locations on the scale reflect the same quantitative difference (e.g., temperature in Celsius or Fahrenheit). *15*

Least Squares. A definition of the mean as that score in a distribution about which the sum of the squared deviation scores is a minimum. In notation, $\Sigma(X - \overline{X})^2 = \text{minimum}$. In the context of regression, $\Sigma(y - y')^2 = \text{minimum}$. *48*

Level of Significance. The probability level (usually .05 or .01) at which we decide to reject the null hypothesis and default to the alternative hypothesis. The alpha (α) level of a test. The probability of Type I error. *189*

Linear Function. A straight line function represented by the equation $Y = a + bX$ where a is the Y-intercept and b is the slope of the line. *90*

Linear Regression Analysis. Solving for the equation that best describes the linear trend between two variables. *93*

Linear Trend. The tendency of an imperfect functional relationship between two variables to resemble a straight line. *94*

Main Effect. An experimental effect that is attributable to different levels of one factor. It is assessed after averaging across all levels of the other factor. *373*

Mann-Whitney *U*-Test. A nonparametric test that may be used as a substitute for the independent groups t-test. The statistical power of the Mann-Whitney U-test is comparable to that of the t-test. *276*

Matched Pairs Design. *See* Correlated Experimental Designs.

Mean. The sum of all the score values in a distribution divided by the number of scores. The mean is also called the *average*. *45*

Median. The score value in a distribution above which and below which half the score values fall. *45*

Mode. The most frequently occurring score value in a distribution. *45*

Monotonicity. A pattern observed in some functions in which, in a positive function, successively greater X values are always paired with successively greater Y values and, in a negative function, successively greater X values are always paired with successively smaller Y values. *129*

MS. Mean square ("MS") is really just a variance. It is the average variation per degree of freedom or, said another way, SS divided by the appropriate *df* as in:

$$MS_{b.t.} = \frac{SS_{b.t.}}{k - 1}$$

317

$MS_{between\ treatment}$. A Mean Square ("MS") is a variance. The $MS_{b.t.}$ is the $SS_{b.t.}$ divided by $(k - 1)$ degrees of freedom and is used as the numerator of the F ratio. *317*

$MS_{within\ cell}$. The variance within cells. An estimate of the error variance that is sometimes written MS_{error}. In the two-factor design, the $MS_{within\ cell} = SS_{within\ cell}/pq(n - 1)$. *390*

$MS_{within\ treatment}$. A mean square ("MS") is a variance. The $MS_{w.t.}$ is the $SS_{w.t.}$ divided by $k(n - 1)$ degrees of freedom and is used as the denominator of the F ratio. *317*

Multiple Comparisons. Evaluating the differences between all possible pairs of treatment means in a multigroup experiment. If done using the *t*-test, this results in alpha inflation and the near certainty of committing a Type I error. *351*

Multiplication Rule. For independent events:

$$P(A \text{ and } B) = P(A) \cdot P(B)$$

For nonindependent events:

$$P(A \text{ and } B) = P(A) \cdot P(A/B)$$

155

Mutually Exclusive. If events are related such that the occurrence of one event denies the possibility of the occurrence of the other, the events are mutually exclusive. For example, the sex of a child is a mutually exclusive variable because identifying a child as a male means that the child cannot be a female. *151*

Negative Relationship. A negative relationship is said to exist between X and Y when high values of variable X tend to be paired with low values of variable Y, and low values of variable X tend to be paired with high values of variable Y. The graph of a negative linear function slopes from upper left to lower right. *92*

Nominal Limits. The limits of a class interval in whole units of measurement. *32*

Nominal Scale. A measurement scale in which numbers are used as labels or names rather than to reflect quantitative information (e.g., the numbers on athletic uniforms). *19*

Nonlinear Relationships. Functional relationships that do not plot as a straight line. *126*

Nonparametric Statistics (also called "distribution free" statistics). Statistical procedures for hypothesis testing that do not require the estimation of population parameters and, in general, do not require meeting many of the assumptions that must be met for legitimate use of the parametric tests. In general, the nonparametric tests do not have the same degree of statistical power as the parametric tests. *270*

Nonpredictable Variation (also called unexplained variation). The variation of a variable (usually Y) that is not predictable with the knowledge of a predictor (usually X). *124*

Normal Distribution (also called the Normal Curve). A bell-shaped symmetrical curve that typifies the distributions of many behavioral (e.g., intelligence) and physical (e.g., height) variables. *70*

Null Hypothesis. In general, the null hypothesis is a working assumption that only chance will affect the results of an experiment. The null hypothesis always states an equality and is retained or rejected following an analysis of the data. *186, 207*

Null Hypothesis Population. The population described in the null hypothesis from which we assume the sample was drawn. *210*

Observed Frequencies. The actual frequency data upon which the chi-square analysis is performed. *292*

Ogive Curve. The S-shaped curve that results from the graphic plot of cumulative frequency or cumulative percent data. *36*

One-tail Test. The statistical test that is employed to test a directional hypothesis. The 5% (or 1%) of area that is enclosed in the critical region is located in either the right tail or the left tail. *216*

Order Effect. An effect that results from the order in which a subject experiences a treatment. For example, if there are four treatment conditions in a repeated measures ANOVA design, the subject may be fatigued by the time data are collected under the fourth treatment condition. To the extent that fatigue influences subject performance, an order effect exists. *338*

Ordinal Scale. A measurement scale in which values reflect only rank order (e.g., the order of finishing a race). *16*

Orthogonal Comparisons. An approach to planned comparisons that involves dividing the $SS_{b.t.}$ into $k - 1$ nonoverlapping ("orthogonal") parts. This allows the exact contribution of each individual comparison to the $SS_{b.t.}$ to be determined, but the comparisons that are orthogonal do not always make sense within the context of the experiment. *361*

Overall (Weighted) Mean. The mean of a set of means. *53*

Parameter. A measurable characteristic of a population. *8*

Partitioning SS. The process of dividing total variation into that portion attributable only to random factors ($SS_{w.t.}$) and the portion(s) that is (are) attributable to nonrandom (systematic) factors. *316*

Pearson *r*. A statistic that describes the extent of the linear relationship between variable X and variable Y on a scale of 0 to 1.00 or 0 to -1.00. *111*

Percentile. The location of a score in a distribution in terms of the percentage of scores that equal or are less than the score value. ("Forty is on the 35th percentile.") *71*

Percentile Rank. A value equal to the percentage of scores in a distribution that are equal to or less than a specific score value. ("The percentile rank of forty is 35.") *71*

Planned Comparisons. Comparisons between treatments that were planned before execution of the experiment. These comparisons usually flow logically from the experimental rationale. *360*

Point Estimation. Estimating a population parameter with a specific score value. For example, the value of a sample mean may be used as a point estimate of μ, the mean of the population from which the sample was drawn. *230*

Population. All members of a specified group. The specification can be broad (e.g., all members of the human race) or relatively narrow (e.g., all male heads of household whose income exceeds $40,000 per year). *5*

Positive Relationship. A positive relationship is said to exist between X and Y when high values of variable X are paired with high values of variable Y and low values of X are paired with low values of Y. The graph of a positive linear function slopes from lower left to upper right. *90*

Post Hoc Tests. *See* a posteriori tests. *351*

Power of a Test. The ability of a test to reject the null hypothesis when it is false and should be rejected. *229*

Predictable Variation (also called explained variation). The variation of a variable (usually Y) that is predictable with the knowledge of a predictor (usually X). *124*

Prediction. Using the equation representing the functional relationship between two variables to predict the value of one variable with the knowledge of the other. *88*

Probability. The proportion of all possible events that are considered successes:

$$P(\text{success}) = \frac{\text{successes}}{\text{successes} + \text{failures}}$$

151

Proportions of Area. Using the z statistic, one can determine the proportion of the total area under any normal curve that is contained in a specific segment of the curve. These proportions of area are listed in the z table according to the area between the mean and the score (column B) and between the score and the tail (column C). *75*

***P* value.** The probability that the event defined as a success will occur in a sampling experiment. *169*

***Q* value.** The probability that the event defined as a failure will occur in a sampling experiment. *169*

Random Sampling. Sampling so that each element or group of elements has an equal chance of being included in the sample. *149*

Range. The highest score in a distribution minus the lowest score plus one. For example, the range of the distribution 11, 12, 12, 12, 13, 13, 14, 15 is $15 - 11 + 1 = 5$. *28*

Ranking. Arranging a set in order of the numerical value of the scores. *132*

Ratio Scale. The highest level of measurement that has all the characteristics of the interval scale plus a true zero point. Physical measures are commonly ratio (e.g., height, weight, distance, pressure, etc.). *15*

Region of Rejection (also called Critical Region). The regions of rejection are the portions on the tails of a statistical distribution that are so far away from the center of the distribution that they contain only 5% (or 1%) of the area under the curve. If the computed value of a statistic falls in a region of rejection we must reject the null hypothesis. *209*

Regression Constants. The slope and axis intercept of a best fit regression line. For example, in using the regression equation $Y' = a_Y + b_Y X$ to predict Y from X, the regression constants are the slope, b_Y, and the Y-intercept, a_Y. *97*

Regression of *X* on *Y*. Predicting X from Y using the X on Y regression constants ($X' = a_X + b_X Y$). *104*

Regression of *Y* on *X*. Predicting Y from X using the Y on X regression constants ($Y' = a_Y + b_Y X$). *104*

Relative Frequency. The proportion of scores in a data set that fall within a specific class interval. *35*

Repeated Measures Design. Each subject is tested under both the control and experimental conditions. The before and after design is one type of repeated measures design. *243*

Residual. The portion of total variation that is unexplained and is attributable to random (unsystematic) factors. *334*

Rounding Convention. Take computations out to three more decimal places than exist in the original data and round back to two places. *12*

Sample. A subset of a population. *5*

Sampling Distribution. The distribution of a statistic that results from a sampling experiment. The distribution displays all possible values the statistic can equal and the probability of obtaining each value. *200*

Scatterplot. A graphic display of bivariate data (i.e., two sets of measurements on a single group of subjects) in which each pair of X and Y scores is represented by a dot at the juncture of the X and Y values. *94*

Scheffé Test. A relatively conservative post hoc test for evaluating differences between all possible pairs of treatments. The probability of Type I error is held to a maximum of alpha. *357*

Sequence Effect. A sequence effect exists in a repeated measures design when the response to a treatment condition is partly determined by a residual effect from a preceding treatment. *338*

Sign Test. A nonparametric substitute for the correlated *t*-test. This relatively weak test is really a binomial test that is done on the frequencies of plus and minus difference scores. *270*

Skewness. A condition that denotes assymetrical dispersion of the scores in a distribution about the central value. *52*

Slope. The slope of the regression (best-fit) line used for predicting Y from X is the rate of change of Y relative to X. The slope of the regression line used to predict X from Y is the rate of change of X relative to Y. *91*

Spearman rho. The correlation coefficient computed on ranked data. *111*

SS. Notation for the variation ("sum of squares") in a set. The SS of any set of raw or composite scores may be computed using the General Rule. *57, 313*

$SS_{\text{between cell}}$. The variation among the $p \cdot q$ cells in a factorial design. Factor A, factor B, and the A $\times$ B interaction all contribute to the $SS_{\text{between cell}}$. *384*

$SS_{\text{between treatment}}$. The $SS_{\text{b.t.}}$ is that portion of the total variation that is, in part, attributable to systematic (nonrandom) differences between the treatments. In the computational method presented in the text, the $SS_{\text{b.t.}}$ is found by computing the variation among the set of treatment totals. According to the null hypothesis, only random factors account for variation among the treatment totals. According to the alternative hypothesis, treatment effects also contribute to differences that exist among the totals. *314*

$SS_{\text{regression}}$. Predictable variation. *124*

SS_{residual}. Unpredictable variation. *124*

$SS_{\text{within cell}}$. The variation among the cells. An estimate of error variation. *384*

$SS_{\text{within treatment}}$. In an independent groups ANOVA the $SS_{w.t.}$ is that portion of the total variation that is attributable to random error. *314*

Standard Deviation. A descriptive statistic that reflects the amount of dispersion that exists in a distribution. The square root of the variance. σ is the symbol for the population standard deviation and s is the symbol for the sample standard deviation. *56*

Standard Deviation Units. A synonym for z score units. A representation of a score in a normal distribution in terms of how far away it is from the mean. *72*

Standard Error. The deviation measure of a distribution of sample means, as distinguished from the standard deviation, the deviation measure of a distribution of raw scores. *203, 221*

Standard Error of the Difference. The deviation measure of a distribution of difference scores. *246*

Standard Error of Estimate. A measure of the dispersal of the dots in a scatterplot about the best-fit line. When the relationship between X and Y is a perfect linear function (i.e., all dots on the same straight line), the standard error of estimate equals zero. *102*

Statistic. A measurable characteristic of a sample. *8*

Structural Model. The mathematical model that equates the value of a datum to the mean of the null hypothesis population, plus some departure from that mean resulting from a treatment effect, plus further departure due to unpredictable random factors. The structural model for the single factor ANOVA is

$$X_{ij} = \mu + T_j + E_{ij}$$

311

Summation Notation. The use of the Greek Σ to stand for the "add" instruction in performing computations. *11*

Synergism. The action of two experimental variables upon a dependent measure that produces an effect greater than the individual contribution of each variable taken independently. A synergistic effect is an interaction. *374*

Tallies (also called "ticks" or "hash marks"). Tallies are used to record frequency counts of events. *292*

The Steps of Hypothesis Testing. The representation of the data analysis phase of all hypothesis testing, no matter which statiscal procedure is employed, as a uniform series of five steps. *See* the text for details. *190*

Transformation. Applying the same change to each member of an original set, such as adding a constant to each member of a set of raw scores. *62, 73*

Treatment Effect. Variation among the treatment totals (or means) that is attributable to an effect of the independent variable. *311*

True Limits. The value of a continuous variable plus and minus one-half a scale measuring unit. For example, the true limits of 10 pounds are 9.5 to 10.5 pounds. *7*

True Limits (of an interval). The range of an interval plus and minus one-half a measuring unit. For example, if the nominal limits of a class interval are 12 to 18, the true limits are 11.5 to 18.5. *32*

Truncated Range. A condition in which the range of a variable in a set of sample data is less than the range found in the population. *126*

***t* statistic.** The t statistic is a difference score (score − mean) divided by an estimate of the distribution's deviation measure. In the current context: score = $\overline{X}$, mean = μ, and deviation estimate = $s_{\overline{X}}$. *223*

Tukey HSD Test. The Honestly Significant Difference post hoc test that permits making all possible paired comparisons while controlling alpha inflation. *352*

Two-tail Test. A test of a nondirectional hypothesis. For example, in the context of the z test, the null hypothesis is rejected if the sample mean is either significantly less than or greater than the value of the population mean specified in the null hypothesis. *216*

Type I Error. Rejecting the null hypothesis when it should not have been rejected. *195, 208*

Type II Error. Failing to reject the null hypothesis when it should have been rejected. *197, 208*

Unbiased Estimate. A sample statistic is an unbiased estimate of a population parameter if, on the average, the sample statistic equals the population parameter. *223*

Ungrouped Frequency Distribution. The sequential arrangement of a distribution presented with the frequency tally for each score value. *30*

Unit Normal Curve (also called the Unit Normal Distribution). Another name for the distribution of the z statistic reflecting the fact that the area under the z curve is unity (1.00). *75*

Variance. The average variation per population value (SS/N) or sample value (SS/n). The square of the standard deviation. σ^2 is the symbol for the variance of a population and s^2 is the symbol for the variance of a sample. *56*

Variation. The sum of the squared deviation scores. Also called sum of squares or SS. *56*

Wilcoxon *T*-Test. This nonparametric test may be regarded as an enhancement of the sign test. Both the sign of the difference score and the magnitude of the difference score influence the value of the Wilcoxon T statistic. *270*

Y'. Y prime is the predicted value of Y that is the solution of the regression equation $Y' = a_Y + b_Y X$. *97*

Y-intercept. The location on the Y-axis where the regression line for predicting Y with the knowledge of X (Y on X) crosses. *91*

Yates Correction for Discontinuity. An adjustment to the chi-square formula that enables the computed statistic more nearly to approximate the distribution of the chi-square statistic when there is only one degree of freedom. *301*

z approximation to the binomial. The use of the z statistic to estimate proportions of area under segments of the binomial distribution. The sample size must be greater than twenty for a reasonable approximation and greater than thirty for a good approximation. *175*

z scores. The location of a raw score in its distribution in relation to how far from the mean of the distribution the score is in standard deviation units. *72*

Index